BIBLIOGRAPHY OF SYSTEMATIC WOOD ANATOMY OF DICOTYLEDONS

by

Mary Gregory

Jodrell Laboratory, Royal Botanic Gardens
Kew, United Kingdom

IAWA Journal, Supplement 1 — 1994

Published for the International Association of Wood Anatomists
at Rijksherbarium / Hortus Botanicus, Leiden, The Netherlands

582. 016 GRE

Cover: *Ternstroemia* sp. Mutis ex L. f. (Theaceae), transverse section. Photograph by courtesy of Peter Gasson (Kew, U. K.) from a slide from IPT, São Paulo (IPT 7857).

CIP-GEGEVENS KONINKLIJKE BIBLIOTHEEK, DEN HAAG

Gregory, Mary

Bibliography of systematic wood anatomy of Dicotyledons /
by Mary Gregory. - Leiden : Rijksherbarium / Hortus Botanicus. -
(IAWA Journal. Supplement ; 1)
Publ. for the International Association of Wood Anatomists.
ISBN 90-71236-22-6
Trefw.: hout ; bibliografieën.

Published at Rijksherbarium / Hortus Botanicus, Leiden University, The Netherlands

IAWA Journal, Supplement 1 (1994) 1–266

BIBLIOGRAPHY OF SYSTEMATIC WOOD ANATOMY OF DICOTYLEDONS

by

Mary Gregory

Jodrell Laboratory, Royal Botanic Gardens, Kew, Richmond, Surrey TW9 3DS, U.K.

INTRODUCTION

After publication of my wood identification bibliography (Gregory 1980), which was arranged primarily on a geographical basis with a small systematic section, some people expressed disappointment that the systematic section was not more comprehensive; this bibliography attempts to remedy that deficiency. My aim is to provide a convenient guide to the available literature, which I hope will be of use to anatomists starting research on a particular family or genus, and to those who are looking for a poorly studied group on which to work. It should also be of assistance to others who need to use anatomical data, e.g. taxonomists, archaeologists, physiologists, and ecologists.

The literature on wood anatomy has been scanned from 1900 (plus a few earlier works) with a closing date of journals published in 1993. The references are all included in the computerised plant anatomy database maintained at the Jodrell Laboratory and most of the books and articles are available at Kew, although some were consulted at the Plant Sciences Library, University of Oxford (incorporating the Forestry Institute Library), or elsewhere, and a few have only been seen in Forestry Abstracts. In order to keep the length down, only references with microscopical details are included, omitting the many works covering macroscopical and lens features, and some where the descriptions are very brief or repeat information on common woods. This means that some familiar reference books have been omitted, e.g. the series on Indian woods (edited by Chowdhury & Ghosh 1958 etc.). Unpublished theses are omitted, apart from a few available on microfilm. Atlases showing microscopical features have been indexed, even when they lack text. The study of fossil woods is an important aspect of systematic anatomy, but a separate bibliography of fossil wood anatomy is in preparation and therefore palaeobotanical papers have mostly been excluded, except where there are significant descriptions of extant species.

Many early accounts of wood anatomy (e.g. ones cited in Solereder 1908) were based largely on twig wood and therefore not representative of mature wood of the species concerned; I have omitted most such papers. Later workers concentrated on obtaining mature wood specimens, but there were often no herbarium vouchers for the material. The possibility of incorrect identification must be borne in mind when using these works. This problem was recognized (e.g. Stern & Chambers 1960, Baas 1980) and articles published in the last twenty or thirty years are usually based on vouchered material. Even so, nomenclatural inaccuracies may exist, since authors rarely track down herbarium vouchers to check for name changes. In recent years, certain anatomists have become interested in studying the secondary xylem of primarily herbaceous groups, and such papers have been included (e.g. Carlquist 1992g).

Layout

Following a brief general section (pp. 3–5), families are listed in alphabetical order (pp. 6–160). They do not follow any specific system of classification, but it is hoped most families are those generally recognized; alternative family names and positions of 'difficult' genera (e. g. *Nyctanthes*) are indicated. The genera described are listed up to a total of about ten; above that the number of genera is given. Generic names are as in the articles, except for the correction of spellings to agree with those in Brummitt (1992). Where Brummitt considers a name to be a synonym, the name accepted at Kew is given in brackets. Publications considered to be of special importance for a family, or occasionally a genus, are indicated by an asterisk (*).

Articles dealing only with specific features, such as anomalous structure, crystals, perforation plates, are listed separately for each family (negative reports for crystals, silica etc. are not indexed), but of course many works in the main family listings will describe these features also. I have indexed mainly broad surveys for these special features and have not tried to make them comprehensive. A few references on tyloses are given in the General section, but these are not indexed under families, because the presence and abundance of tyloses vary considerably with the site and season of collection.

In the references (pp. 161–265), the titles of articles are cited in the original language where possible; otherwise the original language is indicated in square brackets and the presence of an English summary is noted. All names including 'Van' have been indexed under Van for convenience, e. g. Van Wyk, Van der Slooten, Van Vliet, although this practice is not followed in some countries.

The first date mentioned is that on the title page or journal part; the actual date of publication, if different, is given in square brackets.

ACKNOWLEDGEMENTS

I wish to thank all those who have sent me copies of publications over many years, without whose help this bibliography would not have been possible. In particular, Prof. Pieter Baas has encouraged me to continue with this project during its long period of preparation. Special thanks go to the staff of the Library of the Royal Botanic Gardens, Kew, for obtaining many obscure items. I am grateful to the Keeper of the Jodrell Laboratory, Prof. M.D. Bennett, for the use of facilities, and to the staff of the Plant Sciences Library, Oxford, for their help.

GENERAL INDEX

(I) indicates indexed under families

Anomalous structure

Philipson 1990.
Ravololomaniraka & Koechlin 1970 (I).
Schenck 1893.
Snezhkova 1986 (I).
Timonin 1988a, b (I).

Computerized identification
Espinoza de Pernía & Miller 1991.
Ilic 1987, 1993.
Izumoto & Hayashi 1990.
Kuroda 1987.
LaPasha & Wheeler 1987.
Miller 1980.
Miller et al. 1987.
Pearson & Wheeler 1981.
Quirk 1983.
Richter & Trockenbrodt 1993.
Swart & Vos 1985.
Tochigi et al. 1984.
Wagenführ et al. 1988.
Wheeler et al. 1986, 1987, 1989.
Yang & Cheng 1990.
Zhang, Q.C. et al. 1986.

Crystals
Baker 1917 (I).
Chattaway 1955 (I), 1956 (I).
Espinoza de Pernía 1987b (I).
Hess 1936.
Lee et al. 1987.
Meniado et al. 1970 (I).
Oda & Nakasone 1975, 1976.
Scurfield et al. 1973 (I).
Taniguchi et al. 1982 (I).
Yamauchi 1967.

Ecological anatomy
Baas 1982, 1990.
Baas & Carlquist 1985.
Baas & Schweingruber 1987 (I).
Baas et al. 1983 (I).
Barajas Morales 1985 (I).
Bissing 1982.
Carlquist 1974 (I), 1975a, 1977c (I),
    1980a, 1985a (I), 1985 [1986]a (I),
    1989a.
Carlquist & Hoekman 1985a (I).
Den Outer & Van Veenendaal 1976 (I).
Novruzova 1968 (I).
Vales et al. 1983.
Van der Graaff & Baas 1974 (I).
Van Steenis 1973.
Versteegh 1968 (I).

Webber 1936a (I).
Worbes 1986 (I).

Growth rings (excluding dendro-
chronology)
Baas & Vetter 1989.
Carlquist 1980a.
Chowdhury 1938 [1939], 1939 [1940],
    1940, 1964.
Coster 1927, 1928.
Détienne 1989 (I).
Fahn 1953 (I).
Lobzhanidze 1961.
Tomlinson & Craighead 1972.
Worbes 1984 (I).

Helical (spiral) thickenings
Hess 1946a.
Meylan & Butterfield 1978a (I).
Nair 1987 (I).
Ohtani & Ishida 1978b (I).
Parham & Kaustinen 1973 (I).
Record 1936, 1943.

Perforation plates
Carlquist 1983d, 1992d (I).
Chalk 1933.
Li 1993.
MacDuffie 1921.
Meylan & Butterfield 1975 (I).
Ohtani & Ishida 1978a (I).
Parameswaran & Liese 1973 (I).
Record 1943.
Süss 1969 (I).

Pits
Bailey 1933.
Carlquist 1982 [1983].
Côté & Day 1962.
Lemesle 1946a (I).
Meylan & Butterfield 1974 (I).
Ohtani & Ishida 1976 (I).
Record 1943.
Van Vliet 1978 (I).

Rays
Bailey 1912.
Barghoorn 1940, 1941.
Braun 1955 (I), 1967 (I).
Braun & Den Outer 1965 (I).
Braun et al. 1967 (I), 1968 (I).
Carlquist 1970 [1971].
Chalk & Chattaway 1933.
Chattaway 1933a (I), 1951a, b (I).

Cozzo 1946d.
Dadswell & Record 1936 (I).
Huber & Mägdefrau 1953.
Kribs 1935.
McLean & Richardson 1973 [1974] (I).
Nicoloff 1911 (I).
Record 1943, 1944a.
Reinders-Gouwentak 1949 (I), 1950.
Sebastine 1955 (I).
Thompson 1911.
Webber 1938.

Secretory cells and canals
Baas & Gregory 1985.
Fahn 1979.
Fujii 1988 (I).
Gottwald 1980b.
Gregory & Baas 1989.
Rao 1966 [1970].
Record 1918, 1921, 1925a,b, 1944a.
Saitoh et al. 1993.

Silica
Amos 1951, 1952.
Amos & Dadswell 1948.
Balan Menon 1956, 1965.
Bamber & Lanyon 1960 (I).
Besson 1946.
Bianchi 1934.
Burgess 1965.
Espinoza de Pernía 1987b (I).
Frison 1942 (I).
Lim & Lau 1982.
Murthy 1965.
Scurfield et al. 1974 (I).
Sharma & Rao 1970 (I).
Sudo et al. 1967 (I).
Welle 1976a, b (I).

Storied structure
Cozzo 1954.
Cozzo & Cristiani 1950 (I).
Janssonius 1931.
Record 1919, 1944a.

Tracheary elements
Baas 1976, 1986a.
Bailey 1944a.
Bierhorst 1960.
Butterfield & Meylan 1976 (I) Septate fibres
Carlquist 1983b, 1984a, 1985a (I), 1985
   [1986]a (I), 1986a, b, 1987a (I), 1987g,
   1988f (I).
Chalk & Chattaway 1935.
Fahn & Leshem 1963.
Frison 1948b.
Frost 1930, 1931.
Harrar 1946.
Hess 1946a.
Ohtani 1983 (I), 1987 (I).
Purkayastha 1958 (I).
Ragonese 1976 (I).
Record 1942c, 1944a.
Reinders 1935.
Takahashi & Tamura 1990a.
Thompson 1923.
Wolkinger 1969–1971, 1970.

Tyloses
Bonsen & Kučera 1990.
Chattaway 1949.
Gerry 1914.
Gottwald 1972.
Itô & Kishima 1951.
Saitoh et al. 1993.
Zürcher et al. 1985.

Warts
Ohtani et al. 1983 (I).
Parham & Baird 1974.

Xylem parenchyma
Braun & Wolkinger 1970.
Hess 1946a, 1948, 1950a.
Kribs 1937.
Normand 1951.
Ohtani 1986 (I).
Record 1944a.
Tumanyan 1969.
Wagenführ 1961.

FAMILY INDEX

ACANTHACEAE (*Beloperone* = *Justicia*)

*Carlquist & Zona 1988a – 26 genera, 43 spp.
Corothie 1961a – *Bravaisia, Trichanthera.*
Datta & Deb 1968b – *Adhatoda* (= *Justicia*).
Datta & Maiti 1971a – *Adhatoda* (= *Justicia*), *Andrographis, Barleria, Ecbolium, Justicia.*
Dechamps 1979 – *Bravaisia, Trichanthera.*
Den Outer & Van Veenendaal 1983 – *Aphelandra, Barleria, Crossandra, Forsythiopsis* (= *Oplonia*), *Strobilanthes, Trichanthera*; for comparison with Pedaliaceae.
Détienne & Jacquet 1983 – *Bravaisia, Trichanthera.*
Détienne et al. 1982 – *Trichanthera.*
Hess 1946b – *Anisacanthus, Aphelandra, Beloperone, Bravaisia, Pachystachys, Sanchezia, Trichanthera.*
Hess 1950c – *Mendoncia.*
Ilic 1991 – *Graptophyllum, Oplonia, Salpixantha, Trichanthera.*
Jagiella & Kurschner 1987 – *Anisotes.*
Normand & Paquis 1976 [1977] – *Thomandersia.*
Prakash 1972 – *Crossandra* (root).
Record & Hess 1943 – Family description (same genera as Hess 1946b).
Record & Mell 1924 – *Bravaisia.*
Williams 1928 – *Trichanthera.*
Williams 1936 – *Pachystachys, Sanchezia, Trichanthera.*

Anomalous structure
Mullenders 1947 – *Thunbergia.*
Niesemann 1927 – *Afromendoncia* (= *Mendoncia*), *Mendoncia.*
Obaton 1960 – *Afromendoncia* (= *Mendoncia*), *Mendoncia, Thunbergia.*

Crystals
Chattaway 1956 – *Graptophyllum.*

Ecological anatomy
Carlquist 1985a – *Beloperone, Thunbergia.*
Carlquist 1985 [1986]a – *Thunbergia.*
Carlquist & Hoekman 1985a – *Beloperone.*
Webber 1936a – *Beloperone.*

ACERACEAE
(*Acer* only unless otherwise stated)

Anon. 1966.
Brazier & Franklin 1961 – 10 spp.
Carvalho 1954–1955; 1956.
Cheng, C. 1985.
Cheng, J.-Q. 1980 – *Acer, Dipteronia.*
Cheng, J.-Q. et al. 1992.
Chudnoff 1956.
Cutler 1976 (root).
Cutler et al. 1987 (root).
Edlmann & Monaco 1981.
Fahn et al. 1986.
Fegel 1941 (root).
Friedman 1978.
Furuno 1985, 1987.
Greguss 1959.
Grosser 1977.
Hayashi 1991.
Heimsch 1942 – *Acer* 14 spp., *Dipteronia* 1.
Hess 1946b.
Hirai 1979–1985.
Ilic 1991.
Jacquiot et al. 1973.
Kanehira 1921a,b, 1926.
Kribs 1959.
López & Ortega 1989.
Luo 1989.
Moiseeva 1940 (branches).
Moll & Janssonius 1906–1936.
Mork 1946.
Niloofari 1961.
*Ogata 1967.
Oprea & Oprea 1986.
Panshin & Zeeuw 1980.
Parsa Pajouh & Schweingruber 1985.
Pearson & Brown 1932.
Rao 1962.
Record & Hess 1943.
Riedl 1937 (root).
Saiki 1982.
Saint-Laurent 1926, 1928, 1932b, 1934.
Schweingruber 1978, 1990.
Shimaji & Itoh 1982, 1988.
Snezhkova 1974.
*Stark 1954a – 19 spp.
Sudo 1959.
Suzuki et al. 1991.

(ACERACEAE)
Tabatabai 1962.
Tabatabai et al. 1963 (No. 41).
Tang 1973.
Vasiljević 1954.
Vintoniv 1976.
Wagenführ & Scheiber 1974.
Wang 1966.
Wuang 1979.
Yaltirik 1971 – 10 spp.
Yamabayashi 1938.
*Yamauchi 1962 (21 spp.), 1972.
Yao 1988.
Yatsenko-Khmelevsky 1939 – 15 spp.
Zgurovskaya 1958.

Anomalous structure
Korovin 1987.

Crystals
Chattaway 1956.

Ecological anatomy
Baas et al. 1983.
Baas & Schweingruber 1987.
Carlquist & Hoekman 1985a.
Novruzova 1968.
Webber 1936a.
Yaltirik 1968, 1970.

Growth rings
Hanson & Brenke 1936.

Helical thickenings
Ohtani & Ishida 1978b.
Parham & Kaustinen 1973.

Perforation plates
Ohtani & Ishida 1978a.

Rays
Chattaway 1951b.
Holden 1912.
Petrić & Šcukanec 1975.
Reinders-Gouwentak 1949.
Vasiljević 1950.

Tracheary elements
Jing et al. 1989.
Ohtani 1983.

ACHATOCARPACEAE
(*Achatocarpus* only)

Burgerstein 1912.
Corothie 1961b.
Hess 1946b.
Record & Hess 1943.

ACTINIDIACEAE
(incl. SAURAUIACEAE)

Barajas Morales 1980 – *Saurauia*.
Cheng, J.-Q. 1980 – *Saurauia*.
Cheng, J.-Q. et al. 1992 – *Saurauia*.
Chesnais 1941 – *Actinidia*.
Cockrell 1942 – *Saurauia*.
Dadswell & Record 1936 – *Actinidia*.
Ilic 1991 – *Saurauia*.
Kanehira 1921a – *Saurauia*.
Lechner 1914 – *Actinidia, Clematoclethra, Saurauia* (twigs).
Moll & Janssonius 1906–1936 – *Saurauia* 13 spp.
Record 1926a – *Saurauia*.
Record & Hess 1943 – *Saurauia*.
Shimaji & Itoh 1988 – *Actinidia*.
Snezhkova 1986 – *Actinidia*.
Suzuki & Noshiro 1988 – *Actinidia*.
Tang 1973 – *Saurauia*.
Vestal 1937 – Family description (*Actinidia, Saurauia*).
Wang et al. 1991 – *Actinidia*.

Crystals
Chattaway 1955 – *Saurauia*.

Ecological anatomy
Carlquist 1985 [1986]a – *Actinidia*.
Versteegh 1968 – *Saurauia*.

Rays
Braun et al. 1967, 1968 – *Saurauia*.

Tracheary elements
Jing et al. 1989 – *Saurauia*.

AEXTOXICACEAE
(*Aextoxicon* only)

Heimsch 1942.
Hess 1946b.
Ilic 1991.
Ortiz Cespedes 1959.
Rancusi et al. 1987.
Record & Hess 1943.
Sudo 1963.
Wagemann 1949.

Pits and Perforation plates
Carlquist 1992d.

AIZOACEAE (incl. MOLLUGINACEAE)

Anomalous structure
Bhambie et al. 1977 – *Glinus, Orygia*
   (= *Corbichonia*), *Trianthema, Zaleya.*
Theron et al. 1968 – *Plinthus.*
Timonin 1988a, b – *Mesembryanthe-*
   mum.

Crystals
Chattaway 1955 – *Carpobrotus.*

AKANIACEAE (*Akania* only)

Dadswell & Record 1936.
Heimsch 1942.
Ilic 1991.

Crystals
Chattaway 1956.

ALANGIACEAE
(*Alangium* only, incl. *Marlea*)

Cheng, J.-Q. 1980.
Cheng, J.-Q. et al. 1992.
Hayashi et al. 1973.
Ilic 1991.
Kanehira 1921a.
Lebacq & Dechamps 1964.
Lecomte 1926a.
Li & Chao 1954.
Luo 1989.
Moll & Janssonius 1906–1936.
Ogata 1975–1983.
Sudo 1963.
Suzuki et al. 1991.
Wiraj Chunwarin & Damrong Sri-Aran
   1974.
Wuang 1979.
Yao 1988.

Crystals
Chattaway 1956.
Meniado et al. 1970.

ALSEUOSMIACEAE

*Dickison 1986 – *Alseuosmia, Crispiloba,*
   Wittsteinia.
Gardner 1978 – *Alseuosmia, Memecylanthus*
   (= *Wittsteinia*), *Periomphale* (= *Wittsteinia*)
   (brief notes).
Paliwal & Srivastava 1969 – *Alseuosmia.*

(ALSEUOSMIACEAE)
Helical thickenings
Meylan & Butterfield 1978a – *Alseuosmia.*

Septate fibres
Butterfield & Meylan 1976 – *Alseuosmia.*

AMARANTHACEAE

Brown 1922 – *Charpentiera, Nototrichium.*
Ilic 1991 – *Charpentiera.*
Saint-Laurent 1932a – *Aerva.*
Schweingruber 1990 – *Bosea.*

Anomalous structure
Bramwell 1976 [1977] – *Bosea.*
Chalk & Chattaway 1937 – *Bosea.*
Joshi 1937 – *Achyranthes, Alternanthera,*
   Amaranthus, Pupalia.
Lotova & Timonin 1985 – *Amaranthus.*
Schmid 1928 – 52 genera.
Timonin 1987 – General survey.
Viana 1992 – *Amaranthus.*

Ecological anatomy
Baas & Schweingruber 1987 – *Bosea.*
Carlquist 1974 – *Charpentiera.*

AMBORELLACEAE (*Amborella* only)

Bailey 1957b.
Bailey & Swamy 1948 (young).
Den Outer & Van Veenendaal 1982.
Ilic 1991.
Lemesle 1956b, 1963a.
Lemesle & Pichard 1954.
Metcalfe 1987 – General survey.
Money et al. 1950.
Takahashi 1985.

ANACARDIACEAE
(see also JULIANIACEAE)
(*Melanorrhoea* = *Gluta*)

Anon. 1981 (Andes) – *Anacardium,*
   Campnosperma, Spondias.
Anon. 1981 (Curua) – *Astronium.*
Abbate 1964 – *Heeria, Lannea.*
Abbate 1970 – *Lannea.*
Abbate 1973 – *Poupartia.*
Almeida 1973 [1974] – *Lannea.*
Alves de Pinho 1969 – *Lithraea.*

(ANACARDIACEAE)
Araujo & Mattos Filho 1973e – *Campnosperma*.
Ayensu & Bentum 1974 – *Antrocaryon*.
Balan Menon 1955 – *Gluta, Melanorrhoea*.
Balan Menon 1959 – *Campnosperma, Mangifera, Swintonia*.
Barajas Morales & León Gómez 1989 – *Spondias*.
Barajas Morales et al. 1979 – *Astronium, Mosquitoxylon*.
Bargagli-Petrucci 1903 – *Campnosperma, Melanochyla, Melanorrhoea, Pentaspadon*.
Benoist 1931 – *Spondias, Thyrsodium*.
Berger 1922 – *Gluta*.
Brazier & Franklin 1961 – 10 genera.
Brown 1922 – *Rhus*.
Burgerstein 1909 – *Buchanania, Mangifera*.
Burgerstein 1912 – *Lithraea, Schinopsis, Schinus*.
Cardoso 1960 – *Sclerocarya*.
Carreras & Pérez 1988 – *Spondias*.
Chauhan & Dayal 1990 – *Lannea, Spondias*.
Cheng, C. 1985 – *Choerospondias, Pistacia*.
Cheng, J.-Q. 1980 – *Choerospondias, Lannea, Mangifera, Pistacia, Rhus, Spondias*.
Cheng, J.-Q. et al. 1992 – *Choerospondias, Cotinus, Lannea, Mangifera, Pistacia, Rhus, Spondias, Toxicodendron* (= *Rhus*).
Chiang 1964 – *Pistacia*.
Chudnoff 1956 – *Pistacia, Rhus*.
Cockrell 1942 – *Buchanania, Campnosperma, Mangifera*.
Corothie 1960 – *Anacardium, Astronium, Mangifera, Mauria, Spondias, Tapirira*.
Cutler et al. 1987 – *Cotinus, Rhus* (root).
Dadswell & Eckersley 1935 – *Blepharocarya, Euroschinus, Pleiogynium, Rhodosphaera*.
*Dadswell & Ingle 1948 – 22 genera.
Das 1984b – *Buchanania, Gluta, Holigarna, Lannea, Mangifera, Semecarpus, Spondias, Swintonia*.
Dechamps 1979 – *Anacardium, Astronium, Loxopterygium, Schinus, Spondias, Tapirira, Thyrsodium*.
Détienne & Jacquet 1983 – 11 genera.
Détienne et al. 1982 – *Anacardium, Loxopterygium, Spondias, Tapirira, Thyrsodium*.
*Dong & Baas 1993 – 11 genera.

(ANACARDIACEAE)
Edlmann & Monaco 1981 – *Rhus*.
Eeckhout 1951 – *Antrocaryon*.
El-Oqlah 1984 – *Pistacia*.
Fahn et al. 1986 – *Pistacia, Rhus*.
Fasolo 1941–1944 – *Odina* (= *Lannea*).
Fedalto et al. 1989 – *Anacardium, Spondias, Tapirira*.
Fouarge & Gérard 1964 – *Antrocaryon, Lannea, Spondias*.
Freitas 1963 – *Mangifera*.
Freitas 1986 – *Sclerocarya*.
Fundter & Wisse 1977 – *Buchanania, Campnosperma, Dracontomelon, Koordersiodendron*.
Furuno 1977, 1979 – *Buchanania, Campnosperma, Dracontomelon, Gluta, Mangifera, Pleiogynium, Semecarpus, Spondias*.
Furuno 1985, 1987 – *Rhus*.
Gaiotti de Peralta & Edlmann Abbate 1981 – *Anacardium, Spondias*.
Garratt 1931 – *Dracontomelon*.
Gibson 1981 – *Pachycormus*.
Gomes 1984 – *Sclerocarya*.
Greguss 1959 – *Cotinus, Pistacia, Rhus*.
Grisa 1988 – *Poupartia*.
Grundwag & Werker 1976 – *Pistacia*.
Hayashi 1991 – *Rhus*.
Hayashi et al. 1973 – 10 genera.
Hayashi & Nomura 1986 – *Campnosperma, Lannea, Mangifera*.
*Heimsch 1940, 1942 – 53 genera.
Heringer & Paula 1977 – *Anacardium*.
*Hess 1946b – 20 genera.
Hess 1950c – *Tiparvia* (spelling error for *Tapirira*: L.L. Forman, pers. comm.).
Hirai 1979–1985 – *Rhus*.
Hofmann 1955 – *Cotinus*.
Hoheisel et al. 1968 – *Tapirira*.
Huber & Rouschal 1954 – *Cotinus, Pistacia*.
Ilic 1991 – 30 genera.
Jagiella & Kurschner 1987 – *Pistacia, Rhus*.
Kanehira 1921a – *Buchanania, Mangifera, Pistacia, Rhus, Semecarpus*.
Kanehira 1921b – *Rhus*.
Kanehira 1924 – *Buchanania, Dracontomelon, Koordersiodendron, Mangifera, Spondias*.
Kanehira 1926 – *Pistacia, Rhus*.
Kobayashi & Sugawa 1963 – *Dracontomelon, Koordersiodendron, Melanorrhoea*.
Kobayashi & Sugawa 1966a – *Mangifera*.

(ANACARDIACEAE)

Kribs 1928a – *Anacardium, Tapirira.*
Kribs 1959 – 13 genera.
Lebacq & Dechamps 1964 – *Antrocaryon, Heeria, Lannea, Mangifera, Pseudospondias, Sorindeia, Spondias, Trichoscypha.*
Lebacq & Dechamps 1967 – *Antrocaryon, Lannea,* cf. *Sclerocarya,* cf. *Sorindeia, Spondias, Trichoscypha.*
Lebacq et al. 1973 – 10 genera.
Lebacq & Staner 1964 – *Anacardium, Astronium, Trichoscypha.*
Lecomte 1922 – *Protorhus.*
Lecomte 1926a – *Mangifera, Melanorrhoea, Spondias, Swintonia.*
López Naranjo & Espinoza de Pernía 1990 [1992] – *Anacardium.*
Luo 1989 – *Choerospondias, Mangifera, Pistacia, Toxicodendron.*
Machado 1944 – *Anacardium.*
Mainieri 1962 – *Anacardium, Spondias, Tapirira.*
Mainieri 1978 – *Astronium.*
Mainieri & Chimelo 1989 – *Anacardium, Astronium, Tapirira.*
Martawijaya et al. 1986 – *Melanorrhoea.*
Martawijaya et al. 1989 – *Dracontomelon.*
Martijena 1987 – *Lithraea.*
Mattos Filho 1990 – *Apterokarpos* (= *Loxopterygium*), *Loxopterygium.*
Messeri 1938 – *Rhus.*
Moll & Janssonius 1906–1936 – *Bouea, Buchanania, Dracontomelon, Gluta, Mangifera, Melanochyla, Odina* (= *Lannea*), *Semecarpus, Spondias.*
Monteiro & Frade 1960 – *Lannea, Pseudospondias.*
Nardi Berti & Edlmann Abbate 1992 – *Anacardium, Astronium, Campnosperma, Schinopsis.*
Nassonov 1934 – *Pistacia.*
Niloofari 1961 – *Cotinus, Pistacia, Rhus.*
Normand 1955 – *Antrocaryon, Lannea, Pseudospondias, Spondias, Trichoscypha.*
Normand & Paquis 1976 [1977] – *Antrocaryon, Lannea, Pseudospondias, Sorindeia, Spondias, Trichoscypha.*
Ogata 1975–1983 – *Campnosperma, Dracontomelon, Gluta, Mangifera, Melanorrhoea, Spondias* + summary for 17 genera.

(ANACARDIACEAE)

Ortega et al. 1988 – *Mangifera, Tapirira.*
Ortega 1958 – *Spondias.*
Paula 1979, 1981 – *Anacardium.*
Paula & Alves 1973 – *Anacardium.*
Paula & Alves 1980 – *Astronium, Schinopsis, Spondias.*
Pearson & Brown 1932 – *Buchanania, Gluta, Holigarna, Mangifera, Melanorrhoea, Odina* (= *Lannea*), *Parishia, Pistacia, Spondias, Swintonia.*
Pereira 1933 – *Myracrodruon* (= *Astronium*).
Pérez Olvera et al. 1980 [1981] – *Astronium, Metopium, Spondias.*
Pérez Olvera et al. 1982 [1985] – *Schinus.*
Pfeiffer, J.P. 1926 – *Loxopterygium, Spondias, Tapirira.*
Prakash 1972 – *Mangifera, Spondias* (root).
Purkayastha et al. 1976 – *Dracontomelon, Lannea, Mangifera, Parishia.*
*Record 1939d – 18 genera.
Record & Hess 1943 – Family (18 genera).
Rock 1972 – *Metopium, Toxicodendron.*
Saiki 1982 – *Dracontomelon.*
Saint-Laurent 1926, 1928, 1934 – *Pistacia, Rhus.*
Schmid 1915 – *Astronium,* ?*Rhus, Schinopsis.*
Schweingruber 1990 – *Cotinus, Pistacia, Rhus, Schinus.*
Serizawa 1985 – Not seen.
Shimaji & Itoh 1982, 1988 – *Rhus.*
Sudo 1959 – *Poupartia, Rhus.*
Sudo 1963 – 14 genera.
Sudo 1988 – 11 genera.
Sudworth & Mell 1911c – *Cotinus.*
Tabatabai et al. 1963 – *Mangifera, Pistacia, Rhus* (Nos. 42–47).
Tang 1973 – *Choerospondias, Dracontomelon, Mangifera, Pistacia, Rhus, Semecarpus.*
Tavares 1968 – *Thyrsodium.*
Tavares 1970 – *Schinus.*
Terrazas 1993 – 54 genera [Abstr.].
Tortorelli 1956 – *Astronium, Schinopsis, Schinus.*
Wagemann 1949 – *Astronium, Lithraea, Schinopsis.*
Wagenführ & Scheiber 1974 – *Antrocaryon, Astronium, Dracontomelon.*

(ANACARDIACEAE)

Wang 1984–1988 – *Campnosperma, Dracontomelon, Gluta, Mangifera, Melanorrhoea, Spondias.*

Williams 1936 – *Anacardium, Astronium, Mauria, Spondias, Tapirira.*

Wiraj Chunwarin & Damrong Sri-Aran 1973 – *Bouea, Dracontomelon, Mangifera, Melanorrhoea, Odina (= Lannea), Spondias.*

Wuang 1979 – *Pistacia, Rhus.*

Yamabayashi 1938 – *Rhus.*

Yao 1988 – *Rhus.*

Young 1974 – *Cotinus, Malosma (= Rhus), Metopium, Rhus, Schinus, Toxicodendron (= Rhus).*

Young 1982 – *Actinocheita.*

Crystals and silica

Chattaway 1955 – *Rhus.*

Chattaway 1956 – 24 genera.

Dhar & Purkayastha 1973 – *Lannea.*

Espinoza de Pernía 1987b – 10 genera.

Scurfield et al. 1973 – *Rhus.*

Scurfield et al. 1974 – *Anacardium, Melanorrhoea.*

Sudo et al. 1967 – *Gluta, Melanorrhoea, Parishia, Swintonia.*

Welle 1976b – *Anacardium, Loxopterygium.*

Ecological anatomy

Baas et al. 1983 – *Pistacia, Rhus.*

Baas & Schweingruber 1987 – *Cotinus, Pistacia, Rhus.*

Carlquist 1985a – *Rhus.*

Carlquist 1985 [1986]a – *Toxicodendron (= Rhus).*

Carlquist & Hoekman 1985a – *Rhus, Toxicodendron (= Rhus).*

Den Outer & Van Veenendaal 1976 – *Spondias.*

Novruzova 1968 – *Cotinus, Pistacia, Rhus.*

Psaras & Hatzopoulou-Belba 1984 – *Pistacia.*

Van der Graaff & Baas 1974 – *Rhus.*

Webber 1936a – *Rhus.*

Growth rings

Fahn 1953, 1955 – *Pistacia.*

Helical thickenings

Ohtani & Ishida 1978b – *Rhus.*

(ANACARDIACEAE)

Perforation plates

Ohtani & Ishida 1978a – *Rhus.*

Rays

Chattaway 1951a – *Euroschinus, Microstemon (= Pentaspadon), Pistacia, Pleiogynium.*

Sebastine 1955 – *Anacardium.*

Tracheary elements

Gill & Onuja 1984b – *Anacardium, Mangifera.*

Jing et al. 1989 – *Pistacia.*

Ohtani 1983 – *Rhus.*

ANCISTROCLADACEAE

(*Ancistrocladus*)

*Gottwald & Parameswaran 1968.

Ecological anatomy

Carlquist 1985a.

ANISOPHYLLEACEAE

see RHIZOPHORACEAE

ANNONACEAE (*Enantia = Annickia*)

Anon. 1967 – *Polyalthia.*

Anon. 1981 (Curua) – *Onychopetalum, Xylopia.*

Araujo & Mattos Filho 1965 – *Xylopia.*

Balan Menon 1959 – *Alphonsea, Cyathocalyx, Enicosanthum, Mezzettia, Mitrephora, Monocarpia, Platymitra, Polyalthia, Sageraea, Trivalvaria, Xylopia.*

Bargagli-Petrucci 1903 – *Xylopia.*

Benoist 1927, 1931 – *Xylopia.*

Blunden et al. 1974 – *Goniothalamus* (young stem and root).

Brazier & Franklin 1961 – *Cleistopholis, Mezzettia, Oxandra.*

Burgerstein 1909 – *Annona, Cananga.*

Carreras & Vales 1986b – *Oxandra.*

Cheng, J.-Q. 1980 – *Annona, Polyalthia.*

Cheng, J.-Q. et al. 1992 – *Annona, Polyalthia.*

Cockrell 1942 – *Cananga, Polyalthia.*

Cunha Mello 1950 [1951] – *Guatteria.*

Dechamps 1979 – *Duguetia, Guatteria, Oxandra, Rollinia, Unonopsis, Xylopia.*

(ANNONACEAE)

Détienne & Jacquet 1983 – 14 genera.
Détienne et al. 1982 – *Anaxagorea, Cymbopetalum, Duguetia, Guatteria, Oxandra, Rollinia, Unonopsis, Xylopia*.
Fedalto et al. 1989 – *Diclinanona, Onychopetalum*.
Ferreirinha 1958 – *Enantia*.
Ferreirinha & Reis 1969 – *Polyalthia*.
Fouarge & Gérard 1964 – *Cleistopholis, Enantia, Hexalobus, Xylopia*.
Fouarge et al. 1953 – *Anonidium*.
Freitas 1963 – *Polyalthia*.
Furuno 1977, 1979 – *Cananga, Polyalthia, Xylopia*.
Garratt 1933b – Family and relations with Myristicaceae.
Gomide et al. 1972 – *Annona*.
Hayashi et al. 1973 – *Enicosanthum, Xylopia*.
Heringer & Paula 1976 – *Annona*.
*Hess 1946b – 21 genera.
Hess 1950c – *Ephedranthus*.
Hoheisel et al. 1968 – *Xylopia*.
Ilic 1991 – 19 genera.
Ingle & Dadswell 1953 – 12 genera.
Jentsch et al. 1936, 1938 – *Enantia, Xylopia*.
Kanehira 1924 – *Cyathocalyx, Polyalthia*.
Kanehira et al. 1933 – *Annona*.
Kobayashi & Sugawa 1972 – *Mezzettia*.
Kribs 1928a – *Rollinia*.
Kribs 1959 – *Cleistopholis, Enantia, Guatteria, Oxandra*.
Lebacq 1955 – 11 genera.
Lebacq & Dechamps 1964 – 16 genera.
Lebacq & Dechamps 1967 – 11 genera.
Lebacq et al. 1973 – *Anaxagorea, Annona, Cymbopetalum, Diclinanona, Duguetia, Guatteria, Oxandra, Unonopsis, Xylopia*.
Lecomte 1922 – *Artabotrys*.
Lecomte 1926a – *Polyalthia*.
Lepe 1959 – *Oxandra, Rollinia*.
Loureiro 1969 – *Fusaea, Rollinia, Unonopsis, Xylopia*.
Loureiro 1970 – *Bocageopsis, Guatteria, Xylopia*.
Loureiro 1971 [1972] – *Annona, Guatteria*.
Maas & Westra 1984, 1985 – *Anaxagorea*.
Maas et al. 1992 – *Rollinia* (wood by B.J.H. ter Welle, pp. 21–26.)
Mainieri 1978 – *Duguetia*.

(ANNONACEAE)

Mainieri & Chimelo 1989 – *Duguetia*.
Metcalfe 1987 – General survey.
Moll & Janssonius 1906–1936 – 14 genera.
Monteiro 1967 – *Pachypodanthium, Polyalthia*.
Monteiro & França 1971 – *Monodora, Xylopia*.
Normand 1933c – *Enantia*.
Normand 1950b – *Cleistopholis, Enantia, Hexalobus, Monodora, Neostenanthera, Pachypodanthium, Piptostigma, Polyalthia, Xylopia*.
Normand & Paquis 1976 [1977] – *Cleistopholis, Enantia, Pachypodanthium, Polyalthia, Xylopia*.
Ogata 1975–1983 – *Alphonsea, Cananga, Cyathocalyx, Mezzettia, Polyalthia, Xylopia*.
Ortega 1958 – *Guatteria*.
Paula 1979 – *Annona*.
Paula 1981 – *Xylopia*.
Paula & Alves 1989 – *Guatteria*.
Paula & Heringer 1977, 1979 – *Annona*.
Pearson & Brown 1932 – *Miliusa, Polyalthia, Sageraea*.
Pereira 1933 – *Duguetia*.
Pérez Mogollón 1973 – *Rollinia*.
Pfeiffer, J.P. 1926 – ?*Xylopia*.
Pinho et al. 1986b – *Annona, Guatteria, Rollinia, Xylopia*.
Prakash 1972 – *Annona, Monodora* (root).
Purkayastha et al. 1976 – *Sageraea*.
Record & Hess 1943 – Family (21 genera).
Record & Mell 1924 – *Oxandra*.
Riera 1947 – *Enantia, Polyalthia*.
Rogel Gomez 1982 [1985] – *Guatteria*.
Sudo 1963 – *Cananga, Cyathocalyx, Enantia, Oxandra, Polyalthia, Xylopia*.
Sudo 1988 – *Cananga, Cyathocalyx, Polyalthia*.
Tang 1973 – *Polyalthia*.
Vales & Carreras 1987 – *Oxandra*.
*Vander Wyk & Canright 1956 – 61 genera.
*Welle 1984 – Family (77 genera).
Welle & Van Rooden 1982 – *Desmopsis* 4, *Sapranthus* 5, *Stenanona* 2.
Westra 1985 – *Tetrameranthus*.
Williams 1936 – 11 genera.
Wiraj Chunwarin & Damrong Sri-Aran 1973 – *Cananga, Miliusa, Saccopetalum* (= *Miliusa*).

(ANNONACEAE)

Yao 1988 – *Polyalthia.*

Yatsenko-Khmelevsky 1954a – *Asimina.*

Crystals

Chattaway 1956 – *Goniothalamus, Tetrastemma* (= *Uvariopsis*).

Scurfield et al. 1973 – *Goniothalamus, Polyalthia.*

Ecological anatomy

Barajas Morales 1985 – *Cymbopetalum, Rollinia.*

Den Outer & Van Veenendaal 1976 – *Cleistopholis.*

Worbes 1986 – *Annona, Pseudoxandra.*

Rays

Botosso & Gomes 1982 – *Annona, Duguetia, Guatteria, Rollinia.*

APIACEAE see UMBELLIFERAE

APOCYNACEAE

(see also DUCKEODENDRACEAE)

Anon. 1981 (Andes) – *Aspidosperma.*

Anon. 1981 (Curua) – *Couma, Malouetia.*

Abbate 1973 – *Carissa.*

Balan Menon 1959 – *Alstonia, Dyera.*

Bandyopadhyaya & Dutta 1986 [1988] – *Plumeria* 8 spp.

Barajas Morales & León Gómez 1989 – *Alstonia, Thevetia.*

Bargagli-Petrucci 1903 – *Cerbera, Dyera.*

Benoist 1931 – *Aspidosperma, Couma.*

Berger 1922 – *Alstonia.*

Brazier & Franklin 1961 – *Alstonia, Aspidosperma, Dyera, Funtumia, Gonioma, Parahancornia, Picralima.*

Brown 1922 – *Ochrosia, Rauvolfia.*

Burgerstein 1909 – *Cerbera, Gynopogon.*

Burgerstein 1912 – *Aspidosperma, Vallesia.*

Cellai 1971 – *Carissa.*

Chalk et al. 1933 – *Holarrhena.*

Chalk et al. 1935 – *Gonioma.*

Chen 1957 – *Strophanthus.*

Cheng, J.-Q. 1980 – *Alstonia, Wrightia.*

Cheng, J.-Q. et al. 1992 – *Alstonia, Winchia* (= *Alstonia*), *Wrightia.*

Cockrell 1942 – *Dyera.*

(APOCYNACEAE)

Cunha Mello 1950 [1951] – *Tabernaemontana.*

Dadswell & Eckersley 1935 – *Alstonia.*

Datta & Maiti 1971b – *Alstonia, Ervatamia* (= *Tabernaemontana*), *Holarrhena, Lochnera* (= *Catharanthus*), *Plumeria, Rauvolfia, Thevetia.*

Dechamps 1979 – 11 genera.

Détienne & Jacquet 1983 – 14 genera.

Détienne et al. 1982 – *Ambelania, Anartia* (= *Tabernaemontana*), *Aspidosperma, Couma, Geissospermum, Himatanthus, Macoubea, Parahancornia.*

Doležal 1959 – *Alstonia.*

Eeckhout 1951 – *Alstonia, Funtumia.*

Eggeling & Harris 1939 – *Alstonia.*

Esdorn & Zohm 1961 – *Alstonia.*

Fahn et al. 1986 – *Nerium.*

Fouarge & Gérard 1964 – *Alstonia, Funtumia.*

Freitas 1955 – *Alstonia.*

Fundter & Wisse 1977 – *Alstonia.*

Furuno 1977, 1979 – *Alstonia, Cerbera, Wrightia.*

Gaiotti de Peralta & Edlmann Abbate 1981 – *Aspidosperma.*

Giordano 1939 – *Acokanthera.*

Gómez 1959 – *Aspidosperma.*

Greguss 1959 – *Nerium.*

Harvey-Gibson 1911 – *Gonioma.*

Hayashi et al. 1973 – *Alstonia, Dyera.*

Hirai 1979–1985 – *Alstonia, Dyera.*

Hoheisel et al. 1968 – *Aspidosperma.*

Huber & Rouschal 1954 – *Nerium.*

Ilic 1991 – 19 genera.

*Ingle & Dadswell 1953 – 12 genera.

Jagiella & Kurschner 1987 – *Acokanthera, Carissa.*

Jentsch et al. 1936 – *Alstonia, Kickxia* (= *Kibatalia*), *Rauvolfia.*

Kanehira 1924 – *Alstonia, Kopsia, Wrightia.*

Kanehira et al. 1933 – *Alstonia.*

Kobayashi & Sugawa 1963 – *Dyera.*

Kobayashi & Sugawa 1964 – *Alstonia.*

Kribs 1959 – *Alstonia, Aspidosperma, Gonioma, Macoubea, Wrightia.*

Lebacq & Dechamps 1964 – *Alstonia, Conopharyngia* (= *Tabernaemontana*), *Funtumia, Holarrhena, Hunteria, Picralima, Rauvolfia, Voacanga.*

(APOCYNACEAE)

Lebacq & Dechamps 1967 – *Alstonia, Conopharyngia* (= *Tabernaemontana*), *Funtumia, Picralima, Rauvolfia, Voacanga.*

Lebacq et al. 1973 – 15 genera.

Lebacq & Staner 1964 – *Aspidosperma, Rauvolfia.*

Lecomte 1922 – *Carissa, Tanghinia.*

Lecomte 1926a – *Wrightia.*

Lepe 1959 – *Aspidosperma.*

Leprince 1911 – *Adenium.*

Luo 1989 – *Alstonia.*

Mägdefrau & Wutz 1961 – *Ambelania, Malouetia.*

Mainieri 1958 – *Zschokkea* (= *Lacmellea*).

Mainieri 1962 – *Couma, Himatanthus, Parahancornia.*

Mainieri 1964 – *Parahancornia.*

Mainieri 1978 – *Aspidosperma.*

Mainieri & Chimelo 1989 – *Aspidosperma.*

Mariaux 1971 – *Crioceras.*

Martawijaya et al. 1986 – *Alstonia, Dyera.*

Martin 1953 – *Rauvolfia.*

Messeri 1938 – *Nerium.*

Milanez 1938 – *Aspidosperma.*

*Milanez 1939 – *Aspidosperma* 30 spp.

Moll & Janssonius 1906–1936 – *Alstonia, Cerbera, Kickxia* (= *Kibatalia*), *Kopsia, Ochrosia, Orchipeda* (= *Voacanga*), *Rauvolfia, Tabernaemontana, Wrightia.*

Nardi Berti & Edlmann Abbate 1988 – *Alstonia.*

Nardi Berti & Edlmann Abbate 1992 – *Aspidosperma, Parahancornia.*

Normand 1960 – *Alstonia, Conopharyngia* (= *Tabernaemontana*), *Funtumia, Holarrhena, Hunteria, Picralima, Rauvolfia.*

Normand & Paquis 1976 [1977] – *Alstonia, Funtumia, Holarrhena, Hunteria, Picralima, Rauvolfia, Tabernaemontana.*

Ogata 1975–1983 – *Alstonia, Cerbera, Dyera, Wrightia.*

Panshin 1932 – *Cerbera.*

Paula & Alves 1980 – *Aspidosperma.*

Pearson & Brown 1932 – *Alstonia, Holarrhena, Wrightia.*

Pereira 1933 – *Aspidosperma.*

Pereira et al. 1970 – *Aspidosperma.*

Pérez Olvera & Corral López 1980 – *Aspidosperma.*

(APOCYNACEAE)

Pfeiffer, J.P. 1926 – *Aspidosperma, Couma, Macoubea.*

Prakash 1972 – *Landolphia, Mascarenhasia, Picralima, Saba, Strophanthus* (root).

Record & Garratt 1925 – *Aspidosperma, Gonioma.*

Record & Hess 1943 – Family (25 genera).

Record & Mell 1924 – *Aspidosperma.*

Riera 1947 – *Alstonia.*

Saiki 1982 – *Alstonia.*

Saint-Laurent 1926, 1928, 1934 – *Nerium.*

Schmid 1915 – ?*Aspidosperma.*

Schweingruber 1990 – *Nerium.*

Scott 1927 – *Gonioma.*

Sudo 1963 – *Alstonia, Aspidosperma, Dyera, Gonioma, Wrightia.*

Sudo 1988 – *Alstonia, Cerbera, Wrightia.*

Sugawa 1968c – *Dyera.*

Sulochana 1959 – *Rauvolfia* (root).

Tabatabai et al. 1963 – *Nerium* (Nos. 48, 49).

Tang 1973 – *Alstonia.*

Tortorelli 1956 – *Aspidosperma.*

Van Donselaar 1972 – *Aspidosperma* (wood by A.M.W. Mennega).

Vonk & Leeuwenberg 1989 – *Tabernanthe.*

Wagenführ & Scheiber 1974 – *Alstonia, Aspidosperma.*

Wang 1984–1988 – *Alstonia, Dyera.*

Webber 1945 – *Ambelania.*

Williams 1936 – 11 genera.

Wiraj Chunwarin & Damrong Sri-Aran 1974 – *Alstonia, Holarrhena, Wrightia.*

Zarucchi 1987 – *Molongum* (incl. *Ambelania*), *Mucoa, Rhigospira, Spongiosperma.*

Anomalous structure

Obaton 1960 – *Landolphia.*

Crystals and silica

Chattaway 1955 – *Rejoua* (= *Tabernaemontana*).

Chattaway 1956 – 10 genera.

Espinoza de Pernía 1987b – *Aspidosperma.*

Ecological anatomy

Baas et al. 1983 – *Nerium.*

Baas & Schweingruber 1987 – *Nerium.*

Barajas Morales 1985 – *Stemmadenia.*

(APOCYNACEAE)
Carlquist 1985a – *Acokanthera, Beaumontia, Carissa, Condylocarpon, Kopsia, Trachelospermum.*
Carlquist 1985 [1986]a – *Alyxia, Mandevilla, Trachelospermum.*
Den Outer & Van Veenendaal 1976 – *Holarrhena, Rauvolfia.*

Helical thickenings
Meylan & Butterfield 1978a – *Parsonsia.*

Laticifers
Fujii 1988 – *Alstonia.*

Pits and Perforation plates
Jing et al. 1988 – *Alstonia.*
Meylan & Butterfield 1975 – *Parsonsia.*
Nair & Ram 1989 – *Alstonia, Holarrhena, Wrightia.*

Rays
Chattaway 1951b – *Dyera.*
Sebastine 1955 – *Tabernaemontana.*

Tracheary elements
Gill et al. 1985b – *Alstonia, Holarrhena, Plumeria.*
Jing et al. 1989 – *Alstonia.*
Ohtani et al. 1983 – *Parsonsia* (warts).

AQUIFOLIACEAE
(*Ilex* unless otherwise stated)

Abbate 1970.
Araujo & Mattos Filho 1974a.
*Baas 1973 – 81 spp.
*Baas 1975 – *Ilex, Nemopanthus, Oncotheca, Phelline.*
Baas 1984b – *Ilex, Nemopanthus.*
Bargagli-Petrucci 1903.
Brazier & Franklin 1961.
Brown 1922 – *Byronia* (= *Ilex*).
Carpenter & Dickison 1976 – *Oncotheca.*
Carvalho 1954–1956.
Cheng, J.-Q. 1980.
Cheng, J.-Q. et al. 1992.
Cutler et al. 1987 – (root).
Dechamps 1979.
Descole & O'Donell 1937.
Détienne & Jacquet 1983.
Détienne et al. 1982.
Dickison 1982 – *Oncotheca.*
Edlmann & Monaco 1981.

(AQUIFOLIACEAE)
Furuno 1977, 1985, 1987.
Giordano 1939–1940.
Greguss 1959.
Grosser 1977.
Hayashi 1991.
Hirai 1979–1985.
Hu 1967.
Ilic 1991.
Jacquiot et al. 1973.
Kanehira 1921a, b, 1926.
Kribs 1928a.
Lecomte 1922, 1926a.
Luo 1989.
Mork 1946.
Nájera Angulo 1959.
Panshin & Zeeuw 1980.
Peraza Oramas & Lopez de Roma 1967.
Pérez Olvera et al. 1982 [1985].
Record 1938a.
Record & Hess 1943.
Saiki 1982.
Schweingruber 1978, 1990.
Shilkina 1977 – *Oncotheca.*
Shimaji & Itoh 1988.
Sudo 1959, 1988.
Suzuki et al. 1991.
Tabatabai et al. 1963 (No. 50).
Williams 1936.
Wuang 1979.
Yamabayashi 1938.

Crystals
Chattaway 1956.
Espinoza de Pernía 1987b.

Ecological anatomy
Baas & Schweingruber 1987.
Versteegh 1968.
Worbes 1986.

Growth rings
Worbes 1984.

Helical thickenings
Ohtani & Ishida 1978b.
Parham & Kaustinen 1973.

Perforation plates
Ohtani & Ishida 1978a.

Tracheary elements
Ohtani 1983.

ARALIACEAE

(*Acanthopanax* = *Eleutherococcus*;
Didymopanax = *Schefflera*)

Anon. 1966 – *Kalopanax*.
Anon. 1981 (Andes) – *Didymopanax*.
Anon. 1981 (Curua) – *Didymopanax*.
Alves de Pinho 1966 – *Didymopanax*.
Baas et al. 1984 – *Kalopanax*.
Barajas Morales & Echenique-Manrique
    1976 – *Dendropanax, Sciadodendron*.
Barajas Morales & León Gómez 1989 –
    Sciadodendron.
Bastos 1946 [1947] – *Didymopanax*.
Benoist 1931 – *Schefflera*.
Brazier & Franklin 1961 – *Acanthopanax,
    Didymopanax, Hedera*.
Brown 1922 – *Dipanax* (= *Tetraplasandra*),
    Panax, Tetraplasandra.
Burgerstein 1909 – *Meryta, Polyscias*.
Burgerstein 1912 – *Pentapanax*.
Burtt & Dickison 1975 – *Seemannaralia*.
Carreras & Vales 1986b – *Dendropanax*.
Cheng, C. 1985 – *Schefflera*.
Cheng, J.-Q. 1980 – *Kalopanax, Scheff-
    lera*.
Cheng, J.-Q. et al. 1992 – *Kalopanax,
    Schefflera*.
Chiang 1962 – *Schefflera*.
Cutler et al. 1987 – *Hedera* (root).
Dadswell & Eckersley 1935 – *Tieghemo-
    panax* (= *Polyscias*).
Dechamps 1979 – *Didymopanax, Scheff-
    lera*.
Détienne & Jacquet 1983 – *Dendropanax,
    Didymopanax, Schefflera*.
Détienne et al. 1982 – *Didymopanax,
    Schefflera*.
Edlmann & Monaco 1981 – *Dendropanax,
    Kalopanax*.
Fahn et al. 1986 – *Hedera*.
Furuno 1979 – *Polyscias*.
Giordano 1939 – *Polyscias, Schefflera*.
Gonzalez et al. 1971 – *Dendropanax*.
Greguss 1959 – *Hedera*.
Grosser 1977 – *Hedera*.
Hayashi 1991 – *Acanthopanax, Aralia,
    Dendropanax, Evodiopanax* (= *Gamblea*),
    Kalopanax.
Hirai 1979–1985 – *Acanthopanax, Dendro-
    panax, Evodiopanax, Kalopanax*.
Ilic 1991 – 14 genera.

(ARALIACEAE)

Kanehira 1921a – *Aralia, Fatsia, Gilibertia*
    (= *Dendropanax*), *Heptapleuron* (= *Scheff-
    lera*), *Oreopanax, Osmoxylon, Penta-
    panax*.
Kanehira 1921b – *Acanthopanax, Aralia*.
Kanehira 1926 – *Acanthopanax, Aralia,
    Metagalma* (ined.), *Papyropanax* (ined.).
Kribs 1959 – *Didymopanax, Kalopanax*.
Lebacq & Dechamps 1964 – *Cussonia,
    Polyscias*.
Lebacq & Dechamps 1967 – *Polyscias*.
Lebacq et al. 1973 – *Aralia, Didymopanax,
    Gilibertia* (= *Dendropanax*), *Oreopanax*.
Lebacq & Staner 1964 – *Cussonia, Didy-
    mopanax*.
Lebedenko 1962a – *Polyscias*.
Lecomte 1922 – *Cussonia*.
Lecomte 1926a – *Schefflera*.
Lemesle & Dupuy 1966 – *Nothopanax*.
Li & Chao 1954 – Family relations.
Luo 1989 – *Acanthopanax, Kalopanax*.
Mainieri 1962 – *Didymopanax*.
Mainieri 1978 – *Didymopanax, Pentapanax*.
Mainieri & Chimelo 1989 – *Didymopanax,
    Pentapanax*.
Meylan & Butterfield 1978b – *Pseudo-
    panax, Schefflera*.
Moll & Janssonius 1906–1936 – *Aralia,
    Arthrophyllum, Brassaiopsis, Heptapleu-
    rum* (= *Schefflera*), *Horsfieldia* (= *Harm-
    siopanax*), *Macropanax, Polyscias, Tre-
    vesia*.
Nardi Berti & Edlmann Abbate 1992 –
    Didymopanax, Schefflera.
Normand 1960 – *Cussonia*.
Normand & Paquis 1976 [1977] – *Cusso-
    nia, Polyscias*.
Pérez Mogollón 1993 – *Dendropanax*.
Pérez Olvera et al. 1980 [1981] – *Dendro-
    panax, Oreopanax*.
Pinho 1984 – *Didymopanax*.
Ragonese 1961 – *Didymopanax, Gilibertia*
    (= *Dendropanax*), *Pentapanax, Pseudo-
    panax*.
Rancusi et al. 1987 – *Pseudopanax*.
Record & Hess 1943 – Family (*Aralia,
    Dendropanax, Didymopanax, Oreopanax,
    Pseudopanax, Schefflera, Sciadoden-
    dron*).
Record & Mell 1924 – *Didymopanax*.
*Rodríguez 1957a – 26 genera.

(ARALIACEAE)
Rodríguez 1971 – Relations of Umbellulales.
Saiki 1982 – *Kalopanax.*
Saint-Laurent 1926, 1928, 1934 – *Hedera.*
Schweingruber 1978, 1990 – *Hedera.*
Shimaji & Itoh 1982 – *Kalopanax.*
Shimaji & Itoh 1988 – *Acanthopanax, Aralia, Kalopanax.*
Soper 1956–1957 – *Nothopanax* (= *Polyscias*), *Pseudopanax.*
Sudo 1959 – *Acanthopanax, Aralia, Dendropanax, Evodiopanax* (= *Gamblea*), *Kalopanax.*
Sudo 1963 – *Didymopanax, Polyscias.*
Tabatabai & Soleymani 1964 – *Hedera.*
Tang 1973 – *Schefflera.*
Tomazello Filho et al. 1983 – *Didymopanax.*
Tortorelli 1956 – *Didymopanax, Pentapanax.*
Vales & Carreras 1986 – *Dendropanax.*
Van der Slooten 1968 – *Didymopanax.*
Van der Slooten et al. 1970 – *Didymopanax.*
Wagemann 1949 – *Pseudopanax.*
Williams 1936 – *Didymopanax, Gilibertia* (= *Dendropanax*), *Nothopanax* (= *Polyscias*), *Oreopanax.*
Wu & Wang 1976 – *Schefflera.*
Wuang 1979 – *Kalopanax.*
Yamabayashi 1938 – *Acanthopanax, Aralia, Eleutherococcus, Kalopanax, Textoria* (= *Dendropanax*).
Yao 1988 – *Dendropanax.*

Crystals
Chattaway 1956 – *Pseudopanax.*

Ecological anatomy
Baas & Schweingruber 1987 – *Hedera.*
Barajas Morales 1985 – *Dendropanax.*
Carlquist 1985a – *Hedera, Pseudopanax, Tetrapanax.*
Carlquist 1987a – *Fatsia, Hedera, Kalopanax, Pseudopanax, Tetrapanax.*
Versteegh 1968 – *Harmsiopanax, Schefflera.*

Helical thickenings
Meylan & Butterfield 1978a – *Pseudopanax.*

(ARALIACEAE)
Pits and Perforation plates
Meylan & Butterfield 1974 – *Pseudopanax, Schefflera.*
Ohtani & Ishida 1978a – *Acanthopanax, Aralia, Dendropanax, Evodiopanax* (= *Gamblea*), *Kalopanax.*

Rays
Chattaway 1951b – *Panax.*

Septate fibres
Butterfield & Meylan 1976 – *Pseudopanax, Schefflera.*

Tracheary elements
Butterfield et al. 1984 – *Pseudopanax* 14 spp.
Ohtani 1983 – *Acanthopanax, Aralia, Dendropanax, Evodiopanax* (= *Gamblea*), *Kalopanax.*

ARALIDIACEAE see CORNACEAE

ARISTOLOCHIACEAE
(*Aristolochia* unless otherwise stated)

Burgerstein 1909.
*Carlquist 1993 – *Apama, Aristolochia, Asarum, Holostylis, Thottea.*
Dadswell & Record 1936.
Puławska 1982.
Rao, R.V. et al. 1992b – *Thottea* (prev. *Apama*).
Record & Hess 1943.
Snezhkova 1986.
Tippo 1938.
Yatsenko-Khmelevsky 1954a.

Anomalous structure
Obaton 1960 – *Pararistolochia.*

Ecological anatomy
Carlquist 1985 [1986]a.

ASCLEPIADACEAE

Burgerstein 1909 – *Hoya.*
Cellai 1967 – *Calotropis.*
Fahn et al. 1986 – *Calotropis, Periploca.*
Fontella Pereira et al. 1971 – *Oxypetalum.*
Greguss 1959 – *Periploca.*
Huber & Rouschal 1954 – *Periploca.*

(ASCLEPIADACEAE)
Jagiella & Kurschner 1987 – *Calotropis, Leptadenia, Periploca.*
Messeri 1938 – *Calotropis.*
Saint-Laurent 1932a – *Calotropis, Leptadenia.*
Schweingruber 1990 – *Periploca.*
Tabatabai & Soleymani 1964 – *Calotropis.*
Tabatabai et al. 1964 – *?Periploca.*
Vigodsky-De Philippis 1938 [1939] – *Solenostemma.*

Anomalous structure
Handa 1936b – *Marsdenia.*
Milanez 1966 – *Cryptostegia.*
Singh 1943 – *Leptadenia.*

Ecological anatomy
Baas et al. 1983 – *Calotropis, Periploca.*
Baas & Schweingruber 1987 – *Periploca.*
Carlquist 1985a – *Asclepias, Leptadenia, Periploca, Stephanotis, Tacazzea.*
Carlquist 1985 [1986]a – *Araujia, Hoya, Stephanotis, Tacazzea.*
Carlquist & Hoekman 1985a – *Asclepias.*
Umarov & Chavchavadze 1990 – *Periploca.*

ASTERACEAE see COMPOSITAE

ASTEROPEIACEAE see BONNETIACEAE

ATHEROSPERMATACEAE
see MONIMIACEAE

AUSTROBAILEYACEAE
(*Austrobaileya*)

Bailey & Swamy 1949.
Metcalfe 1987 – General survey.
Takahashi 1985.

Ecological anatomy
Carlquist 1985 [1986]a.

Tracheary elements
Carlquist 1988f.

AVICENNIACEAE see VERBENACEAE

BALANITACEAE see ZYGOPHYLLACEAE

BALANOPACEAE (*Balanops*)

*Carlquist 1980b – 6 spp.
Ilic 1991.

Crystals
Chattaway 1956.

BALSAMINACEAE

Gérard 1917 – *Impatiens.*

BARBEYACEAE (*Barbeya*)

Cellai 1971.
Dickison & Sweitzer 1970.
Jagiella & Kurschner 1987.
Moseley 1973 [1974].

BASELLACEAE

Ecological anatomy
Carlquist 1985 [1986]a – *Boussingaultia.*

BATACEAE (*Batis*)

*Carlquist 1978b.
McLaughlin 1959.
Moseley 1973 [1974].

Ecological anatomy
Carlquist & Hoekman 1985a.

BAUERACEAE (*Bauera*)

Dickison 1980.

BEGONIACEAE (*Begonia*)

Carlquist 1962a.
*Carlquist 1985d.

BERBERIDACEAE
(incl. NANDINACEAE; for *Hydrastis* see RANUNCULACEAE)

Barykina 1971 – *Berberis.*
Cutler et al. 1987 – *Berberis, Mahonia* (root).
Greguss 1959 – *Berberis, Mahoberberis, Mahonia.*
Grosser 1977 – *Berberis.*

(BERBERIDACEAE)

Harvey-Gibson & Horsman 1919 – *Berberis* and brief notes on 7 other genera (young stems).
Kanehira 1921a – *Berberis, Mahonia.*
Kanehira 1921b, 1926 – *Berberis.*
Novruzova & Shamsieva 1964 – *Berberis.*
Rancusi et al. 1987 – *Berberis.*
Record & Hess 1943 – *Berberis.*
Saint-Laurent 1926, 1928, 1934 – *Berberis.*
Schmid 1915 – *Berberis.*
Schweingruber 1978, 1990 – *Berberis.*
Shen 1954 – *Berberis, Mahonia, Nandina.*
Sudo 1959 – *Berberis.*
Takahashi 1985 – *Berberis, Mahonia, Nandina.*
Yamabayashi 1938 – *Berberis.*
Yatsenko-Khmelevsky 1954a – *Berberis.*

Crystals
Chattaway 1956 – *Berberis.*

Ecological anatomy
Baas & Schweingruber 1987 – *Berberis.*
Carlquist 1985a – *Berberis, Nandina.*
Carlquist 1987a – *Berberis.*
Carlquist & Hoekman 1985a – *Berberis.*
Novruzova 1968 – *Berberis.*
Webber 1936a – *Berberis.*

Helical thickenings
Ohtani & Ishida 1978b – *Berberis, Nandina.*

Perforation plates
Ohtani & Ishida 1978a – *Berberis, Nandina.*

Tracheary elements
Ohtani 1983 – *Berberis, Nandina.*

BETULACEAE
(incl. CARPINACEAE, CORYLACEAE)

Anon. 1966 – *Alnus, Betula, Ostrya.*
Anon. 1985 – *Carpinus.*
Alekseeva 1962a, b – *Betula.*
Armando Rondon & Hernandez Gil 1987 – *Alnus.*
Barajas Morales 1980 – *Alnus.*
Barykina & Kudryashev 1973 – *Betula.*
Berndt 1963, 1979 – *Betula.*
Bhat & Kärkkäinen 1980, 1981a, b (root), 1982 – *Betula.*

(BETULACEAE)

Biondi & Baldoni 1984 – *Betula.*
Brazier & Franklin 1961 – *Alnus, Betula, Carpinus, Corylus, Ostrya.*
Burgerstein 1912 – *Alnus.*
Carvalho 1954–1955, 1956 – *Alnus, Betula, Carpinus.*
Cheng, C. 1985 – *Alnus, Betula.*
Cheng, J.-Q. 1980 – *Alnus, Betula, Carpinus, Corylus, Ostrya.*
Cheng, J.-Q. et al. 1992 – *Alnus, Betula, Carpinus, Corylus, Ostrya.*
Chiang 1962 – *Alnus.*
Cutler et al. 1987 – *Alnus, Betula, Carpinus, Corylus* (root).
Detzner 1910 – *Alnus, Betula, Carpinus, Corylus, Ostrya, Ostryopsis* (root).
Edlmann & Monaco 1981 – *Alnus, Betula, Carpinus.*
Erak 1972 – *Corylus.*
Fegel 1941 – *Betula* (root).
Friedman 1978 – *Alnus, Betula.*
Furlow 1979 – *Alnus* 8 spp. (brief).
Furuno 1985, 1987 – *Alnus, Betula, Carpinus, Ostrya.*
Greguss 1959 – *Alnus, Betula, Carpinus, Corylus, Ostrya.*
Grosser 1977 – *Alnus, Betula, Carpinus, Corylus, Ostrya.*
*Hall 1952 – *Alnus, Betula, Carpinus, Corylus, Ostrya, Ostryopsis.*
Hayashi 1991 – *Alnus, Betula, Carpinus, Corylus, Ostrya.*
Hayden & Hayden 1984 – *Betula.*
Hejnowicz, A. 1980 – *Alnus.*
Hirai 1979–1985 – *Alnus, Betula, Carpinus, Corylus, Ostrya.*
Huber & Rouschal 1954 – *Corylus.*
Ilic 1991 – *Alnus, Betula, Carpinus, Corylus, Ostrya.*
Jacquiot et al. 1973 – *Alnus, Betula, Carpinus, Corylus, Ostrya.*
Joshi & Suzuki 1992 – *Alnus, Betula, Carpinus, Corylus.*
Kanehira 1921a – *Alnus, Carpinus.*
Kanehira 1921b, 1926 – *Alnus, Betula, Carpinus, Ostrya.*
Kasesalu 1968 – *Betula.*
Kribs 1959 – *Betula, Ostrya.*
Lebacq et al. 1973 – *Alnus.*
Lebedenko 1959 [1960] – *Alnus, Betula, Carpinus, Corylus.*

(BETULACEAE)
Lee et al. 1989 – *Carpinus*.
Luo 1989 – *Alnus, Betula*.
Miller, H.J. 1975 – *Betula*.
Miller & Cahow 1989 – *Betula*.
Mork 1946 – *Alnus, Betula, Corylus*.
Moseley 1973 [1974] – General.
Nájera Angulo & Lopez Fraile 1969 –
  Alnus, Betula.
Niloofari 1961 – *Alnus, Betula, Carpinus*.
Panshin & Zeeuw 1980 – *Alnus, Betula,*
  Carpinus, Ostrya.
Parsa Pajouh & Schweingruber 1985 –
  Alnus, Carpinus, Corylus.
Patel 1965 – *Alnus*.
Pearson & Brown 1932 – *Alnus, Betula*.
Pérez Olvera & Corral López 1980 –
  Alnus.
Pérez Olvera et al. 1982 [1985] – *Carpinus,*
  Ostrya.
Pozhidaeva 1970 – *Carpinus*.
Rebollar Dominguez 1977 – *Alnus*.
Record & Hess 1943 – *Alnus, Betula, Car-*
  pinus, Corylus, Ostrya.
Record & Mell 1924 – *Alnus*.
Riedl 1937 – *Alnus, Betula, Carpinus*
  (root).
Sacchse & Schulte 1991 – *Alnus*.
Saiki 1982 – *Alnus, Betula, Carpinus,*
  Ostrya.
Saint-Laurent 1926, 1928, 1934 – *Alnus*.
Şanli 1988 [1989] – *Ostrya*.
Schweingruber 1978, 1990 – *Alnus, Betu-*
  la, Carpinus, Corylus, Ostrya.
Shimaji & Itoh 1982 – *Alnus*.
Shimaji & Itoh 1988 – *Alnus, Betula, Car-*
  pinus, Ostrya.
Soh & Han 1985 – *Alnus, Betula, Carpi-*
  nus, Corylus, Ostrya.
Sosnowsky 1933 – *Betula*.
Stark 1953a – *Alnus, Betula, Carpinus,*
  Corylus, Ostrya.
Sudo 1959 – *Alnus, Betula, Carpinus,*
  Corylus, Ostrya.
Suzuki et al. 1991 – *Alnus, Betula, Carpi-*
  nus, Corylus.
Tabatabai et al. 1969 – *Alnus, Betula, Car-*
  pinus, Corylus.
Tang 1973 – *Alnus, Betula, Carpinus*.
Ter-Abraamyan 1951 – *Carpinus*.
Thunell & Perem 1947 – *Alnus, Betula,*
  Carpinus, Corylus.

(BETULACEAE)
Tippo 1938 – Family (*Alnus* 10 spp., *Betu-*
  la 20, *Carpinus* 8, *Corylus* 4, *Ostrya* 3,
  Ostryopsis 1).
Tortorelli 1956 – *Alnus*.
Tschchubianischvili 1933 – *Corylus*.
Tumanyan 1975 – *Betula*.
Van der Slooten 1968 – *Alnus*.
Wagenführ & Scheiber 1974 – *Alnus,*
  Betula, Carpinus.
Wang 1965 – *Alnus*.
Wang & Li 1989 – *Alnus*.
Wu & Wang 1976 – *Alnus, Carpinus*.
Wuang 1979 – *Betula, Carpinus, Corylus*.
Yamabayashi 1938 – *Alnus, Betula,*
  Carpinus, Corylus, Ostrya.
Yao 1988 – *Alnus, Betula, Carpinus*.
Yu 1948 – *Betula*.

Anomalous structure
Holdheide 1955 – *Carpinus*.
Korovin 1987 – *Alnus, Betula*.

Crystals
Chattaway 1955 – *Betula, Carpinus,*
  Ostrya.
Chattaway 1956 – *Carpinus, Ostrya*.
Scurfield et al. 1973 – *Carpinus, Ostrya*.

Ecological anatomy
Baas & Schweingruber 1987 – *Alnus,*
  Betula, Carpinus, Corylus, Ostrya.
Carlquist 1985a – *Alnus, Betula, Carpinus,*
  Corylus.
Carlquist & Hoekman 1985a – *Alnus,*
  Betula.
Forsaith 1920 – *Alnus, Betula*.
Lim & Soh 1991a – *Alnus*.
Novruzova 1968 – *Alnus, Betula, Carpi-*
  nus, Corylus.
Tabata 1964 – *Betula* (branches).
Webber 1936a – *Corylus*.

Helical thickenings
Ohtani & Ishida 1978b – *Carpinus, Cory-*
  lus, Ostrya.
Parham & Kaustinen 1973 – *Carpinus,*
  Ostrya.

Perforation plates
Ohtani & Ishida 1978a – *Alnus, Betula,*
  Carpinus, Corylus, Ostrya.
Parameswaran & Liese 1973 – *Alnus*.

(BETULACEAE)

Rays

Bailey 1910 – *Betula, Carpinus.*
Bhat 1983 – *Betula.*
Braun et al. 1968 – *Alnus, Carpinus.*
Erak 1971 – *Corylus.*
Hoar 1916 – *Alnus, Betula, Carpinus,*
Corylus, Ostrya.
Kobayashi 1952 – *Alnus.*
Noskowiak 1978 – *Alnus.*

Tracheary elements

Jing et al. 1989 – *Alnus, Betula.*
Ohtani 1983 – *Alnus, Betula, Carpinus,*
Corylus, Ostrya.
Yaghmaie & Catling 1984 – *Alnus, Betula.*

BIGNONIACEAE

Anon. 1981 (Andes) – *Tabebuia.*
Alves de Pinho 1966 – *Tecoma.*
Alves de Pinho 1969 – *Tabebuia.*
Babos & Borhidi 1978 – *Catalpa, Tabebuia.*
Barajas Morales & Echenique-Manrique
1976 – *Tabebuia.*
Barajas Morales & León Gómez 1989 –
Crescentia, Tabebuia.
Bastos 1946 [1947] – *Jacaranda, Tecoma.*
Benoist 1931 – *Couralia* (= *Tabebuia*),
Jacaranda, Tabebuia.
Brazier & Franklin 1961 – *Catalpa,*
Jacaranda, Paratecoma, Tabebuia.
Brindha et al. 1990 – *Oroxylum* (root).
Burgerstein 1912 – *Tecoma.*
Carlquist 1992c – *Catalpa, Tecoma.*
Carreras & Vales 1986b – *Catalpa,*
Spathodea, Tabebuia.
Carreras & Vales 1987 – *Catalpa.*
Cheng, C. 1985 – *Catalpa.*
Cheng, J.-Q. 1980 – *Catalpa, Markhamia,*
Radermachera.
Cheng, J.-Q. et al. 1992 – *Catalpa, Mark-*
hamia, Radermachera.
Cockrell 1942 – *Deplanchea.*
Cunha Mello 1950 [1951] – *Jacaranda.*
Cunha Mello 1967 – *Zeyheria.*
Cutler et al. 1987 – *Bignonia, Catalpa* (root).
Dechamps 1979 – *Jacaranda, Tabebuia.*
Den Outer & Van Veenendaal 1983 – Notes
on 14 genera and relations.
Détienne & Jacquet 1983 – *Jacaranda, Para-*
tecoma, Saldanhaea (= *Cuspidaria*), *Tabe-*
buia, Tecoma, Zeyheria.

(BIGNONIACEAE)

Détienne et al. 1982 – *Jacaranda, Tabebuia.*
*Dos Santos & Miller 1992 – 11 genera.
Edlmann & Monaco 1981 – *Catalpa.*
Eggeling & Harris 1939 – *Markhamia.*
Fasolo 1941–1944 – *Kigelia.*
Fedalto et al. 1989 – *Jacaranda.*
Furuno 1985, 1987 – *Catalpa.*
Gaiotti de Peralta & Edlmann Abbate 1981 –
Tabebuia.
*Gasson & Dobbins 1991 – 62 genera.
Giordano 1939, 1940 – *Stereospermum.*
Gómez 1959 – *Tabebuia.*
Greguss 1959 – *Campsis, Catalpa.*
Grosser 1977 – *Catalpa.*
Hayashi 1991 – *Catalpa.*
Hess 1950c – *Zeyheria.*
Hoheisel et al. 1968 – *Jacaranda.*
Huber & Rouschal 1954 – *Catalpa.*
Ilic 1991 – 13 genera.
*Jain & Singh 1980 – 14 genera, 17 spp.
Johnston 1952 – *Tabebuia.*
Kanehira 1921a – *Stereospermum.*
Kanehira 1921b – *Catalpa.*
Kanehira 1924 – *Radermachera.*
Kanehira 1926 – *Catalpa.*
Kribs 1959 – *Cybistax, Jacaranda, Para-*
tecoma, Tabebuia.
Lebacq & Dechamps 1964, 1967 – *Ferdi-*
nandia (= *Fernandoa*), *Markhamia,*
Spathodea.
Lebacq et al. 1973 – *Crescentia, Jacaranda,*
Tabebuia, Tecoma.
Lecomte 1926a – *Markhamia, Oroxylum.*
Lepe 1959 – *Tabebuia.*
Lindorf 1988 – *Tabebuia.*
Luo 1989 – *Catalpa, Markhamia, Stereo-*
spermum.
Mainieri 1958 – *Jacaranda, Tabebuia.*
Mainieri 1962 – *Jacaranda.*
Mainieri 1978 – *Jacaranda, Paratecoma,*
Tabebuia.
Mainieri & Chimelo 1989 – *Jacaranda,*
Paratecoma, Tabebuia.
Moll & Janssonius 1906–1936 – *Doli-*
chandrone, Oroxylum, Stereospermum.
Nardi Berti & Edlmann Abbate 1992 – *Jaca-*
randa, Paratecoma, Roseodendron (= *Ta-*
bebuia), *Tabebuia.*
Niloofari 1961 – *Catalpa.*
Normand 1960 – *Markhamia, Spathodea,*
Stereospermum.

(BIGNONIACEAE)

Normand & Paquis 1976 [1977] – *Fernandoa, Kigelia, Markhamia, Newbouldia, Spathodea, Stereospermum.*
Panshin 1932 – *Dolichandrone.*
Panshin & Zeeuw 1980 – *Catalpa.*
Paula & Alves 1989 – *Tabebuia.*
Pearson & Brown 1932 – *Dolichandrone, Heterophragma, Stereospermum.*
Pereira 1933 – *Jacaranda, Tecoma.*
Pereira et al. 1970 – *Tabebuia.*
Pérez Mogollón 1973 – *Tabebuia.*
Pérez Olvera & Corral López 1980 – *Tabebuia.*
Pérez Olvera et al. 1982 [1985] – *Jacaranda.*
Pfeiffer, J.P. 1926 – *Arrabidaea, Jacaranda, Tabebuia, Tecoma.*
Prakash 1972 – *Crescentia, Kigelia* (root).
Purkayastha et al. 1976 – *Pajanelia.*
*Record & Hess 1940b – 15 genera.
Record & Hess 1943 – Family (15 genera).
Record & Mell 1924 – *Jacaranda.*
Rogel Gomez 1982 – *Parmentiera.*
Rogers 1984 – Comparison with 3 genera of Rubiaceae.
Schmid 1915 – *Tecoma.*
Sudo 1959 – *Catalpa.*
Sudo 1963 – *Cybistax, Dolichandrone, Jacaranda, Paratecoma, Radermachera, Tabebuia.*
Tang 1973 – *Catalpa, Markhamia, Mayodendron* (= *Radermachera*), *Oroxylum, Stereospermum.*
Tomazello Filho et al. 1983 – *Tabebuia.*
Tortorelli 1956 – *Jacaranda, Tabebuia.*
Vales & Carreras 1987 – *Spathodea, Tabebuia.*
Wagenführ & Scheiber 1974 – *Paratecoma.*
Williams 1936 – *Crescentia, Jacaranda, Tabebuia.*
Wiraj Chunwarin & Damrong Sri-Aran 1974 – *Millingtonia, Stereospermum.*
Wuang 1979 – *Catalpa.*
Yamabayashi 1938 – *Catalpa.*
Yao 1988 – *Dolichandrone.*

Anomalous structure
Dobbins 1971 – *Doxantha* (=*Macfadyena*).
Dobbins 1981 – *Clytostoma.*
Handa 1936a – *Campsis.*

(BIGNONIACEAE)

Jain 1984 – *Adenocalymna.*
Pfeiffer 1924b – Brief notes on 13 genera.
Pfeiffer 1925 – *Pleonotoma.*

Crystals
Chattaway 1955 – *Radermachera.*
Chattaway 1956 – *Couralia* (= *Tabebuia*), *Diplanthera* (= *Deplanchea*).

Ecological anatomy
Carlquist 1985a – *Doxantha* (=*Macfadyena*).
Carlquist 1985 [1986]a – *Adenocalymma, Phaedranthus* (= *Distictis*).
Carlquist & Hoekman 1985a – *Chilopsis.*
Den Outer & Van Veenendaal 1976 – *Kigelia.*
Vales et al. 1983 – *Tabebuia.*

Growth rings
Détienne 1989 – *Jacaranda.*
Worbes 1988 – *Tabebuia.*

Helical thickenings
Nair 1987 – *Radermachera.*
Ohtani & Ishida 1978b – *Catalpa.*
Parham & Kaustinen 1973 – *Catalpa.*

Perforation plates
Chalk 1933 – *Dolichandrone, Millingtonia, Oroxylum, Stereospermum.*
Ohtani & Ishida 1978a – *Catalpa.*
Parameswaran & Liese 1973 – *Markhamia, Oroxylum.*

Rays
Sebastine 1955 – *Pajanelia.*

Silica
Scurfield et al. 1974 – *Stereospermum.*
Sharma & Rao 1970 – *Stereospermum* (*Radermachera*).

Storied structure
Cozzo & Cristiani 1950 – *Tabebuia.*

Tracheary elements
Gill et al. 1985b – *Jacaranda.*
Jing et al. 1989 – *Catalpa, Stereospermum.*
Ohtani 1983 – *Catalpa.*

BIXACEAE (*Bixa*)

Dechamps 1979.
Détienne & Jacquet 1983.
Fedalto 1982.

(BIXACEAE)

Fedalto et al. 1989.
Ilic 1991.
Keating 1968 [1969].
Lebacq et al. 1973.
Normand 1950b–1960.
Prakash 1972.
Record & Hess 1943.
Tang 1973.
Vestal 1937.
Williams 1936.

Storied structure

Cozzo & Cristiani 1950.

Tracheary elements

Gill & Onuja 1984b.

BOMBACACEAE

Anon. 1981 (Andes) – *Bombacopsis, Catostemma, Ceiba, Huberodendron, Quararibea.*
Abbate & Cavina 1980 – *Cullenia* (= *Durio*).
Baas 1972b – *Kostermansia.*
Babos & Vales 1977 [1978] – *Bombacopsis.*
Balan Menon 1959 – *Boschia, Coelostegia, Durio, Neesia.*
Barajas Morales & León Gómez 1989 – *Ceiba.*
Barajas Morales et al. 1979 – *Ceiba, Quararibea.*
Bargagli-Petrucci 1903 – *Coelostegia, Durio, Neesia.*
Benoist 1931 – *Bombax, Guenetia* (= *Catostemma*).
Braun 1900 – *Adansonia.*
Brazier & Franklin 1961 – *Bombax, Ceiba, Durio, Ochroma.*
Burgerstein 1912 – *Chorisia.*
Carreras & Vales 1986b – *Bombacopsis, Ochroma.*
Carreras & Vales 1987 – *Bombacopsis.*
Cheng, J.-Q. 1980 – *Gossampinus.*
Cheng, J.-Q. et al. 1992 – *Gossampinus, Ochroma.*
Cockrell 1942 – *Durio.*
Dechamps 1979 – *Bombacopsis, Catostemma, Cavanillesia, Ceiba, Eriotheca, Huberodendron, Ochroma, Pachira, Quararibea.*

(BOMBACACEAE)

Détienne & Jacquet 1983 – 15 genera.
Détienne et al. 1982 – *Bombacopsis, Catostemma, Ceiba, Eriotheca, Pachira.*
*Détienne et al. 1983 – 15 genera, 40 spp.
Eeckhout 1951 – *Ceiba.*
Fedalto et al. 1989 – *Ceiba.*
Ferreirinha 1955 – *Bombax.*
Fouarge & Gérard 1964 – *Bombax, Ceiba.*
Freitas 1963, 1971 – *Bombax.*
Furuno 1977 – *Bombax, Ochroma.*
Gaiotti de Peralta & Edlmann Abbate 1981 – *Bombacopsis.*
Gómez 1959 – *Ceiba.*
Gonzalez et al. 1971 – *Bombacopsis.*
Hayashi et al. 1973 – *Coelostegia, Durio.*
Hirai 1979–1985 – *Ochroma.*
Hyde 1925 – *Cavanillesia, Pachira.*
Ilic 1991 – 14 genera.
Kanehira 1921a – *Bombax.*
Kanehira 1924 – *Camptostemon.*
Kanehira et al. 1933 – *Adansonia, Bombax, Cavanillesia, Chorisia, Ochroma.*
Kobayashi & Sugawa 1963 – *Ochroma.*
Kobayashi & Sugawa 1966a – *Durio.*
Kribs 1928a – *Catostemma.*
Kribs 1959 – *Bombacopsis, Catostemma, Ceiba, Ochroma.*
Lebacq & Dechamps 1964 – *Bombax, Ceiba.*
Lebacq & Dechamps 1967 – *Ceiba.*
Lebacq et al. 1973 – 11 genera.
Lecomte 1926a – *Bombax.*
Lepe 1959 – *Ceiba.*
Lomibao 1978 – *Camptostemon.*
Lopes et al. 1983 – *Bombax.*
Luo 1989 – *Bombax, Ochroma.*
Mägdefrau & Wutz 1961 – *Bombax, Pachira.*
Mainieri 1978 – *Eriotheca.*
Mainieri & Chimelo 1989 – *Ceiba, Eriotheca, Pseudobombax.*
Martawijaya et al. 1986 – *Durio.*
Miller 1991 – *Phragmotheca.*
Moll & Janssonius 1906–1936 – *Bombax, Durio, Eriodendron* (= *Ceiba*), *Neesia.*
Moseley 1956 – *Ceiba* (root).
Nardi Berti & Edlmann Abbate 1988 – *Bombax, Ceiba, Rhodognaphalon.*
Nardi Berti & Edlmann Abbate 1992 – *Bombacopsis, Chorisia, Ochroma.*
Normand 1955 – *Bombax, Ceiba.*

(BOMBACACEAE)
Normand & Paquis 1976 [1977] –
  Bombax, Ceiba, Rhodognaphalon.
Ogata 1975–1983 – Bombax, Ceiba, Durio.
Ortega 1958 – Bernoullia, Pachira.
Panshin 1932 – Camptostemon.
Paula 1975 – Catostemma.
Paula 1976a – Catostemma, Scleronema.
Paula 1977 – Catostemma.
Paula 1979 – Catostemma, Scleronema.
Paula 1980 – Pseudobombax.
Pearson & Brown 1932 – Bombax, Cul-
  lenia (= Durio).
Pereira 1933 – Chorisia.
Pérez Mogollón 1991b – Bombacopsis.
Pérez Olvera et al. 1980 [1981] – Ceiba.
Pfeiffer, J.P. 1926 – Ceiba, Ochroma.
Purkayastha et al. 1976 – Bombax.
*Record 1939b – 16 genera.
Record & Hess 1943 – Family (16 genera).
Record & Mell 1924 – ?Quararibea.
Riera 1947 – Ceiba.
Robyns et al. 1977 – Maxwellia (or Ster-
  culiaceae).
Rogel Gomez 1982 – Chiranthodendron (or
  Sterculiaceae), Quararibea.
Saiki 1982 – Durio, Ochroma.
Schmid 1915 – ?Ceiba.
Schmidt 1951–1952 – Ceiba.
Schultz & Wollheim 1962 – Chorisia.
Sudo 1963 – Bombacopsis, Camptostemon,
  Catostemma, Ceiba, Durio, Ochroma.
Sudo 1988 – Bombax, Ochroma.
Tang 1973 – Ceiba, Gossampinus.
Tortorelli 1956 – Chorisia.
Troll 1933 – Camptostemon (root).
Vales & Carreras 1986 – Ochroma.
Vales et al. 1977 – Bombacopsis.
Wagenführ & Scheiber 1974 – Ceiba,
  Ochroma.
Wang 1984–1988 – Boschia, Durio.
Williams 1936 – Bombax, Matisia, Ochro-
  ma, Quararibea.
Wiraj Chunwarin & Damrong Sri-Aran 1973
  – Boschia, Neesia, Salmalia (= Bombax).
Yao 1988 – Gossampinus.

Crystals and silica
Chattaway 1955 – Adansonia, Ochroma.
Chattaway 1956 – Bombax, Camptostemon,
  Ceiba, Coelostegia, Durio, Gossampinus,
  Neesia, Salmalia (= Bombax).

(BOMBACACEAE)
Espinoza de Pernía 1987b – Bombacopsis,
  Bombax, Ceiba, Chorisia, Pachira, Qua-
  raribea, Spirotheca (= Ceiba).
Scurfield et al. 1974 – Boschia, Coelo-
  stegia.
Welle 1976b – Bombax, Quararibea.

Ecological anatomy
Barajas Morales 1985 – Bernoullia.

Perforation plates
Parameswaran & Liese 1973 – Pachira.

Rays
Bargagli-Petrucci 1904 – 16 genera.
Chattaway 1933a – Malvales: general.
Chattaway 1951b – Durio.

Storied structure
Cozzo & Cristiani 1950 – Bombax, Chorisia.

Tracheary elements
Jing et al. 1989 – Bombax.

BONNETIACEAE

*Baretta-Kuipers 1976 – 11 genera +
  Asteropeia.
Bargagli-Petrucci 1903 – Archytaea.
Desch 1954 – Archytaea.
Détienne & Jacquet 1983 – Caraipa, Hap-
  loclathra, Mahurea, Marila.
Détienne et al. 1982 – Caraipa, Mahurea.
Ilic 1991 – Bonnetia, Ploiarium (or Gut-
  tiferae).
Lecomte 1922 – Asteropeia.
Miller, R.B. 1975 – Asteropeia.
Prakash & Lau 1976 – Ploiarium (or Gut-
  tiferae).
Record 1942a – Archytaea, Bonnetia.
Record & Hess 1943 – Archytaea, Bon-
  netia.
Williams 1936 – Bonnetia.

Ecological anatomy
Carlquist 1985a – Bonnetia.

Silica
Espinoza de Pernía 1987b – Archytaea,
  Haploclathra.
Welle 1976b – Archytaea, Haplocla-
  thra.

BORAGINACEAE
Abbate 1964 – *Ehretia.*
Aldridge 1981 – *Echium* 17 spp.
Almeida 1947 – *Cordia.*
Baas et al. 1984 – *Carmona.*
Babos & Borhidi 1981 – *Cordia.*
Barajas Morales 1981 – *Bourreria, Cordia.*
Barajas Morales & Echenique-Manrique
    1976 – *Cordia.*
Barajas Morales & León Gómez 1989 –
    Bourreria, Cordia.
Barbosa et al. 1977–1978 – *Cordia.*
Benoist 1931 – *Cordia.*
Brazier & Franklin 1961 – *Cordia.*
Burgerstein 1912 – *Saccellium.*
Carlquist 1970a – *Echium* 13 spp.
Cellai 1971 – *Cordia.*
Cheng, J.-Q. 1980 – *Ehretia.*
Cheng, J.-Q. et al. 1992 – *Ehretia.*
Cunha Mello 1954 – *Cordia.*
Dadswell & Eckersley 1935 – *Ehretia.*
Dechamps 1979 – *Cordia.*
Détienne & Jacquet 1983 – *Cordia, Lepi-*
    docordia, Tournefortia.
Détienne et al. 1982 – *Cordia.*
Fahn et al. 1986 – *Cordia.*
Fasolo 1939–1940 – *Cordia.*
Fedalto et al. 1989 – *Cordia.*
Furuno 1977, 1979 – *Cordia.*
Gaiotti de Peralta & Edlmann Abbate 1981
    – *Cordia.*
Gasson & Cutler 1990 – *Ehretia* (root).
Giordano 1939, 1940 – *Cordia.*
Gomes 1982 – *Cordia.*
Gottwald 1980a – *Cordia.*
Gottwald 1982 – *Antrophora* (= *Lepido-*
    cordia), Lepidocordia, Pteleocarpa.
Gottwald 1983a – *Cordia* 10 spp.
*Gottwald 1983b – *Auxemma* 2 spp., *Cordia*
    95 spp., *Patagonula* 1 sp.
Gottwald & Noack 1965 [1966] – *Cordia.*
Hayashi 1991 – *Ehretia.*
Hirai 1979–1985 – *Ehretia.*
Hyde 1925 – *Cordia.*
Ilic 1991 – *Bourreria, Cordia, Ehretia,*
    Messerschmidia (= *Tournefortia), Pata-*
    gonula, Rochefortia, Tournefortia.
Jagiella & Kurschner 1987 – *Cordia.*
Kanehira 1921a – *Cordia, Ehretia, Tour-*
    nefortia.
Kanehira 1921b – *Ehretia.*
Kanehira 1926 – *Cordia, Ehretia.*

(BORAGINACEAE)
Kribs 1959 – *Cordia, Patagonula.*
Lebacq & Dechamps 1964 – *Cordia.*
Lebacq et al. 1973 – *Cordia.*
Lebedenko 1962a – *Cordia.*
Luo 1989 – *Ehretia.*
Mainieri 1978 – *Cordia, Patagonula.*
Mainieri & Chimelo 1989 – *Cordia, Pata-*
    gonula.
Metcalfe 1933 – *Cordia.*
Moll & Janssonius 1906–1936 – *Cordia,*
    Ehretia.
Nardi Berti & Edlmann Abbate 1992 – *Cor-*
    dia, Patagonula.
Normand 1960 – *Cordia, Ehretia.*
Normand & Paquis 1976 [1977] – *Cordia,*
    Ehretia.
Ogata 1975–1983 – *Cordia.*
Ortega 1958 – *Cordia.*
Paula 1979, 1981 – *Cordia.*
Pearson & Brown 1932 – *Cordia, Ehretia.*
Pereira 1933 – *Patagonula.*
Pérez Mogollón 1973 – *Cordia.*
Pérez Olvera 1993 – *Cordia, Ehretia.*
Pfeiffer, J.P. 1926 – *Cordia.*
Rao, B.H. et al. 1989 – *Ehretia, Pteleo-*
    carpa, Saccellium.
*Record & Hess 1941b – *Auxemma,*
    Bourreria, Cordia, Ehretia, Patagonula,
    Rochefortia, Saccellium, Tournefortia.
Record & Hess 1943 – Family (8 genera).
Scala 1934 – *Patagonula.*
Schweingruber 1990 – *Echium, Lithodora,*
    Moltkia, Onosma.
Senni 1905 – *Cordia.*
Sudo 1959 – *Ehretia.*
Sudo 1963 – *Cordia, Ehretia, Patagonula.*
Sudo 1988 – *Cordia.*
Surya Kamala et al. 1988 – *Echium.*
Surya Kamala et al. 1989 – *Heliotropium,*
    Mallotonia, Tournefortia.
Tang 1973 – *Cordia, Ehretia.*
Teles & Paula 1980 – *Cordia.*
Tortorelli 1956 – *Cordia, Patagonula.*
Veldkamp 1988 – *Pteleocarpa.*
Wagemann 1949 – *Cordia.*
Wagenführ & Scheiber 1974 – *Cordia.*
Williams 1936 – *Cordia.*

Crystals
Chattaway 1955 – *Cordia, Patagonula.*
Chattaway 1956 – *Bourreria, Ceiba.*

(BORAGINACEAE)
Espinoza de Pernía 1987b – *Cordia, Lepidocordia.*
Heubl et al. 1990 – 17 genera.
Meniado et al. 1970 – *Cordia.*
Scurfield et al. 1973 – *Cordia, Patagonula.*

Ecological anatomy
Baas et al. 1983 – *Cordia.*
Baas & Schweingruber 1987 – *Echium, Lithodora, Moltkia, Onosma.*
Barajas Morales 1985 – *Bourreria, Cordia.*
Carlquist 1977c – *Halgania.*
Carlquist 1985a – *Ehretia, Lepidocordia.*
Versteegh 1968 – *Ehretia.*

Growth rings
Tschinkel 1966 – *Cordia.*

Perforation plates
Bisen & Sharma 1985 – *Cordia.*

Rays
McLean & Richardson 1973 [1974] – *Ehretia.*

Tracheary elements
Gill & Onuja 1984b – *Cordia.*
Gill et al. 1985b – *Cordia.*

Vestured pits
Barajas Morales 1983 [1984] – *Bourreria, Cordia.*
Miller 1977 – 12 genera.
Nair & Ram 1989 – *Cordia.*

BRASSICACEAE see CRUCIFERAE

BRETSCHNEIDERACEAE
(*Bretschneidera*)

Cheng, J.-Q. 1980.
Cheng, J.-Q. et al. 1992.
Heimsch 1942.
Luo 1989.
Tang 1935, 1973.

BREXIACEAE see ESCALLONIACEAE

BRUNELLIACEAE (*Brunellia*)

Cuatrecasas 1970 (Anatomy by Eyde).
Pérez Mogollón 1993.
Record & Hess 1943.
Tippo 1938.
Vales 1984.
Van der Slooten 1968.

BRUNIACEAE

*Carlquist 1978a – 12 genera.
Lemesle 1955b – General.

Pits and Perforation plates
Carlquist 1992d – *Berzelia, Lonchostoma.*

Tracheary elements
Lemesle 1956a – *Audouinia, Brunia, Staavia, Tittmannia.*

BUDDLEJACEAE see LOGANIACEAE

BURSERACEAE

Abbate 1970 – *Boswellia.*
Ayensu & Bentum 1974 – *Canarium.*
Balan Menon 1959 – *Canarium, Dacryodes, Santiria, Scutinanthe, Triomma.*
Barajas Morales & León Gómez 1989 – *Bursera.*
Bargagli-Petrucci 1903 – *Canarium, Santiria.*
Becking 1960 – *Aucoumea.*
Benoist 1931 – *Protium, Tetragastris.*
Brazier & Franklin 1961 – *Aucoumea, Canarium.*
Carreras & Pérez 1988 – *Bursera.*
Chauhan & Dayal 1990 – *Boswellia, Garuga.*
Cheng, J.-Q. 1980 – *Canarium, Garuga.*
Cheng, J.-Q. et al. 1992 – *Canarium, Ganuga.*
Cockrell 1942 – *Canarium, Dacryodes, Santiria.*
Collardet 1929a – *Aucoumea.*
Dadswell & Eckersley 1935 – *Protium.*
Dechamps 1979 – *Dacryodes, Protium, Tetragastris, Trattinnickia.*
Détienne 1976a – *Aucoumea.*
Détienne & Jacquet 1983 – *Bursera, Dacryodes, Hemicrepidospermum (= Crepidospermum), Protium, Tetragastris, Trattinickia.*
Détienne et al. 1982 – *Dacryodes, Protium, Tetragastris, Trattinickia.*
Dixon 1919 – *Aucoumea, Protium.*
Doležal 1959 – *Canarium.*
Dupéron 1979 – *Boswellia.*
Eeckhout 1951 – *Canarium, Pachylobus (= Dacryodes).*

(BURSERACEAE)

Forman et al. 1989 – *Beiselia* + 14 genera for comparison.

Fouarge & Gérard 1964 – *Canarium, Dacryodes*.

Fouarge et al. 1953 – *Canarium*.

Freitas 1958 – *Canarium*.

Freitas 1987 – *Dacryodes*.

Furuno 1977, 1979 – *Canarium, Garuga, Protium*.

Gómez 1959 – *Bursera*.

Gómez-Vázquez & Engleman 1983 – *Bursera*.

Grisa 1988 – *Commiphora*.

Hayashi et al. 1973 – *Canarium, Dacryodes, Santiria, Scutinanthe*.

Heimsch 1942 – Family (19 genera).

Hirai 1979–1985 – *Canarium*.

Hoheisel et al. 1968 – *Protium*.

Ilic 1991 – 11 genera.

Jagiella & Kurschner 1987 – *Commiphora*.

Jentsch et al. 1936 – *Aucoumea*.

Kanehira 1921a – *Canarium*.

Kanehira 1924 – *Canarium, Santiria*.

Kribs 1928a – *Icica* (= *Protium*).

Kribs 1959 – *Aucoumea, Bursera, Canarium, Dacryodes, Protium, Tetragastris*.

Lebacq 1963 – *Canarium, Dacryodes, Santiria*.

Lebacq & Dechamps 1964 – *Aucoumea, Canarium, Dacryodes, Santiria*.

Lebacq & Dechamps 1967 – *Canarium, Dacryodes, Santiria*.

Lebacq et al. 1973 – *Bursera, Crepidospermum, Dacryodes, Protium, Tetragastris, Trattinnickia*.

Lebacq & Staner 1964 – *Canarium, Protium*.

Lecomte 1922, 1926a – *Canarium*.

Lepe 1959 – *Bursera*.

Luo 1989 – *Canarium, Garuga, Protium*.

Mainieri 1962 – *Trattinnickia*.

Mainieri & Chimelo 1989 – *Protium*.

Martin 1953 – *Canarium, Pachylobus* (= *Dacryodes*).

Moll & Janssonius 1906–1936 – *Canarium, Garuga, Protium*.

Nardi Berti & Edlmann Abbate 1988 – *Aucoumea, Canarium, Dacryodes*.

(BURSERACEAE)

Nardi Berti & Edlmann Abbate 1992 – *Protium, Tetragastris*.

Normand 1948b – *Dacryodes, Santiria*.

Normand 1955 – *Canarium, Dacryodes, Santiriopsis* (= *Santiria*).

Normand 1962 – *Dacryodes* 10 spp.

Normand & Mariaux 1962 – *Dacryodes* 9 spp.

Normand & Paquis 1976 [1977] – *Aucoumea, Canarium, Dacryodes, Santiria*.

Ogata 1975–1983 – *Canarium, Dacryodes, Garuga, Protium, Santiria, Triomma*.

Ogata 1992 – *Canarium*.

Paula & Alves 1980 – *Bursera*.

Pearson & Brown 1932 – *Boswellia, Bursera, Canarium, Garuga*.

Pérez Mogollón 1973 – *Tetragastris*.

Pérez Olvera et al. 1980 [1981] – *Bursera*.

Pfeiffer, J.P. 1926 – *Protium, Tetragastris*.

Purkayastha et al. 1976 – *Canarium*.

Record & Hess 1943 – Family (*Bursera, Crepidospermum, Dacryodes, Protium, Tetragastris, Trattinnickia*).

Riera 1947 – *Aucoumea, Pachylobus* (= *Dacryodes*).

Rock 1972 – *Bursera*.

Rogel Gomez 1982 – *Protium*.

Schmidt 1951–1952 – *Aucoumea, Canarium*.

Souza & Gusmão 1984 – *Bursera*.

Sudo 1963 – *Aucoumea, Bursera, Canarium, Dacryodes, Garuga, Protium, Tetragastris*.

Sudo 1988 – *Canarium, Garuga, Protium*.

Tang 1973 – *Canarium, Garuga*.

Teles & Paula 1980 – *Protium*.

Thunell & Perem 1947 – *Aucoumea*.

Tomazello Filho et al. 1983 – *Protium*.

Tôrres 1941 – *Canarium, Garuga*.

Van der Slooten 1968 – *Bursera*.

Van der Slooten & Gonzalez 1971 – *Bursera*.

Wagenführ & Scheiber 1974 – *Aucoumea, Canarium, Dacryodes*.

Wang 1984–1988 – *Canarium*.

*Webber 1941 – 13 genera.

Williams 1936 – *Crepidospermum, Protium*.

Wiraj Chunwarin & Damrong Sri-Aran 1973 – *Canarium, Garuga*.

(BURSERACEAE)

Crystals
Chattaway 1955 – *Haplolobus*.
Chattaway 1956 – *Boswellia, Canarium, Dacryodes, Garuga, Haplolobus, Protium, Triomma*.
Espinoza de Pernía 1987b – *Bursera, Dacryodes, Hemicrepidospermum* (= *Crepidospermum*), *Protium, Tetragastris, Trattinnickia*.
Meniado et al. 1970 – *Canarium, Dacryodes*.
Scurfield et al. 1973 – *Canarium, Santiria*.

Ecological anatomy
Barajas Morales 1985 – *Bursera*.
Carlquist & Hoekman 1985a – *Bursera*.

Growth rings
Détienne 1989 – *Aucoumea, Canarium*.
Mariaux 1970 – *Aucoumea*.

Rays
Chattaway 1951a – *Garuga, Protium*.
Chattaway 1951b – *Canarium*.

Secretory cells
Ghosh & Purkayastha 1960b – *Boswellia*.

Septate fibres
Purkayastha 1958 – *Protium*.

Silica
Espinoza de Pernía 1987b – *Dacryodes, Paraprotium, Protium, Tetragastris, Trattinnickia*.
Mariaux 1980 – *Aucoumea*.
Scurfield et al. 1974 – *Canarium*.
Sudo et al. 1967 – *Canarium, Santiria*.
Welle 1976b – *Dacryodes, Paraprotium, Protium, Trattinnickia*.

Tracheary elements
Gill & Onuja 1984a – *Canarium*.
Jing et al. 1989 – *Garuga*.

BUXACEAE
(*Buxus* unless otherwise stated)

Bailey, D.C. 1980 – *Simmondsia*.
Brazier & Franklin 1961.
*Carlquist 1982c – *Buxus, Notobuxus, Sarcococca, Simmondsia, Styloceras*.
Carvalho 1954–1955, 1956.

(BUXACEAE)

Cheng, J.-Q. 1980.
Cheng, J.-Q. et al. 1992.
Cutler et al. 1987 – *Buxus, Sarcococca* (root).
Den Outer 1985.
Greguss 1959.
Grosser 1977.
Hayashi 1991.
Heim 1971.
Hirai 1979–1985.
Ilic 1991.
Jacquiot et al. 1973.
Kanehira 1921a, b, 1926.
Kribs 1959.
Niloofari 1961.
Parsa Pajouh & Schweingruber 1985.
Pearson & Brown 1932.
Record & Garratt 1925 – *Buxella* (= *Buxus*), *Buxus, Notobuxus*.
Record & Hess 1943 – *Styloceras, Tricera* (= *Buxus*).
Saint-Laurent 1926, 1928, 1934.
Schweingruber 1978, 1990.
Scott 1927.
Shimaji & Itoh 1982, 1988.
Sudo 1959.
Tippo 1938.
Vasilevskaya & Borisovskaya 1981 – *Buxus, Notobuxus, Pachysandra, Sarcococca*.
Wuang 1979.
Yamabayashi 1938.
Yao 1988.
Yatsenko-Khmelevsky 1954a.

Anomalous structure
Chalk & Chattaway 1937 – *Simmondsia*.

Ecological anatomy
Baas & Schweingruber 1987.
Carlquist & Hoekman 1985a – *Simmondsia*.
Novruzova 1968.

Perforation plates
Ohtani & Ishida 1978a.

Tracheary elements
Ohtani 1983.

BYBLIDACEAE (*Byblis*)

*Carlquist 1976b.

CACTACEAE

Bailey 1962, 1963 – *Pereskia*.
Bailey 1964 – *Pereskiopsis, Quiabentia*.
Bailey 1966 – General survey.
Burgerstein 1912 – *Pereskia*.
Carlquist 1962a – *Cereus*.
Crespo 1973 – *Pereskia*.
*Gibson 1973 – 53 genera of Cactoideae.
Gibson 1977a – *Maihuenia*.
Gibson 1977b – *Austrocylindropuntia*
(= *Opuntia*), *Opuntia, Tephrocactus*
(= *Opuntia*).
Gibson 1978a – *Nopalea* (= *Opuntia*),
Opuntia.
Gibson 1978b – *Melocactus, Neoraimon-
dia*.
Mauseth 1989 – *Melocactus*.
Mauseth 1992 – *Armatocereus, Jasmino-
cereus* [Abstr.].
Mauseth & Ross 1988 – *Leptocereus*.
Milanez 1936b – *Rhipsalis* (root).
Record & Hess 1943 – Family (several
genera; not specified).
Record & Mell 1924 – *Cereus*.
Süss 1974 – *Dendrocereus* (= *Acantho-
cereus*).

Anomalous structure
Mauseth 1993b – (medullary bundles: c. 50
genera).

Crystals
Chattaway 1955 – *Pereskia*.
Scurfield et al. 1973 – *Pereskia*.

Ecological anatomy
Carlquist 1985a – 16 genera.
Carlquist & Hoekman 1985a – *Bergerocac-
tus, Carnegiea, Echinocactus, Echino-
cereus, Ferocactus, Mammillaria, Opuntia*.
Mauseth 1993a – 18 genera.

Perforation plates
Süss 1969 – *Cereus, Eriocereus* (= *Harri-
sia*), *Piptanthocereus* (= *Cereus*), *Tricho-
cereus* (= *Echinopsis*).

CALYCANTHACEAE
(for *Idiospermum* see IDIOSPERMACEAE)

*Carlquist 1983e – *Calycanthus, Chimonan-
thus*.
Lemesle 1955a, 1956b – *Calycanthus,
Chimonanthus*.

(CALYCANTHACEAE)
Lemesle & Pichard 1954 – *Calycanthus,
Chimonanthus*.
Metcalfe 1987 – General survey.
Record & Hess 1943 – *Calycanthus*.
Tippo 1938 – *Calycanthus*.

Ecological anatomy
Carlquist 1985a – *Calycanthus, Chimonanthus*.

Pits
Lemesle 1947b – *Calycanthus, Chimonanthus*.

CALYCERACEAE

*Carlquist 1983d – *Calycera*.

CAMPANULACEAE
(see also LOBELIACEAE)

Dadswell & Record 1936 – *Clermontia,
Wahlenbergia*.
Erdtman & Metcalfe 1963 – *Berenice*
(young stem).
Shulkina & Zikov 1980 – *Campanula,
Canarina, Cyananthus, Musschia,
Ostrowskia, Platycodon*.
Vasilevskaya & Shulkina 1976 – *Azorina*.

CANELLACEAE

Brazier & Franklin 1961 – *Warburgia*.
Garratt 1933b – Family.
Ghosh & Shahi 1961 – *Cinnamosma*.
Ilic 1991 – *Canella, Warburgia*.
Lecomte 1922 – *Cinnamosma*.
Lemesle 1950a, 1955a – *Canella, Cinna-
modendron, Cinnamosma, Pleodendron*.
Metcalfe 1933 – *Cinnamosma*.
Metcalfe 1935 – *Cinnamosma, Warburgia*.
Metcalfe 1987 – General survey.
Occhioni 1947, 1948, 1949 – *Cinnamoden-
dron*.
Record & Hess 1943 – *Canella, Capsico-
dendron, Pleodendron*.
Record & Mell 1924 – *Canella*.
Vander Wyk & Canright 1956 – Relations
with Annonaceae.
Vestal 1937 – Family (*Canella, Capsicoden-
dron, Cinnamosma, Warburgia*).

(CANELLACEAE)
*Wilson 1960 – *Canella, Capsicodendron,
Cinnamodendron, Cinnamosma, Pleoden-
dron, Warburgia.*

CANNABACEAE (*Cannabis*)

Anderson 1974.

CANOTIACEAE see CELASTRACEAE

CAPPARACEAE
(see also KOEBERLINIACEAE and
PHYSENACEAE)

Abbate 1963 – *Maerua.*
Abbate 1964 – *Crateva.*
Abbate 1970 – *Boscia.*
Babos et al. 1981, 1982, 1983 – *Capparis.*
Babos et al. 1984 – *Belencita, Steriphoma.*
Babos et al. 1987 – *Crateva, Morisonia.*
Barajas Morales & León Gómez 1989 – *Cap-
paris, Forchhammeria.*
Benoist 1931 – *Capparis.*
Bokhari & Hedge 1975 – *Capparis.*
Burgerstein 1912 – *Atamisquea, Capparis.*
Carlquist 1985b – Relations with *Tovaria.*
Cellai 1971 – *Cadaba, Capparis.*
Cozzo 1946a – *Atamisquea, Capparis.*
Cristiani 1961a – *Atamisquea, Capparis,
Cleome, Crateva.*
Dechamps 1979 – *Crateva.*
Détienne & Jacquiot 1983 – *Capparis, Cra-
teva.*
Détienne et al. 1982 – *Capparis.*
Fahn et al. 1986 – *Capparis, Cleome,
Maerua.*
Fasolo 1941–1944 – *Boscia.*
Gibson 1979 – *Koeberlinia* (transferred
from Koeberliniaceae).
Ilic 1991 – *Boscia, Capparis, Crateva.*
Jagiella & Kurschner 1987 – *Boscia,
Cadaba, Maerua.*
Kanehira 1921a – *Capparis, Crateva.*
Kanehira 1926 – *Crateva.*
Lebacq 1955 – *Buchholzia.*
Lebacq & Dechamps 1964 – *Buchholzia.*
Lebacq et al. 1973 – *Capparis, Crateva.*
Mattos Filho 1959–1961 – *Capparis.*
Moll & Janssonius 1906–1936 – *Capparis,
Crateva.*

(CAPPARACEAE)
Normand 1950b – *Buchholzia, Euadenia.*
Normand & Paquis 1976 [1977] – *Buch-
holzia.*
Record & Hess 1943 – Family (*Atamisquea,
Capparis, Crateva, Isomeris, Morisonia,
Steriphoma, Stuebelia* (= *Belencita*)).
Saint-Laurent 1928, 1932a, 1934 – *Cappa-
ris, Maerua.*
Schmid et al. 1984 – *Oceanopapaver.*
Schweingruber 1990 – *Capparis.*
Senni 1905 – *Boscia.*
Stern et al. 1963 – *Capparis.*
Williams 1936 – *Capparis, Crateva, Steri-
phoma.*

Anomalous structure
Chalk & Chattaway 1937 – Family (*Boscia,
Cadaba, Forchhammeria, Maerua*).
Webber 1936a – *Isomeris.*

Crystals
Miller 1978 – *Capparis.*

Ecological anatomy
Baas et al. 1983 – *Capparis, Cleome,
Maerua.*
Baas & Schweingruber 1987 – *Capparis.*
Carlquist 1985a – *Oceanopapaver.*
Carlquist & Hoekman 1985a – *Isomeris.*
Novruzova 1968 – *Capparis.*

Storied structure
Cozzo 1944, 1945 – *Capparis.*
Cozzo & Cristiani 1950 – *Atamisquea, Cap-
paris.*

CAPRIFOLIACEAE

Brazier & Franklin 1961 – *Sambucus,
Viburnum.*
Burgerstein 1912 – *Sambucus.*
Cheng, J.-Q. 1980 – *Viburnum.*
Cheng, J.-Q. et al. 1992 – *Viburnum.*
Cutler et al. 1987 – *Abelia, Diervilla, Kolk-
witzia, Lonicera, Sambucus, Symphori-
carpos, Viburnum, Weigela* (root).
Dechamps 1985 – *Sambucus.*
Fahn et al. 1986 – *Lonicera, Viburnum.*
Friedman 1978 – *Lonicera, Sambucus.*
Gasson 1979 – *Abelia, Diervilla* (incl. *Wei-
gela*), *Dipelta, Kolkwitzia, Leycesteria,
Lonicera, Symphoricarpos, Viburnum*
(root).

(CAPRIFOLIACEAE)

Giger 1913 – *Linnaea*.

Greguss 1959 – *Linnaea, Lonicera, Sambucus, Symphoricarpos, Viburnum, Weigela*.

Grosser 1977 – *Lonicera, Sambucus, Viburnum*.

Hayashi 1991 – *Sambucus, Viburnum*.

Huber & Rouschal 1954 – *Lonicera, Viburnum*.

Ilic 1991 – *Lonicera, Sambucus, Viburnum*.

Jacquiot et al. 1973 – *Sambucus, Viburnum*.

Kanehira 1921a, b, 1926 – *Viburnum*.

Li & Chao 1954 – Family.

Metcalfe 1948 – *Sambucus*.

Moll & Janssonius 1906–1936 – *Viburnum*.

Niloofari 1961 – *Lonicera, Sambucus*.

*Ogata 1988 – *Abelia* 2 spp., *Lonicera* 11, *Sambucus* 1, *Viburnum* 13, *Weigela* 6, *Zabelia* 1 (= *Abelia*).

*Ogata 1991 – *Zabelia* + brief notes on 10 other genera.

Ogata 1992 – *Zabelia*.

Plank 1976 – *Sambucus*.

Record & Hess 1943 – *Sambucus, Viburnum*.

Saint-Laurent 1928, 1934 – *Lonicera, Sambucus, Viburnum*.

Schweingruber 1978 – *Lonicera, Sambucus, Viburnum*.

Schweingruber 1990 – *Lonicera, Sambucus, Symphoricarpos, Viburnum*.

Shimaji & Itoh 1988 – *Sambucus, Viburnum*.

Sudo 1959 – *Sambucus, Viburnum*.

Urling & Smith 1953 – *Sambucus*.

Wang et al. 1990 – *Metalonicera* (= *Lonicera*).

Yamabayashi 1938 – *Lonicera, Sambucus, Viburnum, Weigela*.

Ecological anatomy

Baas et al. 1983 – *Viburnum*.

Baas & Schweingruber 1987 – *Lonicera, Sambucus, Viburnum*.

Carlquist 1985 [1986]a – *Lonicera*.

Carlquist & Hoekman 1985a – *Sambucus, Symphoricarpos*.

Novruzova 1968 – *Lonicera, Sambucus, Viburnum*.

(CAPRIFOLIACEAE)

Helical thickenings

Ohtani & Ishida 1978b – *Sambucus, Viburnum*.

Perforation plates

Ohtani & Ishida 1978a – *Sambucus, Viburnum*.

Rays

Braun 1955 – *Lonicera*.

Tracheary elements

Ohtani 1983 – *Sambucus, Viburnum*.

CARICACEAE

Barajas Morales & León Gómez 1989 – *Jacaratia*.

Carlquist 1962a – *Carica*.

Fisher 1980 – *Carica*.

Furst 1965 – *Carica*.

Holbrook & Putz 1992 – *Jacaratia* [Abstr.]

Record & Hess 1943 – *Carica, Jacaratia* (very brief).

CARPINACEAE see BETULACEAE

CARYOCARACEAE

Anon. 1981 (Andes) – *Caryocar*.

Alves de Pinho 1966 – *Caryocar*.

Araujo & Mattos Filho 1973a – *Anthodiscus, Caryocar*.

Barghoorn & Renteira 1967 – *Caryocar*.

Benoist 1931 – *Caryocar*.

Cunha Mello 1967, 1970 – *Caryocar*.

Dechamps 1979 – *Anthodiscus, Caryocar*.

Détienne & Jacquiot 1983 – *Anthodiscus, Caryocar*.

Détienne et al. 1982 – *Caryocar*.

Hoheisel et al. 1968 – *Caryocar*.

Ilic 1991 – *Caryocar*.

Kribs 1928a, 1959 – *Caryocar*.

Lebacq et al. 1973 – *Anthodiscus, Caryocar*.

Mainieri 1978 – *Caryocar*.

Mainieri & Chimelo 1989 – *Caryocar*.

Paula 1979 – *Caryocar*.

Pfeiffer, J.P. 1926 – *Caryocar*.

Prance & Freitas da Silva 1973 – *Anthodiscus, Caryocar*.

Record & Hess 1943 – Family.

(CARYOCARACEAE)
Sudo 1963 – *Caryocar.*
Vestal 1937 – *Anthodiscus, Caryocar.*
*Williams 1935 – *Anthodiscus, Caryocar.*
Williams 1936 – *Anthodiscus, Caryocar.*

Growth rings
Détienne 1989 – *Caryocar.*

Silica
Espinoza de Pernía 1987b – *Anthodiscus.*
Welle 1976b – *Anthodiscus.*

CARYOPHYLLACEAE
(incl. ILLECEBRACEAE)

Carlquist 1992h – Several genera [Abstr.].
Fahn et al. 1986 – *Gymnocarpos.*
Rohweder & Urmi-Konig 1975 – *Gymno-carpos.*
Schweingruber 1990 – *Arenaria, Dianthus, Silene.*
Tellini 1939 [1940] – *Dianthus.*

Anomalous structure
Joshi 1936 – *Thylacospermum.*

Ecological anatomy
Baas et al. 1983 – *Gymnocarpos.*
Baas & Schweingruber 1987 – *Arenaria, Dianthus, Silene.*

Silica
Scurfield et al. 1974 – *Achyronychia.*

CASUARINACEAE (*Casuarina*)

Bargagli-Petrucci 1903.
Brazier & Franklin 1961.
Burgerstein 1909.
Cai & Su 1978.
Carvalho 1954–1956.
Cheng, C. 1985.
Cheng, J.-Q. 1980.
Cheng, J.-Q. et al. 1992.
Dadswell & Eckersley 1935.
El-Osta et al. 1981.
Francis 1926.
Freitas 1955.
Furuno 1977.
Greguss 1959.
Hayashi et al. 1973.
Ilic 1991.
Kanehira 1921a.

(CASUARINACEAE)
Kazmi et al. 1989.
López & Ortega 1989.
Moll & Janssonius 1906–1936.
*Moseley 1948 – 29 spp.
Normand & Paquis 1976 [1977].
Ogata 1975–1983.
Pearson & Brown 1932.
Pérez Olvera et al. 1982 [1985].
Schultz et al. 1964.
Sudo 1963, 1988.
Tang 1973.
Tippo 1938.

Crystals
Baker 1917.
Chattaway 1956.

Ecological anatomy
Carlquist 1977c, 1985a.

Helical thickenings
Nair 1987.

Tracheary elements
Gill & Onuja 1984b.

CECROPIACEAE see MORACEAE

CELASTRACEAE
(incl. CANOTIACEAE, GOUPIACEAE, HIP-
POCRATEACAE, SIPHONODONTACEAE)

Anon. 1981 (Curua) – *Goupia.*
Araujo & Mattos Filho 1973d – *Goupia.*
*Archer & Van Wyk 1993 – *Allocassine, Cassine, Crocoxylon, Elaeodendron, Hartogiella, Lauridia* (= *Elaeodendron*), *Maurocenia, Mystroxylon, Pleurostylia.*
Balan Menon 1955 – *Lophopetalum.*
Barajas Morales 1980 – *Perrottetia.*
Benoist 1931 – *Goupia.*
Brazier & Franklin 1961 – *Euonymus, Goupia, Lophopetalum.*
Brown 1922 – *Perrottetia.*
Burgerstein 1912 – *Maytenus.*
Carreras & Pérez 1988 – *Cassine.*
Cheng, J.-Q. 1980 – *Euonymus.*
Cheng, J.-Q. et al. 1992 – *Euonymus.*
Cutler et al. 1987 – *Celastrus, Euonymus* (root).
DeBuhr 1978 – *Forsellesia* (transferred to Crossosomataceae).

(CELASTRACEAE)

Dechamps 1979 – *Goupia, Maytenus.*

Détienne & Jacquet 1983 – *Goniodiscus, Goupia, Maytenus.*

Détienne et al. 1982 – *Goupia, Maytenus.*

Edlmann & Monaco 1981 – *Euonymus.*

Falcão 1969 – *Salacia.*

Furuno 1977, 1979 – *Kokoon*a (alteration in ink by author in 1979 for *Sonneratia* sp. No. 167), *Solenospermum* (= *Lophopetalum*).

Gibson 1979 – *Canotia.*

Goldblatt et al. 1985 – *Empleuridium* (in Rutaceae).

Greguss 1959 – *Celastrus, Euonymus.*

Grosser 1977 – *Euonymus.*

Hayashi 1991 – *Euonymus.*

Hayashi et al. 1973 – *Kokoona, Lophopetalum.*

Hayashi & Nomura 1986 – *Kurrimia* (= *Bhesa*).

Huber & Rouschal 1954 – *Celastrus, Euonymus.*

Ilic 1991 – 10 genera + *Goupia.*

Jacquiot et al. 1973 – *Euonymus.*

Jagiella & Kurschner 1987 – *Catha, Maytenus.*

Janssonius 1914 – *Goupia.*

Kanehira 1921a – *Euonymus, Otherodendron* (= *Microtropis*), *Perrottetia.*

Kanehira 1921b, 1926 – *Euonymus.*

Kobayashi & Sugawa 1964 – *Lophopetalum.*

Kribs 1959 – *Goupia, Maytenus, Schaefferia, Siphonodon.*

Lebacq et al. 1973 – *Goupia, Maytenus.*

Lecomte 1926a – *Capusia* (= *Siphonodon*).

*Li & Zhang 1990 – *Celastrus, Dipentodon, Euonymus, Microtropis, Monocelastrus* (= *Celastrus*), *Pleurostylia, Tripterygium.*

Luo 1989 – *Euonymus.*

Machado 1945 – *Maytenus.*

Mainieri 1978 – *Goupia.*

Mainieri & Chimelo 1989 – *Goupia.*

Martawijaya et al. 1989 – *Lophopetalum.*

*Mennega 1972a – 12 genera of New World Hippocrateaceae.

Moll & Janssonius 1906–1936 – *Caryospermum* (= *Perrottetia*), *Elaeodendron, Euonymus, Lophopetalum, Microtropis, Siphonodon.*

(CELASTRACEAE)

Nardi Berti & Edlmann Abbate 1992 – *Goupia.*

Ogata 1975–1983 – *Lophopetalum.*

Paula 1979 – *Goupia.*

Pearson & Brown 1932 – *Lophopetalum.*

Pérez Olvera & Corral López 1980 – *Zinowiewia.*

Pérez Olvera et al. 1982 [1985] – *Celastrus, Zinowiewia.*

Pfeiffer, J.P. 1926 – *Goupia.*

Rancusi et al. 1987 – *Maytenus.*

Rebollar Dominguez et al. 1987 – *Wimmeria.*

*Record 1938a – 15 genera.

Record & Garratt 1925 – *Schaefferia.*

Record & Hess 1943 – Family (15 genera).

Record & Mell 1924 – *Goupia, Maytenus.*

Saint-Laurent 1928, 1934 – *Euonymus.*

Schweingruber 1978 – *Euonymus.*

Schweingruber 1990 – *Euonymus, Maytenus.*

Shaw et al. 1973 – *Pottingeria* (twig) (or Escalloniaceae or Hydrangeaceae).

Shimaji & Itoh 1982, 1988 – *Euonymus.*

Smith & Bailey 1941 – *Brassiantha.*

Snezhkova 1986 – *Celastrus, Tripterygium.*

Sudo 1959 – *Euonymus.*

Sudo 1963 – *Goupia, Lophopetalum, Maytenus, Siphonodon.*

Sudo 1988 – *Lophopetalum.*

Teles & Paula 1980 – *Goupia.*

Tortorelli 1941, 1956 – *Maytenus.*

Wagemann 1949 – *Maytenus.*

Wang 1984–1988 – *Lophopetalum.*

Wiraj Chunwarin & Damrong Sri-Aran 1973 – *Solenospermum* (= *Lophopetalum*).

Xu et al. 1990 – *Bhesa.*

Yamabayashi 1938 – *Euonymus.*

Zhang, X. et al. 1990 – *Bhesa.*

Anomalous structure

Chalk & Chattaway 1937 – *Salacia.*

Obaton 1960 – *Hippocratea, Salacia, Salacighia.*

Crystals

Chattaway 1955 – *Siphonodon.*

Chattaway 1956 – 11 genera (incl. *Salacia*).

Scurfield et al. 1973 – *Siphonodon.*

Ecological anatomy

Baas & Schweingruber 1987 – *Euonymus, Maytenus.*

(CELASTRACEAE)
Carlquist 1985a – *Goupia, Maytenus, Microtropis.*
Carlquist 1985 [1986]a – *Celastrus, Hippocratea, Tripterygium.*
Carlquist & Hoekman 1985a – *Mortonia.*
Novruzova 1968 – *Euonymus.*

Growth rings
Détienne 1989 – *Goupia.*

Helical thickenings
Nair 1987 – *Cassine.*
Ohtani & Ishida 1978b – *Celastrus, Euonymus.*

Perforation plates
Ohtani & Ishida 1978a – *Celastrus, Euonymus.*
Parameswaran & Liese 1973 – *Goupia.*

Rays
Braun & den Outer 1965 – *Euonymus.*
Braun et al. 1967 – *Euonymus.*

Tracheary elements
Carlquist 1988f – *Catha, Celastrus, Elaeodendron, Maytenus.*
Jing et al. 1989 – *Euonymus.*
Ohtani 1983 – *Celastrus, Euonymus.*

CEPHALOTACEAE *(Cephalotus)*

*Carlquist 1981c.

CERCIDIPHYLLACEAE
(Cercidiphyllum)

Anon. 1966.
Brazier & Franklin 1961.
Chen, G. 1989.
Cheng, J.-Q. 1980.
Cheng, J.-Q. et al. 1992.
Greguss 1959.
Hayashi 1991.
Hirai 1979–1985.
Ilic 1991.
Kanehira 1921b, 1926.
Kribs 1959.
Lemesle 1953, 1956b.
McLaughlin 1933.
Saiki 1982.
Shimaji & Itoh 1982, 1988.
Sudo 1959.
Swamy & Bailey 1949.

(CERCIDIPHYLLACEAE)
Takahashi 1985.
Wang & Gao 1991.
Wuang 1979.

Crystals
Chattaway 1956.

Pits and perforation plates
Lemesle 1946b.
Ohtani & Ishida 1978a.

Rays
Braun et al. 1968.

Tracheary elements
Ohtani 1983.

CHENOPODIACEAE

Artsikhovskii 1928 – *Arthrophytum.*
Bokhari & Wendelbo 1978 – *Anabasis.*
Chudnoff 1956 – *Atriplex, Haloxylon, Suaeda.*
Fahn et al. 1986 – 12 genera.
Gibson 1978c – *Halophytum.*
Jagiella & Kurschner 1987 – *Haloxylon.*
Messeri 1938 – *Salsola.*
Saint-Laurent 1928 – *Atriplex, Salicornia, Salsola, Suaeda, Traganum.*
Saint-Laurent 1932a – *Anabasis, Salsola.*
Schweingruber 1990 – *Arthrocnemum, Atriplex, Chenopodium, Halimione, Halocnemum, Haloxylon, Noaea, Salsola, Suaeda.*
Thunell & Perem 1947 – *Atriplex.*
Yatsenko-Khmelevsky 1954a – *Eurotia* (= *Axyris*), *Noaea, Salsola.*

Anomalous structure
Baird & Blackwell 1980 – *Halogeton.*
Butnik 1983 – General survey: 17 genera.
Chalk & Chattaway 1937 – Family (*Allenrolfea, Atriplex, Chenopodium, Eurotia* (= *Axyris*), *Grayia, Haloxylon, Sarcobatus, Suaeda*).
Cumming 1925 – *Atriplex.*
Fahn 1985 – *Atriplex.*
Fahn & Shchori 1967 [1968] – *Anabasis, Atriplex, Haloxylon, Kochia.*
Gattuso & Gattuso 1985 – *Chenopodium.*
Joshi 1937 – *Atriplex, Chenopodium, Suaeda.*
Vasilevskaya 1972 – *Camphorosma.*
Zhu et al. 1992 – *Ceratoides* (= *Ceratocarpus*).

(CHENOPODIACEAE)

Crystals
Chattaway 1956 – *Kochia*.

Ecological anatomy
Baas et al. 1983 – 12 genera.
Baas & Schweingruber 1987 – *Arthrocnemum, Atriplex, Chenopodium, Halimione, Halocnemum, Haloxylon, Noaea, Salsola, Suaeda*.
Carlquist 1977c – *Atriplex, Kochia, Rhagodia*.
Carlquist 1985a – *Ceratoides* (= *Ceratocarpus*), *Grayia*.
Carlquist & Hoekman 1985a – *Atriplex, Ceratoides* (= *Ceratocarpus*), *Grayia*.
Novruzova 1968 – *Anabasis, Camphorosma, Eurotia* (= *Axyris*), *Halocnemum, Halostachys, Kalidium, Kochia, Salsola, Suaeda*.

CHLORANTHACEAE

Bascopé 1954 – *Hedyosmum*.
Carlquist 1987g – *Sarcandra*.
*Carlquist 1990a – *Ascarina* 8 spp.
*Carlquist 1992a – *Chloranthus* and key to all 4 genera.
*Carlquist 1992i – *Hedyosmum* 14 spp..
Cunha Mello 1950 [1951] – *Hedyosmum*.
Détienne & Jacquet 1983 – *Hedyosmum*.
Ilic 1991 – *Ascarina*.
Lebacq et al. 1973 – *Hedyosmum*.
Lemesle 1963a – *Sarcandra*.
Metcalfe 1987 – General survey.
Meylan & Butterfield 1978b – *Ascarina*.
Occhioni 1954 – *Hedyosmum*.
Patel 1975 – *Ascarina*.
Pérez Mogollón 1993 – *Hedyosmum*.
Record & Hess 1943 – *Hedyosmum*.
*Swamy 1953a – *Ascarina* 5 spp., *Chloranthus* (young), *Hedyosmum* 20, *Sarcandra* (young).
Swamy 1953b – *Ascarina* (transferred to Paracryphiaceae).
Swamy 1953c – *Sarcandra* (young).
Swamy & Bailey 1950 – *Sarcandra* (young).
Takahashi 1984 – Family (*Ascarina, Chloranthus, Sarcandra*).
Takahashi 1985 – *Ascarina, Chloranthus, Sarcandra*.
Takahashi 1988 – *Hedyosmum*.

(CHLORANTHACEAE)

Pits and perforation plates
Carlquist 1992d – *Ascarina*.
Meylan & Butterfield 1974 – *Ascarina*.

Tracheary elements
Takahashi & Tamura 1990b – *Sarcandra*.
Zhang, S.-S. et al. 1990 – *Sarcandra*.

CHRYSOBALANACEAE

(*Parinarium* = *Parinari*)

Anon. 1955–1959 – *Parinari*.
Anon. 1981 (Andes) – *Licania*.
Anon. 1981 (Curua) – *Licania*.
Abbate 1973 – *Hirtella*.
Alves de Pinho 1968 – *Parinari*.
Alves de Pinho & Camargo 1979 – *Couepia*.
Barajas Morales et al. 1979 – *Licania*.
Bargagli-Petrucci 1903 – *Parastemon*.
Benoist 1931 – *Hirtella, Licania, Parinarium*.
Brazier & Franklin 1961 – *Parinari*.
Burgerstein 1909 – *Parinarium*.
Croptier & Kučera 1990 – *Parinari*.
Dechamps 1979 – *Couepia, Hirtella, Licania, Parinari*.
Desch 1954 – *Angelesia* (= *Licania*), *Parastemon, Parinari*.
Détienne & Jacquet 1983 – *Acioa, Chrysobalanus, Couepia, Exellodendron, Hirtella, Licania, Parinari*.
Détienne et al. 1982 – *Chrysobalanus, Couepia, Hirtella, Licania, Parinari*.
Eeckhout 1951 – *Parinari*.
Furuno 1979 – *Parinari*.
Hayashi et al. 1973 – *Parastemon, Parinari*.
Ilic 1991 – *Cyclandrophora* (= *Atuna*), *Licania, Parastemon, Parinari*.
Kanehira 1924 – *Parinarium*.
Kribs 1928a – *Hirtella, Licania, Moquilea* (= *Licania*), *Parinarium*.
Kribs 1959 – *Licania, Parinari*.
Lebacq 1957 – *Parinari*.
Lebacq & Dechamps 1964 – *Parinari*.
Lebacq & Dechamps 1967 – *Acioa*, cf. *Chrysobalanus, Hirtella, Parinari*.
Lebacq et al. 1973 – *Couepia, Hirtella, Licania, Parinari*.
Lecomte 1926a – *Parinarium*.
Mainieri 1978 – *Licania, Moquilea* (= *Licania*).

(CHRYSOBALANCACEAE)

Mainieri & Chimelo 1989 – *Hirtella, Licania, Moquilea* (= *Licania*).
Martawijaya et al. 1989 – *Maranthes.*
Moll & Janssonius 1906–1936 – *Parinarium.*
Normand 1950b – *Acioa, Chrysobalanus, Parinari.*
Normand & Paquis 1976 [1977] – *Parinari.*
Ogata 1975–1983 – *Parinari.*
Ortega 1958 – *Licania.*
Pereira et al. 1970 – *Licania.*
Pérez Mogollón 1973 – *Hirtella, Parinari.*
Pfeiffer, J.P. 1926 – *Couepia, Hirtella, Licania, Parinarium.*
Prakash 1972 – *Licania* (root).
Prance 1965 – *Stylobasium* (or Stylobasiaceae).
*Prance & White 1988 – Family (15 genera).
Record & Hess 1943 – Family (*Chrysobalanus, Couepia, Hirtella, Licania, Moquila* (= *Licania*), *Parinarium*).
Sudo 1963 – *Parinarium.*
Sudo 1988 – *Maranthes.*
Tavares 1957 – *Chrysobalanus.*
Tippo 1938 – Family (many genera).
Tôrres 1941 – *Parinarium.*
Urling & Smith 1953 – *Chrysobalanus.*
Van der Slooten et al. 1962 – *Licania.*
Wagenführ & Scheiber 1974 – *Parinarium.*
Wang 1984–1988 – *Parinari.*
*Welle & Détienne 1986 – *Acioa, Chrysobalanus, Couepia, Exellodendron, Hirtella, Licania, Parinari.*
Williams 1936 – *Couepia, Hirtella, Licania, Parinarium.*
Wiraj Chunwarin & Damrong Sri-Aran 1974 – *Parinarium.*

Crystals
Chattaway 1956 – *Parastemon.*

Helical thickenings
Welle 1975 – 12 genera.

Silica
Espinoza de Pernía 1987b – *Chrysobalanus, Couepia, Exellodendron, Hirtella, Licania.*
Frison 1942 – *Parinari.*
Scurfield et al. 1974 – *Licania, Parinari.*
Sudo et al. 1967 – *Parastemon, Parinarium.*
Welle 1976a, b – 11 genera.

CISTACEAE

Fahn et al. 1986 – *Cistus.*
Greguss 1959 – *Cistus, Fumana, Helianthemum.*
Huber & Rouschal 1954 – *Cistus.*
Saint-Laurent 1928, 1934 – *Cistus.*
Saya 1957 – *Cistus.*
Schweingruber 1990 – *Cistus, Fumana, Halimium, Helianthemum.*
Vestal 1937 – Family (*Cistus, Helianthemum, Hudsonia, Lechea*).

Ecological anatomy
Baas et al. 1983 – *Cistus.*
Baas & Schweingruber 1987 – *Cistus, Fumana, Halimium, Helianthemum.*
Carlquist 1980a – *Cistus.*
Carlquist & Hoekman 1985a – *Helianthemum.*

Pits
Baas & Werker 1981 – *Cistus, Fumana.*

CLETHRACEAE (*Clethra*)

Araujo & Mattos Filho 1982 [1983].
Barajas Morales 1980.
Barbosa et al. 1977–1978.
Cunha Mello 1950 [1951].
Détienne & Jacquet 1983.
*Giebel & Dickison 1976 – 17 spp.
Hayashi 1991.
Hirai 1979–1985.
Ilic 1991.
Kanehira 1921b, 1926.
Lechner 1914 (twig).
Ortega et al. 1988.
Pérez Mogollón 1993.
Pérez Olvera et al. 1982 [1985].
Raturi & Dayal 1988.
Record 1932b.
Record & Hess 1943.
Shimaji & Itoh 1988.
Sudo 1959.
Vales et al. 1988.
Williams 1928.

Ecological anatomy
Van der Graaff & Baas 1974.

Helical thickenings
Ohtani & Ishida 1978b.

(CLETHRACEAE)
Pits and perforation plates
Carlquist 1992d.
Ohtani & Ishida 1978a.

Tracheary elements
Ohtani 1983.

CLUSIACEAE see GUTTIFERAE

CNEORACEAE (*Cneorum*)

*Carlquist 1988c.
Greguss 1959.
Heimsch 1942.
Huber & Rouschal 1954.
Record & Hess 1943.
Schweingruber 1990.

Ecological anatomy
Baas & Schweingruber 1987.
Carlquist 1985a.

COBAEACEAE see POLEMONIACEAE

COCHLOSPERMACEAE

Barajas Morales & León Gómez 1989 – *Cochlospermum*.
Détienne & Jacquet 1983 – *Cochlospermum*.
*Keating 1968 [1969] – *Amoreuxia* 3 spp., *Cochlospermum* 10.
Lebacq et al. 1973 – *Cochlospermum*.
Record & Hess 1943 – *Cochlospermum*.
Vestal 1937 – *Cochlospermum*.
Williams 1936 – *Cochlospermum*.

Crystals
Chattaway 1955 – *Cochlospermum*.

Ecological anatomy
Barajas Morales 1985 – *Cochlospermum*.

Storied structure
Cozzo & Cristiani 1950 – *Cochlospermum*.

COLUMELLIACEAE (*Columellia*)

Record & Hess 1943.
*Stern et al. 1969.

COMBRETACEAE

Anon. 1981 (Andes) – *Buchenavia, Terminalia*.
Abbate 1970 – *Anogeissus, Combretum*.
Abbate 1971a – *Terminalia*.
*Alfonso & Richter 1991 – *Buchenavia* 15 spp., *Terminalia* 5 spp.
Alves de Pinho 1966 – *Terminalia*.
Alves de Pinho & Camargo 1979 – *Terminalia*.
Ayensu & Bentum 1974 – *Terminalia*.
Babos & Vales 1977 [1978] – *Bucida*.
Barajas Morales et al. 1979 – *Terminalia*.
Bargagli-Petrucci 1903 – *Lumnitzera*.
Barreto 1967 – *Combretum, Pteleopsis, Terminalia*.
Bascopé et al. 1959 – *Conocarpus, Laguncularia*.
Benoist 1931 – *Buchenavia, Terminalia*.
Brazier & Franklin 1961 – *Anogeissus, Pteleopsis, Terminalia*.
Brown 1922 – *Terminalia*.
Burgerstein 1909 – *Terminalia*.
Burgerstein 1912 – *Chuncoa* (= *Terminalia*).
Cardoso 1960 – *Terminalia*.
Carreras 1988 – *Conocarpus, Laguncularia*.
Carreras & Vales 1986a – *Bucida*.
Carreras & Vales 1986b – *Bucida, Conocarpus, Laguncularia, Terminalia*.
Cellai 1967 – *Terminalia*.
Chalk et al. 1933 – *Terminalia*.
Cheng, J.-Q. 1980 – *Terminalia*.
Cheng, J.-Q. et al. 1992 – *Terminalia*.
Chowdhury 1936 – *Terminalia*.
Coode 1969 – *Lumnitzera, Terminalia*.
Dechamps 1979 – *Buchenavia, Bucida, Laguncularia, Terminalia*.
Détienne & Jacquet 1983 – *Buchenavia, Combretum, Laguncularia, Terminalia*.
Détienne et al. 1982 – *Buchenavia, Laguncularia, Terminalia*.
Edlmann Abbate & De Luca 1981 – *Terminalia*.
Eeckhout 1951 – *Terminalia*.
Fasolo 1939–1940 – *Combretum*.
Ferreirinha 1955 – *Combretum, Pteleopsis*.
Fouarge & Gérard 1964 – *Pteleopsis, Terminalia*.
Fouarge et al. 1953 – *Pteleopsis*.
Freitas 1955, 1963 – *Terminalia*.
Fundter & Wisse 1977 – *Terminalia*.

(COMBRETACEAE)

Furuno 1977, 1979 – *Terminalia*.
Gaiotti de Peralta & Edlmann Abbate 1981 – *Terminalia*.
Gill & Onuja 1984c – *Terminalia*.
Gómez 1959 – *Bucida*.
Gottwald & Noack 1965 [1966] – *Terminalia*.
Grisa 1988 – *Terminalia*.
Groulez & Wood 1984, 1985 – *Terminalia*.
Hayashi et al. 1973 – *Terminalia*.
Hayashi & Nomura 1986 – *Terminalia*.
*Hooks 1966 – *Terminalia* 17 spp.
Ilic 1991 – *Anogeissus, Buchenavia, Bucida, Lumnitzera, Pteleopsis, Terminalia*.
Jagiella & Kurschner 1987 – *Combretum*.
Janssonius 1950 – Relations.
Jentsch et al. 1936 – *Terminalia*.
Kanehira 1921a, 1924 – *Lumnitzera, Terminalia*.
Kanehira 1926 – *Terminalia*.
Kobayashi & Sugawa 1964 – *Terminalia*.
Kribs 1959 – *Buchenavia, Bucida, Laguncularia, Terminalia*.
Lamb & Ntima 1971 – *Terminalia*.
Lebacq & Dechamps 1964 – *Combretum, Pteleopsis, Terminalia*.
Lebacq & Dechamps 1967 – *Pteleopsis*.
Lebacq et al. 1973 – *Buchenavia, Combretum, Terminalia*.
Lebacq & Staner 1964 – *Buchenavia, Pteleopsis, Terminalia*.
Lecomte 1922 – *Terminaliopsis*.
Lecomte 1926a – *Terminalia*.
Lepe 1959 – *Bucida*.
Lomibao 1973a – *Terminalia*.
Lomibao 1978 – *Lumnitzera*.
López & Ortega 1989 – *Conocarpus, Laguncularia*.
Luo 1989 – *Terminalia*.
Mahmood & Nasir 1991 – *Conocarpus*.
Mainieri 1978 – *Buchenavia, Terminalia*.
Mainieri & Chimelo 1989 – *Buchenavia, Terminalia*.
Marchiori 1986a – *Terminalia*.
Moll & Janssonius 1906–1936 – *Lumnitzera, Terminalia*.
Monteiro & Frade 1960 – *Pteleopsis*.
Nardi Berti & Edlmann Abbate 1988, 1992 – *Terminalia*.
Normand 1960 – *Anogeissus, Laguncularia, Pteleopsis, Strephonema, Terminalia*.

(COMBRETACEAE)

Normand & Paquis 1976 [1977] – *Pteleopsis, Strephonema, Terminalia*.
Ogata 1975–1983 – *Lumnitzera, Terminalia*.
Ogata 1992 – *Terminalia*.
Ortega 1958 – *Terminalia*.
Panshin 1932 – *Lumnitzera*.
Pearson & Brown 1932 – *Anogeissus, Terminalia*.
Pereira et al. 1970 – *Terminalia*.
Pérez Olvera & Corral López 1980 – *Terminalia*.
Pérez Olvera et al. 1980 [1981] – *Bucida*.
Purkayastha et al. 1976 – *Terminalia*.
Rao, B.S. & P.S.P. 1972 – *Terminalia*.
*Rao, P.S.P. 1972 – 15 genera.
Record & Hess 1943 – Family (*Buchenavia, Bucida, Conocarpus, Laguncularia, Ramatuela, Terminalia*).
Record & Mell 1924 – *Terminalia*.
Riera 1947 – *Terminalia*.
Rozmarin et al. 1983 – *Terminalia*.
Saiki 1982 – *Terminalia*.
Schmidt 1951–1952 – *Terminalia*.
Scott 1927 – *Terminalia*.
Seabra & Ferreirinha 1959 – *Terminalia*.
Senni 1905 – *Terminalia*.
Souza et al. 1982 – *Laguncularia*.
Sudo 1963 – *Anogeissus, Buchenavia, Bucida, Lumnitzera, Terminalia*.
Sudo 1988 – *Lumnitzera, Terminalia*.
Tang 1973 – *Terminalia*.
Tôrres 1941 – *Terminalia*.
Tortorelli 1956 – *Terminalia*.
Urling & Smith 1953 – *Conocarpus, Laguncularia*.
Vales & Carreras 1987 – *Laguncularia*.
Van der Slooten 1968 – *Terminalia*.
Van der Slooten & Gonzalez 1970 [1971] – *Terminalia*.
*Van Vliet 1979 – 19 genera, 90 spp.
Van Vliet & Baas 1984 – Relations of myrtalean families.
Venkateswarlu & Rao 1971 – *Strephonema*.
Wagenführ & Scheiber 1974 – *Terminalia*.
Williams 1936 – *Terminalia*.
Wiraj Chunwarin & Damrong Sri-Aran 1974 – *Anogeissus, Lumnitzera, Terminalia*.
Zou et al. 1989 – *Anogeissus*.

Anomalous structure
Chalk & Chattaway 1937 – *Combretum*.

(COMBRETACEAE)
Obaton 1960 – *Combretum*.
Verhoeven & Van der Schijff 1974 [1975] – *Combretum*.

Crystals
Chattaway 1955 – *Anogeissus, Combretum, Terminalia*.
Chattaway 1956 – *Anogeissus, Combretum, Conocarpus, Macropteranthes, Terminalia*.
Espinoza de Pernía 1987b – *Bucida, Combretum, Laguncularia, Terminalia*.
Meniado et al. 1970 – *Terminalia*.
Scurfield et al. 1973 – *Anogeissus, Combretum, Terminalia*.

Ecological anatomy
Carlquist 1985a – *Calopyxis, Calycopteris (= Getonia), Combretum, Guiera, Strephonema, Thiloa*.

Growth rings
Détienne 1989 – *Terminalia*.

Pits
Jing et al. 1988 – *Terminalia*.
Nair & Ram 1989 – *Anogeissus, Terminalia*.
Van Vliet 1978 – 18 genera.

Rays
Braun & den Outer 1965 – *Terminalia*.
Braun et al. 1967 – *Terminalia*.
Dayal & Rao 1983 – *Combretum*.
Van Vliet 1976b – *Combretum, Quisqualis*.

Tracheary elements
Jing et al. 1989 – *Terminalia*.

COMPOSITAE

Aldridge 1978 – *Sonchus*.
Anderson 1963 [1964] – *Chrysothamnus, Haplopappus, Petradoria, Solidago*.
Anderson 1972 – *Bigelowia* (caudex).
Anderson 1983 – *Chrysothamnus*.
Anderson & Weberg 1974 – *Vanclevea*.
Baagøe 1974 – *Guizotia*.
Bascopé 1954 – *Montanoa*.
Brazier & Franklin 1961 – *Brachylaena*.
Brown 1922 – *Dubautia*.
Burgerstein 1912 – *Baccharis, Cnicothamnus, Moquinia, Tessaria*.
Carlquist 1957a – *Fitchia, Oparanthus*.

(COMPOSITAE)
*Carlquist 1957b – Mutisieae 22 genera.
*Carlquist 1958a – Heliantheae 34 genera.
*Carlquist 1958b – *Ambrosia, Baccharis, Bidens, Borrichia, Eupatorium, Flaveria, Haplopappus, Melanthera, Pluchea*.
Carlquist 1958c – *Centaurodendron, Yunquea (= Centaurodendron)*.
*Carlquist 1959a – Madinae 15 genera.
*Carlquist 1959b – Helenieae 11 genera.
*Carlquist 1960a – Cichorieae: *Dendroseris, Lactuca, Malacothrix, Phoenicoseris (= Dendroseris), Rea (= Dendroseris), Sonchus, Stephanomeria, Thamnoseris*.
*Carlquist 1960b – Astereae 14 genera.
*Carlquist 1961 – Inuleae 11 genera.
*Carlquist 1962a – *Chimantaea, Espeletia, Liabum, Neurolaena, Phoenicoseris (= Dendroseris), Senecio, Sonchus, Vernonia, Wunderlichia*.
*Carlquist 1962b – Senecioneae 13 genera.
*Carlquist 1964b – Vernonieae: *Lychnophora, Oliganthes, Piptocarpha, Proteopsis, Vanillosmopsis, Vernonia*.
*Carlquist 1965a – Cynareae: *Centaurea, Centaurodendron, Cirsium, Cnicus, Onopordum, Silybum, Warionia, Yunquea (= Centaurodendron)*.
*Carlquist 1965b – Eupatorieae: *Brickellia, Eupatorium, Mikania, Piqueria*.
*Carlquist 1966a – Anthemideae, Ambrosieae, Calenduleae, Arctotideae: 15 genera.
*Carlquist 1966b – Summary.
*Carlquist 1976d – Tribes and phylogeny.
Carlquist 1982e – *Scalesia*.
Carlquist 1983c – *Crepidiastrum, Dendrocacalia*.
Carlquist & Eckhart 1982 – *Darwiniothamnus, Lecocarpus, Macraea*.
Carlquist & Grant 1963 – *Fitchia*.
Cockrell 1942 – *Vernonia*.
Cozzo & Cristiani 1946 – *Cyclolepis*.
Cunha Mello 1950 [1951] – *Vanillosmopsis*.
Cutler et al. 1987 – *Olearia, Senecio* (root).
Dadswell & Eckersley 1935 – *Olearia*.
Dechamps 1979 – *Oliganthes*.
Détienne & Jacquet 1983 – *Pollalesta, Vernonia*.
Diettert 1938 – *Artemisia*.
Ebel & Kästner 1973 – *Neurolaena, Senecio*.
Eliasson 1971 – *Lecocarpus*.

(COMPOSITAE)

Eliasson 1974 – *Scalesia.*
Fahn & Sarnat 1963 – *Artemisia.*
Fahn et al. 1986 – *Artemisia, Inula, Pluchea.*
Gill & Ogunlowo 1988 – *Inula.*
Henrickson 1976 – *Marshalljohnstonia.*
Ilic 1991 – *Baccharis, Bedfordia, Brachylaena, Dubautia, Fitchia, Olearia, Vernonia.*
Jagiella & Kurschner 1987 – *Psiadia, Tarchonanthus.*
Lebacq & Dechamps 1964 – *Vernonia.*
Lebacq et al. 1973 – *Clibadium, Mikania, Oliganthes, Tessaria, Vernonia.*
Lecomte 1922 – *Apodocephala, Synchodendron, Vernonia.*
Mabberley 1975 – *Senecio.*
Mainieri & Chimelo 1989 – *Moquinia.*
Metcalfe 1935 – *Brachylaena.*
Meylan & Butterfield 1978b – *Brachyglottis, Cassinia, Olearia.*
Moll & Janssonius 1906–1936 – *Anaphalis, Vernonia.*
Nardi Berti & Edlmann Abbate 1988 – *Brachylaena.*
Normand 1960 – *Vernonia.*
Normand & Paquis 1976 [1977] – *Vernonia.*
Pereira 1933 – *Moquinia.*
Pérez Mogollón 1993 – *Montanoa.*
Petriella 1966 – *Vernonia.*
Record & Hess 1943 – Family.
Ruffin 1974 [1975] – *Amphiachyris, Amphipappus, Greenella* (= *Gutierrezia*), *Gutierrezia, Gymnosperma, Thurovia* (= *Gutierrezia*), *Xanthocephalum.*
Saint-Laurent 1928 – *Anvillaea, Artemisia, Inula, Pallenis* (= *Asteriscus*), *Warionia, Zollikoferia.*
Saint-Laurent 1932a – *Artemisia.*
Saint-Laurent 1932b – *Pluchea, Santolina.*
Schweingruber 1990 – 16 genera.
Silva 1991 – *Montanoa, Oyedaea.*
Slatter 1948 – *Senecio.*
Sudo 1963 – *Brachylaena, Vernonia.*
Tortorelli 1956 – *Flotovia, Tessaria.*
Urling & Smith 1953 – *Baccharis.*
Wagemann 1949 – *Flotovia.*
Williams 1936 – *Clibadium, Oliganthes, Tessaria, Vernonia.*

(COMPOSITAE)

Anomalous structure

Adamson 1934 – *Disparago, Elytropappus, Lachnospermum, Metalasia, Perotriche, Phaenocoma, Stoebe.*
Adamson 1937 – *Osteospermum.*
Böcher 1971 – *Tetradymia.*
Moss 1940 – *Artemisia.*
Obaton 1960 – *Mikania.*
Ravololomaniraka & Koechlin 1970 – *Crassocephalum.*
Sajo & Menezes 1986 – *Vernonia.*
Van der Walt et al. 1973 – *Mikania.*
Worsdell 1919 – Miscellaneous comments on several genera.

Crystals

Chattaway 1956 – *Olearia.*
Espinoza de Pernía 1987b – *Baccharis.*

Ecological anatomy

Baas et al. 1983 – *Artemisia, Inula.*
Baas & Schweingruber 1987 – 16 genera.
Carlquist 1974 – *Coreopsis, Dendroseris, Sonchus.*
Carlquist 1985a – 11 genera.
Carlquist & Hoekman 1985a – 18 genera.
Novruzova 1968 – *Artemisia.*
Webber 1936a – *Artemisia, Aster, Chrysothamnus, Encelia, Franseria* (= *Ambrosia*), *Hymenoclea, Tetradymia.*

Growth rings

Ferguson 1964 – *Artemisia.*
Trautner-Jäger 1962 – *Espeletia.*

Helical thickenings

Meylan & Butterfield 1978a – *Cassinia, Olearia, Pachyskegia* (= *Olearia*), *Senecio, Traversia.*

Pits and perforation plates

Meylan & Butterfield 1974 – *Brachyglottis, Cassinia, Olearia, Senecio.*
Ragonese 1980 – *Pterocaulon.*

Septate fibres

Butterfield & Meylan 1976 – *Brachyglottis, Olearia.*

Storied structure

Cozzo & Cristiani 1950 – *Baccharis, Cyclolepis.*

CONNARACEAE

*Den Outer & Van Veenendaal 1989 – 19 genera.
*Dickison 1972 – 14 genera.
 Eimunjeze 1976 – *Hemandradenia* (twig).
 Heimsch 1942 – *Byrsocarpus* (= *Rourea*), *Cnestidium, Connarus, Ellipanthus, Jollydora, Rourea.*
 Ilic 1991 – *Connarus.*
 Janssonius 1950 – Relations.
 Lebacq & Dechamps 1964 – *Cnestis.*
 Lebacq et al. 1973 – *Connarus.*
 Moll & Janssonius 1906–1936 – *Ellipanthus.*
 Normand 1950b – *Hemandradenia.*
 Record & Hess 1943 – Family (*Cnestidium, Connarus, Rourea*).
 Williams 1936 – *Connarus.*
 Worbes 1986 – *Rourea.*

Anomalous structure
 Obaton 1960 – *Agelaea, Connarus, Santaloides* (= *Rourea*), *Spiropetalum* (= *Rourea*).
 Ursem & Welle 1992 – *Rourea.*

Crystals and silica
 Chattaway 1956 – *Connarus.*
 Espinoza de Pernía 1987b – *Connarus, Pseudoconnarus, Rourea.*
 Welle 1976b – *Pseudoconnarus, Rourea.*

Ecological anatomy
 Carlquist 1985a – *Byrsocarpus* (= *Rourea*), *Cnestidium, Connarus, Manotes, Rourea.*

Growth rings
 Worbes 1984 – *Rourea.*

CONVOLVULACEAE
(incl. HUMBERTIACEAE)

 Barajas Morales & León Gómez 1989 – *Ipomoea.*
 Bhattacharyya 1975 – *Cuscuta.*
*Carlquist & Hanson 1991 – 16 genera.
 Détienne & Jacquet 1983 – *Ipomoea.*
 Mariaux 1959 – *Humbertia.*
 McDonald 1992 – *Ipomoea.*
 Mennega 1969, 1972b – *Dicranostyles.*
 Metcalfe 1935 – *Convolvulus* (root).
 Müller 1903 – *Convolvulus.*

(CONVOLVULACEAE)
Anomalous structure
 Bhattacharyya 1988 [1990] – Notes on 8 genera.
 Lowell & Lucansky 1986, 1990 – *Ipomoea.*
 Obaton 1960 – *Bonamia, Neuropeltis, Prevostea* (= *Calycobolus*).
 Pant & Bhatnagar 1975 – *Argyreia.*
 Pfeiffer 1924a – *Erycibe.*
 Pfeiffer 1925 – ?*Dufourea* (= *Breweria*).

Crystals
 Chattaway 1956 – *Ipomoea.*

Ecological anatomy
 Carlquist 1985 [1986]a – *Dicranostyles, Mina* (= *Ipomoea*), *Turbina.*
 Novruzova 1968 – *Convolvulus, Cressa.*

Tracheary elements
 Carlquist 1988f – *Ipomoea.*

CORIARIACEAE (*Coriaria*)

*Carlquist 1985e.
 Cheng, J.-Q. 1980.
 Cheng, J.-Q. et al. 1992.
 Dadswell & Record 1936.
 Heimsch 1942.
 Kanehira 1921a.
 Meylan & Butterfield 1978b.
 Record & Hess 1943.
 Saint-Laurent 1928, 1934.
 Schweingruber 1990.
*Suzuki & Yoda 1986, 1992.
*Yoda & Suzuki 1992.

Ecological anatomy
 Baas & Schweingruber 1987.

Pits
 Meylan & Butterfield 1974.

CORNACEAE
(incl. ARALIDIACEAE, GRISELINIACEAE, HELWINGIACEAE, MELANOPHYLLACEAE; see also NYSSACEAE)

*Adams 1949 – 11 genera.
 Brazier & Franklin 1961 – *Cornus, Curtisia.*
 Brown 1928 – *Lautea* (= *Corokia*).
 Carlquist 1989d – *Kaliphora* (twig).
 Chalk et al. 1935 – *Curtisia.*

(CORNACEAE)

Cheng, J.-Q. 1980 – *Cornus, Dendroben-thamia* (= *Cornus*).
Cheng, J.-Q. et al. 1992 – *Cornus, Den-drobenthamia* (= *Cornus*).
Cutler et al. 1987 – *Aucuba, Cornus* (root).
Détienne & Jacquet 1983 – *Cornus*.
Edlmann & Monaco 1981 – *Cornus*.
Friedman 1978 – *Cornus*.
Furuno 1985, 1987 – *Cornus*.
Greguss 1959 – *Cornus*.
Grosser 1977 – *Cornus*.
Hayashi 1991 – *Aucuba, Cornus*.
Hirai 1979–1985 – *Cornus*.
Ilic 1991 – *Cornus, Curtisia, Mastixia*.
Jacquiot et al. 1973 – *Cornus*.
Kanehira 1921a – *Cornus*.
Kanehira 1921b – *Aucuba, Cornus*.
Kanehira 1926 – *Aucuba, Cornus, Cy-noxylon* (= *Cornus*), *Macrocarpium* (= *Cornus*).
*Li & Chao 1954 – *Aucuba, Cornus, Coro-kia, Griselinia, Helwingia, Mastixia*.
Lomibao 1973c – *Mastixia*.
Luo 1989 – *Cornus*.
Meylan & Butterfield 1978b – *Griselinia*.
Moll & Janssonius 1906–1936 – *Mastixia*.
Niloofari 1961 – *Cornus*.
Panshin & Zeeuw 1980 – *Cornus*.
Patel 1973 – *Corokia, Griselinia*.
Pérez Olvera et al. 1982 [1985] – *Cornus*.
Philipson 1967 – *Griselinia*.
Philipson et al. 1980 – *Aralidium*.
Purkayastha & Bahadur 1977 – *Cornus*.
Record & Garratt 1925 – *Cornus*.
Record & Hess 1943 – *Cornus*.
Rodriguez 1957a – Relations.
Saiki 1982 – *Cornus*.
Schweingruber 1978, 1990 – *Cornus*.
Scott 1927 – *Curtisia*.
Shimaji & Itoh 1982, 1988 – *Cornus*.
Sudo 1959 – *Aucuba, Cornus*.
Sudo 1963 – *Cornus, Mastixia*.
Suzuki et al. 1991 – *Benthamidia* (= *Cor-nus*), *Helwingia, Swida* (= *Cornus*).
Van der Slooten 1968 – *Cornus*.
Yamabayashi 1938 – *Aucuba, Cornus, Cynoxylon* (= *Cornus*), *Macrocarpium* (= *Cornus*).
Yao 1988 – *Cornus, Dendrobenthamia* (= *Cornus*).

(CORNACEAE)

Crystals
Chattaway 1956 – *Curtisia, Griselinia, Mastixia.*

Ecological anatomy
Baas & Schweingruber 1987 – *Cornus.*
Carlquist & Hoekman 1985a – *Cornus.*
Novruzova 1968 – *Cornus, Thelycrania* (= *Cornus*).
Versteegh 1968 – *Mastixia.*

Helical thickenings
Meylan & Butterfield 1978a – *Corokia.*

Pits and perforation plates
Meylan & Butterfield 1974 – *Corokia, Griselinia.*
Ohtani & Ishida 1978a – *Cornus.*

Septate fibres
Butterfield & Meylan 1976 – *Corokia, Griselinia.*

Tracheary elements
Ohtani 1983 – *Cornus.*

CORYLACEAE see BETULACEAE

CORYNOCARPACEAE
(*Corynocarpus*)

Heimsch 1942.
Ilic 1991.
Ingle 1956.
Meylan & Butterfield 1978b.
Patel 1975.

Crystals
Chattaway 1956.

Helical thickenings
Meylan & Butterfield 1978a.

Pits
Meylan & Butterfield 1974.

CRASSULACEAE

Blesa Rodriguez et al. 1979 – *Aeonium, Aichryson, Greenovia, Monanthes.*
Carlquist 1962a – *Sedum.*
Hart & Koek-Noorman 1989 – *Sedum* + notes on other genera.
Schweingruber 1990 – *Aeonium, Sedum.*

(CRASSULACEAE)

Anomalous structure

Hamet 1912 – *Greenovia*.
Hamet 1925 – *Echeveria, Greenovia, Thompsonella*.

Ecological anatomy

Baas & Schweingruber 1987 – *Sedum*.

CROSSOSOMATACEAE

DeBuhr 1978 – *Crossosoma, Forsellesia* (= *Glossopetalon*).
Lemesle 1948b, 1955a – *Crossosoma*.
Record & Hess 1943 – *Crossosoma*.

Ecological anatomy

Carlquist & Hoekman 1985a – *Crossosoma, Forsellesia* (= *Glossopetalon*).

CRUCIFERAE

(*Cheiranthus* = *Erysimum*)

*Carlquist 1971 – *Cheiranthus, Crambe, Descurainia, Lepidium, Matthiola, Parolinia, Sinapidendron, Stanleya*.
Fahn et al. 1986 – *Zilla*.
Kowal & Cutler 1975 – *Fabrisinapis* (= *Hemicrambe*), *Schouwia*.
Messeri 1938 – *Schouwia*.
Metcalfe & Chalk 1950 – *Brassica*.
Saint-Laurent 1928 – *Cheiranthus, Henophyton, Iberis*.
Saint-Laurent 1932a – *Oudneya* (= *Henophyton*).
Schweingruber 1990 – *Biscutella, Brassica, Cheiranthus, Erysimum, Ptilotrichum* (= *Alyssum*), *Sinapidendron, Vella*.

Ecological anatomy

Baas et al. 1983 – *Zilla*.
Baas & Schweingruber 1987 – *Biscutella, Brassica, Cheiranthus, Erysimum, Ptilotrichum* (= *Alyssum*), *Sinapidendron, Vella*.
Carlquist & Hoekman 1985a – *Lepidium, Stanleya*.
Webber 1936a – *Lepidium*.

CRYPTERONIACEAE

Anon. 1977a – *Dactylocladus*.
Baas 1979b – *Alzatea* (or Lythraceae).

(CRYPTERONIACEAE)

Brazier & Franklin 1961 – *Dactylocladus*.
Hayashi et al. 1973 – *Dactylocladus*.
Ilic 1991 – *Crypteronia*.
Janssonius 1950 – Relations.
Kobayashi & Sugawa 1963 – *Dactylocladus*.
Lecomte 1926a – *Crypteronia*.
Martawijaya et al. 1986 – *Dactylocladus*.
Moll & Janssonius 1906–1936 – *Crypteronia*.
Ogata 1975–1983 – *Dactylocladus*.
Pearson & Brown 1932 – *Crypteronia*.
Saiki 1982 – *Dactylocladus* (in Melastomataceae).
Sudo 1963 – *Crypteronia, Dactylocladus* (in Melastomataceae).
Tang 1973 – *Crypteronia*.
*Van Vliet 1975 – *Alzatea* (or Lythraceae), *Axinandra, Crypteronia, Dactylocladus, Rhynchocalyx*.
Van Vliet & Baas 1984 – Relations of myrtalean families.
Wang 1984–1988 – *Dactylocladus*.

Anomalous structure

Chalk & Murthy 1963 – *Dactylocladus*.
Saiki & Ohnishi 1976 – *Dactylocladus*.

CTENOLOPHONACEAE see LINACEAE

CUCURBITACEAE

Carlquist 1992g – *Acanthosicyos, Apodanthera, Coccinia, Zanonia*.

Anomalous structure

Fries 1906 – *Siolmatra*.
Worsdell 1915 – Miscellaneous comments on several genera.
Zimmermann 1922 – 14 genera.

Ecological anatomy

Carlquist 1985 [1986]a – *Zanonia*.

CUNONIACEAE

(*Ackama* = *Caldcluvia, Opocunonia* = *Caldcluvia*)

Araujo & Mattos Filho 1981 [1982]a – *Belangera* (= *Lamanonia*).
Araujo & Mattos Filho 1981 [1982]b – *Weinmannia*.

(CUNONIACEAE)

Barbosa et al. 1977–1978 – *Lamanonia.*
Brazier & Franklin 1961 – *Ceratopetalum, Weinmannia.*
Burgerstein 1909 – *Spiraeanthemum.*
Chalk et al. 1935 – *Cunonia, Platylophus.*
Dadswell & Eckersley 1935 – *Ackama, Anodopetalum, Ceratopetalum, Geissois, Schizomeria, Weinmannia.*
Dadswell & Eckersley 1938b – *Ackama, Anodopetalum, Callicoma, Ceratopetalum, Geissois, Schizomeria, Weinmannia.*
Détienne & Jacquet 1983 – *Weinmannia.*
*Dickison 1977 – *Weinmannia* 35 spp.
*Dickison 1980 – 21 genera, 77 spp. (incl. *Bauera*).
Furuno 1977, 1979 – *Ackama, Ceratopetalum, Opocunonia, Schizomeria.*
Garratt 1924 – *Weinmannia.*
Ilic 1991 – 14 genera.
*Ingle & Dadswell 1956 – 20 genera.
Kribs 1959 – *Ceratopetalum, Weinmannia.*
Lecomte 1922 – *Weinmannia.*
Lomibao 1973c – *Weinmannia.*
Meylan & Butterfield 1978b – *Ackama, Weinmannia.*
Moll & Janssonius 1906–1936 – *Weinmannia.*
Nardi Berti & Edlmann Abbate 1992 – *Weinmannia.*
Ogata 1975–1983 – *Schizomeria.*
Ortiz Cespedes 1959 – *Weinmannia.*
Patel 1990 – *Ackama, Weinmannia.*
Rancusi et al. 1987 – *Caldcluvia, Weinmannia.*
Record & Hess 1943 – Family (*Belangera* (= *Lamanonia*), *Caldcluvia, Weinmannia*).
Record & Mell 1924 – *Weinmannia.*
Scott 1927 – *Cunonia, Platylophus.*
Sudo 1963 – *Ceratopetalum, Weinmannia.*
Sudo 1988 – *Ackama, Aistopetalum, Ceratopetalum, Schizomeria.*
Tippo 1938 – Family (*Ceratopetalum, Cunonia, Weinmannia*).
Tortorelli 1937 [1938] – *Caldcluvia.*
Van der Slooten 1968 – *Weinmannia.*
Wagemann 1949 – *Caldcluvia, Weinmannia.*
Welch 1926 – *Ackama, Callicoma, Ceratopetalum, Geissois, Schizomeria, Weinmannia.*

(CUNONIACEAE)

Crystals

Chattaway 1956 – 13 genera.
Scurfield et al. 1973 – *Ceratopetalum.*

Ecological anatomy

Van der Graaff & Baas 1974 – *Weinmannia.*
Versteegh 1968 – *Ceratopetalum, Schizomeria, Weinmannia.*

Pits

Meylan & Butterfield 1974 – *Ackama, Weinmannia.*

CYRILLACEAE

Araujo & Mattos Filho 1974a – *Cyrilla.*
Babos & Borhidi 1978 – *Cyrilla.*
Heimsch 1942 – *Cliftonia, Cyrilla.*
Record 1932b – *Schizocardia* (= *Purdiaea*).
Record 1938a – *Cyrilla.*
Record & Hess 1943 – *Cyrilla.*
Thomas 1960 – *Cliftonia, Cyrilla.*
Urling & Smith 1953 – *Cyrilla.*

Pits and perforation plates
Carlquist 1992d – *Cliftonia.*

DAPHNIPHYLLACEAE (*Daphniphyllum*)

*Carlquist 1982a.
Cheng, J.-Q. 1980.
Cheng, J.-Q. et al. 1992.
Hayashi 1991.
Hirai 1979–1985.
Huang 1965.
Ilic 1991.
Kanehira 1921a,b, 1926.
Moll & Janssonius 1906–1936.
Shimaji & Itoh 1988.
Sudo 1959.
Suzuki & Noshiro 1988.
Tang 1973.
Yamabayashi 1938 – (under Euphorbiaceae).
Yao 1988.

Ecological anatomy
Versteegh 1968.

Perforation plates
Ohtani & Ishida 1978a.

Tracheary elements
Ohtani 1983.

DATISCACEAE

Abbate & Cavina 1980 – *Tetrameles*.
Brazier & Franklin 1961 – *Octomeles, Tetrameles*.
*Davidson 1976 – *Datisca, Octomeles, Tetrameles*.
Fundter & Wisse 1977 – *Octomeles*.
Furuno 1977 – *Octomeles, Tetrameles*.
Ilic 1991 – *Octomeles, Tetrameles*.
Janssonius 1950 – Relationships.
Kanehira 1924 – *Octomeles*.
Kobayashi & Sugawa 1960 – *Tetrameles*.
Kobayashi & Sugawa 1963 – *Octomeles*.
Martawijaya et al. 1989 – *Octomeles*.
Moll & Janssonius 1906–1936 – *Tetrameles*.
Ogata 1975–1983 – *Octomeles, Tetrameles*.
Pearson & Brown 1932 – *Tetrameles*.
Sudo 1963, 1988 – *Octomeles, Tetrameles*.
Tang 1973 – *Tetrameles*.
Wang 1984–1988 – *Octomeles*.
Wiraj Chunwarin & Damrong Sri-Aran 1974 – *Tetrameles*.

Ecological anatomy
Carlquist & Hoekman 1985a – *Datisca*.

DAVIDIACEAE (*Davidia*)

Cheng, J.-Q. 1980.
Cheng, J.-Q. et al. 1992.
Li & Chao 1954.
Luo 1989.
Moll & Janssonius 1906–1936.
Titman 1949.
Yao 1988.

DAVIDSONIACEAE (*Davidsonia*)

Ingle & Dadswell 1956.

Crystals
Chattaway 1956.

DEGENERIACEAE (*Degeneria*)

Bailey & Smith 1942 – (young).
Carlquist 1989e.
Ilic 1991.
Lemesle & Duchaigne 1955.
Metcalfe 1987 – General survey.
Takahashi 1985.
Vander Wyk & Canright 1956 – Relations.

DESFONTAINIACEAE
see LOGANIACEAE

DIALYPETALANTHACEAE
(*Dialypetalanthus*)

Toledo Rizzini & Occhioni 1949.

DICHAPETALACEAE

Dechamps 1979 – *Tapura*.
Détienne & Jacquet 1983 – *Tapura*.
Détienne et al. 1982 – *Tapura*.
Heimsch 1942 – *Dichapetalum, Gonypetalum* (= *Tapura*), *Tapura*.
Lebacq et al. 1973 – *Tapura*.
Nel et al. 1982 – *Dichapetalum*.
Normand 1955 – *Dichapetalum*.
Normand & Paquis 1976 [1977] – *Dichapetalum, Tapura*.
Prance 1972a – Family (*Dichapetalum, Stephanopodium, Tapura*).
Record 1927b – *Tapura*.
Record & Hess 1943 – Family (*Dichapetalum, Gonypetalum* (= *Tapura*), *Tapura*).
Tippo 1938 – *Tapura*.
*Van Veenendaal & Den Outer 1978 – *Dichapetalum* 54 spp.
Williams 1936 – *Tapura*.

DICRASTYLIDACEAE
(CHLOANTHACEAE)

*Carlquist 1981e – *Cyanostegia, Lachnostachys, Physopsis, Pityrodia*.

Ecological anatomy
Carlquist 1977c – *Cyanostegia, Lachnostachys, Physopsis, Pityrodia*.

DIDIEREACEAE

Den Outer & Van Veenendaal 1980 – *Alluaudia*.
Heimsch 1942 – *Didierea*.
*Rauh & Dittmar 1970 – *Alluaudia, Alluaudiopsis, Decarya, Didierea*.

DIDYMELACEAE (*Didymeles*)

Léandri 1937 – (young).
Takhtajan et al. 1986.

DIEGODENDRACEAE (*Diegodendron*)

Dickison 1988.

DILLENIACEAE (*Wormia* = *Dillenia*)

Alves de Pinho 1966 – *Curatella*.
Araujo & Mattos Filho 1977 – *Curatella*.
Babos & Borhidi 1978 – *Curatella*.
Balan Menon 1955 – *Dillenia*.
Baretta-Kuipers 1972 – *Doliocarpus, Pinzona*.
Bargagli-Petrucci 1903 – *Dillenia*.
Bastos 1946 [1947] – *Curatella*.
Brazier & Franklin 1961 – *Dillenia, Wormia*.
Carreras & Vales 1986b – *Curatella*.
Cheng, J.-Q. 1980 – *Dillenia*.
Cheng, J.-Q. et al. 1992 – *Dillenia*.
Cockrell 1942 – *Dillenia, Wormia*.
Dechamps 1979 – *Curatella*.
Détienne & Jacquet 1983 – *Curatella*.
Détienne et al. 1982 – *Curatella*.
*Dickison 1967 – 10 genera, 40 spp.
*Dickison 1979 – *Dillenia* 31 spp.
*Dickison et al. 1978 – *Hibbertia* 27 spp.
Fundter & Wisse 1977 – *Dillenia*.
Furuno 1979 – *Dillenia*.
Hayashi et al. 1973 – *Dillenia*.
Ilic 1991 – *Curatella, Dillenia, Hibbertia*.
Kanehira 1921a – *Dillenia*.
Kobayashi & Sugawa 1966a – *Dillenia*.
Kribs 1959 – *Dillenia*.
Lecomte 1926a – *Dillenia*.
Martawijaya et al. 1989 – *Dillenia*.
Moll & Janssonius 1906–1936 – *Dillenia, Wormia*.
Ogata 1975–1983 – *Dillenia*.
Pearson & Brown 1932 – *Dillenia*.
Record & Hess 1943 – Family (*Curatella, Davilla, Doliocarpus, Tetracera*).
Sudo 1963, 1988 – *Dillenia*.
Tang 1973 – *Dillenia*.
Vestal 1937 – Family (*Curatella, Davilla, Dillenia, Doliocarpus, Hibbertia, Schumacheria, Tetracera, Wormia*).
Wang 1984–1988 – *Dillenia*.
Williams 1936 – *Curatella*.
Wiraj Chunwarin & Damrong Sri-Aran 1973 – *Dillenia*.

Anomalous structure
Chalk & Chattaway 1937 – *Doliocarpus*.

(DILLENIACEAE)
Crystals
Chattaway 1955 – *Dillenia, Hibbertia*.

Ecological anatomy
Carlquist 1977c – *Hibbertia*.
Carlquist 1985 [1986]a – *Hibbertia, Tetracera*.
Rury & Dickison 1984 – *Hibbertia*.

Pits and perforation plates
Carlquist 1992d – *Hibbertia*.

Silica
Dickison 1984 – *Hibbertia* 13 spp.
Scurfield et al. 1974 – *Dillenia*.

DIONCOPHYLLACEAE
(see also ANCISTROCLADACEAE)

*Gottwald & Parameswaran 1968 – *Dioncophyllum, Habropetalum, Triphyophyllum*.
Miller, R.B. 1975 – *Triphyophyllum*.

Anomalous structure
Chalk & Chattaway 1937 – *Dioncophyllum*.

Ecological anatomy
Carlquist 1985 [1986]a – *Triphyophyllum*.

DIPENTODONTACEAE

Li & Zhang 1990 – *Dipentodon* (in Celastraceae).

DIPSACACEAE

*Carlquist 1982b – *Pterocephalus, Scabiosa*.
Saint-Laurent 1928 – *Scabiosa*.
Schweingruber 1990 – *Pterocephalus*.

Ecological anatomy
Baas & Schweingruber 1987 – *Pterocephalus*.

DIPTEROCARPACEAE
(*Balanocarpus* = *Hopea, Pentacme* = *Shorea*)

Anon. 1961 – *Shorea*.
Abbate 1977 – *Anisoptera, Cotylelobium, Dipterocarpus, Hopea, Pentacme, Shorea*.
Abbate & Cavina 1980 – *Dipterocarpus*.
America 1974 – *Anisoptera*.

(DIPTEROCARPACEAE)

Balan Menon 1955 – *Balanocarpus, Cotylelobium, Dipterocarpus, Dryobalanops, Hopea, Shorea, Vatica.*

Balan Menon 1959 – *Anisoptera, Hopea, Shorea.*

Bancroft 1934 – *Monotes.*

Bancroft 1935a – *Marquesia.*

Bancroft 1935b – *Marquesia, Monotes.*

Bargagli-Petrucci 1903 – *Balanocarpus, Cotylelobium, Dipterocarpus, Dryobalanops, Hopea, Shorea, Vateria.*

Berger 1922 – *Dipterocarpus, Shorea.*

*Brazier 1979 – Family (13 genera).

Brazier & Franklin 1961 – *Anisoptera, Balanocarpus, Dipterocarpus, Dryobalanops, Hopea, Parashorea, Pentacme, Shorea.*

Cheng, C. 1985 – *Dipterocarpus, Hopea, Parashorea, Vatica.*

Cheng, J.-Q. 1980 – *Dipterocarpus, Hopea, Vatica.*

Cheng, J.-Q. et al. 1992 – *Dipterocarpus, Hopea, Vatica.*

Chiba 1989 – Not seen.

Chu 1974 – *Anisoptera, Cotylelobium, Dipterocarpus, Dryobalanops, Hopea, Parashorea, Shorea, Upuna, Vatica.*

Das 1970b, c, 1976b – *Anisoptera, Dipterocarpus, Hopea, Shorea, Vatica.*

Desch 1941 – 11 genera.

Desch & Symington 1936 – *Shorea.*

Dixon 1919 – *Dipterocarpus, Dryobalanops.*

Doležal 1959 – *Parashorea.*

Edlmann Abbate & De Luca 1981 – *Hopea.*

Enchev et al. 1986 – *Anisoptera, Dipterocarpus.*

Fundter & Wisse 1977 – *Anisoptera, Vatica.*

Furuno 1977, 1979 – *Anisoptera, Hopea, Vatica.*

Gottwald 1968 – *Parashorea, Pentacme, Shorea.*

Gottwald & Noack 1972 – *Shorea.*

*Gottwald & Parameswaran 1966a – 17 genera.

Gottwald & Parameswaran 1966b – *Vateria (Vateriopsis).*

Hayashi et al. 1973 – 10 genera.

Hayashi & Nomura 1986 – *Dipterocarpus, Shorea, Vatica.*

Hirai 1979–1985 – *Dipterocarpus, Dryobalanops, Parashorea, Shorea.*

(DIPTEROCARPACEAE)

Huynh-Long 1969 – *Hopea.*

Huynh-Long & Hòmes 1969 – *Hopea.*

Ilic 1991 – 12 genera.

Kanehira 1924 – *Anisoptera, Dipterocarpus, Hopea, Isoptera, Pentacme, Shorea, Vatica.*

Kobayashi 1966 – *Anisoptera, Dipterocarpus, Hopea, Shorea.*

Kobayashi 1967 – *Dryobalanops.*

Kobayashi 1968 – *Shorea.*

Kobayashi & Sugawa 1960 – *Anisoptera, Dipterocarpus.*

Kobayashi & Sugawa 1961 – *Parashorea, Pentacme, Shorea.*

Kobayashi & Sugawa 1962 – *Dipterocarpus.*

Kobayashi & Sugawa 1963 – *Dryobalanops, Hopea, Shorea, Vatica.*

Kobayashi & Sugawa 1966a – *Balanocarpus.*

Kobayashi & Sugawa 1966b – *Shorea.*

Kobayashi et al. 1958 – *Anisoptera, Dipterocarpus, Hopea.*

Kribs 1959 – *Anisoptera, Dipterocarpus, Dryobalanops, Hopea, Parashorea, Pentacme, Shorea.*

Lebacq & Dechamps 1964 – *Monotes.*

Lecomte 1926a – *Dipterocarpus, Hopea, Parashorea, Shorea.*

Lomibao 1973b – Keys to groups of spp. *Anisoptera, Dipterocarpus, Hopea, Parashorea, Pentacme, Shorea, Vatica.*

Luo 1989 – *Dipterocarpus, Hopea, Parashorea, Shorea, Vatica.*

Maguire et al. 1977 – *Pakaraimaea* (wood by De Zeeuw).

Martawijaya et al. 1986 – *Anisoptera, Dipterocarpus, Dryobalanops, Hopea, Shorea, Vatica.*

Martawijaya et al. 1989 – *Cotylelobium, Hopea, Shorea.*

Meniado 1966 – *Parashorea, Pentacme, Shorea.*

Meniado 1971 – *Vatica.*

Meniado et al. 1974 – *Hopea, Parashorea, Pentacme, Shorea.*

Meniado & Valbuena 1966 – *Hopea.*

Moll & Janssonius 1906–1936 – *Dipterocarpus, Hopea, Shorea, Vatica.*

Morton 1993 – New sp. [Abstr.].

Normand & Paquis 1976 [1977] – *Marquesia.*

(DIPTEROCARPACEAE)

Ogata 1975–1983 – 15 genera.

*Parameswaran & Gottwald 1979 – 10 genera.

Pearson & Brown 1932 – *Balanocarpus, Dipterocarpus, Hopea, Parashorea, Pentacme, Shorea, Vateria, Vatica.*

Purkayastha et al. 1976 – *Dipterocarpus, Hopea.*

Reyes 1923 – *Anisoptera, Balanocarpus, Dipterocarpus, Hopea, Isoptera, Parashorea, Pentacme, Shorea.*

Saiki 1982 – *Anisoptera, Dipterocarpus, Dryobalanops, Parashorea, Shorea.*

*Sarayar 1976 – *Shorea* 42 spp.

Schmidt 1951–1952 – *Dipterocarpus.*

Sudo 1963 – 11 genera.

Sudo 1988 – *Anisoptera, Hopea, Vatica.*

Sugawa 1967b, 1968b – *Dipterocarpus.*

Sugawa 1968c – *Cotylelobium, Shorea, Vatica.*

Sugawa 1969 – *Dipterocarpus.*

Sugawa 1971a, b – *Shorea.*

Suzuki et al. 1991 – *Shorea.*

Takaki 1963 – *Cotylelobium, Dryobalanops, Hopea, Shorea, Upuna, Vatica.*

Tang 1973 – *Dipterocarpus, Hopea.*

Vestal 1937 – Family (8 genera).

Wagenführ 1990 – *Anisoptera, Dipterocarpus, Shorea.*

Wagenführ & Scheiber 1974 – *Anisoptera, Dipterocarpus, Hopea, Shorea.*

Wagenführ & Weiss 1990 – *Shorea.*

Wang 1984 – 17 genera.

Wang 1984–1988 – *Anisoptera, Dryobalanops, Hopea, Parashorea, Pentacme, Shorea, Vateria.*

Wiraj Chunwarin & Damrong Sri-Aran 1973 – *Anisoptera, Balanocarpus, Dipterocarpus, Hopea, Parashorea, Pentacme, Shorea.*

Wu & Tsai 1975 – *Shorea.*

Yao 1988 – *Dipterocarpus, Parashorea.*

Zamuco et al. 1964 – *Shorea.*

Crystals and silica

Anon. 1961 – *Shorea.*

Chattaway 1955 – *Hopea, Vatica.*

Chattaway 1956 – *Balanocarpus, Dryobalanops, Hopea, Parashorea, Pentacme, Shorea, Vateria, Vatica.*

(DIPTEROCARPACEAE)

Hirata et al. 1972 – *Anisoptera, Dipterocarpus, Dryobalanops, Parashorea, Pentacme, Shorea.*

Meniado et al. 1970 – *Hopea, Parashorea, Pentacme, Shorea.*

Scurfield et al. 1974 – *Dryobalanops.*

Stern & Zamuco 1964 – *Shorea.*

Sudo et al. 1967 – *Anisoptera, Cotylelobium, Dipterocarpus, Dryobalanops, Shorea.*

Taniguchi et al. 1982 – *Dipterocarpus, Dryobalanops, Pentacme, Shorea.*

Ecological anatomy

Carlquist 1985a – *Balanocarpus, Dipterocarpus, Doona* (= *Shorea*), *Hopea, Parashorea, Pentacme, Shorea.*

Perforation plates

Gottwald & Parameswaran 1964 – *Vateria, Vatica.*

Parameswaran & Liese 1973 – *Vatica.*

Rays

Chattaway 1951b – *Hopea.*

Sugawa 1967a – *Shorea.*

DUCKEODENDRACEAE

(*Duckeodendron*)

*Carlquist 1988b.

Détienne & Jacquet 1983.

Record 1933 – (in Apocynaceae).

Record & Hess 1943 – (in Solanaceae).

EBENACEAE

(*Diospyros* only unless otherwise stated)
(*Maba* = *Diospyros*)

Anon. 1981 (Andes).

Abbate 1963 – *Euclea.*

Abbate & Cavina 1980.

Bargagli-Petrucci 1903.

Benoist 1931 – *Diospyros, Maba.*

Brazier & Franklin 1961.

Brown 1922 – *Maba.*

Burgerstein 1909.

Cheng, J.-Q. 1980.

Cheng, J.-Q. et al. 1992.

Croptier & Kučera 1990.

Dechamps 1979.

(EBENACEAE)
Détienne & Jacquet 1983.
Détienne et al. 1982.
Edlmann Abbate & De Luca 1981.
Fasolo 1941–1944 – *Diospyros, Maba.*
Ferreirinha 1955.
Furuno 1977, 1985, 1987.
Greguss 1959.
Hayashi 1991.
Hayashi et al. 1973.
Hayashi & Nomura 1986.
Hirai 1979–1985.
Huber & Rouschal 1954.
Ilic 1991 – *Diospyros, Royena* (= *Dio-spyros*).
Jagiella & Kurschner 1987 – *Euclea.*
Janssonius 1950 – Relations.
Kanehira 1921a, 1924, 1926 – *Diospyros, Maba.*
Kanehira 1921b.
Kobayashi & Sugawa 1964.
Kribs 1928a, 1959.
Lebacq & Dechamps 1964 – *Diospyros, Euclea, Maba.*
Lebacq & Dechamps 1967 – *Diospyros, Euclea,* cf. *Maba.*
Lebacq et al. 1973.
Lecomte 1926a.
Luo 1989.
Martawijaya et al. 1986.
Martin 1953.
Moll & Janssonius 1906–1936 – *Diospyros, Maba.*
Monteiro & Frade 1960.
Nardi Berti & Edlmann Abbate 1988.
Niloofari 1961.
Normand 1960.
Normand & Paquis 1976 [1977].
Ogata 1975–1983.
Panshin & Zeeuw 1980.
Parsa Pajouh & Schweingruber 1985.
Pearson & Brown 1932.
Prakash 1972 – (root).
Purkayastha et al. 1976.
Record & Hess 1943.
Reinders-Gouwentak & Stahel 1948 – *Ropourea* (= *Diospyros*).
Saiki 1982.
Schweingruber 1990.
Shimaji & Itoh 1982, 1988.
Sudo 1959, 1963, 1988.
Tang 1973.

(EBENACEAE)
Wagenführ & Scheiber 1974.
Wang 1984–1988.
Williams 1936.
Wiraj Chunwarin & Damrong Sri-Aran 1974.
Wu & Wang 1976.
Wuang 1979.
Yamabayashi 1938.

Crystals
Baker 1917.
Chattaway 1956 – *Diospyros, Maba.*
Espinoza de Pernía 1987b.
Meniado et al. 1970.

Ecological anatomy
Novruzova 1968.
Van der Graaff & Baas 1974.

Helical thickenings
Nair 1987.

Perforation plates
Ohtani & Ishida 1978a.

Rays
McLean & Richardson 1973 [1974].

Storied structure
Cozzo & Cristiani 1950.

Tracheary elements
Gill & Onuja 1984a.
Ohtani 1983.

EHRETIACEAE see BORAGINACEAE

ELAEAGNACEAE
(*Elaeagnus* only unless otherwise stated)

Cheng, J.-Q. et al. 1992.
Chudnoff 1956.
Cutler et al. 1987 – (root).
Davtyan 1950 – *Elaeagnus* 7 spp. (+ brief notes on *Hippophae, Shepherdia*).
Fahn et al. 1986.
Ghelmeziu 1958 – *Hippophae.*
Greguss 1959 – *Elaeagnus, Hippophae.*
Grosser 1977 – *Hippophae.*
Hayashi 1991.
Huber & Rouschal 1954.
Kanehira 1921a, b, 1926.
Mork 1946 – *Hippophae.*
Nikolov & Bl"skova 1980.
Niloofari 1961.

(ELAEAGNACEAE)
Saint-Laurent 1928, 1934.
Schweingruber 1978 – *Hippophae*.
Schweingruber 1990 – *Elaeagnus, Hippo-*
phae.
Sudo 1959.
Thunell & Perem 1947 – *Hippophae*.
Wuang 1979 – *Elaeagnus, Hippophae*.
Yamabayashi 1938.
*Yamauchi 1976 – 13 taxa.
Yatsenko-Khmelevsky 1946c – *Hippophae*.

Ecological anatomy
Baas & Schweingruber 1987 – *Elaeagnus,*
Hippophae.
Carlquist & Hoekman 1985a – *Shepherdia*.
Novruzova 1968 – *Elaeagnus, Hippophae*.
Zhang & Cao 1990 – *Hippophae*.

ELAEOCARPACEAE
(*Echinocarpus = Sloanea*; for *Muntingia* see
TILIACEAE)

Brown 1922 – *Elaeocarpus*.
Burgerstein 1909 – *Elaeocarpus*.
Cheng, J.-Q. 1980 – *Elaeocarpus, Sloanea*.
Cheng, J.-Q. et al. 1992 – *Elaeocarpus,*
Sloanea.
Dadswell & Eckersley 1935 – *Elaeocarpus,*
Sloanea.
Dechamps 1979 – *Sloanea*.
Desch 1954 – *Sloanea* (in Tiliaceae).
Descole & O'Donell 1937 – *Crinodendron*.
Détienne & Jacquet 1983 – *Sloanea*.
Détienne et al. 1982 – *Sloanea*.
Freitas 1958 – *Elaeocarpus*.
Fundter & Wisse 1977 – *Elaeocarpus,*
Sloanea.
Furuno 1977 – *Elaeocarpus, Sloanea*.
Garratt 1924 – *Elaeocarpus*.
Hirai 1979–1985 – *Elaeocarpus*.
Ilic 1991 – *Aceratium, Aristotelia, Dubou-*
zetia, Elaeocarpus, Sericolea, Sloanea.
Kanehira 1921a – *Echinocarpus, Elaeocar-*
pus.
Kanehira 1924 – *Elaeocarpus*.
Kanehira 1926 – *Echinocarpus*.
Kribs 1928a – *Sloanea*.
Kukachka 1962 – *Petenaea* (or in Tiliaceae).
*Kukachka & Rees 1943 – *Aristotelia, Echi-*
nocarpus, Elaeocarpus 31 spp., *Sloanea,*
Vallea.

(ELAEOCARPACEAE)
Lebacq et al. 1973 – *Sloanea*.
Lecomte 1922, 1926a – *Elaeocarpus*.
Lim & Soh 1991b – *Elaeocarpus*.
Luo 1989 – *Elaeocarpus*.
Mainieri 1978 – *Sloanea*.
Mainieri & Chimelo 1989 – *Sloanea*.
Meylan & Butterfield 1978b – *Aristotelia,*
Elaeocarpus.
Moll & Janssonius 1906–1936 – *Elaeocar-*
pus, Sloanea.
Mouton & Jacquet 1977 – *Sloanea*.
*Ogata 1975 – *Elaeocarpus* 17 spp., *Sloanea*
6 spp.
Ogata 1975–1983 – *Elaeocarpus, Sloanea*.
Patel 1989 – *Aristotelia, Elaeocarpus*.
Pearson & Brown 1932 – *Echinocarpus,*
Elaeocarpus.
Pereira et al. 1970 – *Aristotelia, Crinoden-*
dron, Sloanea.
Pérez Mogollón 1973 – *Sloanea*.
Rancusi et al. 1987 – *Aristotelia, Crinoden-*
dron.
Record & Hess 1943 – Family (*Aristotelia,*
Crinodendron, Dicraspidia, Muntingia,
Sloanea, Vallea; Dicraspidia and *Muntin-*
gia now in Tiliaceae).
Schultz & Wollheim 1962 – *Sloanea*.
Sudo 1959 – *Elaeocarpus*.
Sudo 1988 – *Elaeocarpus, Sloanea*.
Tang 1973 – *Elaeocarpus*.
Teixeira 1983 – *Sloanea*.
Wagemann 1949 – *Crinodendron*.
Wang 1984–1988 – *Elaeocarpus*.
Williams 1936 – *Sloanea*.
Wu & Wang 1976 – *Elaeocarpus, Sloanea*.

Crystals
Chattaway 1955 – *Sloanea*.
Chattaway 1956 – *Aceratium, Aristotelia,*
Dubouzetia, Elaeocarpus, Sloanea.
Espinoza de Pernía 1987b – *Sloanea*.

Ecological anatomy
Van der Graaff & Baas 1974 – *Elaeocar-*
pus.

Growth rings
Gil 1989 – *Vallea*.

Helical thickenings
Bricker 1991 – *Crinodendron, Dubouzetia*.
Meylan & Butterfield 1978a – *Elaeocarpus*.
Ohtani & Ishida 1978b – *Elaeocarpus*.

(ELAEOCARPACEAE)

Pits and perforation plates
Meylan & Butterfield 1974 – *Aristotelia, Elaeocarpus.*
Ohtani & Ishida 1978a – *Elaeocarpus.*

Septate fibres
Butterfield & Meylan 1976 – *Aristotelia, Elaeocarpus.*

Tracheary elements
Ohtani 1983 – *Elaeocarpus.*

ELATINACEAE

Carlquist 1984d – *Bergia.*

EMBLINGIACEAE

Erdtman et al. 1969 – *Emblingia* (twig).

EMPETRACEAE

*Carlquist 1989f – *Ceratiola, Corema, Empetrum.*
Greguss 1959 – *Empetrum.*
Miller, H.J. 1975 – *Empetrum.*
Mork 1946 – *Empetrum.*
Queiroz & Van der Burgh 1988–1989 [1989] – *Corema, Empetrum.*
Schweingruber 1990 – *Empetrum.*

Ecological anatomy
Baas & Schweingruber 1987 – *Empetrum.*

EPACRIDACEAE

Brown 1922 – *Cyathodes.*
*Etienne 1919 – 26 genera.
Garratt 1924 – *Dracophyllum.*
Ilic 1991 – *Dracophyllum, Leucopogon.*
Meylan & Butterfield 1978b – *Archeria, Cyathodes, Dracophyllum.*
Record 1932b – Family.

Crystals
Chattaway 1956 – *Leucopogon, Monotoca, Trochocarpa.*
Scurfield et al. 1973 – *Trochocarpa.*

Ecological anatomy
Carlquist 1977c – *Andersonia, Cosmelia, Leucopogon, Lysinema, Sphenotoma.*

(EPACRIDACEAE)

Pits
Meylan & Butterfield 1974 – *Cyathodes, Dracophyllum.*

ERICACEAE (incl. VACCINIACEAE)

Baas 1979a – *Vaccinium.*
Carvalho 1954–1956 – *Arbutus.*
Cheng, J.-Q. 1980 – *Lyonia, Rhododendron.*
Cheng, J.-Q. et al. 1992 – *Lyonia, Rhododendron.*
Chevalier 1927 – *Erica.*
Chudnoff 1956 – *Arbutus.*
*Cox 1948a – Rhododendroideae 19 genera (young wood).
*Cox 1948b – Arbutoideae 16 genera (young wood).
Cutler et al. 1987 – *Arbutus, Pieris, Rhododendron* (root).
Fahn et al. 1986 – *Arbutus.*
Fasolo 1941–1944 – *Erica.*
Forsaith 1920 – *Rhododendron.*
Friedman 1978 – *Arbutus, Gaultheria, Menziesia, Rhododendron, Vaccinium.*
Furuno 1985, 1987 – *Arbutus, Oxydendrum.*
Greguss 1959 – 14 genera.
Grosser 1977 – *Rhododendron.*
Grosser 1985 – *Arbutus.*
Hayashi 1991 – *Lyonia, Pieris, Rhododendron, Vaccinium.*
Huber & Rouschal 1954 – *Arbutus, Erica.*
Ilic 1991 – *Arbutus, Dimorphanthera, Oxydendrum, Rhododendron, Vaccinium.*
Jacquiot et al. 1973 – *Arbutus, Erica.*
Jagiella & Kurschner 1987 – *Erica.*
Kanehira 1921a – *Pieris, Rhododendron, Vaccinium.*
Kanehira 1921b, 1926 – *Enkianthus, Rhododendron.*
Lebacq & Dechamps 1964 – *Agauria* (= *Agarista*), *Ficalhoa* (or in Theaceae).
Lecomte 1922 – *Agauria* (= *Agarista*).
Luo 1989 – *Rhododendron.*
Luteyn 1983 – *Cavendishia* 13 spp.
Miller, H.J. 1975 – *Rhododendron, Vaccinium.*
Moll & Janssonius 1906–1936 – *Vaccinium.*
Mork 1946 – *Calluna, Vaccinium.*

(ERICACEAE)

Panshin & Zeeuw 1980 – *Arbutus, Oxydendrum.*

Pearson & Brown 1932 – *Rhododendron.*

Peraza Oramas & Lopez de Roma 1967 – *Arbutus.*

Pérez Olvera et al. 1982 [1985] – *Vaccinium.*

Pérez Olvera & Corral López 1980 – *Arbutus.*

Queiroz & Van der Burgh 1988–1989 [1989] – *Arbutus, Arctostaphylos, Calluna, Daboecia, Erica, Loiseleuria, Phyllodoce, Rhododendron, Vaccinium.*

Record 1932b – Ericales general description.

Record & Hess 1943 – Family (15 genera).

Saccardy & Muzard 1938 – *Erica.*

Saint-Laurent 1928, 1934 – *Arbutus, Erica.*

Saya 1957 – *Erica.*

Schmidt 1951–1952 – *Erica.*

Schweingruber 1990 – 11 genera.

Shimaji & Itoh 1982 – *Vaccinium.*

Shimaji & Itoh 1988 – *Rhododendron, Vaccinium.*

Sudo 1959 – *Lyonia, Pieris, Rhododendron, Vaccinium.*

Sudo 1963 – *Arctostaphylos, Erica.*

Suzuki & Noshiro 1988 – *Agapetes, Enkianthus, Lyonia, Pieris, Rhododendron.*

Suzuki & Ohba 1988 – *Rhododendron.*

Thunell & Perem 1947 – *Calluna.*

*Wallace 1986 – *Cassiope* 21 spp.

Wang 1982 – *Rhododendron.*

Wu & Wang 1976 – *Rhododendron.*

Wuang 1979 – *Rhododendron.*

Yamabayashi 1938 – *Rhododendron, Vaccinium.*

Yatsenko-Khmelevsky 1946b – *Arbutus, Arctostaphylos, Epigaea, Erica, Rhododendron, Vaccinium.*

Crystals

Chattaway 1956 – *Oxydendrum, Vaccinium.*

Ecological anatomy

Baas 1973 – *Vaccinium.*

Baas et al. 1983 – *Arbutus.*

Baas & Schweingruber 1987 – 11 genera.

Carlquist 1985a – *Arbutus, Arctostaphylos, Comarostaphylis, Ornithostaphylos, Xylococcus.*

(ERICACEAE)

Carlquist & Hoekman 1985a – *Arbutus, Arctostaphylos, Comarostaphylis, Ornithostaphylos, Phyllodoce, Rhododendron, Vaccinium, Xylococcus.*

Versteegh 1968 – *Rhododendron, Vaccinium.*

Webber 1936a – *Arctostaphylos.*

Helical thickenings

Ohtani & Ishida 1978b – *Lyonia, Pieris, Vaccinium.*

Pits and perforation plates

Meylan & Butterfield 1974, 1975 – *Gaultheria.*

Ohtani & Ishida 1978a – *Enkianthus, Lyonia, Pieris, Vaccinium.*

Rays

Braun 1967 – *Erica.*

Braun & den Outer 1965 – *Vaccinium.*

Braun et al. 1967 – *Erica.*

Flint 1918 – *Gaylussacia, Vaccinium.*

Septate fibres

Butterfield & Meylan 1976 – *Gaultheria.*

Tracheary elements

Carlquist 1988f – *Arbutus, Arctostaphylos, Comarostaphylis, Vaccinium, Xylococcus.*

Jing et al. 1989 – *Rhododendron.*

Ohtani 1983 – *Enkianthus, Lyonia, Pieris, Vaccinium.*

Rao 1979 – *Vaccinium.*

ERYTHROPALACEAE

see OLACACEAE

ERYTHROXYLACEAE

(*Erythroxylum* only unless otherwise stated)

Barajas Morales & Léon Gómez 1989.

Brazier & Franklin 1961.

Burgerstein 1912.

Détienne & Jacquet 1983.

Détienne et al. 1982.

Heimsch 1942.

Ilic 1991.

Kribs 1959.

Lebacq 1963.

Lebacq & Dechamps 1964.

Lebacq et al. 1973.

Lecomte 1922.

(ERYTHROXYLACEAE)
Metcalfe 1935.
Nardi Berti & Edlmann Abbate 1988.
Normand 1937, 1950b.
Normand & Cavaco 1951 – *Pinacopodium.*
Normand & Paquis 1976 [1977] – *Erythroxylum, Pinacopodium* (in Nectaropetalaceae).
Record & Hess 1943.
Record & Mell 1924.
*Rury 1981 – *Erythroxylum* c. 140 spp.
*Rury 1985 – *Erythroxylum* 65, *Nectaropetalum* 1, *Pinacopodium* 1.
Sudo 1963.
Williams 1936.

Crystals
Chattaway 1956.

Ecological anatomy
Carlquist 1985a.
Rury & Dickison 1984.

Silica
Espinoza de Pernía 1987b.
Welle 1976b.

ESCALLONIACEAE
(incl. BREXIACEAE; for *Corokia* see CORNACEAE; see also ITEACEAE)

Brook 1951 – *Carpodetus.*
Cheng, J.-Q. 1980 – *Polyosma.*
Cheng, J.-Q. et al. 1992 – *Polyosma* (in Saxifragaceae).
Cutler et al. 1987 – *Escallonia* (root).
Détienne & Jacquet 1983 – *Escallonia.*
Duchaigne & Chalard 1952, 1955, 1956 – *Polyosma* (young stem).
Furuno 1979 – *Polyosma.*
Hils et al. 1988 – *Tetracarpaea.*
Ilic 1991 – *Carpodetus, Polyosma, Quintinia.*
Lebacq et al. 1973 – *Escallonia.*
Lemesle 1956b, 1963a – *Polyosma.*
Meylan & Butterfield 1978b – *Carpodetus, Ixerba, Quintinia.*
Moll & Janssonius 1906–1936 – *Polyosma.*
Patel 1973 – *Carpodetus; Ixerba, Quintinia.*
Record 1931b – *Escallonia.*
Record & Hess 1943 – *Escallonia.*
Shaw et al. 1973 – *Pottingeria* (twig) (or Celastraceae or Hydrangeaceae).

(ESCALLONIACEAE)
Stern 1974 – *Escallonia.*
Stern et al. 1969 – *Anopterus, Argophyllum, Brexia, Escallonia, Polyosma.*
Sudo 1988 – *Polyosma.*
Tippo 1938 – Family (*Brexia, Carpodetus, Escallonia*).
Van der Slooten 1968 – *Escallonia.*
Wagemann 1949 – *Escallonia.*
Welch 1926 – *Polyosma, Quintinia.*

Crystals
Chattaway 1956 – *Quintinia.*

Ecological anatomy
Bamber 1984 – *Quintinia.*
Versteegh 1968 – *Polyosma.*

Helical thickenings
Meylan & Butterfield 1978a – *Carpodetus.*

Pits
Meylan & Butterfield 1974 – *Carpodetus, Ixerba, Quintinia.*

EUCOMMIACEAE (*Eucommia*)

Cheng, J.-Q. 1980.
Cheng, J.-Q. et al. 1992.
Ilic 1991.
Lemesle 1946b.
Tippo 1938, 1940.
Wuang 1979.
Yao 1988.
Yatsenko-Khmelevsky 1954a.
Zhang, Z.-Y. et al. 1990.

EUCRYPHIACEAE (*Eucryphia*; for *Paracryphia* see PARACRYPHIACEAE)

Bausch 1938.
Brazier & Franklin 1961.
Dadswell & Eckersley 1935.
*Dickison 1978.
Ilic 1991.
Ingle & Dadswell 1956.
Luca & Edlmann Abbate 1983.
Nardi Berti & Edlmann Abbate 1992.
Ortiz Cespedes 1959.
Rancusi et al. 1987.
Record & Hess 1943.
Record & Mell 1924.
Vestal 1937.
Wagemann 1949.

EUPHORBIACEAE

Anon. 1981 (Andes) – *Hieronima, Hura*.
Anon. 1981 (Curua) – *Drypetes, Glycyden-dron*.
Abbate 1970 – *Euphorbia*.
Abbate 1971a – *Anthostema*.
Araujo & Mattos Filho 1984 – *Drypetes, Hieronima, Paradrypetes, Richeria, Securinega*.
Babos & Borhidi 1978 – *Pera*.
Balan Menon 1959 – *Endospermum*.
Barajas Morales & Echenique-Manrique 1976 – *Celaenodendron, Omphalea*.
Barajas Morales & Léon Gómez 1989 – *Celaenodendron, Cnidoscolus, Jatropha, Sapium*.
Barbosa et al. 1977–1978 – *Sapium*.
Barreto 1967 – *Uapaca*.
Bascopé 1954 – *Alchornea, Tetrorchidium*.
Bastos 1946 [1947] – *Hura*.
Benoist 1931 – *Croton, Hevea*.
Brazier & Franklin 1961 – *Aextoxicon, Croton, Endospermum, Hieronima, Old-fieldia, Ricinodendron, Spirostachys, Uapaca*.
Brown 1922 – *Aleurites, Euphorbia*.
Burgerstein 1909 – *Aleurites, Bischofia, Codiaeum, Homalanthus, Jatropha, Macaranga, Manihot*.
Burgerstein 1912 – *Dactylostemon* (= *Acti-nostemon*), *Sapium*.
Burtt Davy 1928 – *Spirostachys*.
*Carlquist 1970b – *Euphorbia* 16 spp.
Carreras & Vales 1986b – *Grimmeoden-dron, Leucocroton*.
Chalk et al. 1933 – *Ricinodendron*.
Cheng, C. 1985 – *Bischofia*.
Cheng, J.-Q. 1980 – 16 genera.
Cheng, J.-Q. et al. 1992 – 16 genera.
Chiang 1962, 1964 – *Bischofia*.
Cockrell 1942 – 13 genera.
Coimbra Filho & Mattos Filho 1953 – *Hieronima*.
Corral Lopez 1985 – *Sapium*.
Croptier & Kučera 1990 – *Macaranga*.
Cunha Mello 1950 [1951] – *Croton*.
Cutler 1968 – *Givotia* (twig).
Dadswell & Eckersley 1935 – *Aleurites*.
Dahlgren & Van Wyk 1988 – *Andro-stachys*.
Dechamps 1979 – 17 genera.
Dechamps 1985 – *Pera*.

(EUPHORBIACEAE)

Dechamps et al. 1985 – *Hymenocardia*.
Détienne & Jacquet 1983 – 29 genera.
Détienne et al. 1982 – 17 genera.
Doležal 1959 – *Mallotus*.
Dressler 1957 – *Pedilanthus*.
Edlmann & Monaco 1981 – *Mallotus*.
Eeckhout 1951 – *Ricinodendron, Uapaca*.
Fahn et al. 1986 – *Euphorbia, Ricinus*.
Fasolo 1939–1940 – *Croton, Euphorbia*.
Fedalto et al. 1989 – *Joannesia*.
Ferreirinha 1955 – *Androstachys, Ricino-dendron, Spirostachys*.
Ferreirinha 1956 – *Ricinodendron, Spiro-stachys*.
Fouarge & Gérard 1964 – *Discoglypremna, Phyllanthus, Ricinodendron, Uapaca*.
Fouarge et al. 1953 – *Cleistanthus, Uapaca*.
Franco 1990 – *Hieronima*.
Freitas 1958 – *Aleurites, Bischofia, Maca-ranga*.
Freitas 1987 – *Phyllanthus*.
Fundter & Wisse 1977 – *Bischofia*.
Furuno 1977, 1979 – *Aleurites, Annesijoa, Antidesma, Bischofia, Bridelia, Endo-spermum, Macaranga, Neoscortechinia, Pimelodendron*.
Ghosh & Shahi 1961 – *Hemicyclia* (= *Dry-petes*).
Gill & Onuja 1983b – *Hevea, Ricinoden-dron, Uapaca*.
Gilles 1905 – *Hura*.
Giordano 1939 – *Bridelia, Sapium*.
*Giraud 1985 – Statistics (42 genera).
Gomes 1983 – *Hevea*.
Gomes & Silva 1992 [1993] – *Hevea* 11 spp.
Gómez 1959 – *Alchornea*.
Greguss 1959 – *Euphorbia*.
Grisa 1988 – *Givotia*.
Hayashi 1991 – *Mallotus, Sapium*.
Hayashi et al. 1973 – *Aporusa, Elaterio-spermum, Macaranga, Sapium*.
Hayden 1977 – *Picrodendron*.
Hayden 1992 – *Oldfieldioideae* [Abstr.].
Hayden & Brandt 1984 – *Neowawraea* (= *Flueggea*).
Hayden et al. 1993 – *Amanoa* 7 spp.
Heimsch 1942 – 78 genera, 85 spp.
Hirai 1979–1985 – *Aleurites, Mallotus, Sapium, Triadica* (= *Sapium*).
Ilic 1991 – 54 genera + *Uapaca*.
Jagiella & Kurschner 1987 – *Euphorbia*.

(EUPHORBIACEAE)

Janssonius 1929 – Relations.

Jimenez et al. 1978 [1979] – *Euphorbia*.

Kanehira 1921a – 12 genera.

Kanehira 1921b – *Mallotus*.

Kanehira 1924 – *Antidesma, Aporusa, Bischofia, Cyclostemon* (= *Drypetes*), *Endospermum*.

Kanehira 1926 – *Bischofia, Mallotus, Sapium*.

Kazmi & Singh 1988 – *Hevea*.

Kobayashi & Sugawa 1972 – *Bischofia*.

Kribs 1928a *Alchornea, Amanoa, Mabea, Maprounea, Sapium*.

Kribs 1959 – *Excoecaria, Glycydendron, Gymnanthes, Hieronima, Hura, Ricinodendron, Sapium*.

Lebacq & Dechamps 1964 – 27 genera (incl. *Antidesma*).

Lebacq & Dechamps 1967 – 21 genera (incl. *Antidesma*).

Lebacq et al. 1973 – 15 genera.

Lebacq & Staner 1964 – *Hura, Klaineanthus, Sapium*.

Lecomte 1922 – *Macaranga, Savia, Uapaca*.

Lecomte 1926a – *Aleurites, Endospermum, Mallotus, Sapium*.

Léonard 1989 – *Martretia*.

Lepe 1959 – *Alchornea, Sebastiania*.

Lindorf 1988 – *Hura*.

Lomibao 1973c – *Sapium*.

Lomibao 1978 – *Excoecaria*.

Lopes et al. 1983 – *Hevea*.

Loureiro 1968 – *Croton*.

Luo 1989 – *Bischofia, Hevea, Macaranga, Mallotus, Phyllanthus, Sapium*.

Mainieri 1958 – *Alchornea, Croton, Tetrorchidium*.

Mainieri 1962 – *Hura*.

Mainieri 1978 – *Alchornea, Chaetocarpus, Croton, Hieronima, Hura, Joannesia, Pachystroma, Tetrorchidium*.

Mainieri & Chimelo 1989 – *Alchornea, Chaetocarpus, Croton, Hieronima, Hura, Joannesia, Pachystroma, Tetrorchidium*.

Mariaux 1974 – *Leeuwenbergia*.

Martawijaya et al. 1989 – *Aleurites, Bischofia*.

Martin 1953 – *Bridelia, Drypetes, Ricinodendron, Uapaca*.

Mattos Filho 1949 – *Joannesia*.

Mennega 1984 – *Jablonskia*.

(EUPHORBIACEAE)

*Mennega 1987 – 35 genera, 116 spp.

Messeri 1938 – *Ricinus*.

Metcalfe 1933 – *Euphorbia, Excoecaria*.

Milanez 1935 – *Paradrypetes*.

Moll & Janssonius 1906–1936 – 28 genera.

Nardi Berti & Edlmann Abbate 1988 – *Androstachys, Ricinodendron*.

Nardi Berti & Edlmann Abbate 1992 – *Aextoxicon, Hieronima, Hura*.

Normand 1955 – 17 genera.

Normand & Détienne 1992 – *Excoecaria, Spirostachys*.

Normand & Paquis 1976 [1977] – Numerous genera.

Ogata 1975–1983 – *Aleurites, Bischofia, Endospermum, Hevea, Macaranga, Pimelodendron, Sapium*.

Ortega et al. 1988 – *Croton*.

Ortega 1958 – *Drypetes*.

Panshin 1932 – *Excoecaria*.

Paula & Alves 1980 – *Cnidoscolus, Euphorbia*.

Pearson & Brown 1932 – *Bischofia, Bridelia, Excoecaria, Mallotus, Phyllanthus, Trewia*.

Perez-Jimenez 1982 – *Jatropha*.

Pérez Mogollón 1973 – *Pera*.

Pérez Mogollón 1991a – *Tetrorchidium*.

Pérez Mogollón 1993 – *Alchornea, Sapium, Tetrorchidium*.

Pérez Olvera et al. 1980 [1981] – *Croton*.

Pfeiffer, J.P. 1926 – *Chaetocarpus, Conceveiba, Hevea, Hieronima, Hura, Maprounea*.

Pompert 1989 – *Sapium*.

Purkayastha et al. 1976 – *Endospermum*.

Record 1928b – *Celaenodendron*.

*Record 1938b – 49 genera.

Record & Hess 1943 – Family (56 genera + *Picrodendron*).

Record & Mell 1924 – *Gymnanthes, Hieronima, Hippomane, Hura*.

Rogel Gomez 1982 – *Gymnanthes*.

Saint-Laurent 1928, 1934 – *Euphorbia*.

Schmidt 1951–1952 – *Hura*.

Schweingruber 1990 – *Euphorbia, Ricinus*.

Scott 1927 – *Spirostachys*.

Shimaji & Itoh 1988 – *Mallotus, Sapium*.

Smith & Ayensu 1964 – *Calyptosepalum* (= *Drypetes*).

(EUPHORBIACEAE)

*Stern 1967 – *Kleinodendron* + 17 genera of Cluytieae.

Sudo 1959 – *Mallotus, Sapium.*

Sudo 1963 – 10 genera.

Sudo 1988 – 10 genera.

Sugawa 1968a – *Hevea.*

Tang 1973 – *Bischofia, Macaranga, Mallotus, Sapium.*

Tortorelli 1956 – *Alchornea, Sapium.*

Uhlarz & Kunschert 1975 [1976] – *Euphorbia.*

Urling & Smith 1953 – *Gymnanthes.*

Vales & Carreras 1987 – *Grimmeodendron, Leucocroton.*

Van der Slooten 1968 – *Alchornea, Sapium.*

Wagenführ & Scheiber 1974 – *Hura, Ricinodendron.*

Wang 1984–1988 – *Endospermum, Hevea.*

Webber 1936b – *Picrodendron* (in Simaroubaceae).

Webster 1982 – *Kleinodendron.*

Williams 1929 – *Caryodendron.*

Williams 1936 – 14 genera.

Wu & Wang 1976 – *Glochidion, Mallotus.*

Wuang 1979 – *Sapium.*

Yamabayashi 1938 – *Excoecaria, Mallotus, Securinega.*

Yao 1988 – *Endospermum, Macaranga, Vernicia.*

Crystals

Baker 1917 – *Bridelia, Mallotus.*

Chattaway 1955 – *Glochidion, Macaranga, Mallotus, Manihot, Phyllanthus, Sapium, Sauropus.*

Chattaway 1956 – 45 genera.

Espinoza de Pernía 1987b – *Chaetocarpus, Hieronima, Pera, Piranhea.*

Meniado et al. 1970 – *Aleurites, Cleidion, Cleistanthus, Endospermum, Excoecaria, Neotrewia.*

Scurfield et al. 1973 – *Phyllanthus.*

Ecological anatomy

Baas et al. 1983 – *Ricinus.*

Baas & Schweingruber 1987 – *Euphorbia.*

Barajas Morales 1985 – *Alchornea, Celaenodendron, Jatropha, Omphalea.*

Carlquist 1974 – *Euphorbia.*

Carlquist 1977c – *Ricinocarpus.*

Carlquist 1985a – *Bernardia.*

(EUPHORBIACEAE)

Carlquist & Hoekman 1985a – *Acalypha, Bernardia, Tetracoccus.*

Den Outer & Van Veenendaal 1976 – *Antidesma, Bridelia, Phyllanthus.*

Van der Graaff & Baas 1974 – *Drypetes.*

Versteegh 1968 – *Claoxylon.*

Webber 1936a *Bernardia, Croton.*

Fibres

Bamber 1974 – 32 genera.

Helical thickenings

Nair 1987 – *Phyllanthus.*

Laticifers

Fujii 1988 – *Pimelodendron.*

Rudall 1987, 1989 – *Croton.*

Sudo & Fujii 1987 – *Pimelodendron.*

Perforation plates

Giraud 1981 – *Hieronima.*

Ohtani & Ishida 1978a *Aleurites, Mallotus, Sapium.*

Pits

Jing et al. 1988 – *Cleistanthus.*

Nair & Ram 1989 – *Bridelia, Phyllanthus.*

Rays

Chattaway 1951b – *Cyclostemon* (= *Drypetes*), *Endospermum.*

Giraud 1983 – Perforated, in 26 spp.

Nazma et al. 1981 – *Drypetes.*

Sebastine 1955 – *Macaranga.*

Silica

Espinoza de Pernía 1987b – *Actinostemon, Drypetes, Maprounea, Micrandra, Senefeldera.*

Scurfield et al. 1974 – *Antidesma.*

Sudo et al. 1967 – *Sapium.*

Welle 1976b – *Actinostemon, Maprounea, Micrandra, Senefeldera.*

Ziliani 1987 – *Sebastiania.*

Tracheary elements

Jing et al. 1989 – *Baccaurea, Cleistanthus, Macaranga, Mallotus, Sapium.*

Ohtani 1983 – *Aleurites, Mallotus, Sapium.*

EUPOMATIACEAE (*Eupomatia*)

*Carlquist 1992e.

Garratt 1933b – Relations.

Ilic 1991.

(EUPOMATIACEAE)
Lemesle 1936, 1938, 1955a, 1956b.
Metcalfe 1987 – General survey.
Takahashi 1985.
Vander Wyk & Canright 1956 – Relations.

Pits
Lemesle 1946a.

EUPHRONIACEAE see TRIGONIACEAE

EUPTELEACEAE *(Euptelea)*

Chen 1989.
Cheng, J.-Q. 1980.
Cheng, J.-Q. et al. 1992.
Hayashi 1991.
Hirai 1979–1985.
Ilic 1991.
Kanehira 1921b, 1926.
Lemesle 1946b, 1953, 1956b.
McLaughlin 1933.
Nast & Bailey 1946.
Shimaji & Itoh 1988.
Sudo 1959.
Takahashi 1985.
Vander Wyk & Canright 1956 – Relations.

Pits and Perforation plates
Carlquist 1992d.

FABACEAE see LEGUMINOSAE

FAGACEAE
(Cyclobalanopsis = Quercus; Pasania = Lithocarpus)

Anon. 1966 – *Castanea, Cyclobalanopsis, Fagus, Quercus, Shiia* (= *Castanopsis*).
Baas et al. 1984 – *Quercus*.
Babos 1980 [1981] – *Quercus*.
Babos & Borhidi 1981 – *Quercus*.
Bailey 1910 – Family notes and *Quercus*.
Bargagli-Petrucci 1903 – *Quercus*.
Berger 1922 – *Quercus*.
Brazier & Franklin 1961 – *Castanea, Fagus, Nothofagus, Quercus*.
Cambini 1960 – *Castanea*.
Cambini 1967a, b – *Quercus*.
Camus 1936–1954 – *Lithocarpus, Quercus*.

(FAGACEAE)
Carlquist 1987e – *Nothofagus*.
Carvalho 1954–1956 – *Castanea, Fagus, Quercus*.
Cheng, C. 1985 – *Castanea, Castanopsis, Cyclobalanopsis, Fagus, Lithocarpus, Quercus*.
Cheng, J.-Q. 1980 – *Castanea, Castanopsis, Cyclobalanopsis, Fagus, Lithocarpus, Quercus*.
Cheng, J.-Q. et al. 1992 – Same as Cheng 1980.
Chudnoff 1956 – *Quercus*.
Corral Lopez 1981 – *Quercus*.
Cutler 1964 – *Trigonobalanus*.
Cutler et al. 1987 – *Castanea, Fagus, Nothofagus, Quercus* (root).
Dadswell & Eckersley 1935 – *Nothofagus*.
Dadswell & Ingle 1954 – *Nothofagus*.
Detzner 1910 – *Castanea, Fagus, Quercus* (root).
Díaz-Vaz 1987a, b – *Nothofagus*.
Donoso & Landrum 1979 – *Nothofagus*.
Edlmann & Monaco 1981 – *Castanea, Castanopsis, Fagus, Quercus*.
Eeckhout 1951 – *Fagus, Quercus*.
Fahn et al. 1986 – *Quercus*.
Fegel 1941 – *Fagus, Quercus* (root).
Forman & Cutler 1967 – *Trigonobalanus*.
Friedman 1978 – *Quercus*.
Fundter & Wisse 1977 – *Lithocarpus*.
Furuno 1977, 1979 – *Castanopsis, Lithocarpus, Nothofagus*.
Furuno 1985, 1987 – *Castanea, Castanopsis, Fagus, Lithocarpus, Quercus*.
Garratt 1924 – *Nothofagus*.
Gasson & Cutler 1990 – *Nothofagus* (root).
Gorczyński 1951 – *Fagus*.
Gottwald et al. 1982 – *Nothofagus*.
Greguss 1959 – *Castanea, Fagus, Quercus*.
Grosser 1977 – *Castanea, Fagus, Quercus*.
Hafić 1958 – *Quercus*.
Hayashi 1991 – *Castanea, Castanopsis, Fagus, Pasania, Quercus*.
Hayashi et al. 1973 – *Castanopsis, Lithocarpus, Quercus*.
Heim 1971 – *Quercus*.
Hejnowicz 1990 – *Fagus*.
Hernandez Camacho et al. 1980 – *Trigonobalanus*.
Hirai 1979–1985 – *Castanea, Castanopsis, Fagus, Pasania, Quercus*.

(FAGACEAE)

Hjelmqvist 1963 – *Nothofagus*.
Ho 1985 – *Castanopsis*.
Holz & Bruckner 1959 – *Quercus*.
Huber & Rouschal 1954 – *Quercus*.
Huber et al. 1941 – *Quercus*.
Ilic 1991 – *Castanea, Castanopsis, Fagus, Lithocarpus, Nothofagus, Pasania, Quercus*.
Jaccard 1914 – *Fagus* (root).
Jacquiot et al. 1973 – *Castanea, Fagus, Quercus*.
Joshi 1986 – *Castanopsis, Lithocarpus, Quercus* (branches).
Kalinkov 1961 – *Quercus*.
Kalinkov & Shipchanov 1976 – *Quercus*.
Kanehira 1921a – *Castanopsis, Fagus, Quercus* 23 spp.
Kanehira 1921b – *Castanea, Fagus, Pasania*.
Kanehira 1924 – *Quercus*.
Kanehira 1926 – *Castanea, Castanopsis, Fagus, Pasania, Quercus*.
Kobayashi & Sugawa 1959 – *Castanopsis*.
Kribs 1959 – *Fagus, Nothofagus*.
Lebedenko 1959 – *Quercus*.
Lebedenko 1959 [1960] – *Castanea, Fagus, Quercus*.
Lebedenko 1961 – *Castanea*.
Lecomte 1926a – *Castanopsis, Pasania, Quercus*.
Lee 1968 – *Castanea, Castanopsis, Cyclobalanopsis, Fagus, Lithocarpus, Pasania, Quercus*.
Lindorf 1988 – *Quercus* (root).
Luo 1989 – *Castanea, Castanopsis, Cyclobalanopsis, Fagus, Lithocarpus, Quercus*.
Martawijaya et al. 1986 – *Lithocarpus*.
Martawijaya et al. 1989 – *Castanopsis*.
Mennega 1980b – *Trigonobalanus*.
Meylan & Butterfield 1978b – *Nothofagus*.
Middleton 1987c – *Nothofagus*.
Moll & Janssonius 1906–1936 – *Castanea, Quercus* 23 spp.
Mork 1946 – *Fagus, Quercus*.
Mouranche 1951 – *Fagus, Nothofagus*.
Nájera Angulo & López Fraile 1969 – *Castanea, Fagus, Quercus*.
Nardi Berti & Edlmann Abbate 1992 – *Nothofagus*.
Nikolov et al. 1981, 1984 – *Quercus*.
Niloofari 1961 – *Castanea, Fagus, Quercus*.

(FAGACEAE)

Novruzova 1964b – *Quercus*.
Ogata 1975–1983 – *Castanopsis, Lithocarpus, Nothofagus, Quercus, Trigonobalanus*.
Ortega et al. 1988 – *Quercus*.
Ortiz Cespedes 1959 – *Nothofagus*.
Paddon 1953 – *Nothofagus*.
Panshin & Zeeuw 1980 – *Castanea, Castanopsis, Fagus, Lithocarpus, Quercus*.
Papaioannou 1948 – *Quercus*.
Parham 1933 – *Nothofagus*.
Parsa Pajouh & Schweingruber 1985 – *Fagus, Quercus*.
Patel 1986 – *Nothofagus*.
Pearson & Brown 1932 – *Castanopsis, Quercus*.
Pérez Olvera 1974 (2nd ed. 1982), 1976, 1982, 1985 – *Quercus*.
Pérez Olvera & Aguilar Entíquez 1978 – *Quercus*.
Rancusi et al. 1987 – *Nothofagus*.
Record & Hess 1943 – Family (*Castanea, Castanopsis, Fagus, Lithocarpus, Nothofagus, Quercus*).
Record & Mell 1924 – *Nothofagus*.
Riedl 1937 – *Fagus, Quercus* (root).
Rivera 1988 [1989] – *Nothofagus*.
Ryu & Soh 1988 – *Quercus*.
Sachsse 1980 – *Nothofagus*.
Saiki 1982 – *Castanea, Castanopsis, Fagus, Quercus*.
Saint-Laurent 1926, 1934 – *Castanea, Quercus*.
Saint-Laurent 1932b – *Quercus*.
Şanli 1985 [1986] – *Quercus*.
Schultz et al. 1964 – *Quercus*.
Schweingruber 1978, 1990 – *Castanea, Fagus, Quercus*.
*Shimaji 1952 – *Fagus*.
*Shimaji 1954 – *Quercus* 15 spp.
*Shimaji 1959 – *Castanea, Castanopsis, Pasania*.
*Shimaji 1962 – General (*Castanea* 5 spp., *Castanopsis* 13, *Fagus* 8, *Lithocarpus* 8, *Nothofagus* 7, *Quercus* 66).
Shimaji & Itoh 1982, 1988 – *Castanea, Castanopsis, Fagus, Quercus*.
Shipchanov 1973 – *Quercus*.
Šimić 1956–1957 – *Fagus*.
Stieber 1965 – *Quercus*.

(FAGACEAE)

Sudo 1959 – *Castanea, Castanopsis, Fagus, Pasania, Quercus.*
Sudo 1963 – *Nothofagus.*
Sudo 1988 – *Castanopsis, Lithocarpus, Nothofagus.*
Sudworth & Mell 1911a – *Quercus* 35 spp. (mainly macro).
Sugawa 1968c – *Quercus.*
Tabatabai et al. 1967 – *Quercus.*
Tainter 1968 – *Nothofagus.*
Tang 1973 – *Castanopsis, Cyclobalanopsis, Fagus, Lithocarpus, Quercus.*
Taranenko 1972 – *Quercus.*
Tewfik & Al-Dawoody 1982 – *Quercus.*
Thunell & Perem 1947 – *Fagus, Quercus.*
Tillson & Muller 1942 – *Quercus.*
Tippo 1938 – Family (*Castanea, Castanopsis, Fagus, Pasania, Pasaniopsis* (= *Castanopsis*), *Quercus*).
Toker 1963 – *Fagus.*
Tortorelli 1956 – *Nothofagus.*
*Tumanyan 1953 – *Cyclobalanopsis* 4 spp., *Quercus* 49.
Van der Slooten 1968 – *Quercus.*
Van der Slooten et al. 1969 – *Quercus.*
Wagemann 1949 – *Nothofagus.*
Wagenführ & Scheiber 1974 – *Castanea, Fagus, Nothofagus, Quercus.*
Wałek-Czernecka & Smoliński 1956 – *Fagus.*
Walker 1978 – *Quercus.*
Wang 1966 – *Quercus.*
Wang 1984–1988 – *Pasania.*
Willeitner et al. 1982 – *Quercus.*
Williams 1939–1942 – *Quercus* c. 40 spp.
Wiraj Chunwarin & Damrong Sri-Aran 1974 – *Castanopsis, Quercus.*
Wu & Wang 1976 – *Castanopsis, Lithocarpus, Pasania.*
Wu & Xiao 1989 – *Castanea, Trigonobalanus.*
Wuang 1979 – *Castanea, Castanopsis, Fagus, Quercus.*
Yamabayashi 1933 – *Castanea, Fagus, Lithocarpus, Quercus.*
Yao 1988 – *Castanea, Castanopsis, Cyclobalanopsis, Quercus.*
Yatsenko-Khmelevsky 1945 – *Nothofagus.*
Yu 1948 – *Quercus.*
Zgurovskaya 1958 – *Quercus* (root).

(FAGACEAE)

Crystals
Chattaway 1956 – *Castanea, Castanopsis, Fagus, Lithocarpus, Nothofagus, Pasania, Quercus, Shiia* (= *Castanopsis*).

Ecological anatomy
Baas et al. 1983 – *Quercus.*
Baas & Schweingruber 1987 – *Castanea, Fagus, Quercus.*
Carlquist 1985a – *Castanea, Chrysolepis, Lithocarpus, Quercus.*
Carlquist & Hoekman 1985a – *Chrysolepis, Lithocarpus, Quercus.*
Erak 1974 – *Fagus.*
Gasson 1987 – *Fagus, Quercus.*
Lim & Soh 1991a – *Quercus.*
Mariani 1968 – *Fagus.*
Novruzova 1968 – *Castanea, Fagus, Quercus.*
Psaras & Hatzopoulou-Belba 1984 – *Quercus.*
Şanli 1977 – *Fagus.*
Sárkány & Sieber 1959 – *Fagus.*
Tyshkevich 1976 – *Fagus.*
Versteegh 1968 – *Castanopsis, Lithocarpus, Nothofagus, Trigonobalanus.*
Vikhrov 1954 – *Quercus.*
Webber 1936a – *Castanopsis, Quercus.*
Yatsenko-Khmelevsky 1946a – *Fagus.*

Growth rings
Ciampi 1951 – *Castanea.*
Fahn 1953 – *Castanea, Quercus.*
Fahn 1955 – *Quercus.*
Gencsi 1976 [1977] – *Quercus.*
Huber & Keller 1993 – *Quercus.*
Müller-Stoll 1951 – *Fagus.*
Scaramuzzi 1960 – *Quercus.*

Helical thickenings
Ohtani & Ishida 1978b – *Quercus.*

Pits and perforation plates
Gale 1982 – *Nothofagus.*
Meylan & Butterfield 1974 – *Nothofagus.*
Middleton 1987b, 1988 – *Nothofagus.*
Ohtani & Ishida 1978a – *Castanea, Castanopsis, Fagus, Pasania, Quercus.*
Parameswaran & Liese 1973 – *Fagus.*

Rays
Braun 1955 – *Fagus, Quercus.*
Braun & den Outer 1965 – *Castanea, Quercus.*

(FAGACEAE)

Braun et al. 1967 – *Trigonobalanus*.
Braun et al. 1968 – *Castanea, Quercus, Lithocarpus, Trigonobalanus*.
Eames 1910 – *Quercus*.
Groom 1911 – *Quercus*.
Groom 1912 – General Fagaceae.
Kawamura 1984, 1987 – *Quercus*.
Langdon 1918 – *Quercus*.
Linnemann 1953 – *Fagus*.
Middleton 1987a – *Nothofagus*.
Rao, R.V. et al. 1991 – *Castanopsis, Lithocarpus, Quercus*.
Schmidt 1964 – *Fagus*.

Silica

Reid 1947 – *Nothofagus*.

Septate fibres

Butterfield & Meylan 1976 – *Nothofagus*.

Tracheary elements

Jing et al. 1989 – *Quercus*.
Ohtani 1983 – *Castanea, Castanopsis, Fagus, Pasania, Quercus*.

FLACOURTIACEAE

(For *Asteropeia* see BONNETIACEAE and for *Soyauxia* see MEDUSANDRACEAE)

Alves de Pinho & Camargo 1979 – *Casearia*.
Baas 1984a – *Berberidopsis, Streptothamnus* (twig).
Bannan 1943 – *Ryania*.
Barajas Morales & Léon Gómez 1989 – *Casearia*.
Barbosa et al. 1977–1978 – *Casearia*.
Benoist 1931 – *Laetia*.
Berger 1928 – 14 genera.
Brazier & Franklin 1961 – *Gossypiospermum* (= *Casearia*), *Homalium, Scottellia*.
Brown 1922 – *Xylosma*.
Burgerstein 1909 – *Flacourtia*.
Cheng, C. 1985 – *Homalium*.
Cheng, J.-Q. 1980 – *Casearia, Flacourtia, Homalium, Idesia, Xylosma*.
Cheng, J.-Q. et al. 1992 – Same as Cheng 1980.
Cockrell 1942 – *Flacourtia*.
Croptier & Kučera 1990 – *Casearia*.
Dadswell & Record 1936 – *Neumannia* (= *Aphloia*).
Dechamps 1979 – *Casearia, Homalium, Laetia*.

(FLACOURTIACEAE)

Den Outer & Schutz 1981b – 18 genera.
Détienne & Jacquet 1983 – *Banara, Carpotroche, Casearia, Hasseltia* (or in Tiliaceae), *Homalium, Laetia, Lindackeria, Prockia* (or in Tiliaceae), *Tetrathylacium*.
Détienne et al. 1982 – *Casearia, Homalium, Laetia*.
Fedalto et al. 1989 – *Laetia*.
Freitas 1958 – *Homalium*.
Fundter & Wisse 1977 – *Homalium*.
Furuno 1977, 1979 – *Homalium, Pangium, Trichadenia*.
Giordano 1939–1940 – *Oncoba*.
Hallé & Wilde 1978 – *Trichostephanus*.
Hayashi 1991 – *Idesia*.
Hayashi et al. 1973 – *Hydnocarpus*.
Hirai 1979–1985 – *Idesia*.
Ilic 1991 – 24 genera.
*James & Ingle 1956 – 13 genera.
Janssonius 1950 – Relations.
Kanehira 1921a – *Casearia, Homalium, Idesia, Scolopia*.
Kanehira 1924 – *Ahernia, Homalium, Hydnocarpus*.
Kanehira 1926 – *Idesia*.
Kobayashi & Sugawa 1972 – *Homalium*.
Kribs 1928a – *Homalium*.
Kribs 1959 – *Gossypiospermum* (= *Casearia*), *Hasseltiopsis* (or in Tiliaceae), *Scottellia*.
Lebacq & Dechamps 1964 – *Caloncoba, Casearia, Homalium*.
Lebacq & Dechamps 1967 – *Caloncoba, Camptostylus, Homalium, Oncoba, Scottellia*.
Lebacq et al. 1973 – 12 genera.
Lecomte 1922 – *Aphloia, Casearia, Tisonia*.
Lecomte 1926a – *Homalium*.
Lemke 1987 – *Neopringlea*.
Luo 1989 – *Homalium*.
Mainieri & Chimelo 1989 – *Casearia*.
Martawijaya et al. 1989 – *Homalium*.
Martin 1953 – *Caloncoba*.
*Miller, R.B. 1975 – 64 genera.
Moll & Janssonius 1906–1936 – *Bergsmia* (= *Ryparosa*), *Casearia, Flacourtia, Homalium, Pangium, Ryparosa, Scolopia, Taraktogenos* (= *Hydnocarpus*).
Molle 1936 – *Arechavaletaia* (= *Azara*).
Nardi Berti & Edlmann Abbate 1988 – *Scottellia*.

(FLACOURTIACEAE)

Nardi Berti & Edlmann Abbate 1992 – *Gossypiospermum* (= *Casearia*).

Normand 1960 – *Caloncoba, Casearia, Homalium, Lindackeria, Oncoba, Ophiobotrys, Scottellia.*

Normand & Paquis 1976 [1977] – *Homalium, Ophiobotrys, Scottellia.*

Ogata 1975–1983 – *Homalium, Hydnocarpus, Pangium.*

Pearson & Brown 1932 – *Gynocardia, Homalium, Hydnocarpus.*

Pérez Olvera et al. 1980 [1981] – *Zuelania.*

Prakash 1972 – *Hydnocarpus* (root).

Rancusi et al. 1987 – *Azara.*

*Record 1941b – 23 genera.

Record & Garratt 1925 – *Casearia.*

Record & Hess 1943 – Family (23 genera).

Record & Mell 1924 – *Casearia.*

Schmidt 1951–1952 – *Gossypiospermum* (= *Casearia*).

Shimaji & Itoh 1988 – *Idesia, Xylosma.*

Sprague & Boodle 1914 – *Casearia.*

Sudo 1959 – *Idesia, Xylosma.*

Sudo 1963 – *Gossypiospermum* (= *Casearia*), *Homalium, Scottellia, Trichadenia.*

Sudo 1988 – *Erythrospermum, Homalium, Pangium, Trichadenia.*

Tang 1973 – *Casearia, Homalium, Xylosma.*

Teixeira 1983 – *Casearia.*

Tupper 1934 – Family (32 genera).

Vestal 1937 – Family (32 genera).

Wagemann 1949 – *Azara.*

Wang 1984–1988 – *Homalium.*

Williams 1936 – 12 genera.

Wiraj Chunwarin & Damrong Sri-Aran 1973 – *Homalium, Hydnocarpus.*

Yamabayashi 1938 – *Idesia, Myroxylon* (= *Xylosma*).

Yao 1988 – *Homalium, Idesia.*

Crystals and silica

Chattaway 1956 – 15 genera.

Espinoza de Pernía 1987b – *Casearia, Gossypiospermum* (= *Casearia*), *Homalium, Lindackeria, Mayna.*

Meniado et al. 1970 – *Homalium.*

Scurfield et al. 1974 – *Hydnocarpus.*

Sudo et al. 1967 – *Hydnocarpus.*

Ecological anatomy

Carlquist 1985a – *Azara.*

(FLACOURTIACEAE)

Helical thickenings

Nair 1987 – *Flacourtia.*

Perforation plates

Ohtani & Ishida 1978a – *Idesia.*

Tracheary elements

Gill & Onuja 1984a – *Scottellia.*

Jing et al. 1989 – *Gynocardia.*

Ohtani 1983 – *Idesia.*

FLINDERSIACEAE see RUTACEAE

FOUQUIERIACEAE

(*Fouquieria* only, incl. *Idria*)

Henrickson 1969.

Humphrey 1935.

Ilic 1991.

Record & Hess 1943.

Ecological anatomy

Carlquist & Hoekman 1985a.

Webber 1936a.

FRANKENIACEAE (*Frankenia* only)

Schweingruber 1990.

*Whalen 1987 – 11 spp.

Ecological anatomy

Baas & Schweingruber 1987.

Carlquist 1985a.

Carlquist & Hoekman 1985a.

FUMARIACEAE see PAPAVERACEAE

GARRYACEAE (*Garrya* only)

Babos & Borhidi 1978.

Cutler et al. 1987 – (root).

Li & Chao 1954.

Moseley 1973 [1974] – Relations.

*Moseley & Beeks 1955 – 11 spp.

Pérez Olvera et al. 1982 [1985].

Record & Hess 1943.

Ecological anatomy

Carlquist & Hoekman 1985a.

Webber 1936a.

GEISSOLOMATACEAE (*Geissoloma*)

Carlquist 1975c.

GENTIANACEAE

*Carlquist 1984b – *Chelonanthus* (= *Irl-bachia*), *Ixanthus*, *Symbolanthus*.
Maas et al. 1983 – *Lisianthius* [Abstr.].

Ecological anatomy
Carlquist 1974 – *Ixanthus*.

GERANIACEAE

(for *Viviania* see VIVIANIACEAE)

Heimsch 1942 – *Balbisia*, *Geranium*, *Pelargonium*.
Van der Walt et al. 1987 – *Pelargonium* 12 spp.

Ecological anatomy
Carlquist 1985a – *Geranium*.

GESNERIACEAE

Burgerstein 1909 – *Cyrtandra*.
*Carlquist & Hoekman 1986a – 11 genera.
Ilic 1991 – *Cyrtandra*.
Janssonius 1950 – Relations.
Moll & Janssonius 1906–1936 – *Cyrtandra*.
Patel 1990 – *Rhabdothamnus*.
Stern et al. 1969 – *Besleria*, *Columnea*, *Cyrtandra*, *Drymonia*, *Gesneria*, *Rhytidophyllum*, *Solenophora*.
Williams 1936 – *Drymonia*.

Ecological anatomy
Carlquist 1974 – *Cyrtandra*.

GLOBULARIACEAE
(*Globularia*, incl. *Lytanthus*)

Carlquist 1992c.
Saint-Laurent 1928.
Schweingruber 1990.

Ecological anatomy
Baas & Schweingruber 1987.

GOETZEACEAE
(for *Lithophytum* see VERBENACEAE)

*Carlquist 1988b – *Espadaea*, *Henoonia*.
Kramer 1939 – *Henoonia* (in Sapotaceae).
Record 1939c – *Henoonia* (in Sapotaceae).

GOMORTEGACEAE (*Gomortega*)

Dechamps 1979.
Ilic 1991.
Lemesle 1955a.
Metcalfe 1987 – General survey.
Rancusi et al. 1987.
*Stern 1955.
Stern & Greene 1958.

GONYSTYLACEAE (*Gonystylus*; for *Amyxa* see THYMELAEACEAE)

Balan Menon 1959, 1960.
Bargagli-Petrucci 1903.
Brazier & Franklin 1961.
Furuno 1979.
Hayashi et al. 1973.
Hirai 1979–1985.
Ilic 1991.
Kanehira 1924.
Kobayashi & Sugawa 1962.
Martawijaya et al. 1986.
Metcalfe 1933.
Moll & Janssonius 1906–1936.
Ogata 1975–1983.
Saiki 1982.
Sudo 1963, 1988.
Wagenführ & Scheiber 1974.
Wang 1984–1988.

Crystals
Chattaway 1956.
Hirata et al. 1972.

Rays
Braun et al. 1968.

GOODENIACEAE

Carlquist 1962a – *Scaevola*.
*Carlquist 1969b – *Coopernookia* 2 spp., *Dampiera* 22, *Goodenia* 3, *Leschenaultia* 3, *Scaevola* 27, *Verreauxia* 1.
Kanehira 1921a – *Scaevola*.
Stern & Brizicky 1958b – *Scaevola*.

Ecological anatomy
Carlquist 1977c, 1985a, 1985 [1986]a – *Scaevola*.

GOUPIACEAE see CELASTRACEAE

GREYIACEAE (*Greyia*)

Dadswell & Record 1936.
Heimsch 1942.

GRISELINIACEAE see CORNACEAE

GROSSULARIACEAE (*Ribes* only, incl. *Grossularia*)

Cutler et al. 1987 – (root).
Greguss 1959.
Grosser 1977.
Record & Hess 1943.
Saint-Laurent 1928, 1934.
Schweingruber 1978, 1990.
Snezhkova 1990.
Stern et al. 1969.
*Stern et al. 1970 – 61 spp.
Tippo 1938.
Yamabayashi 1938.
Yatsenko-Khmelevsky 1954a.

Ecological anatomy
Baas & Schweingruber 1987.
Carlquist 1985a.
Carlquist & Hoekman 1985a.

Septate fibres
Parameswaran & Liese 1969.

Tracheary elements
Carlquist 1988f.

GRUBBIACEAE (*Grubbia*)

*Carlquist 1977a.

GUTTIFERAE (incl. HYPERICACEAE; see also BONNETIACEAE)
(*Ochrocarpos* and *Rheedia* both = *Garcinia*)

Anon. 1981 (Andes) – *Calophyllum, Symphonia.*
Abbate 1971a – *Calophyllum, Ochrocarpos.*
Abbate 1977 – *Mesua.*
Abbate & Cavina 1980 – *Mesua.*
Alencar et al. 1981 – *Calophyllum.*
Alves de Pinho & Camargo 1979 – *Calophyllum.*
Baas 1970 – *Cratoxylum, Eliea.*
Babos & Borhidi 1978 – *Calophyllum.*

(GUTTIFERAE)

Balan Menon 1959 – *Calophyllum, Cratoxylum.*
Barajas Morales et al. 1979 – *Calophyllum.*
Barbosa et al. 1977–1978 – *Tovomitopsis, Vismia.*
Baretta-Kuipers 1976 – *Kielmeyera* (and *Poeciloneuron* to Bonnetiaceae).
Bargagli-Petrucci 1903 – *Calophyllum, Cratoxylum, Garcinia.*
Bastos 1946 [1947] – *Platonia, Symphonia.*
Benoist 1931 – *Platonia, Symphonia.*
Brazier & Franklin 1961 – *Calophyllum, Cratoxylum, Mammea, Mesua, Symphonia.*
Brown 1922 – *Calophyllum.*
Burgerstein 1909 – *Calophyllum.*
Chalk et al. 1933 – *Garcinia, Ochrocarpos.*
Cheng, C. 1985 – *Calophyllum, Garcinia, Mesua.*
Cheng, J.-Q. 1980 – *Calophyllum, Cratoxylum, Garcinia, Mesua.*
Cheng, J.-Q. et al. 1992 – *Calophyllum, Cratoxylum, Garcinia, Mesua.*
Cockrell 1942 – *Calophyllum.*
Croptier & Kučera 1990 – *Pentadesma, Symphonia.*
Cunha Mello 1967 – *Kielmeyera.*
Cutler et al. 1987 – *Hypericum* (root).
Dadswell & Eckersley 1935 – *Calophyllum.*
Dechamps 1979 – *Calophyllum, Caraipa, Clusia, Platonia, Rheedia, Symphonia, Tovomita, Vismia.*
Détienne 1980 – *Moronobea, Platonia, Symphonia.*
Détienne & Jacquet 1983 – *Calophyllum, Chrysochlamys, Clusia, Moronobea, Platonia, Rheedia, Symphonia, Tovomita.*
Détienne et al. 1982 – *Calophyllum, Clusia, Moronobea, Platonia, Rheedia, Symphonia, Tovomita, Vismia.*
Eeckhout 1951 – *Mammea, Platonia.*
Ferreirinha 1962 – *Mammea.*
Fouarge & Gérard 1964 – *Symphonia.*
Fouarge et al. 1953 – *Garcinia, Mammea.*
Freitas 1958 – *Calophyllum.*
Freitas 1987 – *Harungana, Mammea.*
Frison 1950 – *Lebrunia.*
Fundter & Wisse 1977 – *Calophyllum.*
Furuno 1977 – *Calophyllum, Garcinia.*
Gaiotti de Peralta & Edlmann Abbate 1981 – *Calophyllum.*

(GUTTIFERAE)

Garratt 1936 – *Symphonia*.
Gibson 1980 – *Cratoxylum, Eliea, Hypericum, Psorospermum, Thornea, Triadenum, Vismia*.
Giordano 1940 – *Hypericum*.
Gonzalez et al. 1971 – *Calophyllum*.
Greene 1932 – *Calophyllum*.
Hayashi et al. 1973 – *Calophyllum, Cratoxylum, Garcinia, Mesua*.
Hayashi & Nomura 1986 – *Calophyllum, Mesua*.
Hoheisel et al. 1968 – *Calophyllum*.
Ilic 1991 – 14 genera + *Ploiarium* (in Bonnetiaceae).
Janssonius 1914 – *Platonia*.
Janssonius 1950 – Relations.
Jentsch et al. 1936 – *Symphonia*.
Jentsch et al. 1938 – *Mammea*.
Kanehira 1921a – *Calophyllum, Garcinia*.
Kanehira 1924 – *Calophyllum, Cratoxylum, Garcinia, Kayea*.
Kanehira 1926 – *Calophyllum*.
Kobayashi & Sugawa 1963 – *Calophyllum*.
Kobayashi & Sugawa 1964 – *Cratoxylum*.
Kribs 1928a – *Caopia* (= *Vismia*), *Clusia, Tovomita*.
Kribs 1959 – *Calophyllum, Cratoxylum, Garcinia, Haploclathra, Moronobea, Ochrocarpos, Platonia, Symphonia*.
Latorre et al. 1975 – *Clusia, Vismia*.
Lebacq & Dechamps 1964 – *Allanblackia, Garcinia, Harungana, Lebrunia, Mammea, Pentadesma, Psorospermum, Symphonia, Vismia*.
Lebacq & Dechamps 1967 – *Allanblackia, Garcinia, Mammea, Pentadesma, Psorospermum, Symphonia, Vismia*.
Lebacq et al. 1973 – *Calophyllum, Clusia, Haploclathra, Mammea, Platonia, Rheedia, Symphonia, Vismia*.
Lebacq & Staner 1964 – *Symphonia*.
Lecomte 1922 – *Calophyllum, Haronga* (= *Harungana*), *Ochrocarpos, Psorospermum, Rheedia, Symphonia*.
Lecomte 1926a – *Calophyllum, Cratoxylum, Garcinia, Mesua*.
Lima & Marcati 1989 – *Kielmeyera* (Abstr.).
Luo 1989 – *Garcinia, Mesua*.
Mainieri 1978 – *Calophyllum, Rheedia*.
Mainieri & Chimelo 1989 – *Calophyllum, Platonia, Rheedia, Symphonia*.

(GUTTIFERAE)

Mainieri & Loureiro 1964 – *Moronobea, Platonia, Symphonia*.
Martawijaya et al. 1986 – *Calophyllum, Cratoxylum*.
Moll & Janssonius 1906–1936 – *Calophyllum, Cratoxylum, Garcinia*.
Nardi Berti & Edlmann Abbate 1988 – *Mammea, Symphonia*.
Nardi Berti & Edlmann Abbate 1992 – *Calophyllum, Platonia, Rheedia, Symphonia*.
Normand 1946 – *Endodesmia, Lebrunia*.
Normand 1955 – *Allanblackia, Garcinia, Harungana, Mammea, Pentadesma, Symphonia, Vismia*.
Normand & Paquis 1976 [1977] – *Allanblackia, Endodesmia, Garcinia, Harungana, Hypericum, Lebrunia, Mammea, Pentadesma, Symphonia, Vismia*.
Ogata 1975–1983 – *Calophyllum, Cratoxylum, Garcinia, Kayea, Mesua*.
Ortega et al. 1988 – *Vismia*.
Ortega 1958 – *Calophyllum*.
Paula 1974 – 13 genera.
Paula 1976b – *Caraipa, Clusia, Lorostemon*.
Paula 1979 – 13 genera.
Paula 1981 – *Calophyllum*.
Pearson & Brown 1932 – *Calophyllum, Kayea, Mesua, Poeciloneuron* (or in Bonnetiaceae).
Pereira 1933 – *Calophyllum*.
Pereira et al. 1970 – *Caraipa, Platonia, Symphonia*.
Pérez Olvera et al. 1980 [1981] – *Calophyllum*.
Pfeiffer, J.P. 1926 – *Calophyllum, Platonia, Symphonia*.
Prakash 1972 – *Calophyllum* (root).
Prakash & Lau 1976 – *Ploiarium* (or Bonnetiaceae).
Record & Hess 1943 – Family (18 genera + 2 genera of Hypericaceae).
Record & Mell 1924 – *Calophyllum*.
Saiki 1982 – *Calophyllum*.
Saint-Laurent 1928 – *Androsaemum* (= *Hypericum*).
Schmid 1915 – *Calophyllum*.
Schmidt 1951–1952 – *Symphonia*.
Schultz et al. 1964 – *Rheedia*.
Schweingruber 1990 – *Hypericum*.
Silva 1991 – *Clusia*.

(GUTTIFERAE)

Sudo 1963 – *Calophyllum, Cratoxylum, Garcinia, Kayea, Mammea, Mesua, Symphonia.*
Sudo 1988 – *Calophyllum, Garcinia.*
Tang 1973 – *Calophyllum, Garcinia, Mesua.*
Tôrres 1941 – *Calophyllum.*
Van der Slooten 1968 – *Clusia.*
Vestal 1937 – Family (29 genera, 238 spp.).
Wang 1984–1988 – *Calophyllum.*
Williams 1936 – *Calophyllum, Chrysochlamys, Clusia, Rheedia, Symphonia, Vismia.*
Wiraj Chunwarin & Damrong Sri-Aran 1973 – *Calophyllum, Cratoxylum, Garcinia, Mesua.*
Yao 1988 – *Garcinia.*

Anomalous structure
Duchaigne 1951 – *Lebrunia.*

Crystals and silica
Chattaway 1955 – *Garcinia.*
Chattaway 1956 – 10 genera.
Espinoza de Pernía 1987b – *Calophyllum, Clusia, Mammea, Symphonia, Tovomita.*
Scurfield et al. 1974 – *Cratoxylum.*
Sudo et al. 1967 – *Cratoxylum.*
Welle 1976b – *Clusia, Kielmeyera, Oedematopus, Tovomita.*

Ecological anatomy
Barajas Morales 1985 – *Rheedia.*
Carlquist 1985a – *Calophyllum, Cratoxylum, Harungana, Hypericum, Kayea, Mammea, Mesua, Poeciloneuron* (or Bonnetiaceae), *Vismia.*
Den Outer & Van Veenendaal 1976 – *Harungana.*
Van der Graaff & Baas 1974 – *Calophyllum.*

Growth rings
Détienne 1989 – *Symphonia.*

Tracheary elements
Jing et al. 1989 – *Calophyllum.*
Vestal & Vestal 1940 – *Hypericum.*

GYROCARPACEAE
see HERNANDIACEAE

GYROSTEMONACEAE

*Carlquist 1978b – *Codonocarpus, Gyrostemon, Tersonia.*
Ilic 1991 – *Codonocarpus* (in Phytolaccaceae).
Metcalfe & Chalk 1950 – *Gyrostemon* (in Phytolaccaceae).

HALOPHYTACEAE
see CHENOPODIACEAE

HALORAGACEAE

Orchard 1975 – *Glischrocaryon, Gonocarpus, Haloragis, Haloragodendron* (brief).

HAMAMELIDACEAE

Anon. 1966 – *Distylium.*
Berkel 1955 – *Liquidambar.*
Brazier & Franklin 1961 – *Liquidambar.*
Cheng, C. 1985 – *Altingia, Mytilaria.*
Cheng, J.-Q. 1980 – *Altingia, Distylium, Liquidambar, Loropetalum, Mytilaria, Rhodoleia, Symingtonia* (= *Exbucklandia*).
Cheng, J.-Q. et al. 1992 – Same as Cheng 1980.
Cutler et al. 1987 – *Hamamelis, Liquidambar, Parrotia* (root).
Efe 1987 – *Liquidambar.*
Furuno 1985, 1987 – *Liquidambar.*
Greguss 1959 – *Hamamelis, Liquidambar, Parrotia.*
Hayashi 1991 – *Distylium.*
Hejazi et al. 1961 – *Parrotia.*
Hirai 1979–1985 – *Distylium, Hamamelis.*
Huang 1986 – *Altingia, Eustigma, Exbucklandia, Liquidambar, Loropetalum, Rhodoleia, Semiliquidambar* (= *Liquidambar*), *Sycopsis, Tetrathyrium.*
Huang & Lee 1982 – *Chunia, Mytilaria.*
Huber & Rouschal 1954 – *Liquidambar.*
Ilic 1991 – *Altingia, Bucklandia* (= *Exbucklandia*), *Liquidambar, Sycopsis.*
Jacquiot et al. 1973 – *Liquidambar.*
Janssonius 1950 – Relations.
Kanehira 1921a – *Distylium, Eustigma, Liquidambar.*
Kanehira 1921b – *Distylium.*

(HAMAMELIDACEAE)

Kanehira 1926 – *Distylium, Liquidambar.*

Lecomte 1926a – *Liquidambar.*

Luo 1989 – *Altingia, Exbucklandia, Liquidambar, Mytilaria, Rhodoleia.*

Martawijaya et al. 1989 – *Altingia.*

Moll & Janssonius 1906–1936 – *Altingia, Distylium.*

Niloofari 1961 – *Liquidambar, Parrotia.*

Ogata 1975–1983 – *Altingia.*

Pan et al. 1991 – *Disanthus.*

Panshin & Zeeuw 1980 – *Liquidambar.*

Parsa Pajouh & Schweingruber 1985 – *Liquidambar.*

Pearson & Brown 1932 – *Bucklandia* (= *Exbucklandia*).

Pérez Olvera & Corral Lopez 1980 – *Liquidambar.*

Record & Hess 1943 – Family (*Distylium, Hamamelis, Liquidambar*).

Record & Mell 1924 – *Liquidambar.*

Saiki 1982 – *Distylium.*

Shimaji & Itoh 1982, 1988 – *Distylium.*

Skvortzova 1965 – *Hamamelis.*

*Skvortzova 1975 – 14 genera.

Sudo 1959 – *Distylium, Hamamelis.*

*Tang 1943 – 19 genera.

Tang 1973 – *Altingia, Exbucklandia, Liquidambar, Rhodoleia.*

Tippo 1938 – Family (18 genera).

Wuang 1979 – *Liquidambar.*

Yamabayashi 1938 – *Distylium.*

Yao 1988 – *Liquidambar.*

Yatsenko-Khmelevsky 1954a – *Liquidambar, Parrotia.*

Crystals

Chattaway 1956 – *Altingia, Ostrearia, Rhodoleia, Symingtonia* (= *Exbucklandia*).

Ecological anatomy

Carlquist 1985 [1986]a – *Bucklandia* (= *Exbucklandia*).

Novruzova 1968 – *Parrotia.*

Versteegh 1968 – *Altingia, Distylium.*

Perforation plates

Ohtani & Ishida 1978a – *Distylium, Hamamelis.*

Rays

Braun & den Outer 1965 – *Hamamelis.*

Braun et al. 1968 – *Hamamelis.*

(HAMAMELIDACEAE)

Tracheary elements

Ohtani 1983 – *Distylium, Hamamelis.*

HELWINGIACEAE see CORNACEAE

HERNANDIACEAE

(incl. GYROCARPACEAE)

Abbate 1964 – *Gyrocarpus.*

Brazier & Franklin 1961 – *Hernandia.*

Dechamps 1979 – *Hernandia.*

Détienne & Jacquet 1983 – *Hernandia.*

Détienne et al. 1982 – *Hernandia.*

Furuno 1977 – *Hernandia.*

Garratt 1933b – Family (*Gyrocarpus, Hernandia*).

Grisa 1988 – *Gyrocarpus, Hazomalania* (= *Hernandia*).

Ilic 1991 – *Gyrocarpus, Hernandia.*

Kanehira 1921a, 1926 – *Hernandia.*

Kribs 1959 – *Hernandia.*

Metcalfe 1987 – General survey.

Moll & Janssonius 1906–1936 – *Hernandia* (under Lauraceae).

Ogata 1975–1983 – *Hernandia.*

Pérez Olvera 1993 – *Gyrocarpus.*

Record & Hess 1943 – Family (*Gyrocarpus, Hernandia*).

*Shutts 1960 – *Gyrocarpus, Hernandia, Illigera, Sparattanthelium.*

Sudo 1963, 1988 – *Gyrocarpus, Hernandia.*

Takahashi 1985 – *Hernandia.*

Wu & Tsai 1973 – *Hernandia.*

Crystals & cystoliths

Espinoza de Pernía 1987b – *Hernandia.*

Welle 1980 – *Gyrocarpus, Hernandia, Illigera, Sparattanthelium.*

Ecological anatomy

Carlquist 1985 [1986]a – *Illigera.*

HETEROPYXIDACEAE (*Heteropyxis*)

Baas & Zweypfenning 1979 – Relations.

Dahlgren & Van Wyk 1988.

Schmid 1980.

Stern & Brizicky 1958a.

HIMANTANDRACEAE
(*Galbulimima* only, incl. *Himantandra*)

*Bailey et al. 1943.
Furuno 1979.
Ilic 1991.
Lemesle 1955a, 1956b.
McLaughlin 1933.
Metcalfe 1987 – General survey.
Sudo 1988.
Vander Wyk & Canright 1956 – Relations with Annonaceae.

Crystals
Chattaway 1956.
Scurfield et al. 1973.

HIPPOCASTANACEAE
(*Aesculus* only unless otherwise stated)

Anon. 1966.
Bascopé 1954 – *Billia*.
Brazier & Franklin 1961.
Carvalho 1954–1956.
Cheng, J.-Q. 1980.
Cheng, J.-Q. et al. 1992.
Cutler et al. 1987 – (root).
Détienne & Jacquet 1983 – *Billia*.
Furuno 1985, 1987.
Greguss 1959.
Grosser 1977.
Hayashi 1991.
Heimsch 1942 – *Aesculus, Billia*.
Hirai 1979–1985.
Ilic 1991 – *Aesculus, Billia*.
Jacquiot et al. 1973.
Kanehira 1921b, 1926.
Kramer 1939 – *Aesculus, Billia*.
Nájera Angulo & López Fraile 1969.
Niloofari 1961.
Panshin & Zeeuw 1980.
Patel 1965.
Pearson & Brown 1932.
Pérez Mogollón 1993 – *Billia*.
Record & Hess 1943.
Saiki 1982.
Schweingruber 1978, 1990.
Shimaji & Itoh 1982, 1988.
Sudo 1959.
Suzuki et al. 1991.
Wagenführ & Scheiber 1974.
Wuang 1979.

(HIPPOCASTANACEAE)
Ecological anatomy
Baas & Schweingruber 1987.
Carlquist & Hoekman 1985a.

Helical thickenings
Ohtani & Ishida 1978b.
Parham & Kaustinen 1973.

Perforation plates
Ohtani & Ishida 1978a.

Rays
Braun & den Outer 1965.
Braun et al. 1968.
Holden 1912.

Tracheary elements
Ohtani 1883.

HIPPOCRATEACEAE
see CELASTRACEAE

HOPLESTIGMATACEAE (*Hoplestigma*)

Chesnais 1943 – (twig).
Normand 1950b, 1960.
Normand & Paquis 1976 [1977].

HUACEAE

Baas 1972a – *Afrostyrax, Hua*.
Lebacq & Dechamps 1964 – *Hua*.
Lebacq & Dechamps 1967 – Cf. *Hua*.
Normand & Chatelet 1955 – *Afrostyrax*.
Normand & Paquis 1976 [1977] – *Afrostyrax, Hua*.

HUMBERTIACEAE
see CONVOLVULACEAE

HUMIRIACEAE

Anon. 1981 (Andes) – *Humiria, Humiriastrum*.
Anon. 1981 (Curua) – *Endopleura, Vantanea*.
Araujo & Mattos Filho 1985 – *Humiria, Sacoglottis, Vantanea*.
Barbosa et al. 1977–1978 – *Vantanea*.
Benoist 1931 – *Sacoglottis, Vantanea*.
Dechamps 1979 – *Humiria, Humiriastrum, Sacoglottis, Vantanea*.

(HUMIRIACEAE)

Détienne & Jacquet 1983 – *Duckesia, Endopleura, Humiria, Humiriastrum, Sacoglottis, Vantanea.*

Détienne et al. 1982 – *Humiria, Sacoglottis, Vantanea.*

Heimsch 1942 – *Humiria, Sacoglottis, Vantanea.*

Heimsch & Tschabold 1972 – *Humiria, Sacoglottis, Vantanea.*

Ilic 1991 – *Humiria, Vantanea.*

Kribs 1959 – *Humiria, Sacoglottis.*

Lebacq & Dechamps 1964 – *Sacoglottis.*

Lebacq et al. 1973 – *Humiria, Humiriastrum, Sacoglottis, Vantanea.*

Lopes et al. 1983 – *Sacoglottis.*

Mainieri 1978 – *Vantanea.*

Mainieri & Chimelo 1989 – *Vantanea.*

Martin 1953 – *Sacoglottis.*

Nardi Berti & Edlmann Abbate 1992 – *Humiria.*

Normand 1950b–1960 – *Sacoglottis.*

Normand & Paquis 1976 [1977] – *Sacoglottis.*

Paula 1979 – *Vantanea.*

Pereira 1933 – *Vantanea.*

Pérez Mogollón 1973 – *Sacoglottis.*

Pfeiffer, J.P. 1926 – *Humiria.*

Record 1944b – *Humiria, Sacoglottis, Vantanea* (pp. 8–9).

Record & Hess 1943 – Family (*Humiria, Sacoglottis, Vantanea*).

Sudo 1963 – *Humiria, Sacoglottis.*

Crystals and silica
Chattaway 1956 – *Sacoglottis.*

Espinoza de Pernía 1987b – *Sacoglottis.*

Welle 1976b – *Sacoglottis.*

HYDRANGEACEAE
(incl. PHILADELPHACEAE)

Cutler et al. 1987 – *Deutzia, Hydrangea, Philadelphus* (root).

Friedman 1978 – *Philadelphus.*

Greguss 1959 – *Philadelphus.*

Grosser 1977 – *Philadelphus.*

Hayashi 1991 – *Deutzia, Hydrangea.*

Huber & Rouschal 1954 – *Philadelphus.*

Kanehira 1921a – *Deutzia, Hydrangea.*

Kanehira 1921b, 1926 – *Deutzia.*

Moll & Janssonius 1906–1936 – *Dichroa, Hydrangea.*

(HYDRANGEACEAE)

Record & Hess 1943 – Family (*Fendlera, Philadelphus*).

Schweingruber 1990 – *Hydrangea, Philadelphus.*

Shaw et al. 1973 – *Pottingeria* (twig) (or Celastraceae or Escalloniaceae).

Shimaji & Itoh 1988 – *Deutzia.*

Snezhkova 1986 – *Schizophragma.*

Snezhkova 1990 – *Deutzia, Hydrangea, Philadelphus, Schizophragma.*

*Stern 1978 – *Hydrangea* 13 spp.

Stern et al. 1969 – *Broussaisia, Deutzia, Dichroa, Fendlera, Hydrangea, Philadelphus.*

*Styer & Stern 1979a – *Philadelphus* 32 spp.

*Styer & Stern 1979b – *Deutzia* 33 spp.

Sudo 1959 – *Deutzia, Hydrangea.*

Thunell & Perem 1947 – *Philadelphus.*

Tippo 1938 – Family (*Deutzia, Hydrangea, Philadelphus*).

Yamabayashi 1938 – *Deutzia, Philadelphus.*

Yatsenko-Khmelevsky 1954a – *Philadelphus.*

Ecological anatomy
Baas 1973 – *Hydrangea.*

Carlquist 1985 [1986]a – *Hydrangea.*

Carlquist & Hoekman 1985a – *Fendlera, Jamesia, Philadelphus.*

Versteegh 1968 – *Dichroa, Hydrangea.*

Pits and perforation plates
Carlquist 1992d – *Carpenteria.*

Ohtani & Ishida 1978a – *Deutzia, Hydrangea.*

Tracheary elements
Ohtani 1983 – *Deutzia, Hydrangea.*

HYDRASTIDACEAE
see RANUNCULACEAE

HYDROPHYLLACEAE

*Carlquist et al. 1983 – *Eriodictyon* 9 spp.

*Carlquist & Eckhart 1984 – *Codon, Draperia, Hydrolea, Nama, Phacelia, Turricula, Wigandia.*

Record & Hess 1943 – Family (*Eriodictyon, Nama, Wigandia*).

(HYDROPHYLLACEAE)

Ecological anatomy

Carlquist & Hoekman 1985a – *Eriodictyon, Phacelia, Turricula.*

Webber 1936a – *Eriodictyon.*

HYPERICACEAE see GUTTIFERAE

ICACINACEAE
(incl. LOPHOPYXIDACEAE)

Araujo & Mattos Filho 1974b – *Dendrobangia.*

Araujo & Mattos Filho 1975 – *Discophora; Emmotum.*

Araujo & Mattos Filho 1976 – *Poraqueiba; Villaresia* (= *Citronella*).

*Bailey & Howard 1941 – Family (c. 50 genera).

Balan Menon 1955 – *Cantleya.*

Benoist 1931 – *Emmotum.*

Brazier & Franklin 1961 – *Apodytes.*

Burgerstein 1909 – *Chariessa* (= *Citronella*).

Chalk et al. 1935 – *Apodytes.*

Cheng, J.-Q. 1980 – *Apodytes, Platea.*

Cheng, J.-Q. et al. 1992 – *Apodytes, Platea.*

Dadswell & Eckersley 1935 – *Villaresia* (= *Citronella*).

Dechamps 1979 – *Dendrobangia.*

Détienne & Jacquet 1983 – *Dendrobangia, Discophora, Emmotum, Metteniusa, Poraqueiba.*

Détienne et al. 1982 – *Dendrobangia, Emmotum, Poraqueiba.*

Francis 1926 – *Villaresia* (= *Citronella*).

Hayashi et al. 1973 – *Cantleya.*

Ilic 1991 – 15 genera.

Kanehira 1921a – *Gonocaryum.*

Kanehira 1924 – *Urandra* (= *Stemonurus*).

Kribs 1959 – *Ottoschulzia.*

Lebacq & Dechamps 1964 – *Apodytes.*

Lebacq et al. 1973 – *Calatola, Poraqueiba.*

Lebedenko 1962a – *Apodytes.*

Lecomte 1922, 1926a – *Apodytes.*

Mainieri & Chimelo 1989 – *Emmotum.*

Metcalfe 1935 – *Urandra* (= *Stemonurus*).

Meylan & Butterfield 1978b – *Pennantia.*

Moll & Janssonius 1906–1936 – *Apodytes, Gomphandra, Platea, Stemonurus.*

(ICACINACEAE)

Normand 1950b – *Leptaulus.*

Ogata 1975–1983 – *Cantleya.*

Patel 1975 – *Pennantia.*

Patel & Bowles 1978 – *Pennantia.*

Pérez Mogollón 1993 – *Citronella.*

Record 1938a – *Calatola, Discophora, Emmotum, Mappia, Ottoschulzia, Poraqueiba, Villaresia.*

Record & Hess 1943 – Family (10 genera).

Reed 1955 – *Metteniusa* (in Opiliaceae).

Scott 1927 – *Apodytes.*

Sleumer 1937 – *Peekeliodendron* (= *Merrilliodendron*).

Sleumer 1971 – *Lophopyxis.*

Sudo 1963 – *Gonocaryum, Ottoschulzia.*

Tang 1973 – *Pittosporopsis.*

Thunell & Perem 1947 – *Apodytes.*

Wagemann 1949 – *Citronella.*

Williams 1928 – *Ottoschulzia.*

Williams 1936 – *Poraqueiba.*

Williams 1938 – *Calatola.*

Anomalous structure

Handa 1940 – *Lophopyxis.*

Obaton 1960 – *Icacina, Iodes, Neostachyanthus* (= *Stachyanthus*), *Pyrenacantha, Rhaphiostylis.*

Pfeiffer 1951 – *Lophopyxis.*

Timmermans 1931 – *Phytocrene.*

Ursem & Welle 1992 – *Leretia* (= *Mappia*).

Van der Walt et al. 1970 – *Pyrenacantha.*

Crystals

Baker 1917 – *Villaresia.*

Chattaway 1955 – *Gomphandra.*

Chattaway 1956 – 10 genera.

Heintzelman & Howard 1948 – 23 genera.

Ecological anatomy

Carlquist 1985 [1986]a – General.

Versteegh 1968 – *Platea.*

Helical thickenings

Meylan & Butterfield 1978a – *Pennantia.*

Pits

Meylan & Butterfield 1974 – *Pennantia.*

IDIOSPERMACEAE (*Idiospermum*)

Blake 1972.

Carlquist 1983e.

Foreman 1987, 1988.

(IDIOSPERMACEAE)
Ilic 1991.
Metcalfe 1987 – General survey.
Wilson 1979.

ILLECEBRACEAE
see CARYOPHYLLACEAE

ILLICIACEAE (*Illicium*)

Bailey & Nast 1948.
*Carlquist 1982f – 10 spp.
Cheng, J.-Q. 1980.
Cheng, J.-Q. et al. 1992.
Desch 1954.
Harzmann et al. 1975.
Hayashi 1991.
Hirai 1979–1985.
Ilic 1991.
Kanehira 1921a, b, 1926.
Lemesle 1933, 1953, 1956b.
Luo 1989.
McLaughlin 1933.
Metcalfe 1987 – General survey.
Record & Hess 1943 – (in Winteraceae).
Shimaji & Itoh 1988.
Soh & Park 1985.
Sudo 1959.
Takahashi 1985.
Wu & Wang 1976.
Yamabayashi 1938.
Yao 1988.

Helical thickenings
Ohtani & Ishida 1978b.

Pits and perforation plates
Carlquist 1992d.
Lemesle 1946a.
Ohtani & Ishida 1978a.

Tracheary elements
Ohtani 1983.

IRVINGIACEAE

Baas 1972a – Family.
Chalk et al. 1933 – *Irvingia*.
Desch 1954 – *Irvingia*.
Eeckhout 1951 – *Irvingia, Klainedoxa*.
Fouarge & Gérard 1964 – *Irvingia,
   Klainedoxa*.
Fouarge et al. 1953 – *Irvingia*.

(IRVINGIACEAE)
Hayashi et al. 1973 – *Irvingia*.
Ilic 1991 – *Irvingia, Klainedoxa*.
Jentsch 1936–1939 – *Irvingia*.
Kribs 1959 – *Irvingia*.
Lebacq 1963 – *Desbordesia, Irvingia,
   Klainedoxa*.
Lebacq & Dechamps 1964 – Family
   (*Desbordesia, Irvingia, Klainedoxa*).
Lebacq & Dechamps 1967 – *Irvingia,
   Klainedoxa*.
Martin 1953 – *Irvingia, Klainedoxa*.
Normand 1950b–1960 – *Irvingia,
   Klainedoxa*.
Normand & Paquis 1976 [1977] – *Des-
   bordesia, Irvingia, Klainedoxa*.
Ogata 1975–1983 – *Irvingia*.
Riera 1947 – *Irvingia*.
Sudo 1963 – *Irvingia*.
Webber 1936b – *Desbordesia, Irvingia,
   Klainedoxa*.
Wiraj Chunwarin & Damrong Sri-Aran 1973
   – *Irvingia*.

Crystals
Chattaway 1956 – *Irvingia, Klainedoxa*.

ITEACEAE (*Itea*)

Kanehira 1921a.
Moll & Janssonius 1906–1936.
Stern et al. 1969.
Tippo 1938 – (in Escalloniaceae).

Ecological anatomy
Versteegh 1968.

IXONANTHACEAE
(incl. *Allantospermum*)

Cheng, J.-Q. 1980 – *Ixonanthes*.
Cheng, J.-Q. et al. 1992 – *Ixonanthes*.
Détienne & Jacquet 1983 – *Ochthocosmus*.
Fouarge et al. 1953 – *Ochthocosmus*.
Heimsch 1942 – *Ixonanthes, Ochthocos-
   mus, Phyllocosmus*.
Heimsch & Tschabold 1972 – *Ixonanthes,
   Ochthocosmus, Phyllocosmus*.
Lebacq 1963 – *Ochthocosmus*.
Lebacq & Dechamps 1964 – *Ochthocos-
   mus*.
Lecomte 1926a – *Ixonanthes* (in Sima-
   roubaceae).

(IXONANTHACEAE)

Luo 1989 – *Ixonanthes*.
Metcalfe et al. 1968 – *Allantospermum*
  (young).
Normand 1950b – *Ochthocosmus*.
Normand & Paquis 1976 [1977] – *Ochtho-
cosmus*.
Record 1938a – *Cyrillopsis* (in Cyrillaceae).
Record & Hess 1943 – *Cyrillopsis* (in
  Cyrillaceae), *Ochthocosmus* (in Lina-
  ceae).
Rojo 1968 – *Allantospermum*.
Tang 1973 – *Ixonanthes*.
Thomas 1960 – *Cyrillopsis*.

Ecological anatomy
Carlquist 1985a – *Ixonanthes*.

JUGLANDACEAE

Anon. 1966 – *Juglans, Pterocarya*.
Brazier & Franklin 1961 – *Carya, Engel-
hardtia, Juglans*.
Burgerstein 1912 – *Juglans*.
Carreras & Vales 1986b – *Juglans*.
Carvalho 1954–1956 – *Juglans*.
Cheng, C. 1985 – *Engelhardtia, Juglans,
Pterocarya*.
Cheng, J.-Q. 1980 – *Carya, Engelhardtia,
Juglans, Platycarya, Pterocarya*.
Cheng, J.-Q. et al. 1992 – Same as Cheng
  1980.
Chiang 1964 – *Engelhardtia*.
Cutler et al. 1987 – *Juglans, Pterocarya*
  (root).
Dechamps 1979 – *Juglans*.
Détienne & Jacquet 1983 – *Juglans*.
Detzner 1910 – *Carya, Juglans, Pterocarya*
  (root).
Dupéron 1988 – Extant and fossil woods.
Edlmann & Monaco 1981 – *Juglans, Platy-
carya*.
Eeckhout 1951 – *Juglans*.
Fahn et al. 1986 – *Juglans*.
Furuno 1979 – *Engelhardtia*.
Furuno 1985, 1987 – *Carya, Juglans*.
Gasson & Cutler 1990 – *Carya* (root).
Greguss 1959 – *Carya, Juglans, Ptero-
carya*.
Grosser 1977 – *Juglans*.
Hayashi 1991 – *Juglans, Platycarya, Ptero-
carya*.

(JUGLANDACEAE)

*Heimsch 1942 – *Alfaroa, Carya, Engel-
hardtia, Juglans, Platycarya, Pterocarya*.
Heimsch & Wetmore 1939 – *Alfaroa,
Carya, Engelhardtia, Juglans, Platycarya,
Pterocarya*.
Hill 1983 – *Carya*.
Hirai 1979–1985 – *Juglans, Pterocarya*.
Ilic 1991 – *Carya, Engelhardtia, Juglans*.
Jacquiot et al. 1973 – *Carya, Juglans*.
Kanehira 1921a – *Engelhardtia, Juglans,
Platycarya*.
Kanehira 1921b – *Juglans, Platycarya,
Pterocarya*.
Kanehira 1924 – *Engelhardtia*.
Kanehira 1926 – *Engelhardtia, Juglans,
Platycarya, Pterocarya*.
Kobayashi & Sugawa 1964 – *Carya,
Juglans*.
Kribs 1927 – *Alfaroa, Carya, Engelhardtia,
Juglans, Platycarya, Pterocarya*.
Kribs 1928b – *Carya*.
Kribs 1959 – *Juglans*.
Latorre 1980 – *Juglans*.
Lebacq et al. 1973 – *Juglans*.
Lecomte 1921 – *Carya*.
Lecomte 1926a – *Carya, Engelhardtia*.
Leroy 1953 – *Annamocarya* (= *Carya*).
Leroy 1960 – General.
López & Ortega 1989 – *Carya*.
Luo 1989 – *Annamocarya* (= *Carya*), *Carya,
Engelhardtia, Juglans, Pterocarya*.
Manchester 1983 – Fossils + *Alfaroa, Engel-
hardtia, Oreomunnea*.
Manchester & Wheeler 1993 – Fossils +
Engelhardtia, Platycarya, Pterocarya.
Miller 1976b – *Juglans*.
Miller 1982 – *Carya* [Abstr.]
Miller 1983 – *Alfaroa, Engelhardtia, Oreo-
munnea* [Abstr.].
Moll & Janssonius 1906–1936 – *Engel-
hardtia*.
Nájero Angulo & López Fraile 1969 –
Juglans.
Nardi Berti & Edlmann Abbate 1992 –
Juglans.
Niloofari 1961 – *Juglans, Pterocarya*.
Panshin & Zeeuw 1980 – *Carya, Ju-
glans*.
Parsa Pajouh & Schweingruber 1985 –
Juglans.
Pearson & Brown 1932 – *Juglans*.

(JUGLANDACEAE)

Record & Hess 1943 – Family (*Alfaroa,*
Carya, Engelhardtia, Juglans).
Record & Mell 1924 – *Juglans.*
Saiki 1982 – *Juglans, Pterocarya.*
Schweingruber 1978, 1990 – *Juglans.*
Shimaji & Itoh 1982 – *Juglans, Platy-*
carya.
Shimaji & Itoh 1988 – *Juglans.*
Stark 1953b – *Carya, Juglans.*
Sudo 1959 – *Juglans, Platycarya, Ptero-*
carya.
Sudo 1963 – *Engelhardtia.*
Suzuki et al. 1991 – *Engelhardtia, Juglans.*
Tang 1973 – *Annamocarya* (= *Carya*),
Carya, Engelhardtia, Juglans, Pterocarya.
Taras & Kukachka 1970 – *Carya.*
Thunell & Perem 1947 – *Juglans.*
Tippo 1938 – Family (*Alfaroa, Carya,*
Engelhardtia, Juglans, Pterocarya).
Tortorelli 1956 – *Juglans.*
Wagenführ & Scheiber 1974 – *Carya,*
Juglans.
Williams 1936 – *Juglans.*
Wu & Wang 1976 – *Juglans.*
Wuang 1979 – *Juglans, Platycarya, Ptero-*
carya.
Yamabayashi 1938 – *Juglans, Platycarya.*
Yao 1988 – *Cyclocarya, Juglans, Platy-*
carya.
Yu & Li 1954 – *Annamocarya* (= *Carya*).

Crystals
Chattaway 1956 – *Engelhardtia, Hicoria*
(= *Carya*), *Juglans.*

Ecological anatomy
Baas & Schweingruber 1987 – *Juglans.*
Carlquist & Hoekman 1985a – *Juglans.*
Novruzova 1968 – *Juglans, Pterocarya.*

Helical thickenings
Ohtani & Ishida 1978b – *Platycarya.*

Pits and perforation plates
Miller 1976a – *Juglans.*
Ohtani & Ishida 1978a – *Juglans, Platy-*
carya, Pterocarya.

Rays
Braun et al. 1968 – *Juglans.*

Tracheary elements
Ohtani 1983 – *Juglans, Platycarya, Ptero-*
carya.

JULIANIACEAE
(*Juliania* = *Amphipterygium*)

Barajas Morales & Léon Gómez 1989 –
Amphipterygium.
Heimsch 1942 – *Juliania.*
Kramer 1939 – *Juliania, Orthopterygium.*
Moseley 1973 [1974] – Relations.
Record & Hess 1943 – *Juliania.*
*Stern 1952 – *Juliania, Orthopterygium.*
Youngs 1955 – *Orthopterygium.*

KOEBERLINIACEAE (*Koeberlinia*;
for *Canotia* see CELASTRACEAE)

Gibson 1979.
Record 1926c.
Record & Hess 1943.

Ecological anatomy
Carlquist & Hoekman 1985a.

KRAMERIACEAE (*Krameria*)

Kunz 1913.

Ecological anatomy
Carlquist & Hoekman 1985a.
Webber 1936a.

LABIATAE

*Carlquist 1992f – 27 genera.
Cutler et al. 1987 – *Lavandula, Rosmarinus*
(root).
Fahn et al. 1986 – *Coridothymus, Prasium,*
Rosmarinus, Salvia, Teucrium.
Greguss 1959 – *Lavandula, Rosmarinus.*
Huber & Rouschal 1954 – *Rosmarinus.*
Kästner 1979, 1985 – *Teucrium.*
Rudall 1981 – *Eriope, Hyptis, Marsypian-*
thes, Rhaphiodon.
Saint-Laurent 1928 – *Lavandula, Prasium,*
Rosmarinus, Salvia, Teucrium.
Saint-Laurent 1932a – *Ballota.*
Schweingruber 1990 – 14 genera.

Ecological anatomy
Baas et al. 1983 – *Salvia.*
Baas & Schweingruber 1987 – 14 genera.
Carlquist 1977c – *Prostanthera.*
Carlquist 1985a – *Lavandula, Lepechinia,*
Monardella, Prostanthera, Rosmarinus,
Salvia, Trichostema.

(LABIATAE)

Carlquist & Hoekman 1985a – *Hyptis, Lepechinia, Monardella, Salazaria* (= *Scutellaria*), *Salvia, Trichostema.*
Novruzova 1968 – *Stachys.*
Webber 1936a – *Hyptis, Salazaria* (= *Scutellaria*), *Salvia.*

Rays
Rudall 1985 – *Hyptis.*

LACISTEMACEAE

Détienne & Jacquet 1983 – *Lacistema.*
Détienne et al. 1982 – *Lacistema.*
Lebacq et al. 1973 – *Lacistema.*
Record & Hess 1943 – Family (*Lacistema, Lozania*).
Williams 1936 – *Lacistema.*

Rays
Chalk & Chattaway 1933 – *Lacistema.*

LACTORIDACEAE (*Lactoris*)

*Carlquist 1964a, 1990b.
Lemesle 1955a.
McLaughlin 1933.
Metcalfe 1987 – General survey.
Record & Hess 1943.

LARDIZABALACEAE

*Carlquist 1984f – *Akebia, Boquila, Decaisnea, Holboellia, Lardizabala, Sinofranchetia, Stauntonia.*
Lemesle 1947a, 1955a, 1956b – *Akebia, Boquila, Holboellia, Lardizabala.*
Takahashi 1985 – *Akebia, Decaisnea, Stauntonia.*

Ecological anatomy
Carlquist 1985 [1986]a – General.

LAURACEAE (*Machilus* = *Persea*)

Anon. 1966 – *Cinnamomum, Machilus.*
Anon. 1981 (Andes) – *Nectandra, Ocotea, Persea.*
Anon. 1981 (Curua) – *Aniba, Licaria, Ocotea.*
Abbate 1973 – *Cryptocarya.*
Alves de Pinho 1968 – *Nectandra, Phoebe.*

(LAURACEAE)

Balan Menon 1959 – 10 genera.
Barajas Morales 1980 – *Persea.*
Barbosa et al. 1977–1978 – *Cinnamomum, Ocotea.*
Bargagli-Petrucci 1903 – *Eusideroxylon, Nothaphoebe, Tetranthera* (= *Litsea*).
Bascopé 1954 – *Beilschmiedia.*
Benoist 1931 – *Acrodiclidium* (= *Licaria*), *Cryptocarya, Endlicheria, Ocotea, Silvia* (= *Mezilaurus*).
Berger 1922 – *Dehaasia, Eusideroxylon.*
Borges Florsheim & Barbosa 1983–1985 – *Cryptocarya.*
Botelho 1951 – *Ocotea.*
Brazier & Franklin 1961 – 12 genera.
Brown 1922 – *Cryptocarya.*
Burgerstein 1912 – *Nectandra.*
Carreras & Pérez 1988 – *Cinnamomum, Ocotea.*
Carreras & Vales 1986b – *Cinnamomum.*
Castiglioni 1962 – *Nectandra.*
Chalk et al. 1935 – *Ocotea.*
Cheng, C. 1985 – *Cinnamomum, Machilus, Phoebe, Sassafras.*
Cheng, J.-Q. 1980 – 11 genera.
Cheng, J.-Q. et al. 1992 – 11 genera.
Chiang 1962, 1964 – *Beilschmiedia, Cinnamomum, Machilus.*
Chudnoff 1956 – *Laurus.*
Cockrell 1942 – *Cinnamomum, Litsea.*
Croptier & Kučera 1990 – *Ocotea.*
Cunha Mello 1950 [1951] – *Licaria.*
Cutler et al. 1987 – *Laurus* (root).
Dadswell & Eckersley 1935 – *Beilschmiedia, Cryptocarya, Endiandra, Litsea.*
Dadswell & Eckersley 1940 – *Beilschmiedia, Cinnamomum, Cryptocarya, Endiandra, Litsea, Persea.*
Dechamps 1979 – *Aniba, Endlicheria, Licaria, Mezilaurus, Nectandra, Ocotea, Persea.*
Détienne & Jacquet 1983 – 11 genera.
Détienne et al. 1982 – *Aniba, Endlicheria, Licaria, Mezilaurus, Nectandra, Ocotea.*
Doležal 1959 – *Cinnamomum.*
Edlmann & Monaco 1981 – *Cinnamomum, Lindera, Machilus, Neolitsea.*
Edlmann Abbate & De Luca 1981 – *Litsea.*
Fahn et al. 1986 – *Laurus.*
Falcão 1968 – *Persea.*
Fedalto et al. 1989 – *Mezilaurus, Nectandra.*

(LAURACEAE)
Fouarge et al. 1953 – *Beilschmiedia*.
Francis 1926 – *Cryptocarya*.
Furuno 1977, 1979 – *Cinnamomum, Cryptocarya, Endiandra, Litsea*.
Furuno 1985, 1987 – *Sassafras, Umbellularia*.
Garratt 1924 – *Beilschmiedia, Litsea*.
Garratt 1933b – Relations with Myristicaceae.
Gasson & Cutler 1990 – *Persea, Umbellularia* (root).
Gill & Ogunlowo 1988 – *Ocotea*.
Gómez 1959 – *Licaria*.
Greguss 1959 – *Laurus*.
Hayashi 1991 – *Actinodaphne, Cinnamomum, Machilus, Neolitsea*.
Hayashi et al. 1973 – *Alseodaphne, Beilschmiedia, Cinnamomum, Cryptocarya, Dehaasia, Endiandra, Litsea, Phoebe*.
Hayashi & Nomura 1986 – *Alseodaphne, Cryptocarya*.
Hirai 1979–1985 – *Actinodaphne, Cinnamomum, Machilus, Neolitsea*.
Hoheisel et al. 1968 – *Beilschmiedia*.
Huber & Rouschal 1954 – *Laurus*.
Ilic 1991 – 20 genera.
Jacquiot et al. 1973 – *Laurus*.
Janssonius 1914 – *Nectandra*.
Janssonius 1926 – General.
Janssonius 1950 – Relations.
Jay 1936 – *Alseodaphne, Cinnamomum, Dehaasia, Litsea, Nothaphoebe*.
Kanehira 1921a – 10 genera.
Kanehira 1921b – *Actinodaphne, Cinnamomum, Litsea, Machilus*.
Kanehira 1924 – *Beilschmiedia, Cinnamomum, Cryptocarya, Litsea, Phoebe*.
Kanehira 1926 – *Actinodaphne, Beilschmiedia, Cinnamomum, Cryptocarya, Litsea, Machilus, Sassafras*.
Kasapligil 1962 – *Laurus, Umbellularia*.
Kobayashi & Sugawa 1963 – *Eusideroxylon*.
Kobayashi & Sugawa 1964 – *Litsea*.
Kobayashi & Sugawa 1966a – *Cinnamomum*.
Kostermans 1973 – *Cinnadenia* (twig).
Kostermans et al. 1969 – *Ocotea*.
Kribs 1928a – *Endlicheria, Nectandra, Ocotea*.
Kribs 1959 – 12 genera.

(LAURACEAE)
Kubitzki et al. 1979 – *Clinostemon* (= *Licaria*), *Licaria, Mezilaurus*.
Kubitzki & Richter 1987 – *Williamodendron*.
Lebacq 1955 – *Beilschmiedia, Ocotea*.
Lebacq et al. 1973 – 13 genera.
Lebacq & Dechamps 1964 – *Beilschmiedia, Ocotea*.
Lebacq & Dechamps 1967 – *Beilschmiedia*.
Lebacq & Staner 1964 – *Beilschmiedia, Licaria*.
Lecomte 1922 – *Mespilodaphne* (= *Ocotea*), *Ravensara*.
Lecomte 1926a – *Cinnamomum, Cryptocarya, Lindera, Litsea, Machilus, Phoebe*.
Lepe 1959 – *Licaria*.
Lin 1990 – *Beilschmiedia, Cinnamomum, Cryptocarya, Lindera, Litsea, Machilus, Neolitsea, Phoebe, Sassafras*.
Loureiro 1976 – *Aniba*.
Luo 1989 – *Alseodaphne, Beilschmiedia, Cinnamomum, Lindera, Litsea, Machilus, Phoebe, Sassafras*.
Mainieri 1978 – *Cryptocarya, Mezilaurus, Nectandra, Ocotea, Persea*.
Mainieri & Chimelo 1989 – *Acrodiclidium* (= *Licaria*), *Cryptocarya, Mezilaurus, Nectandra, Ocotea, Persea*.
Martawijaya et al. 1986 – *Cinnamomum*.
Martawijaya et al. 1989 – *Eusideroxylon*.
Mattos Filho 1960 – *Ocotea, Sassafras*.
Metcalfe 1987 – General survey.
Meylan & Butterfield 1978b – *Beilschmiedia, Litsea*.
Moll & Janssonius 1906–1936 – 12 genera.
Nájera Angulo 1959 – *Apollonias, Ocotea, Persea*.
Nardi Berti & Edlmann Abbate 1988 – *Beilschmiedia, Ocotea*.
Nardi Berti & Edlmann Abbate 1992 – *Mezilaurus, Ocotea, Persea, Phoebe*.
Normand 1950b – *Beilschmiedia*.
Normand & Paquis 1976 [1977] – *Beilschmiedia, Ocotea*.
Occhioni & Mattos Filho 1947 – *Ocotea*.
Occhioni & Souza 1949 – *Aniba*.
Ogata 1975–1983 – 10 genera.
Ortega et al. 1988 – *Persea*.
Ortega 1958 – *Nectandra*.
Pal 1981 – *Alseodaphne, Cinnamomum, Phoebe*.

(LAURACEAE)

Panshin & Zeeuw 1980 – *Sassafras, Umbellularia.*

Park & Soh 1984 – *Cinnamomum, Iozoste, Lindera, Litsea, Machilus, Neolitsea.*

Patel 1987 – *Beilschmiedia, Litsea.*

Paula & Alves 1989 – *Ocotea.*

Pearson & Brown 1932 – *Cinnamomum, Litsea, Machilus.*

Peraza Oramas & Lopez de Roma 1967 – *Apollonias, Laurus, Ocotea, Persea.*

Pereira 1933 – *Nectandra, Ocotea, Phoebe.*

Pereira et al. 1970 – *Ocotea.*

Pérez Mogollón 1993 – *Aniba, Beilschmiedia, Ocotea, Persea.*

Pfeiffer, J.P. 1926 – *Acrodiclidium* (= *Licaria*), *Nectandra.*

Prakash 1972 – *Cinnamomum* (root).

Rancusi et al. 1987 – *Beilschmiedia, Cryptocarya, Persea.*

Record & Hess 1942 – 17 genera.

Record & Hess 1943 – Family (17 genera).

Record & Mell 1924 – ?*Aniba, Nectandra, Phoebe.*

Reinders-Gouwentak 1948 – Key to Lauraceae of Java.

*Richter 1981a – *Aniba* 29 spp.

*Richter 1981b – 160 genera, c. 830 spp.

Richter 1985 – *Licaria.*

Richter 1990 – *Aspidostemon* (segregated from *Cryptocarya*).

Richter & Van Wyk 1990 – *Dahlgrenodendron* (= *Cryptocarya*).

Rogel Gomez 1982 [1985] – *Licaria, Nectandra, Persea, Phoebe.*

Rohwer & Richter 1987 – *Aspidostemon, Cryptocarya.*

Rohwer et al. 1991 – *Chlorocardium* (segregated from *Ocotea*), *Paraia.*

Saiki 1982 – *Cinnamomum.*

Saint-Laurent 1928, 1934 – *Laurus.*

Scharai-Rad & Sulistyobudi 1985 – *Eusideroxylon.*

Schmid 1915 – ?*Ocotea,* ?*Oreodaphne.*

Schweingruber 1990 – *Laurus, Ocotea, Persea.*

Scott 1927 – *Ocotea.*

Shimaji & Itoh 1982 – *Cinnamomum.*

Shimaji & Itoh 1988 – *Cinnamomum, Persea.*

Soh & Lim 1987 – *Cinnamomum, Iozoste, Lindera, Litsea, Machilus, Neolitsea.*

(LAURACEAE)

Soh & Park 1984 – Same genera as Soh & Lim 1987 (root).

*Stern 1954 – 29 genera, 48 spp.

Sudo 1959 – *Actinodaphne, Cinnamomum, Lindera, Machilus, Neolitsea.*

Sudo 1963 – *Aniba, Beilschmiedia, Dehaasia, Endiandra, Eusideroxylon, Mezilaurus, Ocotea, Persea, Phoebe.*

Sudo 1988 – *Cinnamomum, Cryptocarya, Endiandra, Litsea.*

Swart & Van der Walt 1985 – *Beilschmiedia, Cryptocarya, Ocotea.*

Takahashi 1985 – *Cinnamomum, Lindera, Litsea, Neolitsea, Persea.*

Tang 1973 – 11 genera.

Thunell & Perem 1947 – *Sassafras.*

Tortorelli 1956 – *Nectandra, Ocotea, Phoebe.*

Vales & Carreras 1986 – *Cinnamomum.*

Van der Slooten 1968 – *Nectandra, Ocotea, Persea.*

Van der Slooten et al. 1962 – *Ocotea.*

Van der Slooten et al. 1970 – *Nectandra, Ocotea, Persea.*

Van der Werff & Richter 1985 – *Caryodaphnopsis.*

Wagemann 1949 – *Beilschmiedia, Cryptocarya, Persea.*

Wagenführ & Scheiber 1974 – *Ocotea, Persea, Phoebe.*

Wang 1965 – *Machilus.*

Wang 1966 – *Cinnamomum.*

Wang 1984–1988 – *Beilschmiedia, Cinnamomum, Litsea.*

Welch 1929a – *Endiandra.*

Williams 1936 – 10 genera.

Wiraj Chunwarin & Damrong Sri-Aran 1974 – *Cinnamomum, Dehaasia, Litsea, Neolitsea, Phoebe.*

Wu & Tsai 1973 – 14 genera.

Wu & Wang 1976 – *Actinodaphne, Beilschmiedia, Cinnamomum, Litsea, Machilus, Neolitsea, Phoebe.*

Yamabayashi 1938 – *Actinodaphne, Benzoin* (= *Lindera*), *Cinnamomum, Litsea, Machilus.*

Yao 1988 – *Cinnamomum, Lindera, Litsea, Machilus, Phoebe, Sassafras.*

Yatsenko-Khmelevsky 1954a – *Cinnamomum, Laurus, Persea.*

Zamora et al. 1988 – *Caryodaphnopsis.*

(LAURACEAE)

Crystals and silica

Bamber & Lanyon 1960 – *Cryptocarya, Endiandra.*

Chattaway 1955 – *Actinodaphne, Cryptocarya, Dehaasia, Iteadaphne (= Lindera), Licaria, Lindera, Litsea.*

Espinoza de Pernía 1987b – *Aniba, Beilschmiedia, Cryptocarya, Endlicheria, Licaria, Mezilaurus, Nectandra, Ocotea, Persea.*

Richter 1979, 1980 – c. 22 genera.

Scurfield et al. 1973 – *Actinodaphne, Cryptocarya, Dehaasia.*

Scurfield et al. 1974 – *Endiandra.*

Sudo et al. 1967 – *Dehaasia.*

Welle 1976b – *Cryptocarya, Licaria, Mezilaurus, Ocotea.*

Ecological anatomy

Baas et al. 1983 – *Laurus.*

Baas & Schweingruber 1987 – *Laurus, Ocotea, Persea.*

Carlquist 1985a – *Iteadaphne (= Lindera), Litsea, Phoebe.*

Carlquist & Hoekman 1985a – *Umbellularia.*

Lim & Soh 1991a – *Lindera.*

Vales et al. 1983 – *Nectandra.*

Van der Graaff & Baas 1974 – *Cryptocarya.*

Versteegh 1968 – *Actinodaphne, Cinnamomum, Lindera, Litsea, Persea, Phoebe.*

Worbes 1986 – *Nectandra, Ocotea.*

Growth rings

Détienne 1989 – *Ocotea.*

Ogden & West 1981 – *Beilschmiedia.*

Worbes 1984 – *Nectandra.*

Helical thickenings

Meylan & Butterfield 1978a – *Beilschmiedia.*

Ohtani & Ishida 1978b – *Actinodaphne, Cinnamomum, Lindera, Machilus, Neolitsea, Parabenzoin (= Lindera).*

Pits and perforation plates

Meylan & Butterfield 1974 – *Beilschmiedia, Litsea.*

Ohtani & Ishida 1978a – Same genera as Ohtani & Ishida 1978b.

Yamauchi 1971 – 9 genera.

(LAURACEAE)

Tracheary elements

Jing et al. 1989 – *Cinnamomum, Litsea.*

Ohtani 1983 – Same genera as Ohtani & Ishida 1978b.

LECYTHIDACEAE (incl. BARRINGTONIACEAE, NAPOLEONACEAE)

(*Combretodendron = Petersianthus; Holopyxidium = Lecythis*)

Anon. 1981 (Andes) – *Cariniana, Gustavia.*

Anon. 1981 (Curua) – *Couratari, Eschweilera, Lecythis.*

Ayensu & Bentum 1974 – *Combretodendron.*

Barbosa et al. 1977–1978 – *Cariniana.*

Benoist 1931 – *Gustavia, Lecythis.*

Brazier & Franklin 1961 – *Cariniana, Combretodendron.*

Cardoso 1960 – *Barringtonia.*

Dechamps 1979 – *Bertholletia, Couratari, Couroupita, Eschweilera, Gustavia, Lecythis.*

Desch 1954 – *Barringtonia* (in Myrtaceae).

Détienne & Jacquet 1983 – 11 genera incl. *Asteranthos* (in Asteranthaceae).

Détienne et al. 1982 – *Couratari, Couroupita, Eschweilera, Gustavia, Lecythis.*

*Diehl 1935 – 17 genera, 56 spp.

Dixon 1919 – *Cariniana.*

Eeckhout 1951 – *Petersia (= Petersianthus).*

Fedalto et al. 1989 – *Bertholettia, Couratari.*

Fouarge & Gérard 1964 – *Combretodendron.*

Freitas 1961 – *Combretodendron.*

Freitas 1963 – *Careya.*

Furuno 1977, 1979 – *Barringtonia, Planchonia.*

Gonzalez et al. 1971 – *Couratari.*

Hayashi et al. 1973 – *Barringtonia.*

Hoheisel et al. 1968 – *Couratari, Eschweilera.*

Ilic 1991 – *Barringtonia, Careya, Cariniana, Couratari, Couroupita, Eschweilera, Lecythis, Planchonia.*

Kanehira 1921a – *Barringtonia.*

Kanehira 1924 – *Petersianthus, Planchonia.*

Kobayashi & Sugawa 1963 – *Planchonia.*

Kribs 1928a – ?*Eschweilera.*

(LECYTHIDACEAE)

Kribs 1959 – *Barringtonia, Bertholletia, Cariniana, Combretodendron, Couratari, Eschweilera, Holopyxidium, Lecythis.*

Lebacq & Dechamps 1964 – *Combretodendron.*

Lebacq & Dechamps 1967 – *Combretodendron, Napoleonaea.*

Lebacq et al. 1973 – *Bertholletia, Couratari, Couroupita, Eschweilera, Grias, Gustavia, Lecythis.*

Lebacq & Staner 1964 – *Bertholletia, Combretodendron, Couratari.*

Lecomte 1922 – *Foetidia.*

Lecomte 1926a – *Careya.*

Mainieri 1978 – *Cariniana, Holopyxidium, Lecythis.*

Mainieri & Chimelo 1989 – *Bertholletia, Cariniana, Couratari, Couroupita, Eschweilera, Holopyxidium, Lecythis.*

Moll & Janssonius 1906–1936 – *Barringtonia, Chydenanthus, Planchonia.*

Nardi Berti & Edlmann Abbate 1988 – *Petersianthus.*

Nardi Berti & Edlmann Abbate 1992 – *Cariniana, Couratari, Couroupita.*

Normand 1960 – *Combretodendron, Napoleonaea.*

Normand & Paquis 1976 [1977] – *Napoleonaea, Petersianthus.*

Ogata 1975–1983 – *Barringtonia, Combretodendron, Planchonia.*

Pearson & Brown 1932 – *Barringtonia, Careya.*

Pereira et al. 1970 – *Eschweilera, Lecythis.*

Pérez Mogollón 1973 – *Couratari, Eschweilera.*

Pérez Mogollón 1993 – *Eschweilera.*

Pfeiffer, J.P. 1926 – *Couratari, Eschweilera, Gustavia.*

Primo 1971 – *Eschweilera, Holopyxidium.*

Purkayastha et al. 1976 – *Planchonia.*

Record 1932a – *Cariniana.*

Record & Hess 1943 – Family (10 genera).

Richter 1982 – *Couratari, Couroupita.*

Schmidt 1951–1952 – *Cariniana.*

Sudo 1963 – *Barringtonia, Cariniana, Combretodendron, Eschweilera, Planchonia.*

Sudo 1988 – *Barringtonia, Planchonia.*

Tang 1973 – *Barringtonia.*

Tomazello Filho et al. 1983 – *Cariniana, Lecythis.*

(LECYTHIDACEAE)

Wagenführ & Scheiber 1974 – *Cariniana.*

Williams 1936 – *Grias, Gustavia, Lecythis.*

*Zeeuw 1990 – 11 genera, 114 spp.

Zeeuw 1992 [1993] – *Bertholletia, Corythophora, Couratari, Couroupita, Eschweilera, Gustavia, Lecythis.*

Zeeuw & Mori 1987 – *Corythophora, Couratari, Eschweilera, Gustavia, Lecythis.*

Crystals and silica

Chattaway 1956 – *Barringtonia, Bertholletia, Couroupita, Eschweilera, Lecythis, Planchonia.*

Espinoza de Pernía 1987b – *Allantoma, Bertholletia, Cariniana, Corythophora, Couratari, Eschweilera, Gustavia, Holopyxidium, Lecythis.*

Parameswaran & Richter 1984 – *Allantoma, Bertholletia, Corythophora, Couratari, Couroupita, Grias, Gustavia.*

Scurfield et al. 1974 – *Eschweilera.*

Van Iterson 1934 – *Eschweilera.*

Welle 1976b – *Allantoma, Cariniana, Corythophora, Couratari, Eschweilera, Holopyxidium, Lecythis.*

Helical thickenings

Nair 1987 – *Careya.*

LEEACEAE (*Leea*)

Adkinson 1913.

Ilic 1991.

Janssonius 1950 – Relations.

Kanehira 1921a.

Moll & Janssonius 1906–1936.

Watari 1951 – Extant and fossils.

Crystals

Chattaway 1955.

Meniado et al. 1970.

LEGUMINOSAE: CAESALPINIOIDEAE
(For *Swartzia* etc. see PAPILIONOIDEAE)

Anon 1955–1959 – *Afzelia, Daniellia, Detarium, Dialium, Erythrophleum.*

Anon. 1963 – *Gossweilerodendron.*

Anon. 1981 (Andes) – *Copaifera, Hymenaea, Mora, Peltogyne, Schizolobium, Sclerolobium.*

Anon. 1981 (Curua) – *Dialium, Hymenaea, Sclerolobium, Tachigali.*

(LEGUMINOSAE – CAESALP.)

Abbate 1963 – *Cassia, Pterolobium, Tamarindus.*
Abbate 1971a – *Intsia.*
Abbate 1977 – *Sindora.*
Alves de Pinho 1966 – *Copaifera.*
America & Meniado 1975 – *Intsia, Pahudia* (= *Afzelia*).
Ayensu & Bentum 1974 – *Copaifera, Distemonanthus.*
Babos & Cumana 1988 – *Caesalpinia, Cassia.*
Balan Menon 1955 – *Dialium, Intsia, Koompassia.*
Balan Menon 1959 – *Cynometra, Sindora.*
Banks & Kromhout 1966 – *Burkea.*
Barajas Morales & León Gómez 1989 – *Caesalpinia, Haematoxylum, Poeppigia.*
Barajas Morales et al. 1979 – *Dialium, Schizolobium.*
Barbosa 1981–1982 – *Copaifera.*
Barbosa & Gurgel Filho 1982 – *Copaifera.*
*Baretta-Kuipers 1981 – General survey: 85 genera of Caesalpinioideae.
Bargagli-Petrucci 1903 – *Abauria* (= *Koompassia*), *Afzelia, Dialium, Koompassia, Sindora.*
Barreto 1967 – *Brachystegia, Julbernardia.*
Bastos 1946 [1947] – *Batesia, Campsiandra.*
Benoist 1931 – *Cassia, Dicorynia, Dimorphandra, Eperua, Hymenaea, Peltogyne, Sclerolobium, Tachigali, Vouacapoua.*
Berger 1922 – *Dialium, Intsia.*
Brazier 1957–1958 [1959] – *Pseudosindora.*
Brazier & Franklin 1961 – Many genera.
Brown 1922 – *Mezoneuron* (= *Caesalpinia*).
Burgerstein 1909 – *Poinciana* (= *Caesalpinia*).
Burgerstein 1912 – *Bauhinia, Caesalpinia, Cassia, Gleditsia, Peltogyne.*
Canessa 1989 – *Copaifera.*
Cardoso & Cardoso 1960 – *Afzelia.*
Carlquist 1989b – *Cercidium* (= *Parkinsonia*).
Carvalho 1954–1956 – *Cercis, Gleditsia.*
Cavaco 1954 – *Afzelia, Copaifera.*
Chalk et al. 1932 – *Afzelia, Baikiaea, Copaifera.*
Chalk et al. 1933 – *Afzelia, Hymenostegia.*
Cheng, C. 1985 – *Cassia, Erythrophleum.*

(LEGUMINOSAE – CAESALP.)

Cheng, J.-Q. 1980 – *Bauhinia, Cassia, Delonix, Erythrophleum, Gleditsia, Gymnocladus, Sindora, Tamarindus.*
Cheng, J.-Q. et al. 1992 – Same genera as Cheng 1980.
Chevalier & Normand 1931 – *Bussea, Erythrophleum.*
Chudnoff 1956 – *Ceratonia, Cercis.*
Cockrell 1942 – *Cassia, Koompassia.*
Cowan 1979 – *Harleyodendron* (wood by Bedell) (or in Papilionoideae).
*Cozzo 1951b – 20 genera.
Cunha Mello 1950 [1951] – *Cassia, Melanoxylon, Peltophorum.*
*Dechamps 1980 – 23 genera.
Détienne & Jacquet 1983 – 37 genera.
Détienne et al. 1982 – 17 genera.
Détienne & Thiel 1988 [1989] – *Eperua.*
Détienne & Welle 1989 – 11 genera.
Dixon 1919 – *Hymenaea.*
Doležal 1959 – *Peltophorum.*
Duchesne 1932 – *Daniellia.*
Edlmann & Monaco 1981 – *Gleditsia.*
Eeckhout 1951 – *Afzelia, Cynometra, Dialium, Erythrophleum, Gossweilerodendron, Guibourtia, Macrolobium, Pterygopodium* (= *Oxystigma*), *Tessmannia.*
Eggeling & Harris 1939 – *Cynometra.*
Fahn et al. 1986 – *Ceratonia, Cercis.*
Fedalto et al. 1989 – *Copaifera, Tachigali.*
Ferreirinha 1955 – *Afzelia, Burkea, Colophospermum, Dialium, Erythrophleum, Piliostigma* (= *Bauhinia*).
Ferreirinha 1962 – *Guibourtia, Oxystigma.*
Ferreirinha & Reis 1969 – *Guibourtia.*
Fouarge et al. 1953 – *Cynometra, Dialium, Erythrophleum, Gilbertiodendron, Gilletiodendron, Oxystigma, Pachyelasma, Tessmannia.*
Fouarge & Gérard 1964 – *Berlinia, Cynometra, Gossweilerodendron, Hylodendron, Julbernardia, Oxystigma.*
Freitas 1955 – *Intsia, Tamarindus.*
Freitas 1958 – *Cassia.*
Freitas 1961 – *Erythrophleum.*
Freitas & Oliveira 1969 – *Afzelia.*
Fundter & Wisse 1977 – *Intsia.*
Furuno 1977, 1979 – *Bauhinia, Intsia, Kingiodendron, Koompassia, Maniltoa.*
Furuno 1985, 1987 – *Gleditsia.*

(LEGUMINOSAE – CAESALP.)

Gaiotti de Peralta & Edlmann Abbate 1981 – *Copaifera, Hymenaea, Prioria, Schizolobium.*

Gill et al. 1983 – *Afzelia, Berlinia, Brachystegia, Daniellia, Gilbertiodendron, Gossweilerodendron, Tamarindus.*

Gill & Ogunlowo 1986 – *Hymenaea, Kingiodendron, Koompassia, Libidibia (= Caesalpinia), Peltogyne, Peltophorum.*

Gottwald et al. 1968 – *Didelotia, Loesenera, Tetraberlinia.*

Gottwald & Noack 1965 [1966] – *Afzelia, Burkea.*

Gottwald & Noack 1968 – *Distemonanthus.*

Gottwald & Schwab 1978 – *Guibourtia.*

Greguss 1959 – *Ceratonia, Cercis, Gleditsia.*

Grisa 1988 – *Colvillea.*

Grosser 1977 – *Gleditsia.*

Hayashi 1991 – *Gleditsia.*

Hayashi et al. 1973 – *Cynometra, Dialium, Koompassia, Peltophorum, Saraca, Sindora.*

Heringer & Paula 1974 – *Apuleia.*

Hirai 1979–1985 – *Gleditsia.*

Huber & Rouschal 1954 – *Ceratonia, Cercis.*

Ilic 1991 – Many genera.

Jacquiot et al. 1973 – *Cercis, Gleditsia, Gymnocladus.*

Jagiella & Kurschner 1987 – *Delonix, Tamarindus.*

Jentsch et al. 1936–1939 – *Copaifera, Daniellia, Oxystigma.*

Kanehira 1921a – *Caesalpinia, Erythrophleum, Gleditsia.*

Kanehira 1921b – *Gleditsia.*

Kanehira 1924 – *Cassia, Erythrophleum, Kingiodendron, Pahudia (= Afzelia), Sindora.*

Kanehira 1926 – *Gleditsia.*

Kobayashi & Sugawa 1962 – *Sindora.*

Kobayashi & Sugawa 1963 – *Intsia, Koompassia.*

Kobayashi & Sugawa 1972 – *Afzelia.*

Koeppen 1963 – *Androcalymma.*

Koeppen 1967 – *Dicorynia.*

Koeppen & Iltis 1962 – *Martiodendron.*

Kribs 1928a – *Dimorphandra, Eperua, Peltogyne, Tachigali, Vouapa (= Macrolobium).*

Kribs 1959 – Many genera.

(LEGUMINOSAE – CAESALP.)

Kusheva Nadson 1964 – *Gymnocladus.*

Laming 1966 – *Colophospermum, Guibourtia.*

Latorre 1983 – *Caesalpinia.*

Lebacq 1957 – 32 genera.

Lebacq & Dechamps 1964 – 36 genera.

Lebacq & Dechamps 1967 – 23 genera.

Lebacq et al. 1973 – 22 genera.

Lebacq & Staner 1964 – *Anthonotha, Daniellia, Gilletiodendron, Scorodophloeus, Tachigali, Vouacapoua.*

Lecomte 1926a – *Dialium, Erythrophleum, Pahudia (= Afzelia), Peltophorum, Sindora.*

Letouzey & Mouranche 1952 – *Berlinia, Brachystegia, Cynometra, Didelotia, Monopetalanthus, Paraberlinia (= Julbernardia).*

López & Ortega 1989 – *Haematoxylum.*

Louis & Fouarge 1949 – *Macrolobium.*

Loureiro 1971 [1973] – *Dialium.*

Loureiro & Silva 1973 – *Crudia, Dimorphandra, Hymenaea, Macrolobium.*

Loureiro & Silva 1981 – *Dimorphandra.*

Loureiro et al. 1983 – *Sclerolobium, Tachigali.*

Loureiro et al. 1984 – *Dimorphandra.*

Luo 1989 – *Acrocarpus, Bauhinia, Caesalpinia, Cassia.*

Machado et al. 1966 – *Bauhinia.*

Mägdefrau 1970 – *Haematoxylum.*

Mainieri 1960 – *Caesalpinia.*

Mainieri 1978 – 10 genera.

Mainieri & Chimelo 1989 – 16 genera.

Mariaux 1963 – *Cassia, Recordoxylon, Vouacapoua.*

Martawijaya et al. 1989 – *Intsia, Koompassia.*

Martin 1953 – *Berlinia.*

Matejčić 1974 – *Dicorynia.*

Mattos Filho 1954, 1973 – *Peltogyne.*

Mattos Filho 1962–1965 – *Goniorrhachis.*

Meniado et al. 1974 – *Erythrophleum, Intsia, Kingiodendron, Pahudia (= Afzelia), Sindora.*

Milanez & Mattos Filho 1959 – *Dicorynia.*

Moll & Janssonius 1906–1936 – 12 genera.

Monteiro 1967 – *Oxystigma.*

Monteiro & França 1965 – *Guibourtia.*

Monteiro & França 1971 – *Afzelia, Brachystegia, Gilletiodendron.*

(LEGUMINOSAE – CAESALP.)

Nardi Berti & Edlmann Abbate 1988 –
18 genera.
Nardi Berti & Edlmann Abbate 1992 –
14 genera.
Niloofari 1961 – *Cercis, Gleditsia.*
Normand 1938 – *Ibadja* (= *Loesenera*).
Normand 1939 – *Afzelia.*
Normand 1947 – *Cynometra, Microber-
linia, Monopetalanthus, Tamarindus,
Tessmannia.*
Normand 1948a – *Copaifera, Daniellia,
Detarium, Gossweilerodendron, Oxy-
stigma, Pterygopodium* (= *Oxystigma*),
Sindora.
Normand 1950a – *Copaifera, Guibourtia.*
Normand 1950b – 22 genera.
Normand 1952 – *Tetraberlinia.*
Normand 1958 – *Didelotia, Tetraberlinia.*
Normand 1993 – *Leonardoxa.*
Normand & Chatelet 1955 – *Gilletioden-
dron.*
Normand & Paquis 1976 [1977] – 52 gen-
era.
Ogata 1975–1983 – *Cassia, Cynometra,
Dialium, Guibourtia, Intsia, Kalappia,
Koompassia, Maniltoa, Pseudosindora,
Sindora.*
Okeke 1966 – *Afzelia.*
Ortega 1958 – *Dialium, Schizolobium.*
Panshin & Zeeuw 1980 – *Gleditsia, Gym-
nocladus.*
Parsa Pajouh & Schweingruber 1985 – *Gle-
ditsia.*
Paula 1979 – *Apuleia, Cassia, Hymenaea,
Schizolobium, Tachigali.*
Paula 1981 – *Apuleia, Caesalpinia, Copai-
fera.*
Paula & Alves 1980 – *Caesalpinia, Parkin-
sonia.*
Paula & Alves 1989 – *Peltophorum.*
Pearson & Brown 1932 – *Acrocarpus, Bau-
hinia, Cassia, Cynometra, Hardwickia.*
Pereira 1933 – *Dimorphandra, Hymenaea,
Sclerolobium.*
Pereira et al. 1970 – *Cassia, Hymenaea,
Sclerolobium.*
Pérez Mogollón 1973 – *Cassia, Sclerolo-
bium.*
Pérez Olvera et al. 1979 – *Dialium.*
Pérez Olvera et al. 1980 [1981] – *Caesal-
pinia, Schizolobium.*

(LEGUMINOSAE – CAESALP.)

Perrot & Gérard 1907 – *Bauhinia, Berlinia,
Burkea, Cassia, Daniellia, Detarium, Ta-
marindus.*
Pfeiffer, J.P. 1926 – *Copaifera, Dicorynia,
Dimorphandra, Eperua, Hymenaea, Ma-
crolobium, Martiusia* (= *Martiodendron*),
Peltogyne, Sclerolobium.
Purkayastha et al. 1976 – *Intsia.*
Quirk 1983 – *Acrocarpus, Cynometra,
Dialium, Intsia, Koompassia, Pseudo-
sindora, Sindora.*
Ranjani & Krishnamurthy 1988 – *Cassia*
(root).
Rasa 1981 – *Bauhinia, Delonix, Tamarin-
dus.*
Rebollar Dominguez et al. 1987 – *Caesal-
pinia.*
Record 1932a – *Jacqueshuberia, Melano-
xylon.*
Record 1945 – *Dicymbe.*
Record & Hess 1943 – Family (numerous
genera).
*Reinders-Gouwentak & Rijsdijk 1955 –
Key to subfamilies.
*Reinders-Gouwentak & Rijsdijk 1968 –
*Copaifera, Dicorynia, Dimorphandra,
Eperua, Hymenaea, Mora, Peltogyne,
Sclerolobium.*
Riera 1947 – *Berlinia, Erythrophleum,
Macrolobium.*
Rizzini & Mattos Filho 1972 – *Arapatiella.*
*Rojo 1992 – *Dialium* 27 spp.
Saiki 1982 – *Cassia, Koompassia, Sindora.*
Saint-Laurent 1926, 1928, 1934 – *Ceratonia.*
Samant & Shete 1989 [1990] a, b – *Cassia.*
Schmid 1915 – *Caesalpinia, ?Coulteria,
Peltogyne.*
Schmidt 1951–1952 – *Afzelia, Distemonan-
thus, Gossweilerodendron, Hymenaea.*
Schweingruber 1990 – *Ceratonia, Cercis,
Gleditsia.*
Scott 1927 – *Afzelia.*
Seabra & Ferreirinha 1960 – *Gossweilero-
dendron.*
Shimaji & Itoh 1988 – *Gleditsia.*
Sillans & Normand 1953 – *Neochevaliero-
dendron.*
Silva 1971 – *Brachystegia.*
Silva et al. 1989 – *Bauhinia, Cassia.*
Sudo 1959 – *Gleditsia.*
Sudo 1963 – 37 genera.

(LEGUMINOSAE-CAESALP.)

Sudo 1988 – *Cynometra, Gigasiphon (= Bauhinia), Intsia, Kingiodendron, Koompassia, Maniltoa.*

Tang 1973 – *Caesalpinia, Cassia, Tamarindus.*

Teles & Paula 1980 – *Cassia, Schizolobium.*

Temu 1990a, b – *Scorodophloeus* (transferred from *Cynometra*), *Zenkerella.*

Tomazello Filho et al. 1983 – *Copaifera, Hymenaea.*

Tôrres 1941 – *Intsia.*

Tortorelli 1956 – *Apuleia, Caesalpinia, Cercidium (= Parkinsonia), Gleditsia, Peltophorum, Pterogyne.*

Wagenführ & Scheiber 1974 – 12 genera.

Wang 1984–1988 – *Cassia, Intsia, Koompassia, Pseudosindora, Sindora.*

Williams 1936 – 14 genera.

Wiraj Chunwarin & Damrong Sri-Aran 1974 – 10 genera.

Wuang 1979 – *Gleditsia.*

Yamabayashi 1938 – *Cercis, Gleditsia.*

Yao 1988 – *Cassia, Erythrophleum, Gleditsia.*

Yatsenko-Khmelevsky 1954a – *Cercis, Gleditsia.*

Anomalous structure

Basson & Bierhorst 1967 – *Bauhinia.*

Handa 1937, 1938 – *Bauhinia.*

Pfeiffer 1925 – *Bauhinia.*

Roth & Ascensio 1977 – *Bauhinia.*

Wagner 1946 – *Bauhinia.*

Wong & Lim 1983 – *Cynometra.*

Crystals and silica

Chattaway 1955 – *Gleditsia.*

Chattaway 1956 – many genera.

Espinoza de Pernía 1987b – *Cassia, Copaifera, Dialium, Dicorynia, Hymenaea, Mora, Peltogyne, Sclerolobium.*

Frison 1942 – *Dialium.*

Koeppen 1980 – In 8 out of 382 genera.

Meniado et al. 1970 – *Afzelia, Caesalpinia, Cassia, Erythrophleum, Intsia, Kingiodendron, Koompassia, Sindora.*

Milanez & Mattos Filho 1956 – *Dialium, Dicorynia.*

Ranjani & Krishnamurthy 1991 – 11 genera.

(LEGUMINOSAE-CAESALP.)

Scurfield et al. 1974 – *Dialium.*

Welle 1976b – *Dialium, Dicorynia, Sclerolobium.*

Ecological anatomy

Baas & Schweingruber 1987 – *Ceratonia, Cercis.*

Baas et al. 1983 – *Ceratonia, Cercis.*

Barajas Morales 1985 – *Caesalpinia, Haematoxylum, Poeppigia.*

Carlquist 1985a – *Cassia.*

Carlquist & Hoekman 1985a – *Cassia, Cercidium, Cercis.*

Den Outer & Van Veenendaal 1976 – *Berlinia.*

Novruzova 1968 – *Gleditsia.*

Psaras & Hatzopoulou-Belba 1984 – *Ceratonia.*

Webber 1936a – *Cercis.*

Worbes 1986 – *Macrolobium.*

Growth rings

De Felice Mastelloni 1960 – *Ceratonia.*

Détienne 1975a – *Afzelia.*

Détienne 1989 – *Afzelia, Dicorynia.*

Fahn 1953 – *Ceratonia.*

Helical thickenings

Nair 1987 – *Piliostigma, Saraca.*

Ohtani & Ishida 1978b – *Caesalpinia, Gleditsia.*

Parham & Kaustinen 1973 – *Gleditsia, Gymnocladus.*

Pits and perforation plates

Cozzo 1953 – *Cercidium.*

Jing et al. 1988 – *Cassia.*

Machado & Schmid 1962–1965 – *Goniorrhachis.*

Nair & Ram 1989 – *Cassia, Delonix, Peltophorum, Saraca, Tamarindus.*

Ohtani & Ishida 1976, 1978a – *Caesalpinia, Gleditsia.*

Quirk & Miller 1983 – *Koompassia.*

Quirk & Miller 1985 – 19 genera.

Schmid & Machado 1963, 1964 – *Goniorrhachis.*

Storied structure

Cozzo & Cristiani 1950 – *Apuleia, Caesalpinia, Cercis, Pterogyne, Zuccagnia.*

Reinders-Gouwentak 1955 – 11 genera.

(LEGUMINOSAE–CAESALP.)
Tracheary elements
Jing et al. 1989 – *Acrocarpus, Cassia.*
Ohtani 1983 – *Caesalpinia, Gleditsia.*

LEGUMINOSAE: MIMOSOIDEAE

(*Samanea = Albizia*)

Anon. 1955–1959 – *Parkia, Prosopis.*
Anon. 1981 (Andes) – *Cedrelinga, Dinizia, Inga, Parkia, Pentaclethra, Piptadenia, Pithecellobium.*
Anon. 1981 (Curua) – *Enterolobium, Inga, Parkia, Piptadenia.*
Abbate 1963, 1970 – *Acacia.*
Abbate 1964 – *Albizia.*
Abbate 1977 – *Xylia.*
Acuña & Flores 1987 – *Stryphnodendron.*
Almeida 1973 [1974] – *Acacia.*
Alves de Pinho 1969 – *Inga.*
Alves de Pinho & Camargo 1979 – *Piptadenia.*
Araujo 1962–1965 – *Plathymenia.*
Ayensu & Bentum 1974 – *Cylicodiscus.*
Babos & Borhidi 1978 – *Lysiloma.*
Balan Menon 1959 – *Pithecellobium.*
Barajas Morales & León Gómez 1989 – *Acacia, Albizia, Lysiloma, Mimosa, Piptadenia, Pithecellobium, Prosopis.*
Barajas Morales et al. 1979 – *Lysiloma.*
*Baretta-Kuipers 1973 – *Inga* 35 spp.
Baretta-Kuipers 1978 – *Pithecellobium.*
Baretta-Kuipers 1979 – *Archidendron* 6 spp.
*Baretta-Kuipers 1981 general survey: 35 genera of Mimosoideae.
Bargagli-Petrucci 1903 – *Pithecellobium.*
Bastos 1946 [1947] – *Pithecellobium.*
Benoist 1931 – *Enterolobium, Inga, Parkia, Pithecellobium, Stryphnodendron.*
Brandão 1954 – *Mimosa.*
*Brazier 1958 – *Anadenanthera, Goldmania, Indopiptadenia, Monoschisma (= Pseudopiptadenia), Newtonia, Piptadenia, Piptadeniastrum, Pityrocarpa (= Piptadenia).*
Brazier & Franklin 1961 – Many genera.
Brown 1922 – *Acacia.*
Burgerstein 1909 – *Acacia, Adenanthera, Entada.*
Burgerstein 1912 – *Acacia, Enterolobium, Piptadenia, Pithecellobium, Prosopis, Stryphnodendron.*

(LEGUMINOSAE–MIMOS.)
Burkart 1947 – *Acacia.*
Cardoso 1960 – *Acacia.*
Cardoso 1966 – *Albizia.*
Carreras & Vales 1986b – *Lysiloma, Samanea.*
Carvalho 1954–1956 – *Acacia.*
*Cassens & Miller 1981 – *Pithecellobium* s.l. 83 spp. (incl. 15 segregate genera).
Cellai 1967 – *Acacia* (incl. *Faidherbia*).
Chalk et al. 1932, 1933 – *Piptadenia.*
Chauhan & Dayal 1985 – *Albizia.*
Chehaibar & Grether 1990 – *Mimosa.*
Cheng, C. 1985 – *Albizia.*
Cheng, J.-Q. 1980 – *Acacia, Adenanthera, Albizia, Enterolobium, Pithecellobium.*
Cheng, J.-Q. et al. 1992 – Same genera as Cheng 1980.
Chevalier 1928 – *Acacia.*
Chevalier & Normand 1931 – *Calpocalyx, Tetrapleura, Xylia.*
Chiang 1964 – *Acacia.*
Chudnoff 1956 – *Acacia.*
Corral Lopez 1985 – *Enterolobium, Inga, Prosopis.*
Cozzo 1951b – 13 genera.
Croptier & Kučera 1990 – *Albizia, Newtonia.*
Cunha Mello 1950 [1951] – *Inga, Piptadenia, Pithecellobium.*
Cunha Mello 1967 – *Enterolobium.*
Cutler 1969 – *Acacia (= Faidherbia).*
Dadswell & Eckersley 1935 – *Acacia, Albizia.*
*Dechamps 1980 – 13 genera.
Détienne & Jacquet 1983 – 25 genera.
Détienne et al. 1982 – 11 genera.
Dixon 1919 – *Acacia, Lysiloma.*
Eeckhout 1951 – *Albizia, Piptadenia.*
Fahn 1959 – *Acacia.*
Fahn et al. 1986 – *Acacia, Prosopis.*
Fasolo 1939–1940 – *Acacia.*
Fedalto et al. 1989 – *Enterolobium, Parkia, Piptadenia.*
Ferreirinha 1955 – *Albizia, Amblygonocarpus, Piptadenia.*
Ferreirinha 1956 – *Amblygonocarpus.*
Fouarge & Gérard 1964 – *Albizia, Newtonia, Parkia, Pentaclethra.*
Fouarge et al. 1953 – *Albizia.*
Freitas 1955 – *Albizia.*
Freitas 1961, 1971 – *Newtonia.*

(LEGUMINOSAE–MIMOS.)

Freitas 1963 – *Acacia, Albizia, Xylia.*

Freitas 1987 – *Albizia, Pentaclethra.*

Fundter & Wisse 1977 – *Adenanthera.*

Furuno 1977, 1979 – *Acacia, Albizia, Cathormion* (= *Albizia*).

Gaiotti de Peralta & Edlmann Abbate 1981 – *Enterolobium.*

Gill et al. 1983 – *Acacia, Albizia, Cylicodiscus, Pentaclethra.*

Giordano 1939–1940 – *Acacia, Albizia.*

Gómez 1959 – *Acacia.*

Gottwald & Noack 1965 [1966] – *Acacia, Albizia, Prosopis.*

Greguss 1959 – *Albizia.*

Grisa 1988 – *Albizia.*

Gros 1991 – *Acacia.*

Gros 1992 – *Albizia.*

Hayashi 1991 – *Albizia.*

Hayashi et al. 1973 – *Adenanthera, Parkia, Pithecellobium.*

Hirai 1979–1985 – *Albizia.*

Hoheisel et al. 1968 – *Enterolobium, Piptadenia.*

Ilic 1991 – Many genera.

Jacquiot et al. 1973 – *Acacia.*

Jagiella & Kurschner 1987 – *Acacia* (incl. *Faidherbia*).

Kanehira 1921a – *Acacia, Albizia, Leucaena.*

Kanehira 1921b – *Albizia.*

Kanehira 1924 – *Adenanthera, Albizia, Parkia, Pithecellobium, Samanea, Wallaceodendron.*

Kanehira 1926 – *Acacia, Albizia.*

Kazmi et al. 1990 – *Acacia.*

Kazmi & Singh 1989 – *Leucaena.*

Kazmi & Singh 1992 – *Prosopis.*

Kobayashi 1966 – *Parkia.*

Kobayashi & Sugawa 1963 – *Xylia.*

Kobayashi & Sugawa 1964 – *Samanea.*

Kobayashi & Sugawa 1966a – *Acacia, Albizia.*

Kribs 1928a – *Inga, Pentaclethra, Pithecellobium.*

Kribs 1959 – Many genera.

Latorre 1983 – *Acacia, Cedrelinga, Leucaena, Pithecellobium, Prosopis.*

Lebacq 1957 – 13 genera.

Lebacq & Dechamps 1964 – 16 genera.

Lebacq & Dechamps 1967 – 10 genera.

Lebacq et al. 1973 – 10 genera.

(LEGUMINOSAE–MIMOS.)

Lebacq & Staner 1964 – *Pentaclethra, Pithecellobium.*

Lebedenko 1962a – *Albizia.*

Lecomte 1922 – *Albizia, Piptadenia.*

Lecomte 1926a – *Albizia, Pithecellobium, Xylia.*

Lepe 1959 – *Acacia.*

Lopes et al. 1983 – *Pithecellobium, Stryphnodendron.*

Loureiro & Silva 1972 – *Parkia.*

Luo 1989 – *Acacia, Albizia.*

Mainieri 1962 – *Cedrelinga, Parkia.*

Mainieri 1978 – *Acacia, Piptadenia, Plathymenia.*

Mainieri & Chimelo 1989 – 10 genera.

Mainieri & Primo 1964, 1968 – *Dinizia, Pithecellobium.*

Marcati & Lima 1989 – *Stryphnodendron.* [Abstr.]

Martawijaya et al. 1989 – *Paraserianthes.*

Martin 1953 – *Pentaclethra, Piptadenia.*

Maruzzo & America 1981 – *Leucaena.*

Mattos Filho 1959 – *Plathymenia.*

Mattos Filho 1971 – *Mimosa.*

Mattos Filho 1989 – *Pithecellobium.*

Meniado et al. 1974 – *Albizia, Parkia, Samanea, Serialbizzia* (= *Albizia*), *Wallaceodendron.*

Mennega 1973 – *Cedrelinga.*

Messeri 1938 – *Acacia.*

Metcalfe 1935 – *Adenanthera.*

Meyer et al. 1971 – *Prosopis.*

Miller 1989 – *Obolinga, Pithecellobium* s.l.

Moll & Janssonius 1906–1936 – *Acacia, Adenanthera, Albizia, Dichrostachys, Parkia, Pithecellobium.*

Monteiro & França 1971 – *Albizia, Tetrapleura.*

Nájera Angulo & López Fraile 1969 – *Acacia.*

Nardi Berti & Edlmann Abbate 1988 – *Albizia, Amblygonocarpus, Cylicodiscus, Piptadeniastrum.*

Nardi Berti & Edlmann Abbate 1992 – 10 genera.

Nielsen & Baretta-Kuipers 1984 – *Archidendron.*

Nielsen et al. 1983, 1984 – *Archidendropsis, Pararchidendron, Paraserianthes, Serianthes, Wallaceodendron.*

Niloofari 1961 – *Albizia.*

(LEGUMINOSAE–MIMOS.)
Normand 1950b – 10 genera.
Normand & Paquis 1976 [1977] – 12 genera.
Ogata 1975–1983 – *Albizia, Leucaena, Parkia, Samanea, Xylia.*
Ortega et al. 1988 – *Inga, Leucaena.*
Ortega 1958 – *Pithecellobium.*
Parsa Pajouh & Schweingruber 1985 – *Albizia.*
Paula 1979 – *Dinizia, Parkia.*
Paula 1981 – *Mimosa, Piptadenia.*
Paula & Alves 1980 – *Mimosa.*
Paula & Alves 1989 – *Acacia, Parkia.*
Pearson & Brown 1932 – *Acacia, Albizia, Xylia.*
Pereira 1933 – *Enterolobium, Piptadenia.*
Pereira et al. 1970 – *Parkia, Plathymenia.*
Pérez Mogollón 1973 – *Inga.*
Pérez Olvera 1993 – *Lysiloma.*
Pérez Olvera & Corral Lopez 1980 – *Inga.*
Pérez Olvera et al. 1979 – *Pithecellobium.*
Pérez Olvera et al. 1980 [1981] – *Acacia, Pithecellobium.*
Pérez Olvera et al. 1982 [1985] – *Inga.*
Perrot & Gérard 1907 – *Acacia, Albizia, Dichrostachys, Parkia, Prosopis, Tetrapleura.*
Pfeiffer, J.P. 1926 – *Inga, Parkia, Pentaclethra, Pithecellobium, Stryphnodendron.*
Prakash 1972 – *Prosopis* (root).
Purkayastha et al. 1976 – *Adenanthera, Albizia.*
Quirk 1983 – *Acacia, Albizia, Wallaceodendron, Xylia.*
Ranjani & Krishnamurthy 1987 – *Acacia, Adenanthera, Albizia, Dichrostachys, Enterolobium, Leucaena, Pithecellobium, Prosopis.*
Rasa 1981 – *Acacia, Leucaena, Pithecellobium, Samanea.*
Record & Hess 1943 – Family (many genera).
*Reinders-Gouwentak & Rijsdijk 1955 – Key to subfamilies.
*Reinders-Gouwentak & Rijsdijk 1968 – *Inga, Parkia, Pentaclethra, Piptadenia, Pithecellobium, Zygia.*
Richter & Charvet 1973 – *Mimosa.*
Riera 1947 – *Calpocalyx.*
Rizzini & Mattos Filho 1962–1965 – *Mimosa.*
Rizzini & Mattos Filho 1967 – *Piptadenia.*

(LEGUMINOSAE–MIMOS.)
*Robbertse et al. 1980 – *Acacia* (incl. *Faidherbia*) 37 spp.
Robbertse & Teichman 1979 – *Acacia.*
Sahri et al. 1993 – *Acacia.*
Saint-Laurent 1932a – *Acacia* (incl. *Faidherbia*).
Scharai-Rad & Kambey 1989 – *Acacia.*
Schmid 1915 – ?*Enterolobium, Piptadenia, Prosopis.*
Schmidt 1951–1952 – *Piptadenia.*
Schweingruber 1990 – *Acacia.*
Scott 1927 – *Acacia, Albizia.*
Seabra et al. 1957 – *Acacia.*
Senni 1905 – *Acacia, Albizia.*
Shimaji & Itoh 1982, 1988 – *Albizia.*
Silva 1991 – *Inga.*
Silva et al. 1989 – *Acacia, Calliandra, Leucaena, Pithecellobium.*
Stahel 1971 – *Piptadeniastrum* (root).
Sudo 1959 – *Albizia.*
Sudo 1963 – 14 genera.
Sudo 1988 – *Acacia, Adenanthera, Albizia, Cathormion* (= *Albizia*).
Tang 1973 – *Adenanthera, Albizia, Pithecellobium.*
Tavares 1959 – *Parkia.*
Teles & Paula 1980 – *Parkia.*
Tomazello Filho et al. 1983 – *Enterolobium, Piptadenia.*
Tortorelli 1948a, b – *Piptadenia.*
Tortorelli 1956 – *Acacia, Arthrosamanea* (= *Albizia*), *Enterolobium, Inga, Piptadenia, Pithecellobium, Prosopis.*
Urling & Smith 1953 – *Leucaena.*
Vales & Carreras 1986 – *Lysiloma.*
Van der Slooten et al. 1962 – *Dinizia.*
Villalba 1985 – *Prosopis.*
Wagemann 1949 – *Acacia.*
Wagenführ & Scheiber 1974 – *Piptadeniastrum, Xylia.*
Wang 1984–1988 – *Albizia, Samanea.*
Williams 1936 – *Acacia, Calliandra, Entada, Inga, Piptadenia, Pithecellobium.*
Wiraj Chunwarin & Damrong Sri-Aran 1974 – *Acacia, Albizia, Xylia.*
Wu et al. 1988 – *Acacia.*
Wu & Wang 1976 – *Acacia.*
Wuang 1979 – *Albizia.*
Yamabayashi 1938 – *Albizia.*
Yatsenko-Khmelevsky 1954a – *Acacia, Albizia, Prosopis.*

(LEGUMINOSAE–MIMOS.)

Anomalous structure
Obaton 1960 – *Acacia*.

Crystals and silica
Chattaway 1956 – Many genera.
Espinoza de Pernía 1987b – *Acacia, Entero-lobium, Inga, Parkia, Piptadenia, Pithe-cellobium.*
Hirata et al. 1972 – *Samanea.*
Meniado et al. 1970 – *Abarema, Adenan-thera, Albizia, Enterolobium, Samanea, Serialbizia (= Albizia), Wallaceoden-dron.*
Scurfield et al. 1973 – *Archidendron.*

Ecological anatomy
Baas et al. 1983 – *Acacia, Prosopis.*
Barajas Morales 1985 – *Pithecello-bium.*
Carlquist 1977c – *Acacia.*
Carlquist & Hoekman 1985a – *Acacia, Calliandra, Prosopis.*
Ford 1984 – *Acacia.*
Lim & Soh 1991a – *Albizia.*
Novruzova 1968 – *Albizia, Lagonychium (= Prosopis).*
Van der Graaff & Baas 1974 – *Acacia.*
Webber 1936a – *Acacia.*
Wilkins & Papassotiriou 1989 – *Acacia.*
Worbes 1986 – *Parkia, Pithecellobium.*

Growth rings
Gourlay & Kanowski 1991 – *Acacia* (incl. *Faidherbia*).
Mariaux 1966 – *Acacia.*
Worbes 1984 – *Parkia.*

Helical thickenings
Nair 1987 – *Albizia.*
Ohtani & Ishida 1978b – *Albizia.*

Pits and perforation plates
Cassens 1980 – *Arthrosamanea (= Albizia), Ebenopsis (= Havardia), Marmaroxylon, Pithecellobium* 83 spp., *Pseudosamanea, Samanea, Zygia.*
Nair & Ram 1989 – *Acacia, Adenanthera, Albizia, Leucaena, Pithecellobium, Pro-sopis, Samanea.*
Ohtani & Ishida 1976, 1978a – *Acacia, Albizia.*
Schmid & Machado 1963, 1964 – *Plathy-menia.*

(LEGUMINOSAE–MIMOS.)

Storied structure
Cozzo 1949a – *Mimosa.*
Cozzo & Cristiani 1950 – *Mimosa.*
Ghouse & Yunus 1974 – *Acacia.*
Reinders-Gouwentak 1955 – *Inga, Parkia, Pentaclethra, Piptadenia, Pithecellobium.*

Tracheary elements
Jing et al. 1989 – *Albizia.*
Ohtani 1983 – *Acacia, Albizia.*

LEGUMINOSAE: PAPILIONOIDEAE
(incl. SWARTZIEAE)
(For *Vouacapoua* see CAESALPINIOIDEAE; *Afrormosia = Pericopsis*)

Anon. 1955–1959 – *Cordyla, Pterocar-pus.*
Anon. 1966 – *Maackia.*
Anon. 1981 (Andes) – *Myroxylon, Ormo-sia, Pterocarpus, Taralea.*
Anon. 1981 (Curua) – *Bowdichia, Dipteryx, Hymenolobium, Ormosia, Vatairea.*
Abbate 1963 – *Sesbania.*
Abbate 1964 – *Erythrina.*
Abbate 1977 – *Dalbergia, Pterocarpus.*
Abbate & Cavina 1980 – *Pericopsis.*
Almeida 1951 – *Dalbergia.*
Alves de Pinho 1969 – *Ferreirea (= Sweetia), Myroxylon.*
Barajas Morales 1980 – *Erythrina.*
Barajas Morales & León Gómez 1989 – *Apo-planesia, Dalbergia, Erythrina, Loncho-carpus, Platymiscium.*
Barajas Morales et al. 1979 – *Lonchocar-pus, Platymiscium, Vatairea.*
Barbosa et al. 1977–1978 – *Machaerium.*
*Baretta-Kuipers 1981 – General survey: 68 genera of Papilionoideae.
*Baretta-Kuipers 1982 – *Erythrina* 38 spp.
Bargagli-Petrucci 1903 – *Pongamia.*
Barreto 1967 – *Ostryoderris (= Aganope).*
Bastos 1946 [1947] – *Hymenolobium, Lonchocarpus.*
Bastos 1952 – *Centrolobium.*
Benoist 1931 – *Andira, Bocoa, Bowdichia, Coumarouna (= Dipteryx), Machaerium, Ormosia, Swartzia.*
Brazier & Franklin 1961 – Many genera.
Brizicky 1960 – *Paramachaerium.*
Brown 1922 – *Erythrina, Sophora.*

(LEGUMINOSAE–PAPIL.)

Burgerstein 1909 – *Desmodium, Erythrina, Indigofera, Inocarpus, Mucuna.*

Burgerstein 1912 – *Erythrina, Gourliea* (= *Geoffroea*), *Myrocarpus.*

Cao & Zhang 1991 – *Caragana.*

Cardoso 1968 – *Pterocarpus.*

Cardoso 1969 – *Cordyla.*

Carvalho 1954–1956 – *Robinia.*

Cavaco 1954 – *Pterocarpus.*

Chalk et al. 1932 – *Pterocarpus.*

Cheng, C. 1985 – *Dalbergia, Ormosia, Robinia, Sophora.*

Cheng, J.-Q. 1980 – *Dalbergia, Erythrina, Ormosia, Robinia, Sophora.*

Cheng, J.-Q. et al. 1992 – Same genera as Cheng 1980.

Chudnoff 1956 – *Genista, Spartium.*

Coimbra Filho 1950 – *Machaerium.*

Corral Lopez 1985 – *Lonchocarpus, Myroxylon.*

Cowan 1979 – *Harleyodendron* (wood by Bedell) (or in Caesalpinioideae).

Cozzo 1946b – *Erythrina.*

Cozzo 1949b – Approx. 45 genera.

*Cozzo 1950 – 48 genera.

*Cozzo 1951a – Key to leguminous woods.

*Cumbie 1960 – c. 100 genera (young).

Cumbie & Mertz 1962 – *Sophora.*

Cunha Mello 1950 [1951] – *Dalbergia, Machaerium, Platypodium.*

Cunha Mello 1972 – *Machaerium.*

Cutler et al. 1987 – *Cytisus, Laburnum, Robinia, Sophora, Wisteria* (root).

Dadswell & Eckersley 1935 – *Castanospermum.*

Datta & Ghosh 1984b – *Dalbergia, Derris, Pongamia, Pterocarpus.*

Datta & Maiti 1968 – *Indigofera, Millettia, Psoralea, Sesbania.*

Datta & Saha 1971 [1972] – 15 genera of Phaseoleae.

*Dechamps 1980 – 29 genera.

*Den Outer & Van Veenendaal 1992 – *Airyantha, Baphia, Baphiastrum, Dalhousiea, Leucomphalos, Ormosia.*

Détienne & Jacquet 1983 – 30 genera.

Détienne et al. 1982 – 16 genera (incl. *Swartzia*).

Détienne & Welle 1989 – *Swartzia* (in Caesalpinioideae).

Dixon 1919 – *Pterocarpus.*

(LEGUMINOSAE–PAPIL.)

Dugand 1962 – *Uribea.*

Edlmann & Monaco 1981 – *Maackia, Sophora.*

Eeckhout 1951 – *Afrormosia, Millettia, Pterocarpus.*

Eggeling & Harris 1939 – *Dalbergia.*

Fahn et al. 1986 – *Anagyris, Calicotome, Colutea, Genista, Gonocytisus, Ononis, Retama, Spartium.*

Fahn & Sarnat 1963 – *Retama.*

Fasolo 1939–1940 – *Dalbergia.*

Fasolo 1941–1944 – *Lonchocarpus.*

Fedalto et al. 1989 – *Alexa.*

Ferreirinha 1955 – *Afrormosia, Cordyla, Dalbergia, Millettia, Ostryoderris* (= *Aganope*), *Pterocarpus, Swartzia.*

Fouarge & Gérard 1964 – *Amphimas, Pterocarpus.*

Fouarge et al. 1953 – *Afrormosia, Pterocarpus.*

Franklin 1952 – *Amburana.*

Freitas 1955 – *Pterocarpus.*

Freitas 1961 – *Swartzia.*

Freitas 1963 – *Dalbergia.*

Freitas 1986 – *Millettia, Pterocarpus, Swartzia.*

Freitas et al. 1968 – *Pterocarpus.*

Fujii & Baas 1992 – *Ammodendron, Bolusanthus, Calpurnia, Cladrastis, Maackia, Sakoanala, Sophora.*

Fundter & Wisse 1977 – *Pericopsis, Pterocarpus.*

Furuno 1977, 1979 – *Pericopsis, Pterocarpus.*

Furuno 1985, 1987 – *Robinia.*

Gaiotti de Peralta & Edlmann Abbate 1981 – *Centrolobium, Coumarouna* (= *Dipteryx*), *Vatairea.*

Gasson 1993 – Swartzieae [Abstr.].

Gill et al. 1983 – *Pterocarpus.*

Gill & Ogunlowo 1986 – *Amburana, Centrolobium, Hymenolobium, Machaerium, Pericopsis, Pterocarpus.*

Gómez 1959 – *Acosmium, Ormosia, Platymiscium.*

Greguss 1959 – 16 genera.

Grisa 1988 – *Cordyla, Dalbergia.*

Grosser 1977 – *Cytisus, Laburnum, Robinia.*

Hayashi 1991 – *Cladrastis, Maackia, Robinia, Sophora, Wisteria.*

(LEGUMINOSAE – PAPIL.)

Hayashi et al. 1973 – *Derris, Millettia, Pongamia.*

Hayashi & Nomura 1986 – *Pericopsis.*

Heringer et al. 1987 – *Dalbergia.*

Hirai 1979–1985 – *Cladrastis, Dalbergia, Maackia, Sophora.*

Hofmann 1955 – *Cytisus.*

Hoheisel et al. 1968 – *Clathrotropis.*

Huber & Rouschal 1954 – *Colutea, Coronilla, Retama, Spartium.*

Ilic 1991 – Many genera.

Inokuma & Shimaji 1950 – *Cladrastis, Platyosprion* (= *Cladrastis*).

Jacquiot et al. 1973 – *Cytisus, Robinia, Sophora.*

Jagiella & Kurschner 1987 – *Indigofera.*

Jentsch et al. 1936–1939 – *Andira, Pterocarpus.*

Kanehira 1921a – *Desmodium, Erythrina, Ormosia, Pongamia.*

Kanehira 1921b – *Maackia, Pongamia, Robinia, Sophora.*

Kanehira 1924 – *Dalbergia, Erythrina, Indigofera, Pterocarpus.*

Kanehira 1926 – *Maackia, Robinia, Styphnolobium.*

Kanehira et al. 1933 – *Aeschynomene, Erythrina, Herminiera* (= *Aeschynomene*).

Kauffmann Fidalgo 1955 – *Lonchocarpus.*

Kim & Yang 1988 – *Lespedeza.*

Kobayashi & Sugawa 1963 – *Pterocarpus.*

Kramer 1939 – *Cashalia* (= *Dussia*).

Kribs 1928a – *Diplotropis, Ormosia, Tounatea* (= *Swartzia*).

Kribs 1959 – Many genera.

Latorre 1983 – *Centrolobium, Geoffroea, Myroxylon, Piscidia, Platymiscium.*

Lebacq 1957 – *Afrormosia, Baphia, Craibia, Erythrina, Millettia, Platysepalum, Pterocarpus, Schefflerodendron.*

Lebacq & Dechamps 1964 – 11 genera.

Lebacq & Dechamps 1967 – *Baphia,* cf. *Craibia, Erythrina, Millettia, Platysepalum, Pterocarpus.*

Lebacq et al. 1973 – 12 genera.

Lebacq & Staner 1964 – *Coumarouna* (= *Dipteryx*), *Hymenolobium, Millettia, Swartzia.*

Lecomte 1922 – *Dalbergia.*

Lecomte 1926a – *Dalbergia, Pterocarpus.*

Lepe 1959 – *Ormosia, Platymiscium.*

(LEGUMINOSAE – PAPIL.)

Liese 1924 – *Robinia* (root).

López & Ortega 1989 – *Eysenhardtia.*

Louis & Fouarge 1943 – *Afrormosia.*

Loureiro & Lisboa 1979 – *Ormosia* 6 spp.

Loureiro & Rodrigues 1975 – *Swartzia.*

Loureiro & Silva 1973 – *Lecointea.*

Luo 1989 – *Dalbergia, Erythrina, Ormosia, Pterocarpus.*

Mainieri 1962 – *Pterocarpus.*

Mainieri 1978 – 15 genera.

Mainieri & Chimelo 1989 – 19 genera.

Mainieri & Primo 1964, 1968 – *Amburana, Andira, Hymenolobium, Platycyamus, Vatairea, Vataireopsis.*

Mainieri & Primo 1971 – *Coumarouna* (= *Dipteryx*), *Ferreirea* (= *Sweetia*), *Pterodon, Taralea.*

Mariaux 1963 – *Clathrotropis, Diplotropis, Haplormosia, Pericopsis.*

Martawijaya et al. 1986 – *Dalbergia, Pterocarpus.*

Mattos Filho 1967, 1969 – *Dalbergia.*

Mattos Filho 1980 – *Itaobimia* (= *Riedeliella*).

Mattos Filho & Coimbra Filho 1957 – *Dalbergia.*

Meniado et al. 1974 – *Pterocarpus.*

Messeri 1938 – *Retama.*

Metcalfe 1935 – *Pterocarpus.*

Meylan & Butterfield 1978b – *Sophora.*

Miller 1920 – *Machaerium.*

Moll & Janssonius 1906–1936 – *Butea, Dalbergia, Derris, Desmodium, Erythrina, Inocarpus, Pongamia, Pterocarpus.*

Molnar 1986 [1987] – *Robinia.*

Monnier 1909 – *Ulex* 10 spp.

Monteiro & Frade 1960 – *Pterocarpus.*

Monteiro & França 1965 – *Swartzia.*

Monteiro & França 1971 – *Lonchocarpus.*

Nair & Ram 1992 – *Aeschynomene.*

Nájera Angulo & López Fraile 1969 – *Robinia.*

Nardi Berti & Edlmann Abbate 1988 – *Dalbergia, Millettia, Pericopsis, Pterocarpus, Swartzia.*

Nardi Berti & Edlmann Abbate 1992 – 17 genera.

Niloofari 1961 – *Robinia.*

Normand 1950b – *Afrormosia, Baphia, Erythrina, Haplormosia, Lonchocarpus, Millettia, Pterocarpus, Swartzia.*

(LEGUMINOSAE–PAPIL.)

Normand 1988 [1990] – *Dalbergia.*

Normand & Paquis 1976 [1977] – *Angylocalyx, Baphia, Erythrina, Haplormosia, Lonchocarpus, Millettia, Pericopsis, Pterocarpus, Schefflerodendron, Swartzia.*

Novruzova 1963b – *Astragalus.*

Ogata 1975–1983 – *Dalbergia, Pericopsis, Pterocarpus.*

Ortega et al. 1988 – *Dalbergia, Diphysa.*

Ortega 1958 – *Pterocarpus, Swartzia, Vatairea.*

Page 1993 – *Robinia.*

Panshin 1937 – *Derris, Lonchocarpus.*

Panshin & Zeeuw 1980 – *Cladrastis, Robinia.*

Paula 1979 – *Alexa.*

Paula & Alves 1989 – *Bowdichia, Clitoria.*

Pearson & Brown 1932 – *Butea, Dalbergia, Erythrina, Millettia, Ougeinia* (= *Desmodium*), *Pongamia, Pterocarpus.*

Pedro et al. 1955 – *Pterocarpus.*

Pereira 1933 – *Machaerium, Myrocarpus, Platycyamus, Platypodium, Toluifera* (= *Myroxylon*).

Pereira et al. 1970 – *Bowdichia, Zollernia.*

Pérez Mogollón 1973 – *Alexa, Lonchocarpus, Pterocarpus.*

Pérez Mogollón 1993 – *Dussia, Ormosia.*

Pérez Olvera 1993 – *Platymiscium.*

Pérez Olvera et al. 1979 – *Swartzia, Sweetia.*

Pérez Olvera et al. 1980 [1981] – *Platymiscium, Pterocarpus, Vatairea.*

Perrot & Gérard 1907 – *Dalbergia, Erythrina, Herminiera* (= *Aeschynomene*), *Ormosia, Pterocarpus, Swartzia.*

Pfeiffer, J.P. 1926 – 10 genera.

Pickel et al. 1961 – *Machaerium.*

Prakash 1961 – *Aeschynomene.*

Prakash 1972 – *Lonchocarpus, Myroxylon* (root).

Purkayastha et al. 1976 – *Pterocarpus.*

Quirk 1983 – *Dalbergia, Pterocarpus.*

Rasa 1981 – *Gliricidia, Pterocarpus, Sesbania.*

Record & Garratt 1923 – *Dalbergia.*

Record & Hess 1943 – Family (many genera).

*Reinders-Gouwentak & Rijsdijk 1955 – Key to subfamilies.

*Reinders-Gouwentak & Rijsdijk 1968 – 12 genera.

(LEGUMINOSAE–PAPIL.)

Riedl 1937 – *Robinia* (root).

Riera 1947 – *Pterocarpus.*

Rizzini & Mattos Filho 1960–1961 – *Dalbergia.*

Rizzini & Mattos Filho 1967 – *Dalbergia, Diplotropis, Swartzia.*

Rizzini & Mattos Filho 1977 – *Luetzelburgia.*

Roig 1986 – *Adesmia.*

Rozmarin et al. 1983 – *Millettia, Pterocarpus.*

Saiki 1982 – *Dalbergia.*

Saint-Laurent 1926, 1928 – 12 genera.

Saint-Laurent 1934 – *Anagyris, Calicotome, Cytisus, Genista, Retama, Spartium.*

Saya 1959 – *Calicotome, Cytisus, Spartium.*

Schmid 1915 – *Andira, ?Machaerium, Myroxylon.*

Schmidt 1951–1952 – *Pterocarpus.*

Schweingruber 1978 – *Laburnum, Robinia.*

Schweingruber 1990 – 13 genera + brief notes on several others.

Scott 1927 – *Erythrina, Pterocarpus.*

Shilova 1965 – *Ammopiptanthus, Piptanthus.*

Shimaji & Itoh 1982 – *Maackia.*

Shimaji & Itoh 1988 – *Cladrastis, Maackia, Wisteria.*

Silva et al. 1989 – *Coursetia, Erythrina, Lonchocarpus.*

Small 1914 – *Eysenhardtia.*

Špoljarić 1953 – *Petteria.*

Sudo 1959 – *Cladrastis, Maackia, Platyosprion* (= *Cladrastis*), *Robinia, Sophora.*

Sudo 1963 – 23 genera.

Sudo 1988 – *Castanospermum, Ormosia, Pericopsis, Pterocarpus.*

Tang 1973 – *Dalbergia, Erythrina, Ormosia, Pterocarpus.*

Teixeira et al. 1978 – *Dalbergia.*

Thunell & Perem 1947 – *Caragana, Laburnum, Pterocarpus.*

Tineo et al. 1992 [1993] – *Machaerium.*

Tomazello Filho et al. 1983 – *Dipteryx, Zollernia.*

Tôrres 1941 – *Pterocarpus.*

Tortorelli 1956 – *Amburana, Erythrina, Geoffroea, Holocalyx, Muellera, Myrocarpus, Myroxylon, Tipuana.*

Urling & Smith 1953 – *Erythrina.*

Van der Slooten 1968 – *Pterocarpus.*

(LEGUMINOSAE–PAPIL.)

Van der Slooten & Gonzalez 1971 – *Pterocarpus.*

Vasilevskaya 1933 – *Ammodendron, Eremosparton.*

Wagemann 1949 – *Sophora.*

Wagenführ 1990 – *Pterocarpus.*

Wagenführ & Scheiber 1974 – *Afrormosia, Dalbergia, Millettia, Pterocarpus, Robinia.*

Wang 1984–1988 – *Dalbergia, Pericopsis, Pterocarpus.*

Wellendorf 1966 – *Millettia.*

Williams 1936 – *Dalbergia, Erythrina, Lonchocarpus, Machaerium, Myroxylon, Pterocarpus, Swartzia, Tephrosia.*

Wiraj Chunwarin & Damrong Sri-Aran 1974 – *Dalbergia, Millettia, Pterocarpus.*

Wuang 1979 – *Cladrastis, Dalbergia, Robinia, Sophora.*

Yakovlev et al. 1968 – *Angylocalyx.*

Yamabayashi 1938 – *Lespedeza, Maackia, Robinia, Styphnolobium.*

Yao 1988 – *Cladrastis, Dalbergia, Ormosia, Robinia, Sophora.*

Yatsenko-Khmelevsky 1954a – 10 genera.

Anomalous structure

Chalk & Chattaway 1937 – Family (*Machaerium, Pueraria, Wisteria*).

Handa 1932 – *Pueraria, Wisteria.*

Hill 1901 – *Dalbergia.*

Kuo & Pate 1981 – *Macrotyloma.*

Nair 1993 – *Spatholobus.*

Nair & Ram 1990 – *Dalbergia.*

Obaton 1960 – *Centrosema, Millettia, Mucuna.*

Pfeiffer 1925 – *Machaerium.*

Ursem & Welle 1992 – *Dioclea.*

Crystals

Chattaway 1956 – Many genera.

Espinoza de Pernía 1987b – *Bowdichia, Centrolobium, Dipteryx, Lonchocarpus, Platymiscium, Pterocarpus, Robinia, Swartzia.*

Gonzales 1976 [1978] – *Pterocarpus.*

Meniado et al. 1970 – *Pterocarpus.*

Ecological anatomy

Baas & Schweingruber 1987 – 23 genera.

Baas et al. 1983 – *Anagyris, Calicotome, Colutea, Genista, Gonocytisus, Retama, Spartium.*

(LEGUMINOSAE–PAPIL.)

Barajas Morales 1985 – *Apoplanesia, Dalbergia, Dussia, Lonchocarpus, Myrospermum, Pterocarpus.*

Carlquist 1977c – *Bossiaea, Hovea, Pultenaea, Templetonia.*

Carlquist 1985a – *Hardenbergia, Pickeringia, Spartium, Wisteria.*

Carlquist 1985 [1986]a – *Hardenbergia, Mucuna, Wisteria.*

Carlquist & Hoekman 1985a – *Amorpha, Dalea, Lotus, Lupinus, Olneya, Pickeringia.*

Den Outer & Van Veenendaal 1976 – *Baphia, Pterocarpus.*

Lim & Soh 1991a – *Lespedeza.*

Novruzova 1968 – *Astragalus, Caragana, Colutea, Eversmannia, Halimodendron.*

Van der Graaff & Baas 1974 – *Erythrina.*

Waisel & Fahn 1965 – *Robinia.*

Webber 1936a – *Parosela (= Dalea), Pickeringia.*

Worbes 1986 – *Swartzia.*

Growth rings

Détienne 1974b – *Pterocarpus.*

Détienne 1989 – *Andira, Pterocarpus.*

Worbes 1984 – *Clathrotropis.*

Helical thickenings

Meylan & Butterfield 1978a – *Carmichaelia, Chordospartium, Corallospartium, Notospartium, Sophora.*

Nair 1987 – *Erythrina.*

Ohtani & Ishida 1978b – *Caragana, Cladrastis, Euchresta, Maackia, Millettia, Robinia, Sophora, Wisteria.*

Parham & Kaustinen 1973 – *Robinia.*

Pits and perforation plates

Jing et al. 1988 – *Dalbergia, Erythrina.*

Meylan & Butterfield 1974 – *Carmichaelia, Chordospartium, Corallospartium, Notospartium, Sophora.*

Müller-Stoll & Süss 1969 [1970] – *Aeschynomene.*

Nair & Ram 1989 – *Butea, Dalbergia, Derris, Erythrina, Ougeinia (= Desmodium), Pterocarpus, Sesbania.*

Ohtani & Ishida 1976, 1978a – 10 genera.

Schmid & Machado 1964 – *Amburana.*

Rays

Sebastine 1955 – *Erythrina.*

(LEGUMINOSAE–PAPIL.)

Secretory elements
Nikitin 1962 – *Astragalus.*

Storied structure
Cozzo 1949a – 13 genera.
Cozzo 1952 – *Cyclolobium.*
Cozzo 1976 – *Sesbania.*
Cozzo & Cristiani 1950 – 46 genera.
Descole & O'Donell 1938 – *Casca-
     ronia.*
Reinders-Gouwentak 1955 – 13 genera.
Tortorelli 1945 – *Muellera.*

Tracheary elements
Jing et al. 1989 – *Dalbergia, Erythrina.*
Ohtani 1983 – 10 genera.

LEITNERIACEAE (*Leitneria*)

Cumbie 1967.
Record & Hess 1943.

LEPIDOBOTRYACEAE
see LINACEAE

LINACEAE (incl. CTENOLOPHONACEAE,
LEPIDOBOTRYACEAE)

Benoist 1931 – *Roucheria.*
Brazier & Franklin 1961 – *Ctenolophon.*
Dechamps 1985 – *Hebepetalum.*
Desch 1954 – *Ctenolophon.*
Détienne & Jacquet 1983 – *Hebepetalum,
     Roucheria.*
Détienne et al. 1982 – *Hebepetalum,
     Roucheria.*
Hayashi et al. 1973 – *Ctenolophon.*
Heimsch 1942 – *Ctenolophon, Hebepeta-
     lum, Hugonia, Indorouchera, Linum,
     Reinwardtia, Roucheria, Tirpitzia.*
*Heimsch & Tschabold 1972 – *Ctenolophon,
     Hebepetalum, Hesperolinon, Hugonia,
     Indorouchera, Linum, Reinwardtia,
     Roucheria.*
Ilic 1991 – *Ctenolophon.*
Lebacq & Dechamps 1964 – *Lepidobotrys.*
Lebacq & Dechamps 1967 – cf. *Hugonia.*
Mennega 1993 – *Lepidobotrys, Ruptilio-
     carpon.*
Normand & Cavaco 1951 – *Ctenolophon.*

(LINACEAE)
Normand & Paquis 1976 [1977] – *Cteno-
     lophon, Lepidobotrys.*
Ogata 1975–1983 – *Ctenolophon.*
Record & Hess 1943 – Family (*Hebepeta-
     lum, Roucheria*).
Schweingruber 1990 – *Linum.*
Sudo 1963, 1988 – *Ctenolophon.*

Crystals
Chattaway 1956 – *Ctenolophon.*

Ecological anatomy
Baas & Schweingruber 1987 – *Linum.*
Carlquist 1985a – *Ctenolophon.*

LISSOCARPACEAE (*Lissocarpus*)

Dickison & Phend 1985.
Record & Hess 1943.

LOASACEAE

*Carlquist 1984c – *Cevallia, Eucnide,
     Fuertesia, Kissenia, Loasa, Mentzelia,
     Petalonyx.*
Carlquist 1987d – *Plakothira.*
Record & Hess 1943 – *Mentzelia.*

Ecological anatomy
Carlquist 1985 [1986]a – *Fuertesia.*
Carlquist & Hoekman 1985a – *Eucnide,
     Mentzelia, Petalonyx.*
Webber 1936a – *Petalonyx.*

LOBELIACEAE

Carlquist 1962a – *Brighamia, Delissea,
     Lobelia, Trematolobelia* (= *Trematocar-
     pus*).
*Carlquist 1969a – 12 genera.
Mabberley 1974b – *Lobelia.*
Record & Hess 1943 – *Siphocampylus.*

LOGANIACEAE
(incl. ANTONIACEAE, BUDDLEJACEAE,
DESFONTAINIACEAE, POTALIACEAE,
SPIGELIACEAE, STRYCHNACEAE)
(For *Pagamea* see RUBIACEAE)

Abbate 1964 – *Nuxia.*
Abbate 1970 – *Buddleja.*
Balan Menon 1955 – *Fagraea.*

(LOGANIACEAE)
Brazier & Franklin 1961 – *Strychnos*.
Burgerstein 1909 – *Fagraea, Geniostoma*.
Carlquist 1992c – *Buddleja*.
*Cockrell 1941 – *Strychnos* 26 spp.
Cockrell & Monachino 1947 – *Strychnos*.
*Coulaud 1988, 1989 – 11 genera.
Cutler et al. 1987 – *Buddleja* (root).
D'Arcy & Keating 1973 – *Lithophytum*
    (= *Plocosperma*) (or in Verbenaceae).
Datta & Ghosh 1983, 1984a – *Strychnos*.
Dechamps 1971 – *Strychnos*.
Dechamps 1979 – *Antonia*.
Dechamps 1985 – *Strychnos*.
Détienne & Jacquet 1983 – *Antonia, Bonyunia, Buddleja, Strychnos*.
Détienne et al. 1982 – *Antonia, Strychnos*.
*Duvigneaud et al. 1952 – *Strychnos* 33 spp.
    (branches).
Fasolo 1941–1944 – *Nuxia*.
Furuno 1977 – *Neuburgia*.
Giordano 1939 – *Nuxia*.
Grotta 1961 – *Buddleja*.
Hayashi et al. 1973 – *Fagraea*.
Ilic 1991 – *Anthocleista, Fagraea, Geniostoma, Neuburgia, Nuxia, Strychnos*.
Jagiella & Kurschner 1987 – *Buddleja, Nuxia*.
Kanehira 1921a, 1924 – *Fagraea*.
Lebacq & Dechamps 1964, 1967 – *Anthocleista, Strychnos*.
Lebacq et al. 1973 – *Potalia, Strychnos*.
Lecomte 1922 – *Nuxia*.
Martawijaya et al. 1989 – *Fagraea*.
Martin 1953 – *Anthocleista*.
*Mennega 1980a – 23 genera (incl. *Retzia*, see Solanaceae).
Meylan & Butterfield 1978b – *Geniostoma*.
Moll & Janssonius 1906–1936 – *Buddleja, Fagraea, Geniostoma*.
Normand 1950b–1960 – *Anthocleista, Lachnopylis* (= *Nuxia*), *Strychnos*.
Normand & Paquis 1976 [1977] – *Anthocleista, Nuxia, Strychnos*.
Ogata 1975–1983 – *Fagraea*.
Paula 1972a, 1979 – *Antonia*.
Pearson & Brown 1932 – *Fagraea, Strychnos*.
Pérez Olvera et al. 1980 [1981] – *Buddleja*.
Prakash 1972 – *Strychnos* (root).
Record 1938c – *Bonyunia, Buddleja, Potalia, Strychnos*.

(LOGANIACEAE)
Record & Hess 1943 – Family (*Antonia, Bonyunia, Buddleja, Potalia, Strychnos*).
Scott 1927 – *Strychnos*.
Sudo 1963 – *Fagraea*.
Sudo 1988 – *Fagraea, Neuburgia*.
Van der Slooten 1968 – *Buddleja*.
Williams 1936 – *Potalia, Strychnos*.
Wiraj Chunwarin & Damrong Sri-Aran 1974
    – *Fagraea, Strychnos*.

Anomalous structure
Chalk & Chattaway 1937 – Family (*Bonyunia, Norrisia, Strychnos*).
Obaton 1960 – *Strychnos, Usteria*.
Van Veenendaal & Den Outer 1993 – *Strychnos*.

Crystals
Baker 1917 – *Strychnos*.
Chattaway 1956 – *Strychnos*.

Ecological anatomy
Carlquist 1985a – *Buddleja, ?Gomphostigma, Logania, Strychnos, Usteria*.
Carlquist 1985 [1986]a – *Gelsemium, Strychnos, Usteria*.
Carlquist & Hoekman 1985a – *Buddleja*.
Den Outer & Van Veenendaal 1976 – *Strychnos*.
Van der Graaff & Baas 1974 – *Fagraea*.

Pits
Meylan & Butterfield 1974 – *Geniostoma*.

Rays
Dayal et al. 1984 – *Strychnos*.

Septate fibres
Butterfield & Meylan 1976 – *Geniostoma*.

LOPHOPYXIDACEAE see ICACINACEAE

LORANTHACEAE (incl. VISCACEAE)

Burgerstein 1909 – *Loranthus*.
Fahn et al. 1986 – *Loranthus, Viscum*.
Greguss 1959 – *Loranthus, Viscum*.
Huber & Rouschal 1954 – *Loranthus, Viscum*.
Lebacq et al. 1973 – *Gaiadendron*.
*Patel 1991 – *Alepis, Ileostylus, Peraxilla, Trilepidea, Tupeia*.

(LORANTHACEAE)
Record 1938a – *Gaiadendron.*
Record & Hess 1943 – *Gaiadendron.*
Schweingruber 1978 – *Viscum.*
Schweingruber 1990 – *Loranthus, Viscum.*

Ecological anatomy
Baas & Schweingruber 1987 – *Loranthus, Viscum.*
Carlquist & Hoekman 1985a – *Phoradendron.*

Crystals
Chattaway 1956 – *Loranthus.*

LYTHRACEAE
(incl. ALZATEACEAE; see also PUNICACEAE & SONNERATIACEAE)

Anon. 1977a – *Lagerstroemia.*
Abbate 1977 – *Lagerstroemia.*
Baas 1979b – *Alzatea.*
*Baas 1986b – *Capuronia, Galpinia, Haitia, Orias* (= *Lagerstroemia*), *Pleurophora.*
*Baas & Zweypfenning 1979 – 18 genera.
Barbosa et al. 1977–1978 – *Lafoensia.*
Brazier & Franklin 1961 – *Lagerstroemia.*
Cheng, J.-Q. 1980 – *Lagerstroemia.*
Cheng, J.-Q. et al. 1992 – *Lagerstroemia.*
Chiang 1964 – *Lagerstroemia.*
Das 1976a – *Lagerstroemia.*
Dechamps 1985 – *Lafoensia.*
Détienne & Jacquet 1983 – *Lafoensia.*
Freitas 1963 – *Lagerstroemia.*
Furuno 1979 – *Lagerstroemia.*
Graham & Lorence 1978 – *Tetrataxis* (twig).
Graham et al. 1986 – *Koehneria.*
Graham et al. 1987 – *Lourtella.*
Hayashi et al. 1973 – *Lagerstroemia.*
Hirai 1979–1985 – *Lagerstroemia.*
Ilic 1991 – *Lafoensia, Lagerstroemia, Pemphis.*
Janssonius 1950 – Relations.
Kanehira 1921a – *Lagerstroemia, Pemphis.*
Kanehira 1924, 1926 – *Lagerstroemia.*
Kobayashi & Sugawa 1972 – *Lagerstroemia.*
Kribs 1959 – *Lagerstroemia.*
Lecomte 1926a – *Lagerstroemia.*
Luo 1989 – *Lagerstroemia.*
Martawijaya et al. 1989 – *Lagerstroemia.*
Moll & Janssonius 1906–1936 – *Lagerstroemia.*

(LYTHRACEAE)
Ogata 1975–1983 – *Lagerstroemia.*
Pearson & Brown 1932 – *Lagerstroemia.*
Purkayastha et al. 1976 – *Lagerstroemia.*
Record 1929b – *Physocalymma* misidentified.
Record & Hess 1943 – Family (*Adenaria, Ginoria, Grislea* (= *Pehria*), *Lafoensia, Physocalymma*).
Sudo 1963, 1988 – *Lagerstroemia.*
Tang 1973 – *Lagerstroemia.*
Van Vliet 1975 – *Alzatea* (in Crypteroniaceae).
Van Vliet & Baas 1984 – Relations of myrtalean families.
Venkateswarlu & Rao 1964 – Relations with Sonneratiaceae.
Williams 1936 – *Adenaria, Physocalymma.*
Wiraj Chunwarin & Damrong Sri-Aran 1974 – *Lagerstroemia.*
Wu & Wang 1976 – *Lagerstroemia.*

Crystals
Chattaway 1956 – *Lagerstroemia.*

Pits and perforation plates
Nair & Ram 1989 – *Lagerstroemia.*
Ohtani & Ishida 1976, 1978a – *Lagerstroemia.*

Rays
McLean & Richardson 1973 [1974] – *Lagerstroemia.*

Septate fibres
Purkayastha 1958 – *Lagerstroemia.*

Tracheary elements
Jing et al. 1989 – *Lagerstroemia.*
Ohtani 1983 – *Lagerstroemia.*

MAGNOLIACEAE
(*Alcimandra, Aromadendron, Manglietiastrum, Parakmeria* and *Talauma* = *Magnolia; Paramichelia* and *Tsoongiodendron* = *Michelia*)

Anon 1966 – *Magnolia.*
Anon. 1977a – *Michelia.*
Abbate 1977 – *Michelia.*
Babos & Vales 1977 [1978] – *Magnolia.*
Bargagli-Petrucci 1903 – *Talauma.*
Berger 1922 – *Michelia.*
Brazier & Franklin 1961 – *Liriodendron, Magnolia.*

(MAGNOLIACEAE)

*Canright 1955 – *Alcimandra, Aromadendron, Elmerrillia, Kmeria, Liriodendron, Magnolia* 22 spp., *Manglietia* 8 spp., *Michelia* 12 spp., *Talauma* 12 spp.

Carreras & Vales 1986b – *Magnolia, Talauma.*

Carreras & Vales 1987 – *Magnolia.*

Carvalho 1954–1955, 1956 – *Liriodendron.*

Chang 1974 – *Tsoongiodendron.*

Chang 1982 – *Manglietiastrum.*

Chauhan & Dayal 1992 – *Michelia* 8 spp.

Chen 1985 – *Magnolia.*

Chen 1989 – *Manglietia* 8 spp.

*Chen et al. 1993 – *Kmeria, Liriodendron, Magnolia* 21 spp., *Manglietia* 12 spp., *Michelia* 25 spp.

Cheng, C. 1985 – *Magnolia, Manglietia, Michelia.*

Cheng, J.-Q. 1980 – *Alcimandra, Liriodendron, Magnolia, Manglietia, Michelia, Paramichelia, Tsoongiodendron.*

Cheng, J.-Q. et al. 1992 – Same genera as Cheng 1980.

Chiang 1962 – *Michelia.*

Cockrell 1942 – *Aromadendron.*

Cutler et al. 1987 – *Liriodendron, Magnolia* (root).

Dechamps 1985 – *Talauma.*

Détienne & Jacquet 1983 – *Talauma.*

Doležal 1959 – *Talauma.*

Foulger et al. 1975 – *Liriodendron.*

Furuno 1979 – *Elmerrillia.*

Furuno 1985, 1987 – *Liriodendron, Magnolia.*

Garratt 1933b – Family; relations.

Greguss 1959 – *Liriodendron, Magnolia.*

Grosser 1977 – *Liriodendron.*

Hayashi 1991 – *Magnolia, Michelia.*

Hirai 1979–1985 – *Magnolia, Michelia.*

Ho 1949 – *Manglietia.*

Ilic 1991 – *Aromadendron, Elmerrillia, Liriodendron, Magnolia, Michelia, Talauma.*

Jacquiot et al. 1973 – *Liriodendron, Magnolia.*

Kanehira 1921a – *Michelia.*

Kanehira 1921b, 1926 – *Magnolia, Michelia.*

Kribs 1959 – *Magnolia, Michelia.*

Lecomte 1926a – *Manglietia, Michelia.*

Lemesle 1933 – *Michelia, Talauma.*

(MAGNOLIACEAE)

Lemesle 1953, 1956b – *Alcimandra, Elmerrillia, Liriodendron, Magnolia, Manglietia, Michelia, Talauma.*

Liu et al. 1987 – *Magnolia, Michelia.*

López & Ortega 1989 – *Magnolia.*

Luo 1989 – *Liriodendron, Magnolia, Manglietia, Manglietiastrum, Michelia, Parakmeria, Paramichelia.*

McLaughlin 1933 – *Aromadendron, Elmerrillia, Liriodendron, Magnolia, Manglietia, Michelia, Talauma.*

Mainieri 1978 – *Talauma.*

Mainieri & Chimelo 1989 – *Talauma.*

Medonça & Paula 1979 – *Talauma.*

Metcalfe 1987 – General survey.

Moll & Janssonius 1906–1936 – *Magnolia, Manglietia, Michelia, Talauma.*

Nooteboom 1985 – Family summary (wood notes by H. Gottwald).

Ogata 1975–1983 – *Elmerrillia, Michelia.*

Panshin & Zeeuw 1980 – *Liriodendron, Magnolia.*

Pearson & Brown 1932 – *Michelia, Talauma.*

Qian et al. 1989 – *Magnolia.*

Record & Hess 1943 – Family (*Liriodendron, Magnolia, Talauma*).

Record & Mell 1924 – *Talauma.*

Rogel Gomez 1982 [1985] – *Talauma.*

Saiki 1982 – *Magnolia.*

Schultz et al. 1964 – *Talauma.*

Shimaji & Itoh 1982, 1988 – *Magnolia.*

Soh & Park 1985 – *Liriodendron, Magnolia, Michelia.*

Stark 1954b – *Liriodendron, Magnolia.*

Sudo 1959 – *Magnolia, Michelia.*

Sudo 1963 – *Michelia.*

Sudo 1988 – *Elmerrillia.*

Sugawa 1968c – *Michelia.*

Takahashi 1985 – *Liriodendron, Magnolia.*

Takahashi 1989 – *Aromadendron, Elmerrillia, Talauma.*

Tang 1973 – *Alcimandra, Liriodendron, Magnolia, Manglietia, Michelia, Paramichelia.*

*Tiêp 1980 – *Manglietia* 22 spp.

Vales et al. 1977 – *Magnolia.*

Vales & Carreras 1986 – *Talauma.*

Van der Slooten 1968 – *Magnolia.*

Van der Slooten et al. 1970 – *Magnolia.*

(MAGNOLIACEAE)
Vander Wyk & Canright 1956 – Relations.
Wagenführ & Scheiber 1974 – *Manglietia, Talauma.*
Wang 1984–1988 – *Elmerrillia.*
Wiraj Chunwarin & Damrong Sri-Aran 1973 – *Manglietia, Michelia.*
Wu & Wang 1976 – *Michelia.*
Wu & Li 1988 – *Alcimandra, Aromadendron, Liriodendron, Manglietia, Manglietiastrum, Parakmeria, Paramichelia, Tsoongiodendron.*
Yamabayashi 1938 – *Magnolia.*
Yao 1988 – *Liriodendron, Magnolia, Manglietia, Michelia, Paramichelia.*
Yatsenko-Khmelevsky 1954a – *Liriodendron, Magnolia.*
Zhang 1984 – *Manglietia, Paramichelia.*

Ecological anatomy
Van der Graaff & Baas 1974 – *Magnolia.*

Helical thickenings
Ohtani & Ishida 1978b – *Magnolia, Michelia.*
Parham & Kaustinen 1973 – *Magnolia.*
Wu & Li 1989 – 10 genera.

Pits and perforation plates
Lemesle 1946a – *Alcimandra, Elmerrillia, Liriodendron, Magnolia, Manglietia, Michelia, Talauma.*
Ohtani & Ishida 1978a – *Liriodendron, Magnolia, Michelia.*

Rays
Wu et al. 1993 – *Alcimandra, Liriodendron, Magnolia, Manglietia, Manglietiastrum, Michelia, Parakmeria, Paramichelia, Tsoongiodendron.*

Silica
Scurfield et al. 1974 – *Talauma.*

Tracheary elements
Jing et al. 1989 – *Magnolia, Michelia, Paramichelia, Talauma.*
Ohtani 1983 – *Liriodendron, Magnolia, Michelia.*
Yadav & Bhattacharyya 1989 [1990] – *Michelia.*

MALESHERBIACEAE (*Malesherbia*)
*Carlquist 1984 [1985]b.

(MALESHERBIACEAE)
Ecological anatomy
Carlquist 1985a.

MALPIGHIACEAE

Alves de Pinho & Camargo 1979 – *Byrsonima.*
Barbosa et al. 1977–1978 – *Byrsonima.*
Benoist 1931 – *Byrsonima.*
Brazier & Franklin 1961 – *Byrsonima.*
Cozzo 1947 – *Tricomaria.*
Dechamps 1985 – *Bunchosia, Byrsonima, Spachea, Tetrapterys.*
Détienne & Jacquet 1983 – *Acmanthera, Bunchosia, Burdachia, Byrsonima, Spachea.*
Détienne et al. 1982 – *Byrsonima, Spachea.*
Heimsch 1942 – 13 genera, 40 spp.
Ilic 1991 – *Bunchosia, Byrsonima, Malpighia.*
Kribs 1928a – *Byrsonima, Tetrapodenia* (= *Burdachia*).
Kribs 1959 – *Byrsonima.*
Lebacq et al. 1973 – *Bunchosia, Byrsonima.*
Lins 1982 – *Heteropterys.*
Mainieri 1978 – *Byrsonima.*
Mainieri & Chimelo 1989 – *Byrsonima.*
Ortega et al. 1988 – *Byrsonima.*
Pereira et al. 1970 – *Byrsonima.*
Pérez Olvera et al. 1980 [1981] – *Byrsonima.*
Pfeiffer, J.P. 1926 – *Byrsonima.*
Record 1927d – *Tetrapodenia* (= *Burdachia*).
Record & Hess 1943 – Family (12 genera).
Record & Mell 1924 – *Byrsonima.*
Sudo 1963 – *Byrsonima.*
Williams 1936 – *Banisteria* (= *Heteropterys*), *Bunchosia, Byrsonima, Spachea.*

Anomalous structure
Obaton 1960 – *Flabellaria, Triaspis.*

Crystals
Chattaway 1956 – *Bunchosia.*

MALVACEAE

Barajas Morales & León Gómez 1989 – *Gossypium.*
Brazier & Franklin 1961 – *Hibiscus.*
Brown 1922 – *Gossypium, Hibiscus.*

(MALVACEAE)

Burgerstein 1909 – *Hibiscus, Sida, Thespesia.*

Carreras & Vales 1986b – *Hibiscus.*

Cellai 1971 – *Thespesia.*

Cutler et al. 1987 – *Hibiscus* (root).

Dariev & Valichek 1980 – *Gossypium.*

Détienne & Jacquet 1983 – *Hibiscus.*

Fahn et al. 1986 – *Abutilon, Hibiscus.*

Freitas 1955 – *Hibiscus.*

Freitas 1958 – *Thespesia.*

Furuno 1977, 1979 – *Hibiscus, Thespesia.*

Garratt 1924 – *Hoheria* or *Plagianthus.*

Greguss 1959 – *Hibiscus.*

Huber & Rouschal 1954 – *Hibiscus.*

Hyde 1925 – *Wercklea.*

Ilic 1991 – *Bastardiopsis, Bombycidendron, Hibiscus, Hoheria, Kydia, Lagunaria, Tetrasida, Thespesia.*

Janssonius 1950 – Relations.

Kanehira 1921a, 1926 – *Hibiscus.*

Kanehira 1924 – *Bombycidendron.*

Kribs 1959 – *Hibiscus.*

Lecomte 1922, 1926a – *Hibiscus.*

Lim & Soh 1991b – *Hibiscus.*

Mainieri & Chimelo 1989 – *Bastardiopsis.*

Meylan & Butterfield 1978b – *Hoheria, Plagianthus.*

Moll & Janssonius 1906–1936 – *Hibiscus, Thespesia.*

Pearson & Brown 1932 – *Kydia.*

Pérez Olvera et al. 1980 [1981] – *Robinsonella.*

Pinto 1978 – *Uladendron.*

Record 1935 – *Cephalohibiscus.*

Record & Hess 1943 – Family (*Abutilon, Bastardiopsis, Hibiscus, Montezuma, Tetrasida, Thespesia, Wercklea*).

Record & Mell 1924 – *Hibiscus.*

Saint-Laurent 1928, 1934 – *Lavatera.*

Schultz & Wollheim 1962 – *Hibiscus.*

Schweingruber 1990 – *Hibiscus, Lavatera.*

Sudo 1963 – *Bombycidendron, Hibiscus, Thespesia.*

Sudo 1988 – *Hibiscus, Thespesia.*

Tang 1973 – *Kydia.*

Tortorelli 1956 – *Bastardiopsis.*

*Walsh 1975 – *Hibiscus* 21 spp.

Webber 1934a – *Hibiscus.*

*Webber 1934b – Family (29 genera).

Williams 1936 – *Hibiscus, Pavonia, Tetrasida.*

(MALVACEAE)

Wiraj Chunwarin & Damrong Sri-Aran 1973 – *Kydia.*

Crystals

Chattaway 1955 – *Cienfuegosia, Hibiscus, Malvaviscus.*

Chattaway 1956 – *Abutilon, Cephalohibiscus, Cienfuegosia, Hibiscus, Kydia, Lagunaria, Malvaviscus, Papuodendron, Thespesia.*

Espinoza de Pernía 1987b – *Uladendron.*

Ecological anatomy

Baas et al. 1983 – *Abutilon, Hibiscus.*

Baas & Schweingruber 1987 – *Lavatera.*

Barajas Morales 1985 – *Robinsonella.*

Carlquist 1977c – *Hibiscus.*

Carlquist 1985a – *Hoheria, Malacothamnus, Selenothamnus* (= *Lawrencia*), *Sphaeralcea.*

Carlquist & Hoekman 1985a – *Lavatera, Malacothamnus, Sphaeralcea.*

Webber 1936a – *Sphaeralcea.*

Helical thickenings

Meylan & Butterfield 1978a – *Hoheria, Plagianthus.*

Ohtani & Ishida 1978b – *Hibiscus.*

Pits and perforation plates

Meylan & Butterfield 1974 – *Hoheria, Plagianthus.*

Ohtani & Ishida 1978a – *Hibiscus.*

Storied structure

Cozzo & Cristiani 1950 – *Abutilon, Bastardiopsis, Hibiscus.*

Tracheary elements

Bhat et al. 1990 – *Hibiscus.*

Ohtani 1983 – *Hibiscus.*

MARCGRAVIACEAE

Dadswell & Record 1936 – *Marcgravia.*

Dechamps 1985 – *Norantea, Souroubea.*

Record & Hess 1943 – Family (*Marcgravia, Norantea, Souroubea*).

Vestal 1937 – Family (*Marcgravia, Norantea, Souroubea*).

Williams 1936 – *Marcgravia.*

MARTYNIACEAE (*Martynia*)

Carlquist 1987c.
Kulkarni & Kazi 1969–1970.

MASTIXIACEAE see CORNACEAE

MEDUSAGYNACEAE

*Dickison 1990 – *Medusagyne*.

MEDUSANDRACEAE

Metcalfe 1952a – *Medusandra*.
Metcalfe & Chalk 1950 – *Soyauxia* (in Pas-
sifloraceae).
Miller, R.B. 1975 – *Soyauxia* (in Flacour-
tiaceae).
Normand 1960 – *Soyauxia*.
Normand & Paquis 1976 [1977] – *Soyauxia*.

MELANOPHYLLACEAE
see CORNACEAE

MELASTOMATACEAE (for *Dactylocladus*
see CRYPTERONIACEAE)

Anon 1981 – (Andes) *Mouriri*.
Barbosa et al. 1977–1978 – *Miconia, Mouriri*.
Bascopé 1954 – *Miconia*.
Benoist 1931 – *Bellucia, Loreya, Mouriri*.
Burgerstein 1909 – *Astronia, Melastoma*.
Cheng, J.-Q. 1980 – *Memecylon*.
Cheng, J.-Q. et al. 1992 – *Memecylon*.
Cockrell 1942 – *Memecylon*.
Cunha Mello 1950 [1951], 1976 – *Mico-
nia*.
Dechamps 1985 – *Bellucia, Henriettea,
Loreya, Memecylon, Miconia, Mouriri,
Pternandra*.
Desch 1954 – *Memecylon, Pternandra*.
Détienne & Jacquet 1983 – *Bellucia, Blakea,
Henriettea, Henriettella, Loreya, Meriania,
Miconia, Mouriri*.
Détienne et al. 1982 – *Bellucia, Henriettea,
Henriettella, Loreya, Miconia, Mouriri*.
Hayashi et al. 1973 – *Memecylon*.
Ilic 1991 – *Astronia, Astronidium, Meme-
cylon, Miconia, Mouriri, Pternandra*.
Janssonius 1950 – Relations.

(MELASTOMATACEAE)
Kanehira 1921a – *Astronia, Blastus,
Melastoma*.
Kanehira 1924 – *Medinilla*.
*Koek-Noorman et al. 1979 – *Blakea,
Huilaea, Topobea;* Miconieae.
Kribs 1928a – *Bellucia, Miconia*.
Lebacq et al. 1973 – *Clidemia, Miconia*.
Lecomte 1922 – *Dichaetanthera, Meme-
cylon*.
Lopes et al. 1983 – *Mouriri*.
Mainieri 1978 – *Mouriri*.
Mainieri & Chimelo 1989 – *Mouriri*.
Moll & Janssonius 1906–1936 – *Astronia,
Kibessia (= Pternandra), Medinilla,
Melastoma, Memecylon*.
Normand 1960 – *Dichaetanthera, Meme-
cylon*.
Normand & Paquis 1976 [1977] – *Dichae-
tanthera, Memecylon*.
Paula & Alves 1989 – *Miconia*.
Pérez Mogollón 1973 – *Mouriri*.
Pérez Mogollón 1993 – *Axinaea*.
Pfeiffer, J.P. 1926 – *Mouriri*.
Ramalho et al. 1981 – *Miconia*.
Record & Hess 1943 – Family (29 genera).
Record & Mell 1924 – *Mouriri*.
Renner 1989 – *Bellucia, Loreya, Macairea*.
[Notes on Welle & Koek-Noorman 1981.]
Schmid 1915 – *Mouriri*.
Tôrres 1941 – *Memecylon*.
*Van Vliet 1981 – 37 genera, 107 spp.
*Van Vliet et al. 1981 – Summary.
Van Vliet & Baas 1984 – Relations of myr-
talean families.
Welle & Détienne 1993 – 20 genera.
Welle & Koek-Noorman 1978 – *Miconia*
6 spp.
*Welle & Koek-Noorman 1981 – 47 genera,
160 spp.
Williams 1936 – 12 genera.
Wiraj Chunwarin & Damrong Sri-Aran 1974
– *Memecylon*.

Anomalous structure

Chalk & Chattaway 1937 – Family (*Memecylon, Mouriri, Pternandra*).

Crystals

Welle & Mennega 1977 – *Calycogonium,
Henriettea*.

(MELASTOMATACEAE)
Pits
Van Vliet 1978 – *Dichaetanthera, Dissotis, Marumia, Medinilla.*

MELIACEAE (*Amoora = Aglaia*)

Anon. 1955–1959 – *Khaya.*
Anon. 1977a – 32 genera.
Anon. 1981 (Andes) – *Carapa, Guarea.*
Anon. 1981 (Curua) – *Trichilia.*
Abbate 1973 – *Khaya.*
Abbate 1977 – *Amoora, Sandoricum, Xylocarpus.*
Almeida 1973 [1974] – *Kirkia* (or in Simaroubaceae).
Arnaez & Flores 1988 – *Cedrela.*
Ayensu & Bentum 1974 – *Entandrophragma, Guarea, Khaya, Lovoa, Turraeanthus.*
Babos & Borhidi 1978 – *Guarea, Trichilia.*
Bahadur 1988 – *Cedrela, Toona.*
Barajas Morales & Echenique-Manrique 1976 – *Guarea.*
Barajas Morales & León Gómez 1989 – *Swietenia.*
Barajas Morales et al. 1979 – *Cedrela, Guarea, Swietenia.*
Bargagli-Petrucci 1903 – *Carapa, Dysoxylum, Sandoricum.*
Bascopé 1954 – *Guarea.*
Bascopé et al. 1957 – *Cedrela.*
Bastos 1946 [1947] – *Carapa.*
Benoist 1931 – *Carapa, Cedrela, Trichilia.*
Brazier & Franklin 1961 – 15 genera.
Burgerstein 1909 – *Aglaia, Dysoxylum, Melia.*
Burgerstein 1912 – *Cedrela.*
Carreras & Pérez 1982 – *Swietenia.*
Carreras & Vales 1986b – *Cedrela, Guarea, Swietenia, Trichilia.*
Carreras & Vales 1987 – *Trichilia.*
Chalk et al. 1933 – *Lovoa, Pseudocedrela.*
Chalk et al. 1935 – *Ekebergia.*
Chattaway 1931 – *Entandrophragma.*
Cheng, C. 1985 – *Aglaia, Chukrasia, Melia, Toona.*
Cheng, J.-Q. 1980 – *Aglaia, Aphanamixis, Chukrasia, Melia, Toona.*
Cheng, J.-Q. et al. 1992 – Same genera as Cheng 1980.
Chiang 1964 – *Melia.*

(MELIACEAE)
Collardet 1929b – *Guarea.*
Croptier & Kučera 1990 – *Carapa, Cedrela, Entandrophragma.*
Cunha Mello 1950 [1951] – *Cabralea.*
Dadswell & Eckersley 1935 – *Cedrela, Dysoxylum, Melia.*
*Dadswell & Ellis 1939 – *Amoora, Carapa, Cedrela, Dysoxylum, Melia, Owenia, Synoum.*
Dahms 1989 – *Swietenia.*
*Datta & Samanta 1983 – 18 genera.
Dechamps 1985 – *Carapa, Cedrela, Guarea, Swietenia, Trichilia.*
Desch 1954 – 11 genera.
Détienne & Jacquet 1983 – *Cabralea, Carapa, Cedrela, Guarea, Ruagea, Swietenia, Trichilia.*
Détienne et al. 1982 – *Carapa, Cedrela, Guarea, Trichilia.*
Dixon 1919 – *Carapa, Cedrela, Dysoxylum, Entandrophragma, Khaya, Swietenia, Trichilia.*
Doležal 1959 – *Chukrasia.*
Donaldson 1984 – *Cedrela, Swietenia.*
Duchesne 1930 – *Khaya, Leplaea* (= *Guarea*).
Edlmann & Monaco 1981 – *Cedrela, Melia.*
Eeckhout 1951 – *Entandrophragma, Guarea, Khaya, Lovoa, Melia, Turraeanthus.*
Eggeling & Harris 1939 – *Carapa, Entandrophragma, Khaya, Lovoa.*
Espinoza de Pernía 1987a – *Cedrela, Toona.*
Fahn et al. 1986 – *Melia.*
Fanshawe 1947 – *Carapa.*
Fedalto et al. 1989 – *Carapa.*
Ferreirinha 1955 – *Khaya.*
Ferreirinha 1962 – *Melia.*
Fouarge & Gérard 1964 – *Entandrophragma, Lovoa, Trichilia.*
Fouarge et al. 1953 – *Carapa, Entandrophragma, Guarea, Turraeanthus.*
Freitas 1955, 1973 [1974] – *Cedrela.*
Freitas 1971 – *Khaya.*
Freitas 1987 – *Carapa.*
Fundter & Wisse 1977 – *Aglaia, Azadirachta, Toona.*
Furuno 1977, 1979 – *Aglaia, Amoora, Cedrela, Chisocheton, Dysoxylum, Sandoricum, Xylocarpus.*
Gaiotti de Peralta & Edlmann Abbate 1981 – *Carapa, Cedrela, Guarea, Swietenia.*

(MELIACEAE)

Garratt 1924 – *Dysoxylum.*
Gasson & Cheek 1992 – *Pseudobersama, Trichilia.*
Gill & Ogunlowo 1988 – *Aglaia, Amoora, Carapa, Cedrela.*
Gill & Onuja 1984d – *Entandrophragma, Guarea, Khaya, Lovoa.*
Giraud 1977a, 1979, 1980 – *Entandrophragma.*
Gleason & Panshin 1936 – *Swietenia.*
Gottwald & Schwab 1975 – *Entandrophragma.*
Greguss 1959 – *Melia.*
Grisa 1988 – *Neobeguea.*
Harms 1940 – Family.
Hayashi 1991 – *Melia.*
Hayashi et al. 1973 – *Aglaia, Amoora, Cedrela, Dysoxylum, Sandoricum, Xylocarpus.*
Hayashi & Nomura 1986 – *Chukrasia, Melia, Walsura.*
*Hedayetullah & Chakravarty 1942 – 10 genera.
Heimsch 1942 – 31 genera.
Hess 1950b – *Carapa, Swietenia.*
Hirai 1979–1985 – *Cedrela, Entandrophragma, Khaya, Melia, Swietenia.*
Huber & Rouschal 1954 – *Melia.*
Ilic 1991 – 28 genera.
Jayawardana 1932 – *Azadirachta, Chukrasia, Melia.*
Jenkin 1962 – *Vavaea.*
Kanehira 1921a – *Aglaia, Chisocheton, Dysoxylum, Melia.*
Kanehira 1921b – *Cedrela, Melia.*
Kanehira 1924 – *Aglaia, Amoora, Chisocheton, Dysoxylum, Melia, Reinwardtiodendron, Sandoricum, Toona, Xylocarpus.*
Kanehira 1926 – *Aglaia, Melia.*
Kobayashi & Sugawa 1963 – *Khaya, Swietenia, Toona.*
Kribs 1928a – *Carapa.*
*Kribs 1930 – 36 genera, 112 spp.
Kribs 1959 – 14 genera.
Lamb 1968, 1969 – *Cedrela.*
Lebacq 1963 – *Carapa, Ekebergia, Entandrophragma, Guarea, Khaya, Leplaea (= Guarea), Lovoa, Melia, Trichilia, Turraeanthus.*
Lebacq & Dechamps 1964 – 11 genera.

(MELIACEAE)

Lebacq & Dechamps 1967 – *Carapa, Entandrophragma, Guarea, Lovoa, Trichilia.*
Lebacq et al. 1973 – *Carapa, Cedrela, Guarea, Lovoa, Melia, Schmardaea, Swietenia.*
Lebacq & Istas 1950 – *Carapa, Entandrophragma, Guarea, Khaya, Leplaea (= Guarea), Lovoa, Trichilia, Turraeanthus.*
Lebacq & Staner 1964 – *Carapa, Entandrophragma, Khaya, Swietenia.*
Lebedenko 1962a – *Ekebergia.*
Lecomte 1922 – *Trichilia.*
Lecomte 1926a – *Aglaia, Chisocheton, Chukrasia, Dysoxylum, Sandoricum.*
Leroy 1960 – *Khaya, Neobeguea.*
Leroy 1964 – *Malleastrum.*
Liben & Dechamps 1966 – *Entandrophragma.*
Louis & Fouarge 1944, 1947, 1948 – *Entandrophragma, Guarea.*
Luo 1989 – *Aphanamixis, Chukrasia, Dysoxylum, Melia, Toona.*
Mainieri 1978 – *Cabralea, Carapa, Cedrela, Swietenia.*
Mainieri & Chimelo 1989 – *Cabralea, Carapa, Cedrela, Swietenia.*
Martawijaya et al. 1986 – *Swietenia.*
Martawijaya et al. 1989 – *Dysoxylum, Melia, Toona.*
Meylan & Butterfield 1978b – *Dysoxylum.*
Moll & Janssonius 1906–1936 – *Aglaia, Amoora, Carapa, Cedrela, Chisocheton, Dysoxylum, Lansium, Melia, Sandoricum, Walsura.*
Monteiro & Frade 1960 – *Khaya, Melia.*
Monteiro et al. 1962 – *Carapa.*
Nair 1988 – *Azadirachta.*
Nair 1991 [1992] – *Azadirachta, Melia, Soymida, Swietenia.*
Nardi Berti & Edlmann Abbate 1988 – *Carapa, Entandrophragma, Guarea, Khaya, Lovoa, Turraeanthus.*
Nardi Berti & Edlmann Abbate 1992 – *Cabralea, Carapa, Cedrela, Swietenia.*
Normand 1933a – *Guarea.*
Normand 1955 – *Carapa, Ekebergia, Entandrophragma, Guarea, Khaya, Lovoa, Trichilia, Turraeanthus.*
Normand & Paquis 1976 [1977] – *Carapa, Ekebergia, Entandrophragma, Guarea, Khaya, Leplaea (= Guarea), Lovoa, Melia, Trichilia, Turraeanthus.*

(MELIACEAE)

Normand & Sallenave 1958 – *Khaya, Swietenia.*

Ogata 1975–1983 – *Aglaia, Amoora, Azadirachta, Dysoxylum, Sandoricum, Xylocarpus.*

Ortega 1958 – *Guarea.*

Panshin 1932 – *Xylocarpus.*

*Panshin 1933 – *Chukrasia, Entandrophragma, Khaya, Lovoa, Pseudocedrela, Soymida, Swietenia.*

Patel 1974 – *Dysoxylum.*

Pearson & Brown 1932 – *Amoora, Azadirachta, Carapa, Cedrela, Chukrasia, Dysoxylum, Melia, Soymida.*

Pennington 1969 – *Vavaea.*

*Pennington & Styles 1975 – General; brief notes on many genera excluding Swietenioideae.

Pereira 1933 – *Cabralea, Cedrela.*

Pérez Mogollón 1973 – *Carapa, Cedrela, Trichilia.*

Pérez Mogollón 1993 – *Cedrela, Guarea.*

Pérez Olvera 1993 – *Cedrela.*

Pérez Olvera et al. 1980 [1981] – *Cedrela, Swietenia.*

Pfeiffer, J.P. 1926 – *Carapa, Cedrela, Guarea, Swietenia.*

Purkayastha et al. 1976 – *Aglaia, Amoora.*

Record 1921a – *Swietenia.*

Record 1931a – *Turraeanthus.*

*Record 1941a – *Cabralea, Carapa, Cedrela, Elutheria, Guarea, Swietenia, Trichilia.*

Record & Hess 1943 – Family (*Cabralea, Carapa, Cedrela, Elutheria, Guarea, Swietenia, Trichilia*).

Record & Mell 1924 – *Cabralea, Carapa, Cedrela, Guarea, Trichilia.*

Riera 1947 – *Entandrophragma, Khaya, Lovoa.*

Rock 1972 – *Swietenia.*

Rogel Gomez 1982 – *Guarea.*

Rozmarin et al. 1983 – *Entandrophragma, Khaya, Lovoa.*

Saiki 1982 – *Swietenia.*

Schmid 1915 – ?*Cedrela, Swietenia.*

Schmidt 1951–1952 – *Cedrela, Entandrophragma, Guarea, Khaya, Turraeanthus.*

Schweingruber 1990 – *Melia.*

Scott 1927 – *Ekebergia, Trichilia.*

Shimaji & Itoh 1988 – *Melia.*

Sieber 1985 – *Khaya* (root).

(MELIACEAE)

Stahel 1971 – *Khaya* (root).

Sudo 1959 – *Cedrela, Melia.*

Sudo 1963 – 18 genera.

Sudo 1988 – *Aglaia, Amoora, Chisocheton, Dysoxylum, Sandoricum, Swietenia, Toona, Xylocarpus.*

Tang 1973 – *Aglaia, Aphanamixis, Chukrasia, Dysoxylum, Melia, Toona.*

Tewari 1992 – *Azadirachta* (summary of literature).

Tomazello Filho et al. 1983 – *Cedrela.*

Tôrres 1941 – *Dysoxylum, Melia.*

Tortorelli 1956 – *Cabralea, Cedrela.*

Vales & Carreras 1986 – *Swietenia, Trichilia.*

Van der Slooten 1968 – *Carapa.*

Van der Slooten & Gonzalez 1970 [1971] – *Carapa.*

Verna 1979 – *Cabralea, Cedrela, Guarea, Trichilia.*

Wagenführ & Scheiber 1974 – *Carapa, Cedrela, Chukrasia, Entandrophragma, Guarea, Khaya, Lovoa, Swietenia, Turraeanthus.*

Wagenführ & Steiger 1963 – *Entandrophragma, Khaya, Swietenia.*

Wagenführ & Steiger 1986 – *Entandrophragma.*

Wang 1984–1988 – *Aglaia, Amoora, Azadirachta, Cedrela, Dysoxylum, Toona.*

Webber 1936b – *Kirkia* (or in Simaroubaceae).

Williams 1936 – *Carapa, Cedrela, Guarea, Swietenia, Trichilia.*

Wiraj Chunwarin & Damrong Sri-Aran 1973 – *Aglaia, Amoora, Azadirachta, Cedrela, Chukrasia, Melia, Sandoricum, Walsura, Xylocarpus.*

Wuang 1979 – *Melia, Toona.*

Yamabayashi 1938 – *Melia, Toona.*

Yao 1988 – *Aglaia, Melia, Toona.*

Crystals and silica

Chattaway 1955 – *Cedrela, Entandrophragma, Toona.*

Chattaway 1956 – 27 genera.

Espinoza de Pernía 1987b – *Carapa, Cedrela, Guarea, Swietenia, Trichilia.*

Meniado et al. 1970 – *Aglaia, Azadirachta, Dysoxylum, Melia, Sandoricum, Vavaea, Xylocarpus.*

(MELIACEAE)
Scurfield et al. 1974 – *Aphanamixis.*
Welle 1976b – *Guarea, Trichilia.*

Ecological anatomy
Barajas Morales 1985 – *Guarea, Trichilia.*
Den Outer & Van Veenendaal 1976 –
    Carapa, Trichilia.
Van der Graaff & Baas 1974 – *Melia.*

Growth rings
Détienne 1989 – *Cedrela, Entandrophragma,*
    Guarea, Khaya, Lovoa.
Détienne & Mariaux 1977 – *Cedrela, Entan-*
    drophragma, Guarea, Khaya, Lovoa.
Hummel 1946 – *Entandrophragma, Khaya.*

Helical thickenings
Nair 1987 – *Azadirachta, Melia, Soymida,*
    Swietenia.
Ohtani & Ishida 1978b – *Cedrela, Melia.*

Pits and perforation plates
Meylan & Butterfield 1974 – *Dysoxylum.*
Nair & Ram 1989 – *Soymida.*
Ohtani & Ishida 1978a – *Cedrela, Melia.*

Rays
Giraud 1977b – *Entandrophragma.*

Secretory canals
Groom 1926 – *Carapa, Lovoa.*

Septate fibres
Butterfield & Meylan 1976 – *Dysoxylum.*

Tracheary elements
Jing et al. 1989 – *Chukrasia, Melia, Toona.*
Ohtani 1983 – *Cedrela, Melia.*

MELIANTHACEAE (*Bersama* only)

Heimsch 1942.
Ilic 1991.
Lebacq & Dechamps 1964.
Normand 1955.
Normand & Paquis 1976 [1977].

MELIOSMACEAE
(for *Sabia* see SABIACEAE)
(*Meliosma* only unless otherwise indicated)

Cheng, J.-Q. 1980.
Cheng, J.-Q. et al. 1992.
Dadswell & Record 1936.
Desch 1954.

(MELIOSMACEAE)
Hayashi 1991.
Heimsch 1942 – *Meliosma, Ophiocaryon.*
Ilic 1991.
Kanehira 1921a, b, 1926.
Kobayashi 1949.
Lecomte 1926a.
Luo 1989.
Moll & Janssonius 1906–1936.
Pérez Mogollón 1993.
Record & Hess 1943.
Shimaji & Itoh 1988.
Sudo 1959.
Watari 1950 – *Meliosma* 12 spp.
Williams 1936 – *Ophiocaryon.*
Wu & Wang 1976.
Wuang 1979.
Yamabayashi 1938.
Yao 1988.

Ecological anatomy
Versteegh 1968.

Perforation plates
Ohtani & Ishida 1978a.

Silica
Espinoza de Pernía 1987b.
Welle 1976b.

Tracheary elements
Jing et al. 1989.
Ohtani 1983.

MENISPERMACEAE

Bonde & Upadhye 1989 – *Tinospora.*
Dechamps 1985 – *Abuta, Anomospermum,*
    Chondrodendron, Sciadotenia, Telitoxi-
    cum.
Détienne & Jacquet 1983 – *Abuta.*
Détienne et al. 1982 – *Abuta.*
Fahn et al. 1986 – *Cocculus.*
Garratt 1933b – Family.
Lebacq & Dechamps 1964 – *Penianthus.*
Lecomte 1922 – *Burasaia.*
*Mennega 1982 – 15 genera.
Moll & Janssonius 1906–1936 – *Cocculus.*
Record & Hess 1943 – Family (*Abuta,*
    Hyperbaena).
Saint-Laurent 1932a – *Cocculus.*
Singh 1945 – *Tiliacora.*
Williams 1936 – *Abuta.*

(MENISPERMACEAE)

Anomalous structure

Chalk & Chattaway 1937 – Family (*Abuta, Cocculus, Hyperbaena, Tiliacora*).

Kundu & Guha 1975 [1978] – *Tiliacora.*

Obaton 1960 – *Rhigiocarya, Stephania, Tiliacora, Triclisia.*

Pfeiffer 1925 – *Abuta.*

Ravololomaniraka & Koechlin 1970 – *Cissampelos.*

Santos 1931 – *Anamirta, Arcangelisia.*

Van der Walt et al. 1970 – *Cocculus.*

Ecological anatomy

Baas et al. 1983 – *Cocculus.*

Carlquist 1985 [1986]a – General.

MISODENDRACEAE (*Misodendron*)

*Carlquist 1985c – 9 spp.

MOLLUGINACEAE see AIZOACEAE

MONIMIACEAE

(incl. ATHEROSPERMATACEAE)

Araujo & Mattos Filho 1973c – *Bracteanthus, Siparuna.*

Araujo & Mattos Filho 1973–1977 – *Bracteanthus.*

Araujo & Mattos Filho 1974a, b – *Mollinedia, Siparuna.*

Brazier & Franklin 1961 – *Laurelia.*

Dadswell & Eckersley 1935 – *Atherosperma, Daphnandra, Doryphora.*

Dechamps 1985 – *Siparuna.*

Den Outer & Van Veenendaal 1982 – 10 genera.

Détienne & Jacquet 1983 – *Bracteanthus, Siparuna.*

Détienne et al. 1982 – *Siparuna.*

Díaz-Vaz 1988a, b – *Laurelia.*

Garratt 1924 – *Laurelia.*

Garratt 1933b – Family (11 genera).

*Garratt 1934 – Family (12 genera).

Gasson & Cutler 1990 – *Laurelia* (root).

Ilic 1991 – *Atherosperma, Daphnandra, Doryphora, Dryadodaphne, Hedycarya, Kibara, Laurelia, Levieria, Siparuna, Xymalos.*

Lebacq 1955 – *Xymalos.*

Lebacq & Dechamps 1964 – *Xymalos.*

(MONIMIACEAE)

Lebacq et al. 1973 – *Mollinedia, Siparuna.*

Lecomte 1922 – *Tambourissa.*

Lemesle 1956b – Notes on 16 genera.

Lemesle 1963b – *Monimia.*

*Lemesle & Pichard 1954 – 17 genera.

Metcalfe 1987 – General survey.

Meylan & Butterfield 1978b – *Hedycarya, Laurelia.*

Moll & Janssonius 1906–1936 – *Kibara.*

*Money et al. 1950 – c. 20 genera (some young stems).

Nardi Berti & Edlmann Abbate 1992 – *Laurelia.*

Ortiz Cespedes 1959 – *Laurelia.*

Patel 1973 – *Hedycarya, Laurelia.*

Rancusi et al. 1987 – *Laurelia, Peumus.*

Record & Hess 1943 – Family (*Boldea* [= *Peumus*], *Bracteanthus, Laurelia, Mollinedia, Siparuna*).

Scott 1927 – *Xymalos.*

Stern 1954 – Relations.

Sudo 1963 – *Doryphora, Laurelia.*

Sudo 1988 – *Dryadodaphne.*

Wagemann 1949 – *Laurelia, Peumus.*

Wagenführ & Scheiber 1974 – *Laurelia.*

Welch 1929b – *Atherosperma, Daphnandra, Doryphora, Hedycarya, Mollinedia.*

Williams 1936 – *Mollinedia, Siparuna.*

Crystals

Chattaway 1955 – *Tetrasynandra.*

Chattaway 1956 – *Hedycarya, Kibara, Matthaea, Tetrasynandra.*

Scurfield et al. 1973 – *Tetrasynandra.*

Pits and perforation plates

Carlquist 1992d – *Atherosperma.*

Meylan & Butterfield 1974 – *Hedycarya, Laurelia.*

Septate fibres

Butterfield & Meylan 1976 – *Hedycarya, Laurelia.*

MONTINIACEAE

*Carlquist 1989d – *Kaliphora* (twig), *Montinia.*

Milne-Redhead 1956 – *Grevea, Montinia* (anatomy by C.R. Metcalfe).

Rakouth 1989 – *Grevea, Kaliphora, Montinia.* [Abstr.]

MORACEAE (incl. CECROPIACEAE)
(*Chlorophora = Maclura, Cudrania =
Maclura, Bosqueia = Trilepisium*)

Anon. 1955–1959 – *Chlorophora.*
Anon. 1966 – *Morus.*
Anon. 1977a – *Antiaris, Artocarpus,
Parartocarpus.*
Anon. 1981 (Andes) – *Brosimum, Chloro-
phora, Clarisia, Ficus, Poulsenia, Pseud-
olmedia.*
Anon. 1981 (Curua) – *Clarisia.*
Abbate 1964 – *Ficus.*
Abbate & Cavina 1980 – *Artocarpus.*
Aubréville et al. 1947 – *Chlorophora.*
Ayensu & Bentum 1974 – *Antiaris, Chloro-
phora, Musanga.*
Balan Menon 1955 – *Artocarpus.*
Balan Menon 1959 – *Artocarpus, Pararto-
carpus.*
Barajas Morales & Echenique-Manrique
1976 – *Brosimum, Poulsenia, Trophis.*
Barajas Morales & León Gómez 1989 –
Chlorophora.
Bargagli-Petrucci 1903 – *Artocarpus, Sloe-
tia (= Streblus).*
Benoist 1931 – *Bagassa, Cecropia, Ficus,
Helicostylis, Noyera (= Perebea), Pirati-
nera (= Brosimum), Pourouma, Pseud-
olmedia.*
Berg et al. 1990 – *Coussapoa* (anatomy by
K. Bonsen).
*Bonsen & Welle 1983 – *Cecropia* 10 spp.,
Coussapoa 8, *Musanga* 2, *Myrianthus* 4,
Poikilospermum 4, *Pourouma* c. 17.
Boulton & Price 1931 – *Chlorophora.*
Brazier & Franklin 1961 – *Antiaris, Artocar-
pus, Bosqueia, Brosimum, Chlorophora,
Maclura, Morus, Piratinera (= Brosimum).*
Brown 1922 – *Artocarpus.*
Burgerstein 1909 – *Antiaris, Artocarpus,
Ficus.*
Burgerstein 1912 – *Maclura.*
Carreras & Vales 1986b – *Ficus, Pseudol-
media.*
Cellai 1967 – *Ficus.*
Cheng, C. 1985 – *Artocarpus, Morus.*
Cheng, J.-Q. 1980 – *Artocarpus, Brousso-
netia, Cudrania, Ficus, Morus, Streblus.*
Cheng, J.-Q. et al. 1992 – Same genera as
Cheng 1980 + *Antiaris.*
Chudnoff 1956 – *Ficus.*

(MORACEAE)
Cockrell 1942 – *Artocarpus, Ficus, Sloetia
(= Streblus).*
Cutler et al. 1987 – *Ficus, Morus* (root).
Dadswell & Eckersley 1935 – *Ficus, Pseu-
domorus (= Streblus).*
Dechamps 1985 – 15 genera (incl. *Cecropia,*
etc.)
Desch 1954 – *Antiaris, Artocarpus, Cudra-
nia, Ficus, Parartocarpus, Prainea, Sloetia
(= Streblus), Taxotrophis (= Streblus).*
Détienne & Jacquet 1983 – 22 genera (incl.
Cecropia, etc.).
Détienne et al. 1982 – 10 genera (incl. *Cecro-
pia,* etc.).
Dixon 1919 – *Chlorophora.*
Edlmann & Monaco 1981 – *Morus.*
Edlmann Abbate & De Luca 1981 – *Arto-
carpus.*
Eeckhout 1951 – *Chlorophora, Morus,
Musanga.*
Eggeling & Harris 1939 – *Chlorophora.*
Fahn et al. 1986 – *Ficus, Morus.*
Fasolo 1939–1940 – *Ficus.*
Fedalto et al. 1989 – *Brosimum, Maquira.*
Ferreirinha 1955 – *Chlorophora, Morus.*
Ferreirinha 1958 – *Morus.*
Flamigni 1948 – *Morus.*
Flores Rodríguez 1968 – *Pseudolmedia.*
Fouarge & Gérard 1964 – *Antiaris, Bos-
queia, Chlorophora, Ficus, Musanga.*
Fouarge et al. 1953 – *Chlorophora, Mu-
sanga.*
Freitas 1958, 1963 – *Artocarpus, Ficus.*
Freitas 1971 – *Chlorophora.*
Freitas 1987 – *Artocarpus, Chlorophora.*
Furuno 1977 – *Antiaris, Artocarpus,
Ficus.*
Furuno 1985, 1987 – *Maclura, Morus.*
Gasson & Cutler 1990 – *Broussonetia,
Maclura* (root).
Gill & Ogunlowo 1988 – *Artocarpus.*
Giordano 1939 – *Bosqueia, Morus.*
Gómez 1959 – *Brosimum, Ficus, Pseudol-
media.*
Greguss 1959 – *Broussonetia, Ficus,
Maclura, Morus.*
Grisa 1988 – *Allaeanthus (= Broussonetia).*
Grosser 1977 – *Morus.*
Grosser 1983, 1984 – *Ficus.*
Hayashi 1991 – *Broussonetia, Ficus,
Morus.*

(MORACEAE)

Hayashi et al. 1973 – *Artocarpus, Ficus, Parartocarpus, Streblus.*

Hayashi & Nomura 1986 – *Artocarpus.*

Hirai 1979–1985 – *Artocarpus, Broussonetia, Ficus, Morus.*

Hoheisel et al. 1968 – *Clarisia, Pourouma, Pseudolmedia.*

Huber & Rouschal 1954 – *Ficus, Morus.*

Ilic 1991 – 21 genera.

Jacquiot et al. 1973 – *Ficus, Morus.*

Jagiella & Kurschner 1987 – *Ficus.*

Jayawardana 1932 – *Artocarpus.*

Jentsch et al. 1936–1939 – *Chlorophora, Musanga.*

Joshi 1987 – *Ficus* (branches).

Joshi 1988 – *Artocarpus, Ficus, Maclura, Morus, Streblus* (branches).

Kachroo & Bhat 1982 – *Ficus.*

Kanehira 1921a – *Artocarpus, Broussonetia, Cudrania, Ficus, Morus.*

Kanehira 1921b – *Ficus, Morus.*

Kanehira 1924 – *Artocarpus, Ficus, Gymnartocarpus* (= *Parartocarpus*).

Kanehira 1926 – *Artocarpus, Ficus, Morus.*

Kedrov 1971 – *Ficus.*

*Koek-Noorman et al. 1984a – *Antiaris, Castilla, Helicostylis, Maquira, Mesogyne, Naucleopsis, Perebea, Pseudolmedia.*

*Koek-Noorman et al. 1984b – *Bosqueiopsis, Brosimum, Dorstenia, Helianthostylis, Trilepisium, Trymatococcus.*

*Koek-Noorman et al. 1984c – *Ficus* 25 spp.

Kribs 1928a – *Ficus.*

Kribs 1959 – *Antiaris, Artocarpus, Bagassa, Brosimum, Chlorophora, Clarisia, Helicostylis, Musanga, Piratinera* (= *Brosimum*), *Trophis.*

Lebacq 1955 – *Antiaris, Bosqueia, Chlorophora, Ficus, Morus, Musanga, Myrianthus, Treculia.*

Lebacq & Dechamps 1964 – *Antiaris, Bosqueia, Bosqueiopsis, Chlorophora, Ficus, Morus, Musanga, Myrianthus, Treculia.*

Lebacq & Dechamps 1967 – 11 genera.

Lebacq et al. 1973 – 12 genera.

Lebacq & Staner 1964 – *Brosimum, Chlorophora, Morus, Treculia.*

Lecomte 1922 – *Bosqueia, Ficus.*

Lecomte 1926a – *Artocarpus, Broussonetia, Cudrania, Ficus, Morus.*

(MORACEAE)

Lepe 1959 – *Brosimum, Ficus, Pseudolmedia.*

Leroy 1960 – *Morus.*

Luo 1989 – *Antiaris, Artocarpus, Ficus, Morus.*

Mainieri 1960, 1962 – *Brosimum.*

Mainieri 1978 – *Brosimum, Chlorophora, Clarisia, Ficus.*

Mainieri & Chimelo 1989 – *Bagassa, Brosimum, Cecropia, Chlorophora, Clarisia, Ficus.*

Martin 1953 – *Musanga, Myrianthus.*

*Mennega & Lanzing-Vinkenborg 1977 – *Castilla, Helicostylis, Maquira, Naucleopsis, Olmedia* (= *Trophis*), *Perebea, Pseudolmedia.*

Meylan & Butterfield 1978b – *Paratrophis* (= *Streblus*).

Moll & Janssonius 1906–1936 – *Antiaris, Artocarpus, Ficus, Gymnartocarpus* (= *Parartocarpus*), *Morus, Streblus.*

Monteiro & Frade 1960 – *Bosqueia, Chlorophora, Musanga.*

Monteiro & França 1971 – *Morus, Musanga.*

Nájero Angulo & López Fraile 1969 – *Morus.*

Nardi Berti & Edlmann Abbate 1988 – *Antiaris, Chlorophora, Morus.*

Nardi Berti & Edlmann Abbate 1992 – *Bagassa, Brosimum, Chlorophora, Clarisia.*

Niloofari 1961 – *Ficus, Maclura, Morus.*

Normand 1934 – *Morus.*

Normand 1950b – *Antiaris, Bosqueia, Chlorophora, Ficus, Morus, Musanga, Myrianthus, Treculia.*

Normand & Paquis 1976 [1977] – 10 genera.

Novruzova 1962c – *Ficus.*

Ogata 1975–1983 – *Antiaris, Artocarpus, Ficus, Parartocarpus.*

Ortega et al. 1988 – *Ficus.*

Ortega 1958 – *Ficus, Poulsenia.*

Panshin & Zeeuw 1980 – *Maclura, Morus.*

Parsa Pajouh & Schweingruber 1985 – *Ficus, Morus.*

Patel & Bowles 1978 – *Paratrophis* (= *Streblus*).

Pearson & Brown 1932 – *Artocarpus, Ficus, Morus.*

Pérez Mogollón 1973, 1993 – *Ficus.*

Pérez Olvera et al. 1980 [1981] – *Brosimum, Maclura.*

(MORACEAE)

Pfeiffer, J.P. 1926 – *Bagassa, Piratinera*
  (= *Brosimum*).
Pfeiffer 1953 – *Cecropia, Chlorophora,*
  Ficus, Maclura, Morus, Sorocea.
Prakash 1972 – *Artocarpus* (root).
Purkayastha et al. 1976 – *Artocarpus.*
Record 1932a – *Brosimum, Helico-*
  stylis.
*Record & Hess 1940a – Family (27
  genera, incl. *Cecropia*, etc.).
Record & Hess 1943 – Family (30 genera).
Record & Mell 1924 – 11 genera.
Riera 1947 – *Chlorophora.*
Rozmarin et al. 1983 – *Chlorophora.*
Saint-Laurent 1928, 1932a, 1934 – *Ficus,*
  Morus.
Schmid 1915 – *Chlorophora.*
Schmidt 1951–1952 – *Chlorophora.*
Schweingruber 1990 – *Ficus, Morus.*
Senni 1905 – *Ficus.*
Shah & Kachroo 1979 – *Ficus, Morus.*
Sharma 1962 – *Artocarpus.*
Shimaji & Itoh 1982, 1988 – *Ficus, Morus.*
Silva 1991 – *Ficus.*
Steigleder 1970 – *Chlorophora, Ficus,*
  Sorocea.
Sudo 1959 – *Broussonetia, Ficus, Morus.*
Sudo 1963 – *Allaeanthus* (= *Broussonetia*),
  Antiaris, Artocarpus, Brosimum, Cecro-
  pia, Chlorophora, Clarisia, Piratinera
  (= *Brosimum*).
Sudo 1988 – *Antiaris, Artocarpus, Ficus,*
  Parartocarpus.
Sudworth & Mell 1911c – *Chlorophora,*
  Toxylon (= *Maclura*).
Sugawa 1968c – *Artocarpus.*
Tang 1973 – *Antiaris, Artocarpus, Ficus,*
  Morus, Pseudostreblus (= *Streblus*),
  Streblus.
Thunell & Perem 1947 – *Chlorophora.*
*Tippo 1938 – Family (50 genera, 100 spp.).
Tomazello Filho et al. 1983 – *Bagassa.*
Tondeur 1939 – *Chlorophora.*
Topper & Koek-Noorman 1980 – *Artocar-*
  pus, Bagassa.
Tortorelli 1956 – *Chlorophora.*
Vales & Carreras 1987 – *Pseudolmedia.*
Van der Slooten 1968 – *Brosimum, Ficus,*
  Poulsenia.
Van der Slooten & Gonzalez 1970 [1971] –
  Brosimum.

(MORACEAE)

Van der Slooten & Gonzalez 1971 – *Ficus,*
  Poulsenia.
Wagenführ & Scheiber 1974 – *Antiaris,*
  Chlorophora, Musanga.
Wang 1966 – *Morus.*
Wang 1984–1988 – *Antiaris, Artocarpus.*
Welle 1985 – *Streblus.*
*Welle et al. 1986 – Moreae (22+ genera).
Williams 1936 – 17 genera (incl. *Cecropia,*
  etc.).
Wiraj Chunwarin & Damrong Sri-Aran 1974
  – *Artocarpus.*
Wu & Wang 1976 – *Broussonetia, Morus.*
Wuang 1979 – *Broussonetia, Cudrania,*
  Morus.
Yamabayashi 1938 – *Broussonetia, Cudra-*
  nia, Morus.
Yao 1988 – *Antiaris, Morus.*
Yatsenko-Khmelevsky 1954a – *Brousso-*
  netia, Ficus, Maclura, Morus.
Zamuco 1967 – *Antiaris, Artocarpus,*
  Broussonetia.

Crystals

Chattaway 1956 – 12 genera.
Espinoza de Pernía 1987b – *Brosimum,*
  Cecropia, Chlorophora, Clarisia, Ficus,
  Pourouma.
Rao, K.K. & Ramayya 1984 – *Ficus.*

Ecological anatomy

Baas et al. 1983 – *Ficus.*
Baas & Schweingruber 1987 – *Ficus,*
  Morus.
Barajas Morales 1985 – *Brosimum, Cecro-*
  pia, Chlorophora, Poulsenia, Trophis.
Carlquist 1985 [1986]a – *Ficus.*
Den Outer & Van Veenendaal 1976 – *Ficus.*
Novruzova 1968 – *Ficus, Morus.*
Van der Graaff & Baas 1974 – *Streblus.*
Worbes 1986 – *Sorocea.*

Growth rings

Détienne 1976b, 1989 – *Chlorophora.*
Worbes 1984 *Sorocea.*

Helical thickenings

Meylan & Butterfield 1978a – *Paratrophis*
  (= *Streblus*).
Nair 1987 – *Ficus.*
Ohtani & Ishida 1978b – *Broussonetia,*
  Ficus, Morus.
Parham & Kaustinen 1973 – *Morus.*

(MORACEAE)

Laticifers

Fujii 1988 – *Antiaris, Artocarpus, Ficus, Parartocarpus.*

Pits and perforation plates

Meylan & Butterfield 1974 – *Paratrophis* (= *Streblus*).
Ohtani & Ishida 1978a – *Broussonetia, Ficus, Morus.*

Silica

Scurfield et al. 1974 – *Artocarpus.*
Sudo et al. 1967 – *Artocarpus, Sloetia* (= *Streblus*).

Tracheary elements

Ohtani 1983 – *Broussonetia, Ficus, Morus.*

MORINGACEAE (*Moringa*)

Cellai 1971.
Dutt et al. 1978.
Fahn et al. 1986.
Gill et al. 1985a.
Jagiella & Kurschner 1987.
Moll & Janssonius 1906–1936.

Ecological anatomy

Baas et al. 1983.

MYOPORACEAE

Brown 1922 – *Myoporum.*
*Carlquist & Hoekman 1986b – *Bontia, Eremophila, Myoporum.*
Ilic 1991 – *Eremophila, Myoporum.*
Metcalfe 1935 – *Eremophila.*
Meylan & Butterfield 1978b – *Myoporum.*
Record & Hess 1943 – *Bontia.*

Ecological anatomy

Carlquist 1977c – *Eremophila, Myoporum.*

Pits and perforation plates

Meylan & Butterfield 1974, 1975 – *Myoporum.*

MYRICACEAE

(*Myrica* only unless otherwise stated)

Abbate 1963.
Abbe & Abbe 1971.
Carreras & Vales 1986b, 1987.
Cheng, J.-Q. 1980.

(MYRICACEAE)

Cheng, J.-Q. et al. 1992.
Dechamps 1985.
Desch 1954.
Détienne & Jacquet 1983.
Friedman 1978.
Giordano 1939.
Greguss 1959.
Hayashi 1991.
Hirai 1979–1985.
Ilic 1991.
Kanehira 1921a, b, 1926.
Lecomte 1926a.
Moll & Janssonius 1906–1936.
Moseley 1973 [1974] – Relations.
Müller-Stoll & Mädel 1962 – Extant and fossil spp.
Nájera Angulo 1959.
Peraza Oramas & Lopez de Roma 1967.
Record & Hess 1943.
Schweingruber 1990.
Shimaji & Itoh 1988.
Sudo 1959.
Suzuki et al. 1991.
Vales et al. 1982.
Wu & Wang 1976.
Yamabayashi 1938.

Ecological anatomy

Baas & Schweingruber 1987.
Carlquist & Hoekman 1985a.
Versteegh 1968.

Perforation plates

Ohtani & Ishida 1978a.

Rays

Braun & den Outer 1965.

Tracheary elements

Muhammad 1984 – *Comptonia.*
Ohtani 1983.

MYRISTICACEAE (*Dialyanthera* = *Otoba*)

Anon. 1977a – 15 genera.
Anon. 1981 (Andes) – *Dialyanthera, Virola.*
Alves de Pinho 1969 – *Virola.*
*Armstrong & Wilson 1980 – *Horsfieldia* 31 spp.
Balan Menon 1959 – *Gymnacranthera, Horsfieldia, Knema, Myristica.*
Bargagli-Petrucci 1903 – *Myristica.*
Benoist 1931 – *Myristica.*

(MYRISTICACEAE)
Brazier & Franklin 1961 – *Pycnanthus, Staudtia, Virola.*
Burgerstein 1909 – *Myristica.*
Cheng, J.-Q. 1980 – *Knema.*
Cheng, J.-Q. et al. 1992 – *Knema.*
Cunha Mello 1950 [1951], 1971a – *Virola.*
Dechamps 1985 – *Dialyanthera, Iryanthera, Osteophloeum, Virola.*
Desch 1954 – *Gymnacranthera, Horsfieldia, Knema, Myristica.*
Détienne & Jacquet 1983 – *Dialyanthera, Iryanthera, Osteophloeum, Virola.*
Détienne et al. 1982 – *Iryanthera, Virola.*
Eeckhout 1951 – *Pycnanthus, Staudtia.*
Fedalto et al. 1989 – *Iryanthera, Virola.*
Ferreirinha 1962 – *Staudtia.*
Fouarge & Gérard 1964 – *Pycnanthus, Staudtia.*
Freitas 1987 – *Pycnanthus, Staudtia.*
Furuno 1977 – *Horsfieldia, Myristica.*
*Garratt 1933a – Family (15 genera).
*Garratt 1933b – Family and relations.
Hayashi et al. 1973 – *Gymnacranthera, Horsfieldia, Knema, Myristica.*
Hoheisel et al. 1968 – *Virola.*
Honda 1971 [1972] – *Virola.*
Ilic 1991 – 10 genera.
Jentsch et al. 1936 – *Pycnanthus, Staudtia.*
Kanehira 1921a – *Myristica.*
Kanehira 1924 – *Knema, Myristica.*
Kanehira 1926 – *Myristica.*
Kribs 1928a – *Virola.*
Kribs 1959 – *Dialyanthera, Iryanthera, Myristica, Pycnanthus, Staudtia, Virola.*
Lebacq 1955 – *Coelocaryon, Pycnanthus, Staudtia.*
Lebacq & Dechamps 1964 – *Coelocaryon, Pycnanthus, Staudtia.*
Lebacq & Dechamps 1967 – *Coelocaryon, Pycnanthus.*
Lebacq et al. 1973 – *Dialyanthera, Iryanthera, Osteophloeum, Virola.*
Lecomte 1926a – *Horsfieldia, Knema.*
Lisboa 1982, 1990 – *Iryanthera.*
*Lisboa 1989b – *Iryanthera* 21 spp.
*Loureiro et al. 1989 – *Virola* 24 spp.
Luo 1989 – *Horsfieldia.*
Mainieri 1962 – *Iryanthera, Osteophloeum, Virola.*
Mainieri 1978 – *Virola.*
Mainieri & Chimelo 1989 – *Virola.*

(MYRISTICACEAE)
Metcalfe 1987 – General survey.
Moll & Janssonius 1906–1936 – *Myristica.*
Nardi Berti & Edlmann Abbate 1988 – *Coelocaryon, Pycnanthus, Scyphocephalium, Staudtia.*
Nardi Berti & Edlmann Abbate 1992 – *Dialyanthera, Virola.*
Normand 1933b – *Coelocaryon, Scyphocephalium.*
Normand 1950b – *Coelocaryon, Pycnanthus.*
Normand & Paquis 1976 [1977] – *Coelocaryon, Pycnanthus, Scyphocephalium, Staudtia.*
Ogata 1975–1983 – Family.
Paula 1979, 1981 – *Virola.*
Pearson & Brown 1932 – *Myristica.*
Pereira et al. 1970 – *Virola.*
Pfeiffer, J.P. 1926 – *Iryanthera, Virola.*
*Rao, R.V. et al. 1992a – *Gymnacranthera, Horsfieldia, Knema, Myristica* and notes on 5 other genera.
Record 1932a – *Iryanthera.*
Record & Hess 1943 – Family (*Compsoneura, Dialyanthera, Iryanthera, Osteophloeum, Virola*).
Richter et al. 1975 – *Virola.*
Riera 1947 – *Pycnanthus, Staudtia.*
Rodrigues 1972 – *Virola.*
Rozmarin et al. 1983 – *Staudtia.*
Schmidt 1951–1952 – *Pycnanthus, Staudtia, Virola.*
Siddiqi & Wilson 1974 – *Knema.*
Stern 1954 – Relations.
Sudo 1963 – *Dialyanthera, Iryanthera, Myristica, Pycnanthus, Virola.*
Sudo 1988 – *Horsfieldia, Myristica.*
Tang 1973 – *Horsfieldia, Knema.*
Tavares, S. & E.J.S. 1967 – *Virola.*
Teles & Paula 1980 – *Virola.*
Van der Slooten 1968 – *Virola.*
Van der Slooten & Gonzalez 1970 [1971] – *Virola.*
Vander Wyk & Canright 1956 – Relations.
Wagenführ & Scheiber 1974 – *Pycnanthus, Staudtia, Virola.*
Wang 1984–1988 – *Myristica.*
Williams 1936 – *Compsoneura, Iryanthera, Osteophloeum, Virola.*
Wiraj Chunwarin & Damrong Sri-Aran 1974 – *Myristica.*

(MYRISTICACEAE)
Wu & Tsai 1973 – *Myristica*.
Yao 1988 – *Horsfieldia*.

Anomalous structure
Obaton 1960 – *Pycnanthus*.

Growth rings
Détienne 1989 – *Virola*.

Silica
Sudo et al. 1967 – *Myristica*.

Tannin tubes
Fujii 1988 – *Horsfieldia, Iryanthera, Knema, Myristica, Virola*.

Tracheary elements
Gill & Onuja 1984a – *Pycnanthus*.
Lisboa et al. 1987 – *Compsoneura, Iryanthera, Osteophloeum, Otoba, Virola*.

MYROTHAMNACEAE (*Myrothamnus*)

Carlquist 1976a.
Tippo 1938.

MYRSINACEAE
(*Conomorpha = Cybianthus*)

Anon. 1981 (Andes) – *Ardisia*.
Babos & Borhidi 1978 – *Myrsine*.
Brazier & Franklin 1961 – *Rapanea*.
Brown 1922 – *Myrsine*.
Chalk et al. 1935 – *Rapanea*.
Cheng, J.-Q. 1980 – *Ardisia, Rapanea*.
Cheng, J.-Q. et al. 1992 – *Ardisia, Rapanea*.
Dechamps 1985 – *Conomorpha, Rapanea, Weigeltia* (= *Cybianthus*).
Desch 1954 – *Aegiceras, Ardisia*.
Détienne & Jacquet 1983 – *Conomorpha, Cybianthus, Rapanea*.
Détienne et al. 1982 – *Conomorpha, Rapanea*.
Hayashi 1991 – *Rapanea*.
Hirai 1979–1985 – *Myrsine*.
Ilic 1991 – *Ardisia, Conandrium, Rapanea, Stylogyne*.
Jagiella & Kurschner 1987 – *Maesa*.
Kanehira 1921a – *Ardisia, Rapanea*.
Lebacq & Dechamps 1964 – *Maesa*.
Lecomte 1922 – *Oncostemum*.

(MYRSINACEAE)
Lomibao 1978 – *Aegiceras*.
Luo 1989 – *Rapanea*.
Meylan & Butterfield 1978b – *Myrsine*.
Moll & Janssonius 1906–1936 – *Aegiceras, Ardisia, Maesa, Myrsine, Pimelandra* (= *Ardisia*).
Normand 1960 – *Maesa*.
Panshin 1932 – *Aegiceras*.
Peraza Oramas & Lopez de Roma 1967 – *Heberdenia, Myrsine*.
Pipoly 1983, 1987 – *Cybianthus*.
Record & Hess 1943 – Family (*Ardisia, Conomorpha, Cybianthus, Geissanthus, Grammadenia* (= *Cybianthus*), *Parathesis, Rapanea, Stylogyne, Wallenia* (= *Cybianthus*)).
Scott 1927 – *Myrsine*.
Shimaji & Itoh 1988 – *Myrsine*.
Sudo 1959 – *Rapanea*.
Suzuki & Noshiro 1988 – *Maesa*.
Tang 1973 – *Rapanea*.
Williams 1928 – *Cybianthus*.
Williams 1936 – *Conomorpha, Rapanea, Stylogyne*.
Wu & Wang 1976 – *Myrsine*.

Crystals
Chattaway 1955 – *Aegiceras*.
Chattaway 1956 – *Aegiceras, Discocalyx, Rapanea, Suttonia* (= *Myrsine*), *Tapeinosperma*.

Ecological anatomy
Versteegh 1968 – *Maesa, Myrsine*.

Helical thickenings
Meylan & Butterfield 1978a – *Myrsine*.
Ohtani & Ishida 1978b – *Myrsine*.

Pits and perforation plates
Meylan & Butterfield 1974, 1975 – *Myrsine*.
Ohtani & Ishida 1978a – *Myrsine*.

Rays
Dayal et al. 1984 – *Embelia, Myrsine*.

Septate fibres
Butterfield & Meylan 1976 – *Myrsine*.

Tracheary elements
Ohtani 1983 – *Myrsine*.

MYRTACEAE
(see also HETEROPYXIDACEAE and PSILOXYLACEAE)

Anon. 1981 (Andes) – *Eucalyptus*.
Abbate 1973 – *Eugenia*.
Agarwal & Chauhan 1988 – *Eucalyptus*.
Baas 1977 – *Leptospermum*.
Balan Menon 1955 – *Eugenia*.
Barajas Morales 1980 – *Psidium*.
Barajas Morales & León Gómez 1989 – *Psidium*.
Barbosa et al. 1977–1978 – *Gomidesia*.
Bargagli-Petrucci 1903 – *Eugenia, Tristania*.
Bascopé 1954 – *Myrcia*.
Benoist 1931 – *Calycolpus*.
Boland & Kleinig 1983 [1984] – *Eucalyptus*.
Brazier & Franklin 1961 – *Backhousia, Eucalyptus, Syncarpia, Tristania*.
Brown 1922 – *Eugenia, Metrosideros*.
Burgerstein 1909 – *Eugenia, Psidium*.
Burgerstein 1912 – *Myrtus*.
Cardoso 1961 – *Syzygium*.
Carreras & Vales 1986b – *Syzygium*.
Carvalho 1954–1955, 1956 – *Eucalyptus*.
Cheng, C. 1985 – *Eucalyptus, Syzygium*.
Cheng, J.-Q. 1980 – *Decaspermum, Eucalyptus, Melaleuca, Psidium, Rhodamnia, Syzygium*.
Cheng, J.-Q. et al. 1992 – Same genera as Cheng 1980 + *Pyrenocarpa*.
Cockrell 1942 – *Decaspermum, Eugenia, Rhodamnia*.
Cozzo & Rodriguez 1959 – *Eucalyptus*.
Cutler et al. 1987 – *Eucalyptus* (root).
*Dadswell 1972 – *Eucalyptus* 108 spp.
*Dadswell & Burnell 1932 – *Eucalyptus* 37 spp.
*Dadswell et al. 1934 – *Eucalyptus* 41 spp.
Dadswell & Eckersley 1935 – *Angophora, Eugenia, Melaleuca, Syncarpia, Tristania*.
Dadswell & Ingle 1947 – *Acmena, Cleistocalyx, Eugenia, Syzygium*.
Dadswell & Ingle 1951 – *Eucalyptopsis*.
Das 1970a – *Syzygium*.
Dechamps 1985 – *Aulomyrcia (= Myrcia), Calyptranthes, Campomanesia, Eugenia, Marlierea, Myrcia, Myrciaria, Psidium, Syzygium*.
Desch 1954 – *Eugenia, Leptospermum, Melaleuca, Rhodamnia, Tristania*.

(MYRTACEAE)
Détienne & Jacquet 1983 – *Calycolpus, Calyptranthes, Campomanesia, Eugenia, Marlierea, Myrcia, Myrciaria, Syzygium*.
Détienne et al. 1982 – *Calycolpus, Calyptranthes, Campomanesia, Eugenia, Marlierea, Myrcia, Myrciaria*.
Donaldson 1984 – *Eucalyptus*.
Edlmann Abbate & De Luca 1981 – *Syzygium*.
Erdtman & Metcalfe 1963 – *Kania, Tristania* (young stems).
Fahn 1959 – *Eucalyptus*.
Fahn et al. 1986 – *Myrtus*.
Fasolo 1939–1940 – *Syzygium*.
Fonseca 1971 – *Eucalyptus*.
Freitas 1958 – *Decaspermum, Melaleuca*.
Freitas 1963 – *Eugenia*.
Freitas 1973 [1974] – *Melaleuca*.
Fundter & Wisse 1977 – *Tristania*.
Furuno 1977, 1979 – *Eucalyptus, Eugenia, Melaleuca, Syzygium, Tristania*.
Garratt 1924 – *Leptospermum, Metrosideros*.
Giordano 1940 – *Syzygium*.
Gouwentak 1935 – *Eucalyptus*.
Greguss 1959 – *Eucalyptus, Myrtus*.
Hayashi et al. 1973 – *Eugenia, Melaleuca, Tristania*.
Huber & Rouschal 1954 – *Myrtus*.
Ilic 1991 – 26 genera.
*Ingle & Dadswell 1953 – 30 genera.
Jacquiot et al. 1973 – *Eucalyptus*.
*Johnson 1984 – *Leptospermum* 13 spp.
Kanehira 1921a – *Decaspermum, Eugenia, Psidium*.
Kanehira 1924 – *Eugenia, Xanthostemon*.
Kobayashi 1966 – *Tristania*.
Kobayashi & Sugawa 1963 – *Eucalyptus*.
Kribs 1928a – *Calycolpus*.
Kribs 1959 – *Eucalyptus, Pimenta, Syncarpia, Xanthostemon*.
Landrum 1981 – *Luma, Myrceugenia*.
Lebacq & Dechamps 1964 – *Caryophyllus (= Syzygium), Eucalyptus, Syzygium*.
Lebacq & Dechamps 1967 – *Syzygium*.
Lebacq et al. 1973 – *Myrciaria, Psidium*.
Lebedenko 1962a – *Syzygium*.
Lecomte 1922 – *Eugenia*.
Lecomte 1926a – *Eugenia, Melaleuca, Tristania*.

(MYRTACEAE)

Luo 1989 – *Eucalyptus, Syzygium.*
Mainieri 1960, 1978 – *Psidium.*
Mainieri & Chimelo 1989 – *Eugenia, Psidium.*
Martawijaya et al. 1989 – *Eucalyptus.*
Martin & Cossalter 1976 – *Eucalyptus.*
Mattos & Pinho 1968 – *Pseudocaryophyllus* (= *Pimenta*).
Meylan & Butterfield 1978b – *Eugenia, Leptospermum, Lophomyrtus, Metrosideros, Neomyrtus.*
Moll & Janssonius 1906–1936 – *Aphanomyrtus* (= *Syzygium*), *Decaspermum, Eugenia, Leptospermum, Rhodamnia.*
Nájera Angulo & López Fraile 1969 – *Eucalyptus.*
Nardi Berti & Edlmann Abbate 1992 – *Myrtus.*
Normand 1960 – *Eugenia, Syzygium.*
Normand & Paquis 1976 [1977] – *Eucalyptus, Syzygium.*
Ogata, K. 1975–1983 – *Eucalyptus, Melaleuca, Syzygium, Tristania* and summary table for 32 genera.
Ogata, S. 1953 – *Eucalyptus.*
Oliveira et al. 1970 – *Eucalyptus.*
Ortega et al. 1988 – *Eugenia, Psidium.*
Panshin 1932 – *Osbornia.*
Parsa Pajouh & Schweingruber 1985 – *Eucalyptus.*
Paula & Alves 1989 – *Myrcia.*
Pearson & Brown 1932 – *Eugenia.*
Pereira 1933 – *Eucalyptus.*
Pérez Mogollón 1973 – *Eugenia.*
Pérez Mogollón 1993 – *Myrcia.*
Prakash 1972 – *Pimenta* (root).
Rabechault 1955 – *Syzygium.*
Ragonese 1977 [1978] – *Amomyrtus, Blepharocalyx, Campomanesia, Eugenia, Myrceugenella* (= *Luma*), *Myrceugenia, Psidium.*
Rancusi et al. 1987 – *Amomyrtus, Myrceugenella* (= *Luma*), *Myrceugenia, Temu* (= *Blepharocalyx*), *Tepualia.*
Record & Hess 1943 – Family (17 genera).
Rozmarin et al. 1983 – *Eucalyptus.*
Saiki 1982 – *Eucalyptus.*
Saint-Laurent 1928, 1932a, 1934 – *Eucalyptus, Myrtus.*
Sastrapradja & Lamoureux 1969 – *Metrosideros.*

(MYRTACEAE)

Schmid 1980 – Relations of *Heteropyxis, Psiloxylon.*
Schweingruber 1990 – *Myrtus.*
Silva 1991 – *Myrcia.*
Sudo 1963 – *Eucalyptus, Eugenia, Metrosideros, Syncarpia, Tristania, Xanthostemon.*
Sudo 1988 – *Decaspermum, Eucalyptopsis, Eucalyptus, Lophostemon, Melaleuca, Rhodomyrtus, Syzygium, Tristania, Xanthomyrtus, Xanthostemon.*
Sugawa 1968b – *Eugenia.*
Tainter 1968 – *Amomyrtus.*
Tang 1973 – *Eucalyptus, Syzygium.*
Taylor 1973 – *Eucalyptus.*
Tomazello Filho 1985 – *Eucalyptus.*
Tortorelli 1956 – *Blepharocalyx, Myrceugenella* (= *Luma*).
Urling & Smith 1953 – *Eugenia, Psidium.*
Van Vliet & Baas 1984 – Relations of myrtalean families.
Van Wyk et al. 1983 – *Eugenia.*
Wagemann 1949 – *Amomyrtus, Myrceugenella* (= *Luma*), *Myrceugenia, Temu* (= *Blepharocalyx*), *Tepualia.*
Wagenführ & Scheiber 1974 – *Eucalyptus.*
Wang 1984–1988 – *Eucalyptus, Eugenia, Syzygium.*
Wei 1984 – *Acmena.*
Welch 1924 [1925]a, 1925 [1926], 1926 [1927] – *Eucalyptus.*
Welch 1929 [1930] – *Syncarpia.*
Wilkes 1988 – *Eucalyptus.*
Williams 1936 – *Psidium.*
Wiraj Chunwarin & Damrong Sri-Aran 1974 – *Melaleuca, Syzygium.*
Wu & Wang 1976 – *Eugenia.*
Yao 1988 – *Cleistocalyx, Eucalyptus.*

Crystals

Baker 1917 – *Eucalyptus.*
Chattaway 1955 – *Eugenia, Psidium, Rhodamnia.*
Chattaway 1956 – 16 genera.
Espinoza de Pernía 1987b – *Eugenia.*
Scurfield et al. 1973 – *Psidium, Tristania.*

Ecological anatomy

Baas et al. 1983 – *Myrtus.*
Baas & Schweingruber 1987 – *Myrtus.*
Barajas Morales 1985 – *Eugenia, Psidium.*

(MYRTACEAE)

Carlquist 1977c – *Eremaeopsis* (= *Eremaea*), *Leptospermum, Melaleuca, Pileanthus.*
Carlquist 1985a – *Callistemon, Eremaea, Leptospermum, Melaleuca, Psidium, Verticordia.*
Carlquist 1985 [1986]a – *Metrosideros.*
Psaras & Hatzopoulou-Belba 1984 – *Myrtus.*
Versteegh 1968 – *Baeckea, Leptospermum, Rhodamnia.*

Growth rings
Tupper 1931 – *Eucalyptus.*

Pits
Jing et al. 1988 – *Syzygium.*
Meylan & Butterfield 1974 – *Leptospermum, Lophomyrtus, Metrosideros, Neomyrtus.*
Nair 1992 – *Syzygium.*
Nair & Ram 1989 – *Callistemon, Syzygium.*

Rays
Braun et al. 1968 – *Tristania.*
Chattaway 1951b – *Eucalyptus.*

Septate fibres
Butterfield & Meylan 1976 – *Eugenia.*

Silica
Amos & Dadswell 1948 – *Syncarpia.*
Bamber & Lanyon 1960 – *Melaleuca, Syncarpia, Tristania.*
Hillis & Silva 1979 – *Syncarpia, Tristania.*
Scurfield et al. 1974 – *Tristania.*
Sudo et al. 1967 – *Melaleuca, Metrosideros, Tristania.*

Tracheary elements
Gill & Onuja 1984b – *Eucalyptus, Psidium.*
Jing et al. 1989 – *Syzygium.*
Ragonese 1976 – *Amomyrtus, Blepharocalyx, Campomanesia, Eugenia, Myrceugenella* (= *Luma*), *Myrceugenia, Psidium.*
Schmid & Baas 1984 – 53 genera.

NANDINACEAE see BERBERIDACEAE

NAUCLEACEAE see RUBIACEAE

NECTAROPETALACEAE
see ERYTHROXYLACEAE

NEPENTHACEAE (*Nepenthes*)

*Carlquist 1981d.

Ecological anatomy
Carlquist 1985 [1986]a.

NOLANACEAE (*Nolana*)

*Carlquist 1987b – 6 spp.

Anomalous structure
Alfaroa & Mesa 1979.
Mirande 1922.

NYCTAGINACEAE
(*Torrubia* = *Pisonia*)

Barajas Morales & León Gómez 1989 – *Guapira.*
Brown 1922 – *Pisonia.*
Burgerstein 1912 – *Bougainvillea.*
Dechamps 1985 – *Neea, Pisonia, Torrubia.*
Desch 1954 – *Bougainvillea.*
Détienne & Jacquet 1983 – *Neea, Pisonia, Rockia* (= *Pisonia*), *Torrubia.*
Détienne et al. 1982 – *Neea, Pisonia.*
Fahn et al. 1986 – *Commicarpus.*
Ilic 1991 – *Pisonia, Torrubia.*
Kanehira et al. 1933 – *Calpidia* (= *Pisonia*), *Pisonia.*
Lopes et al. 1983 – *Neea.*
Mainieri & Chimelo 1989 – *Neea.*
Meylan & Butterfield 1978b – *Heimerliodendron* (= *Pisonia*).
Moll & Janssonius 1906–1936 – *Pisonia.*
Pérez Mogollón 1973 – *Torrubia.*
Record & Hess 1943 – Family (*Bougainvillea, Colignonia, Neea, Pisonia, Reichenbachia, Torrubia*).
Record & Mell 1924 – *Pisonia.*
Schweingruber 1990 – *Bougainvillea.*
Sudo 1963 – *Pisonia.*
Tortorelli 1956 – *Pisonia.*
Williams 1936 – *Neea, Torrubia.*

Anomalous structure
Bhargava 1932 – *Boerhavia.*
Chalk & Chattaway 1937 – Family (*Bougainvillea, Colignonia, Neea, Pisonia, Torrubia*).
Dassanayake & Paranavithana 1976 – *Bougainvillea.*
Esau & Cheadle 1969 – *Bougainvillea.*

(NYCTAGINACEAE)

Maheshwari 1930 – *Boerhavia.*
Puglia & Norverto 1990 – *Pisonia.*
Pu ł awska 1973 – *Bougainvillea.*
Studholme & Philipson 1966 – *Heimer-liodendron* (= *Pisonia*).

Crystals

Chattaway 1955 – *Pisonia, Torrubia.*
Scurfield et al. 1973 – *Pisonia.*

Ecological anatomy

Baas et al. 1983 – *Commicarpus.*
Carlquist 1985 [1986]a – *Bougainvillea.*
Van der Graaff & Baas 1974 – *Pisonia.*

Storied structure

Cozzo & Cristiani 1950 – *Bougainvillea, Pisonia.*

NYSSACEAE

(*Nyssa* only unless otherwise stated)

Beck 1945.
Brazier & Franklin 1961.
Cheng, C. 1985.
Cheng, J.-Q. 1980 – *Camptotheca, Nyssa.*
Cheng, J.-Q. et al. 1992 – *Camptotheca, Nyssa.*
Desch 1954.
Furuno 1985, 1987.
Gasson & Cutler 1990 – (root).
Ilic 1991.
Jacquiot et al. 1973.
Kanehira et al. 1933.
*Li & Chao 1954 – *Camptotheca, Nyssa.*
Luo 1989 – *Camptotheca.*
Moll & Janssonius 1906–1936.
Panshin & Zeeuw 1980.
Pearson & Brown 1932.
Record & Hess 1943.
Sudworth & Mell 1911b.
*Titman 1949 – *Camptotheca, Nyssa.*
Yao 1988.

Crystals

Chattaway 1956.

Ecological anatomy

Versteegh 1968.

Helical thickenings

Parham & Kaustinen 1973.

Tracheary elements

Jing et al. 1989 – *Camptotheca.*

OCHNACEAE

Anon. 1954, 1955–1959 – *Lophira.*
Anon. 1981 (Andes) – *Cespedesia.*
Abbate 1964 – *Ochna.*
Alves de Pinho 1966 – *Ouratea.*
Ayensu & Bentum 1974 – *Lophira.*
Brazier & Franklin 1961 – *Lophira.*
Chalk et al. 1933 – *Lophira.*
Chalk et al. 1935 – *Ochna.*
Dechamps 1985 – *Elvasia, Ouratea.*
*Decker 1966 – 28 genera.
Den Outer & Schütz 1981b – *Campylosper-mum* (= *Ochna*), *Diporidium* (= *Ochna*), *Elvasia, Idertia* (= *Ouratea*), *Lophira, Ochna, Ouratea, Rhabdophyllum* (= *Oura-tea*), *Schuurmansia.*
Desch 1954 – *Ouratea.*
Détienne & Jacquet 1983 – *Blastemanthus, Cespedesia, Elvasia, Ouratea, Wallacea.*
Détienne et al. 1982 – *Elvasia, Ouratea.*
Dickison 1981 – Relations.
Duchaigne & Chalard 1951 – *Distephania* (= *Indosinia*) (twig).
Ilic 1991 – *Brackenridgea, Lophira, Schuur-mansia, Testulea.*
Jentsch et al. 1936 – *Lophira.*
Kribs 1959 – *Lophira, Testulea.*
Lebacq & Dechamps 1964 – *Lophira.*
Lebacq & Dechamps 1967 – *Ochna.*
Lebacq et al. 1973 – *Ouratea.*
Lecomte 1922, 1926b – *Ouratea.*
Mendes & Paula 1980 – *Ouratea.*
Nardi Berti & Edlmann Abbate 1988 – *Lo-phira, Testulea.*
Normand 1955 – *Lophira, Ochna, Oura-tea.*
Normand & Chatelet 1955 – *Fleurydora.*
Normand & Paquis 1976 [1977] – *Lophira, Ochna, Ouratea, Testulea.*
Persinos & Quimby 1968 – *Lophira.*
Record & Hess 1943 – Family (*Blasteman-thus, Cespedesia, Elvasia, Ouratea, Tyle-ria, Wallacea*).
Record & Mell 1924 – *Cespedesia.*
Riera 1947 – *Lophira.*
Rozmarin et al. 1983 – *Testulea.*
Sastré 1975a – General.
Sastré 1975b – *Cespedesia.*
Satabié 1991 – *Lophira.*
Sudo 1963 – *Lophira, Testulea.*
Thieme 1929 – *Lophira.*
Vestal 1937 – Family (8 genera).

(OCHNACEAE)
Wagenführ & Scheiber 1974 – *Lophira.*
Williams 1936 – *Cespedesia, Ouratea.*

Crystals
Chattaway 1956 – *Lophira, Ochna, Testulea.*

Ecological anatomy
Carlquist 1985a – *Lophira.*
Den Outer & Van Veenendaal 1976 – *Campylospermum* (= *Ochna*).
Van der Graaff & Baas 1974 – *Schuurmansia.*

Tracheary elements
Gill & Onuja 1984a – *Lophira.*

OCTOKNEMACEAE

Ilic 1991 – *Octoknema.*
Lebacq & Dechamps 1964, 1967 – *Okoubaka.*
Normand 1944 – *Octoknema, Okoubaka.*
Normand 1950b – *Octoknema, Okoubaka.*
Normand & Paquis 1976 [1977] – *Octoknema, Okoubaka.*
*Reed 1955 – *Octoknema, Okoubaka.*
Van den Oever 1984 – *Octoknema* (in Olacaceae).

OENOTHERACEAE see ONAGRACEAE

OLACACEAE
(see also OCTOKNEMACEAE)

Anon. 1981 (Andes) – *Minquartia.*
Balan Menon 1955 – *Scorodocarpus.*
Bargagli-Petrucci 1903 – *Scorodocarpus.*
Brazier & Franklin 1961 – *Ongokea, Strombosia.*
Burgerstein 1912 – *Ximenia.*
Cockrell 1942 – *Ochanostachys.*
Coradin et al. 1992 – *Brachynema.*
Croptier & Kučera 1990 – *Strombosia.*
Dechamps 1985 – *Chaunochiton, Heisteria, Minquartia, Ptychopetalum.*
Desch 1954 – *Harmandia, Ochanostachys, Scorodocarpus, Strombosia.*
Détienne & Jacquet 1983 – *Aptandra, Chaunochiton, Dulacia, Heisteria, Minquartia, Ptychopetalum.*
Détienne et al. 1982 – *Chaunochiton, Minquartia, Ptychopetalum.*

(OLACACEAE)
Eeckhout 1951 – *Ongokea.*
Fouarge & Gérard 1964 – *Ongokea, Strombosia.*
Fouarge et al. 1953 – *Ongokea, Strombosiopsis.*
Freitas 1961 – *Ongokea.*
Hayashi et al. 1973 – *Ochanostachys, Scorodocarpus, Strombosia.*
Ilic 1991 – *Anacolosa, Coula, Minquartia, Ongokea, Ptychopetalum, Scorodocarpus, Strombosia, Ximenia.*
Janssonius 1950 – Relations.
Jentsch et al. 1939 – *Coula, Strombosia, Strombosiopsis.*
Kanehira 1924 – *Strombosia.*
Kribs 1959 – *Minquartia, Ongokea, Strombosia, Ximenia.*
Lebacq 1955 – *Coula, Heisteria, Ongokea, Strombosia, Strombosiopsis.*
Lebacq & Dechamps 1964 – *Coula, Heisteria, Ongokea, Strombosia, Strombosiopsis.*
Lebacq & Dechamps 1967 – Cf. *Aptandra, Coula, Heisteria, Olax, Ongokea, Strombosia, Strombosiopsis.*
Lebacq et al. 1973 – *Heisteria.*
Lebacq & Staner 1964 – *Ongokea.*
Lecomte 1922 – *Olax.*
Luo 1989 – *Malania.*
Maas et al. 1992 – *Maburea.*
Mainieri 1967 – *Minquartia, Tetrastylidium.*
Mainieri 1978 – *Tetrastylidium.*
Mainieri & Chimelo 1989 – *Minquartia, Tetrastylidium.*
Martawijaya et al. 1989 – *Ochanostachys, Scorodocarpus.*
Martin 1953 – *Lavalleopsis* (= *Strombosia*), *Ongokea.*
Metcalfe 1935 – *Ximenia.*
Moll & Janssonius 1906–1936 – *Anacolosa, Strombosia.*
Monteiro & França 1965 – *Ongokea.*
Nardi Berti & Edlmann Abbate 1988 – *Ongokea.*
Normand 1950b – *Coula, Ongokea, Strombosia.*
Normand & Paquis 1976 [1977] – *Coula, Diogoa, Ongokea, Strombosia, Strombosiopsis.*
Ogata 1975–1983 – *Scorodocarpus.*
Paula 1979 – *Minquartia.*

(OLACACEAE)

Pfeiffer, J.P. 1926 – *Minquartia.*
*Record 1938a – *Aptandra, Chaunochiton, Heisteria, Liriosma* (= *Dulacia*), *Minquartia, Ptychopetalum, Schoepfia, Ximenia.*
Record & Hess 1943 – Family (13 genera).
Record & Mell 1924 – *Minquartia.*
*Reed 1955 – 25 genera.
Sudo 1963 – *Minquartia, Scorodocarpus, Strombosia.*
Sudo 1988 – *Anacolosa.*
Urling & Smith 1953 – *Ximenia.*
Van den Oever 1984 – Family (incl. *Erythropalum*).
Van den Oever et al. 1993 – 10 genera.
Williams 1928 – *Heisteria.*
Williams 1936 – *Aptandra, Heisteria, Liriosma.*

Crystals and silica

Chattaway 1956 – *Ochanostachys, Strombosia.*
Espinoza de Pernía 1987b – *Liriosma* (= *Dulacia*).
Welle 1976b – *Liriosma* (= *Dulacia*).

Rays

Chalk & Chattaway 1933 – *Ptychopetalum.*

OLEACEAE

(*Nyctanthes* is indexed both here and under VERBENACEAE)
(*Linociera* = *Chionanthus*)

Anon. 1955–1959 – *Schrebera.*
Anon. 1966 – *Fraxinus.*
Anon. 1968 – *Notelaea.*
Amaldi 1929 – *Olea.*
*Baas et al. 1988 – 24 genera, 137 spp. (incl. *Myxopyrum* and *Nyctanthes*).
*Baas & Zhang 1986 – *Chionanthus, Fontanesia, Forsythia, Fraxinus, Jasminum, Ligustrum, Olea, Osmanthus, Syringa.*
Babos & Borhidi 1978 – *Linociera.*
Brazier & Franklin 1961 – *Fraxinus, Olea.*
Brown 1922 – *Osmanthus.*
Carvalho 1954–1956 – *Fraxinus, Phillyrea.*
Chakroun 1983 – *Olea.*
Chalk et al. 1935 – *Olea.*
Cheng, C. 1985 – *Fraxinus.*
Cheng, J.-Q. 1980 – *Fraxinus, Ligustrum, Linociera, Olea, Osmanthus.*

(OLEACEAE)

Cheng, J.-Q. et al. 1992 – Same genera as Cheng 1980.
Chiang 1962 – *Fraxinus.*
Chudnoff 1956 – *Fraxinus, Olea, Phillyrea.*
Cockrell 1942 – *Ligustrum.*
Croptier & Kučera 1990 – *Olea.*
Cutler 1976 – *Fraxinus* (root).
Cutler et al. 1987 – *Forestiera, Forsythia, Fraxinus, Jasminum, Ligustrum, Osmanthus, Phillyrea, Syringa* (root).
Desch 1954 – *Linociera, Olea.*
Edlmann & Monaco 1981 – *Fraxinus, Syringa.*
Eeckhout 1951 – *Fraxinus.*
Fahn et al. 1986 – *Fraxinus, Jasminum, Olea, Phillyrea.*
Fasolo 1939–1940 – *Olea.*
Fegel 1941 – *Fraxinus* (root).
Friedman 1978 – *Fraxinus.*
Furuno 1985, 1987 – *Fraxinus.*
Garratt 1924 – *Olea.*
Giordano 1940 – *Olea.*
Greguss 1959 – *Forsythia, Fraxinus, Jasminum, Ligustrum, Olea, Phillyrea, Syringa.*
Grosser 1977 – *Fraxinus, Ligustrum, Syringa.*
Gziryan 1950 – *Fraxinus.*
Hayashi 1991 – *Fraxinus, Ligustrum, Osmanthus, Syringa.*
Hirai 1979–1985 – *Fraxinus.*
Huber & Rouschal 1954 – *Forsythia, Fraxinus, Olea, Phillyrea, Syringa.*
Ilic 1991 – *Chionanthus, Forestiera, Fraxinus, Ligustrum, Linociera, Notelaea, Olea, Schrebera.*
Jaccard 1914 – *Fraxinus* (root).
Jacquiot et al. 1973 – *Fraxinus, Ligustrum, Olea.*
Jagiella & Kurschner 1987 – *Olea.*
Janssonius 1950 – Relations.
Kanehira 1921a – *Fraxinus, Ligustrum, Linociera, Osmanthus.*
Kanehira 1921b – *Fraxinus, Ligustrum, Osmanthus.*
Kanehira 1926 – *Chionanthus, Fraxinus, Ligustrum, Osmanthus, Syringa.*
Kaya 1991 [1993] – *Olea.*
Kiew & Baas 1984 – *Nyctanthes.*
Kim & Hong 1984a – *Forsythia.*
Kollmann 1941 – *Fraxinus.*

(OLEACEAE)
Kribs 1959 – *Fraxinus, Olea.*
Kundu & De 1968 [1969] – *Nyctanthes.*
Lacey & Jahnke 1984 – *Notelaea.*
Lebacq & Dechamps 1964, 1967 – *Schrebera.*
Lebedenko 1962a – *Olea.*
Lecomte 1922 – *Noronhia.*
Lecomte 1926a – *Linociera.*
Luo 1989 – *Fraxinus, Ligustrum, Olea, Osmanthus.*
Marano 1953 – *Phillyrea* (branches).
Meniado et al. 1978 – *Linociera.*
Metcalfe 1938 – *Fraxinus.*
Meylan & Butterfield 1978b – *Nestegis.*
Moll & Janssonius 1906–1936 – *Chionanthus, Fraxinus, Ligustrum, Olea.*
Mork 1946 – *Fraxinus.*
Nájera Angulo & López Fraile 1969 – *Fraxinus.*
Niloofari 1961 – *Fraxinus, Ligustrum, Olea.*
Normand 1960 – *Linociera, Olea, Schrebera.*
Normand & Paquis 1976 [1977] – *Linociera, Olea, Schrebera.*
Noshiro & Suzuki 1987 – *Chionanthus* (root).
Panshin & Zeeuw 1980 – *Fraxinus.*
Parsa Pajouh & Schweingruber 1985 – *Fraxinus, Olea.*
Patel 1965 – *Fraxinus.*
Patel 1978 – *Nestegis.*
Pearson & Brown 1932 – *Fraxinus, Olea, Schrebera.*
Peraza Oramas & Lopez de Roma 1967 – *Notelaea.*
Pérez Olvera & Corral Lopez 1980 – *Fraxinus.*
Record & Hess 1943 – Family (*Chionanthus, Forestiera, Forsythia, Fraxinus, Jasminum* (twig), *Ligustrum, Olea, Syringa*) + *Menodora.*
Riedl 1937 – *Fraxinus* (root).
Saiki 1982 – *Fraxinus, Osmanthus.*
Saint-Laurent 1928, 1932a, 1934 – *Fraxinus, Olea, Phillyrea.*
Sax & Abbe 1932 – *Chionanthus, Forestiera, Forsythia, Fraxinus, Jasminum, Ligustrum, Olea, Syringa.*
Schweingruber 1978 – *Fraxinus, Ligustrum.*

(OLEACEAE)
Schweingruber 1990 – *Fraxinus, Jasminum, Ligustrum, Olea, Phillyrea, Picconia, Syringa.*
Scott 1927 – *Olea.*
Senni 1905 – *Olea.*
Shimaji & Itoh 1982 – *Fraxinus, Osmanthus.*
Shimaji & Itoh 1988 – *Fraxinus, Ligustrum, Osmanthus.*
Sudo 1959 – *Fraxinus, Ligustrum, Osmanthus, Syringa.*
Sudo 1963 – *Olea.*
Suzuki & Nishida 1974 – *Chionanthus.*
Suzuki & Noshiro 1988 – *Fraxinus, Jasminum, Ligustrum, Osmanthus, Syringa.*
Tang 1973 – *Fraxinus, Olea.*
Thunell & Perem 1947 – *Fraxinus.*
Wagenführ & Scheiber 1974 – *Fraxinus.*
Wang 1966 – *Fraxinus.*
Wuang 1979 – *Fraxinus.*
Yamabayashi 1938 – *Chionanthus, Forsythia, Fraxinus, Ligustrum, Syringa.*
Yao 1988 – *Fraxinus, Osmanthus.*
Zgurovskaya 1958 – *Fraxinus* (root).

Anomalous structure
Majumdar 1941 – *Nyctanthes.*

Crystals
Chattaway 1955 – *Ligustrum, Linociera, Notelaea, Olea.*
Meniado et al. 1970 – *Linociera.*
Scurfield et al. 1973 – *Ligustrum.*

Ecological anatomy
Baas et al. 1983 – *Fraxinus, Jasminum, Phillyrea.*
Baas et al. 1984 – *Olea.*
Baas & Schweingruber 1987 – *Fraxinus, Jasminum, Ligustrum, Olea, Phillyrea, Picconia, Syringa.*
Carlquist 1985a – *Chionanthus, Ligustrum, Nestegis, Osmanthus, Phillyrea.*
Carlquist 1985 [1986]a – *Jasminum.*
Carlquist & Hoekman 1985a – *Forestiera, Fraxinus, Menodora.*
Deng & Zhang 1989 – *Syringa.*
Krasnitskij 1959 – *Fraxinus.*
Lim & Soh 1991a – *Fraxinus.*
Matović 1977 [1978] – *Fraxinus.*
Novruzova 1968 – *Fraxinus, Ligustrum.*
Psaras & Hatzopoulou-Belba 1984 – *Olea.*
Zhang et al. 1988 – *Syringa.*

(OLEACEAE)

Growth rings
Hanson & Brenke 1936 – *Fraxinus.*

Helical thickenings
Meylan & Butterfield 1978a – *Nestegis.*
Nair 1987 – *Schrebera.*
Ohtani & Ishida 1978b – *Ligustrum, Osmanthus, Syringa.*

Pits and perforation plates
Dute & Rushing 1987 – *Osmanthus.*
Meylan & Butterfield 1974, 1975 – *Nestegis.*
Nair & Ram 1989 – *Schrebera.*
Ohtani & Ishida 1976 – *Ligustrum.*
Ohtani & Ishida 1978a – *Fraxinus, Ligustrum, Osmanthus, Syringa.*
Parameswaran & Gomes 1981 – *Ligustrum.*
Wheeler 1981 – *Fraxinus.*

Rays
Braun et al. 1967 – *Fraxinus.*
McLean & Richardson 1973 [1974] – *Olea.*
Szalai & Varga 1955 – *Fraxinus.*

Tracheary elements
Chalk 1970 – *Fraxinus.*
Jing et al. 1989 – *Fraxinus.*
Murthy et al. 1978 – 12 genera (incl. *Nyctanthes*).
Ohtani 1983 – *Fraxinus, Ligustrum, Osmanthus, Syringa.*

OLINIACEAE (*Olinia*)

Ilic 1991.
Mujica & Cutler 1974.
Scott 1927.
Van Vliet & Baas 1984 – Relations of myrtalean families.

ONAGRACEAE (incl. OENOTHERACEAE)

Berry et al. 1988 – *Fuchsia.*
*Carlquist 1975b – 14 genera.
Carlquist 1977 [1978] – *Epilobium, Fuchsia, Hauya.*
*Carlquist 1982 [1983] – *Circaea, Fuchsia, Lopezia, Ludwigia, Oenothera.*
Carlquist 1987 [1988] – *Ludwigia.*
Carlquist & Raven 1966 – *Gongylocarpus.*
Cutler et al. 1987 – *Fuchsia* (root).

(ONAGRACEAE)
Ilic 1991 – *Fuchsia.*
Meylan & Butterfield 1978b – *Fuchsia.*
Record & Hess 1943 – Family (*Fuchsia, Jussiaea* (= *Ludwigia*), *Oenothera*).
Van Vliet & Baas 1984 – Relations of myrtalean families.
Williams 1936 – *Jussiaea* (= *Ludwigia*).

Anomalous structure
Coineau & Duchaigne 1967 – *Oenothera.*
Moss 1936 – *Epilobium.*

Ecological anatomy
Carlquist & Hoekman 1985a – *Camissonia, Clarkia, Epilobium, Gaura, Heterogaura, Oenothera, Zauschneria* (= *Epilobium*).

Pits
Meylan & Butterfield 1974 – *Fuchsia.*

Septate fibres
Butterfield & Meylan 1976 – *Fuchsia.*

ONCOTHECACEAE see AQUIFOLIACEAE

OPILIACEAE

Dechamps 1985 – *Agonandra.*
Desch 1954 – *Champereia.*
Détienne & Jacquet 1983 – *Agonandra.*
Ilic 1991 – *Champereia.*
Kanehira 1921a – *Champereia.*
*Koek-Noorman & Rijckevorsel 1983 – *Agonandra, Cansjera, Champereia, Gjellerupia, Lepionurus, Melientha, Opilia, Rhopalopilia, Urobotrya.*
Lebacq et al. 1973 – *Agonandra.*
Record 1938a – *Agonandra.*
Reed 1955 – *Agonandra, Cansjera, Champereia, Lepionurus, Melientha, Opilia, Rhopalopilia, Urobotrya.*

Crystals
Espinoza de Pernía 1987b – *Agonandra.*
Scurfield et al. 1973 – *Opilia.*

OXALIDACEAE

Bargagli-Petrucci 1903 – *Connaropsis* (= *Sarcotheca*).
Cheng, J.-Q. 1980 – *Averrhoa.*
Cheng, J.-Q. et al. 1992 – *Averrhoa.*

(OXALIDACEAE)
Desch 1954 – *Averrhoa, Connaropsis*
  (= *Sarcotheca*).
Heimsch 1942 – *Averrhoa, Oxalis, Sarco-*
  theca.
Ilic 1991 – *Sarcotheca.*
Kanehira 1921a – *Averrhoa.*
Moll & Janssonius 1906–1936 – *Averrhoa.*
Prakash 1972 – *Averrhoa* (root).
Tang 1973 – *Averrhoa.*

Crystals
Chattaway 1956 – *Averrhoa, Sarcotheca.*

Septate fibres
Ghosh & Purkayastha 1960a – *Averrhoa.*

PAEONIACEAE (*Paeonia*)

Barykina & Gulanyan 1976, 1978.
Keefe & Moseley 1978.
Kumazawa 1935.
Lemesle 1948a, 1955a, 1956b.
Takahashi 1985.
Yatsenko-Khmelevsky 1954a.

PANDACEAE

Baas 1972a – Relations.
Kribs 1959 – *Panda.*
Lebacq 1963 – *Panda.*
Lebacq & Dechamps 1964 – *Microdesmis*
  (in Euphorbiaceae), *Panda.*
Lebacq & Dechamps 1967 – *Panda.*
Moll & Janssonius 1906–1936 – *Bennettia*
  (= *Galearia*).
Normand 1950b – *Panda.*
Normand & Paquis 1976 [1977] – *Micro-*
  desmis, Panda.
Parameswaran & Metcalfe 1966 – *Galearia,*
  Panda.
Perrot 1912 – *Panda.*
Stern 1967 – *Microdesmis.*
Vigne & Record 1929 – *Panda.*

PAPAVERACEAE (incl. FUMARIACEAE)

*Carlquist & Zona 1988b – *Bocconia, Den-*
  dromecon, Hunnemannia, Romneya.
Cumbie 1983 – *Bocconia.*
Dadswell & Record 1936 – *Bocconia.*
Lidén 1986 – *Rupicapnos, Sarcocapnos.*

(PAPAVERACEAE)
Pérez Olvera 1993 – *Bocconia.*
Record & Hess 1943 – *Bocconia, Dendro-*
  mecon.

Ecological anatomy
Carlquist 1985a – *Dendromecon, Romneya.*
Carlquist & Hoekman 1985a – *Dendrome-*
  con, Romneya.
Webber 1936a – *Dendromecon.*

PAPILIONACEAE see LEGUMINOSAE

PARACRYPHIACEAE (*Paracryphia*)

*Dickison & Baas 1977.
Swamy 1953b – *Ascarina* transferred to
  Paracryphia.

PASSIFLORACEAE
(for *Soyauxia* see MEDUSANDRACEAE)

*Ayensu & Stern 1964 – *Crossostemma,*
  Dilkea, Mitostemma, Paropsia, Passi-
  flora, Smeathmannia.
Burgerstein 1909 – *Passiflora.*
Cutler et al. 1987 – *Passiflora* (root).
Desch 1954 – *Paropsia.*
Hemsley & Verdcourt 1956 – *Viridivia*
  (wood by C.R. Metcalfe).
Lebacq & Dechamps 1967 – Cf. *Barteria,*
  Paropsia, Smeathmannia.
Metcalfe & Chalk 1950 – *Androsiphonia,*
  Crossostemma, Dilkea, Smeathmannia,
  Tacsonia (= *Passiflora*).
Miller, R.B. 1975 – *Barteria, Paropsia.*
Normand 1960 – *Smeathmannia.*
Normand & Paquis 1976 [1977] – *Barteria,*
  Smeathmannia.
Pérez Mogollón 1993 – *Passiflora.*
Stern & Brizicky 1958c – *Passiflora.*
Woodworth 1935 – *Passiflora.*

Anomalous structure
Obaton 1960 – *Adenia, Crossostemma.*
Ravololomaniraka & Koechlin 1970 – *Pas-*
  siflora.
Swamy 1975 – *Adenia.*
Ursem & Welle 1992 – *Passiflora.*
Van der Walt et al. 1969 – *Adenia.*
Van Vuuren 1973 – *Adenia.*

(PASSIFLORACEAE)

Ecological anatomy
Carlquist 1985a – *Passiflora*, etc.
Carlquist 1985 [1986]a – *Passiflora*.
Den Outer & Van Veenendaal 1976 – *Smeathmannia*.

PEDALIACEAE
(see also MARTYNIACEAE)

*Carlquist 1987c – *Ceratotheca, Holubia, Pedalium, Sesamothamnus, Sesamum*.
Den Outer & Van Veenendaal 1983 – *Uncarina*.
Pawar & Kulkarni 1971 – *Sesamum*.

PELLICIERACEAE (*Pelliciera*)

Baretta-Kuipers 1976.
Record 1942a – (in Theaceae).

PENAEACEAE

*Carlquist & DeBuhr 1977 – *Brachysiphon, Endonema, Penaea, Saltera, Sonderothamnus, Stylapterus*.
Van Vliet & Baas 1984 – Relations of myrtalean families.

PENTAPHRAGMATACEAE

Ecological anatomy
Carlquist 1975a – *Pentaphragma*.

PENTAPHYLACACEAE (*Pentaphylax*)

*Carlquist 1984 [1985]a.
Cheng, J.-Q. 1980.
Cheng, J.-Q. et al. 1992.
Desch 1954 – (in Theaceae).
Heimsch 1942.

PENTHORACEAE (*Penthorum*)

Haskins & Hayden 1987.

PERIDISCACEAE

Détienne & Jacquet 1983 – *Peridiscus*.
Metcalfe 1962 – *Peridiscus, Whittonia*.
Miller, R.B. 1975 – *Peridiscus*.
Record 1941b – *Peridiscus* (in Flacourtiaceae).

PHELLINACEAE see AQUIFOLIACEAE

PHILADELPHACEAE
see HYDRANGEACEAE

PHYSENACEAE (*Physena*)

Dickison & Miller 1993.

PHYTOLACCACEAE (see also ACHATO-CARPACEAE, GYROSTEMONACEAE, RHABDODENDRACEAE, STEGNOSPERMA-CEAE)

Anon. 1981 (Andes) – *Gallesia*.
Dechamps 1985 – *Gallesia*.
Lebacq et al. 1973 – *Gallesia, Phytolacca*.
Mainieri & Chimelo 1989 – *Gallesia, Seguieria*.
Record & Hess 1943 – Family (*Gallesia, Phytolacca, Seguieria*).
Record & Mell 1924 – *Gallesia*.

Anomalous structure
Chalk & Chattaway 1937 – Family (*Gallesia, Seguieria*).
Fahn 1985 – *Phytolacca*.
Kirchoff & Fahn 1984 – *Phytolacca*.
Mikesell 1979 – *Phytolacca*.
Wheat 1977 – *Phytolacca*.

PICRODENDRACEAE
see EUPHORBIACEAE

PIPERACEAE

Araujo & Mattos Filho 1974a – *Piper*.
Burgerstein 1909, 1912 – *Piper*.
Callejas 1986 – *Piper* 7 spp.
Carlquist 1962a – *Macropiper*.
Dadswell & Record 1936 – *Piper*.
Dechamps 1985 – *Piper*.
Ilic 1991 – *Piper*.
Meylan & Butterfield 1978b – *Macropiper*.
Patel & Bowles 1980 – *Macropiper*.
Prakash 1972 – *Piper* (root).
Record & Hess 1943 – *Piper*.
Williams 1936 – *Piper*.

Anomalous structure
Obaton 1960 – *Piper*.
Ravololomaniraka & Koechlin 1970 – *Piper*.

(PIPERACEAE)

Ecological anatomy
Carlquist 1974 – *Macropiper.*

Pits
Meylan & Butterfield 1974 – *Macropiper.*

Septate fibres
Butterfield & Meylan 1976 – *Macropiper.*

Storied structure
Cozzo & Cristiani 1950 – *Piper.*

PITTOSPORACEAE (*Pittosporum* only
unless otherwise indicated)

Brown 1922.
*Carlquist 1981a – *Billardiera, Bursaria,
    Citriobatus, Hymenosporum, Marianthus*
    (= *Billardiera*), *Pittosporum, Sollya.*
Chen & Huang 1986.
Cockrell 1942.
Cutler et al. 1987 – (root).
Desch 1954.
Giordano 1939.
Ilic 1991 – *Hymenosporum, Pittospo-
    rum.*
Kanehira 1921a.
Lecomte 1922.
Lomibao 1973c.
Meylan & Butterfield 1978b.
Moll & Janssonius 1906–1936.
Tang 1973.
Yamabayashi 1938.

Crystals
Baker 1917.
Chattaway 1956 – *Citriobatus, Hymeno-
    sporum, Pittosporum.*

Ecological anatomy
Carlquist 1977c – *Sollya.*
Carlquist 1985a – *Billardiera, Bursaria,
    Marianthus* (= *Billardiera*), *Pittosporum,
    Sollya.*
Van der Graaff & Baas 1974.

Helical thickenings
Meylan & Butterfield 1978a.

Pits
Meylan & Butterfield 1974.

Septate fibres
Butterfield & Meylan 1976.

PLAGIOPTERACEAE (*Plagiopteron*)

Baas et al. 1979 – (twig).

PLANTAGINACEAE (*Plantago*)

Carlquist 1962a, 1970 [1971].
Schweingruber 1990.

Ecological anatomy
Baas & Schweingruber 1987.

PLATANACEAE (*Platanus*)

Baas 1969 – (twig).
Baird 1915.
Barajas Morales 1980.
Brazier & Franklin 1961.
Brush 1917.
Carvalho 1954.
Cheng, C. 1985.
Cheng, J.-Q. 1980.
Cheng, J.-Q. et al. 1992.
Chudnoff 1956.
Cutler et al. 1987 – (root).
Fahn et al. 1986.
Furuno 1985, 1987.
Gajvoronskij 1969 – Fossil and extant spp.
Greguss 1959.
Grosser 1977.
Gziryan 1953.
Hirai 1979–1985.
Ilic 1991.
Jacquiot et al. 1973.
Nájera Angulo & López Fraile 1969.
Niloofari 1961.
Panshin & Zeeuw 1980.
Parsa Pajouh & Schweingruber 1985.
Pérez Olvera & Corral Lopez 1980.
Pérez Olvera et al. 1982 [1985].
Record & Hess 1943.
Schweingruber 1978, 1990.
*Süss & Müller-Stoll 1973, 1975.
Tippo 1938.
Wagenführ & Scheiber 1974.
Wuang 1979.
Yatsenko-Khmelevsky 1954a.

Crystals
Chattaway 1956.

Ecological anatomy
Baas et al. 1983.
Baas & Schweingruber 1987.

(PLATANACEAE)

Carlquist & Hoekman 1985a.
Novruzova 1968.

PLUMBAGINACEAE

Bokhari 1982 – *Limonium.*
Saint-Laurent 1928, 1932a – *Limoniastrum.*
Schweingruber 1990 – *Limoniastrum,*
Limonium.

Ecological anatomy

Baas & Schweingruber 1987 – *Limonias-*
trum, Limonium.

POLEMONIACEAE (incl. COBAEACEAE)

*Carlquist et al. 1984 – *Acanthogilia, Can-*
tua, Cobaea, Eriastrum, Huthia, Ipomop-
sis, Leptodactylon, Loeselia, Phlox.

Ecological anatomy

Carlquist 1985 [1986]a – *Cobaea.*
Carlquist & Hoekman 1985a – *Eriastrum,*
Ipomopsis, Leptodactylon, Phlox.
Patterson & Tanowitz 1989 – *Eriastrum.*

POLYGALACEAE (incl. DICLIDANTHERA-
CEAE, XANTHOPHYLLACEAE)

Böcher & Lyshede 1968 – *Bredemeyera.*
*Bridgwater & Baas 1982 – *Xanthophyllum*
23 spp.
Cheng, J.-Q. 1980 – *Xanthophyllum.*
Cheng, J.-Q. et al. 1992 – *Xanthophyllum.*
Dechamps 1985 – *Bredemeyera.*
Desch 1954 – *Xanthophyllum.*
Détienne 1991 – *Balgoya.*
Falcão et al. 1973 – *Polygala.*
Furuno 1977 – *Xanthophyllum.*
Greguss 1959 – *Polygala.*
Hayashi et al. 1973 – *Xanthophyllum.*
Heimsch 1942 – Family (7 genera).
Ilic 1991 – *Eriandra, Polygala, Securidaca,*
Xanthophyllum.
Lecomte 1926a – *Xanthophyllum.*
Moll & Janssonius 1906–1936 – *Xantho-*
phyllum.
Normand 1955 – *Carpolobia.*
Ogata 1975–1983 – *Xanthophyllum.*
Record & Hess 1943 – Family (*Badiera,*
Bredemeyera, Diclidanthera, Monnina,
Moutabea, Phlebotaenia, Polygala,
Securidaca).

(POLYGALACEAE)

*Styer 1977 – *Barnhartia, Diclidanthera,*
Eriandra, Moutabea.
Sudo 1963, 1988 – *Xanthophyllum.*
Tang 1973 – *Xanthophyllum.*
Yao 1988 – *Xanthophyllum.*

Anomalous structure

Chalk & Chattaway 1937 – Family
(*Polygala, Securidaca*).
O'Donell 1941 – *Diclidanthera.*
Pfeiffer 1925 – *Securidaca.*

Ecological anatomy

Carlquist 1985a – *Monnina, Securidaca.*
Carlquist 1985 [1986]a – *Securidaca.*
Carlquist & Hoekman 1985a – *Polygala.*

POLYGONACEAE

Anon. 1981 (Andes) – *Triplaris.*
Barajas Morales & León Gómez 1989 –
Coccoloba, Ruprechtia.
Benoist 1931 – *Coccoloba.*
Bogdanova 1971 – *Polygonum.*
Burgerstein 1912 – *Ruprechtia.*
Chudnoff 1956 – *Calligonum.*
Cutler et al. 1987 – *Polygonum* (root).
Datta & Deb 1968a – *Rumex.*
Dechamps 1985 – *Coccoloba, Ruprechtia,*
Triplaris.
Détienne & Jacquet 1983 – *Coccoloba,*
Symmeria, Triplaris.
Détienne et al. 1982 – *Coccoloba, Tripla-*
ris.
Fahn & Sarnat 1963 – *Calligonum.*
Fahn et al. 1986 – *Calligonum.*
Greguss 1959 – *Polygonum.*
Horton 1960 – *Delopyrum, Dentoceras,*
Polygonella, Thysanella (all = *Polygo-*
nella) [Abstr.].
Horton 1963 – *Polygonella.*
Ilic 1991 – *Coccoloba, Triplaris.*
Kribs 1928a, 1959 – *Triplaris.*
Lebacq et al. 1973 – *Coccoloba, Triplaris.*
Lepe 1959 – *Coccoloba.*
Messeri 1938 – *Calligonum.*
Parente 1959–1961 – *Triplaris.*
Pérez Mogollón 1973 – *Triplaris.*
Pérez Olvera et al. 1980 [1981] – *Cocco-*
loba.
Pfeiffer, J.P. 1926 – *Triplaris.*
Prakash 1972 – *Coccoloba* (root).

(POLYGONACEAE)

Record & Hess 1943 – Family (*Coccoloba, Gymnopodium, Neomillspaughia, Podopterus, Ruprechtia, Symmeria, Triplaris*).
Record & Mell 1924 – *Coccoloba, Ruprechtia, Triplaris.*
Saint-Laurent 1928, 1932a, 1934 – *Calligonum.*
Schweingruber 1990 – *Polygonum.*
Tortorelli 1956 – *Ruprechtia.*
Urling & Smith 1953 – *Coccoloba.*
Vasilevskaya 1933 – *Calligonum.*
Williams 1936 – *Coccoloba, Symmeria, Triplaris.*
Yatsenko-Khmelevsky 1954a – *Atraphaxis, Calligonum.*

Anomalous structure
Joshi 1931 – *Rumex.*
Men'shchikova 1964, 1965 – *Rumex.*

Crystals and silica
Chattaway 1956 – *Muehlenbeckia, Triplaris.*
Espinoza de Pernía 1987b – *Coccoloba, Ruprechtia, Symmeria, Triplaris.*
Scurfield et al. 1973 – *Triplaris.*
Welle 1976b – *Neomillspaughia, Ruprechtia, Symmeria, Triplaris.*
Ziliani 1987 – *Ruprechtia.*

Ecological anatomy
Baas et al. 1983 – *Calligonum.*
Baas & Schweingruber 1987 – *Polygonum.*
Barajas Morales 1985 – *Coccoloba.*
Carlquist 1985 [1986]a – *Antigonon, Polygonum.*
Carlquist & Hoekman 1985a – *Eriogonum.*
Novruzova 1968 – *Atraphaxis, Calligonum.*
Webber 1936a – *Eriogonum.*

Helical thickenings
Meylan & Butterfield 1978a – *Muehlenbeckia.*

Perforation plates
Meylan & Butterfield 1975 – *Muehlenbeckia.*

Septate fibres
Meylan & Butterfield 1976 – *Muehlenbeckia.*

PORTULACACEAE

Carlquist 1962a – *Talinum.*
*Prabhakar & Ramayya 1979 – *Portulaca, Talinum.*

(PORTULACACEAE)
Ecological anatomy
Carlquist 1974 – *Talinum.*

PRIMULACEAE

Aymard 1968 [1969] – *Lysimachia.*

Ecological anatomy
Carlquist 1974 – *Lysimachia.*

PROTEACEAE

Araujo & Mattos Filho 1974a – *Panopsis.*
Baker 1919 – *Cardwellia, Embothrium, Grevillea, Orites.*
Brazier & Franklin 1961 – *Cardwellia, Grevillea.*
Briggs et al. 1975 – *Placospermum, Sphalmium.*
Carvalho 1954–1956 – *Grevillea.*
Chalk et al. 1935 – *Faurea.*
*Chattaway 1948a – 26 genera.
Cheng, C. 1985 – *Grevillea.*
Cheng, J.-Q. 1980 – *Grevillea, Helicia, Heliciopsis.*
Cheng, J.-Q. et al. 1992 – Same genera as Cheng 1980.
Croptier & Kučera 1990 – *Faurea.*
Dadswell & Eckersley 1935 – *Banksia, Cardwellia, Embothrium, Grevillea, Orites.*
Dechamps 1985 – *Euplassa, Lomatia, Oreocallis, Panopsis, Roupala.*
Desch 1954 – *Helicia.*
Détienne & Jacquet 1983 – *Embothrium, Euplassa, Panopsis, Roupala.*
Détienne et al. 1982 – *Euplassa, Panopsis, Roupala.*
Ferreirinha 1962 – *Faurea.*
Furuno 1977, 1979 – *Cardwellia, Finschia, Oreocallis.*
Garratt 1924 – *Knightia.*
Gasson & Cutler 1990 – *Embothrium* (root).
Giordano 1939 – *Protea.*
Hayashi 1991 – *Helicia.*
Hayashi et al. 1973 – *Helicia.*
Ilic 1991 – 22 genera.
Johnson & Briggs 1975 – Evolution.
Kanehira 1921a, 1926 – *Helicia.*
Kobayashi & Sugawa 1963 – *Grevillea.*
Kribs 1928a – *Panopsis.*
Kribs 1959 – *Cardwellia, Knightia.*

(PROTEACEAE)

Lanyon 1979 – *Dilobeia, Garnieria, Placospermum.*
Lebacq 1955 – *Faurea.*
Lebacq & Dechamps 1964 – *Faurea.*
Lebacq et al. 1973 – *Embothrium, Panopsis, Roupala.*
Lebacq & Staner 1964 – *Faurea, Panopsis.*
Lecomte 1922 – *Dilobeia.*
Luo 1989 – *Grevillea, Helicia.*
Mainieri & Chimelo 1989 – *Euplassa.*
Mennega 1966 – *Euplassa, Panopsis, Roupala.*
Meylan & Butterfield 1978b – *Knightia, Persoonia.*
Moll & Janssonius 1906–1936 – *Helicia.*
Ortiz Cespedes 1959 – *Gevuina.*
Patel 1992 – *Knightia, Persoonia, Toronia.*
Pereira et al. 1970 – *Roupala.*
Pérez Olvera et al. 1982 [1985] – *Grevillea.*
Rancusi et al. 1987 – *Embothrium, Gevuina, Lomatia.*
Record & Hess 1943 – Family (*Embothrium, Gevuina, Lomatia, Panopsis, Roupala*).
Record & Mell 1924 – *Roupala.*
Saiki 1982 – *Cardwellia.*
Scala 1924 – *Lomatia.*
Scala 1929 – *Embothrium.*
Scott 1927 – *Faurea.*
Silva 1971 – *Faurea.*
Stern 1954 – Relations.
Sudo 1959 – *Helicia.*
Sudo 1963 – *Cardwellia, Grevillea.*
Sudo 1988 – *Gevuina, Grevillea.*
Suzuki et al. 1991 – *Helicia.*
Tainter 1968 – *Embothrium, Gevuina, Lomatia.*
Tang 1973 – *Grevillea.*
Tortorelli 1956 – *Embothrium, Lomatia.*
Visser 1966 – *Leucadendron, Protea.*
Wagemann 1949 – *Embothrium, Gevuina, Lomatia.*
Welch 1924 [1925]b – *Carnarvonia, Darlingia, Grevillea, Musgravea, Stenocarpus.*
Williams 1936 – *Embothrium, Panopsis, Roupala.*
Yao 1988 – *Helicia, Heliciopsis.*

Crystals
Chattaway 1955 – *Hakea.*
Chattaway 1956 – *Hakea, Roupala, Stenocarpus.*

(PROTEACEAE)

Hillis & Silva 1979 – *Cardwellia, Orites.*

Ecological anatomy
Carlquist 1977c – *Isopogon, Persoonia, Stirlingia, Xylomelum.*
Carlquist 1985a – 13 genera.

Helical thickenings
Meylan & Butterfield 1978a – *Persoonia.*
Ohtani & Ishida 1978b – *Helicia.*

Pits and perforation plates
Meylan & Butterfield 1974 – *Persoonia.*
Ohtani & Ishida 1978a – *Helicia.*

Rays
Chattaway 1948b – *Banksia.*

Silica
Bamber & Lanyon 1960 – *Stenocarpus.*
Espinoza de Pernía 1987b – *Euplassa, Panopsis, Roupala.*
Butterfield et al. 1974 – *Roupala.*
Welle 1976b – *Euplassa, Panopsis, Roupala.*

Tracheary elements
Ohtani 1983 – *Helicia.*

PSILOXYLACEAE (*Psiloxylon*)

Baas & Zweypfenning 1979.
Schmid 1980.
Van Vliet & Baas 1984 – Relations of myrtalean families.

PTAEROXYLACEAE

Chalk et al. 1935 – *Ptaeroxylon* (in Meliaceae).
Grisa 1988 – *Cedrelopsis.*
Jenkin 1962 – *Ptaeroxylon.*
Leroy 1960 – *Cedrelopsis, Ptaeroxylon.*
Pennington & Styles 1975 – *Cedrelopsis, Ptaeroxylon* (in Meliaceae).
Scott 1927 – *Ptaeroxylon* (in Meliaceae).

PUNICACEAE (*Punica*)

*Bridgwater & Baas 1978.
Fahn et al. 1986.
Greguss 1959.
Hofmann 1955.
Huber & Rouschal 1954.

(PUNICACEAE)
Jacquiot et al. 1973.
Parsa Pajouh & Schweingruber 1985.
Schweingruber 1990.
Shilkina 1973.
Van Vliet & Baas 1984 – Relations of myr-
talean families.

Ecological anatomy
Baas & Schweingruber 1987.
Novruzova 1968.

QUIINACEAE

Dechamps 1985 – *Quiina, Touroulia.*
Détienne & Jacquet 1983 – *Lacunaria, Qui-
ina, Touroulia.*
Détienne et al. 1982 – *Lacunaria, Touroulia.*
*Gottwald & Parameswaran 1967 – *Froesia* 2
spp., *Lacunaria* 8, *Quiina* 24, *Touroulia* 2.
Metcalfe & Chalk 1950 – *Lacunaria, Quiina,
Touroulia.*
Record & Hess 1943 – Family (*Lacunaria,
Quiina*).
Vestal 1937 – *Quiina.*

Crystals
Chattaway 1955 – *Quiina.*

Ecological anatomy
Carlquist 1985a – *Lacunaria, Quiina, Touroulia.*

RANUNCULACEAE
(incl. HYDRASTIDACEAE)

Cutler et al. 1987 – *Clematis* (root).
Fahn et al. 1986 – *Clematis.*
Greguss 1959 – *Clematis.*
Grosser 1977 – *Clematis.*
Lal & Dayal 1984 – *Clematis.*
Lemesle 1948b – *Hydrastis.*
Lemesle 1950b – *Coptis, Hydrastis,
Xanthorhiza* (rhizomes).
Lemesle 1955a – *Hydrastis* relations.
Lemesle 1963a – *Coptis.*
Saint-Laurent 1928, 1934 – *Clematis.*
Schweingruber 1978 – *Clematis.*
Schweingruber 1990 – *Clematis, Helle-
borus, Thalictrum.*
Sieber & Kučera 1980 – *Clematis.*
Takahashi 1985 – *Clematis, Xanthorhiza.*
Yatsenko-Khmelevsky 1954a – *Clematis.*

(RANUNCULACEAE)
Ecological anatomy
Baas & Schweingruber 1987 – *Clematis,
Helleborus, Thalictrum.*
Carlquist 1985a – *Clematis.*
Carlquist & Hoekman 1985a – *Clematis.*

RESEDACEAE

Fahn et al. 1986 – *Ochradenus.*
Schweingruber 1990 – *Reseda.*

Ecological anatomy
Baas et al. 1983 – *Ochradenus.*
Baas & Schweingruber 1987 – *Reseda.*

RETZIACEAE see SOLANACEAE

RHABDODENDRACEAE
(*Rhabdodendron*)

Détienne & Jacquet 1983.
Heimsch 1942.
Milanez 1943 – (in Rutaceae).
*Prance 1968, 1972b.
Record 1933.
Record & Hess 1943 – (in Phytolaccaceae).

Anomalous structure
Chalk & Chattaway 1937.

Silica
Espinoza de Pernía 1987b.
Welle 1976b.

RHAMNACEAE (*Frangula = Rhamnus*)

Anon. 1968 – *Rhamnus.*
Brazier & Franklin 1961 – *Frangula, Maes-
opsis, Rhamnus.*
Brown 1922 – *Alphitonia, Colubrina.*
Burgerstein 1909 – *Alphitonia.*
Burgerstein 1912 – *Ziziphus.*
Cardoso 1960 – *Rhamnus.*
Cellai 1967 – *Ziziphus.*
Cheng, C. 1985 – *Ziziphus.*
Cheng, J.-Q. 1980 – *Hovenia.*
Cheng, J.-Q. et al. 1992 – *Hovenia, Rham-
nus, Ziziphus.*
Chudnoff 1956 – *Paliurus, Rhamnus, Zizi-
phus.*
Chun & Lee 1989 – *Berchemia, Hovenia.*
Cunha Mello 1950 [1951] – *Colubrina.*

(RHAMNACEAE)

Cutler et al. 1987 – *Ceanothus, Rhamnus* (root).

Dechamps 1985 – *Ziziphus.*

Desch 1954 – *Colubrina.*

Détienne & Jacquet 1983 – *Colubrina, Cormonema* (= *Colubrina*), *Rhamnidium, Ziziphus.*

Edlmann & Monaco 1981 – *Berchemia, Hovenia.*

Eeckhout 1951 – *Maesopsis.*

Eggeling & Harris 1939 – *Maesopsis.*

Eyde & Olson 1983 – *Colubrina.*

Fahn et al. 1986 – *Paliurus, Rhamnus, Ziziphus.*

Fasolo 1939–1940 – *Ziziphus.*

Friedman 1978 – *Rhamnus.*

Furuno 1977, 1979 – *Alphitonia, Colubrina, Ziziphus.*

Greguss 1959 – *Paliurus, Rhamnus, Ziziphus.*

Grisa 1988 – *Colubrina.*

Grosser 1977 – *Rhamnus.*

Hayashi 1991 – *Hovenia.*

Heim 1971 – *Rhamnus.*

Hirai 1979–1985 – *Hovenia, Ziziphus.*

Hofmann 1955 – *Paliurus, Rhamnus.*

Huber & Rouschal 1954 – *Paliurus, Rhamnus, Ziziphus.*

Ilic 1991 – *Alphitonia, Colubrina, Emmenosperma, Maesopsis, Pomaderris, Reynosia, Rhamnus, Ziziphus.*

Jacquiot et al. 1973 – *Frangula, Rhamnus.*

Jagiella & Kurschner 1987 – *Rhamnus, Ziziphus.*

Janssonius 1950 – Relations.

Kanehira 1921a – *Paliurus, Rhamnus.*

Kanehira 1921b – *Hovenia.*

Kanehira 1924 – *Ziziphus.*

Kanehira 1926 – *Hovenia.*

Kribs 1959 – *Colubrina, Krugiodendron, Maesopsis, Rhamnus.*

Lebacq & Dechamps 1964 – *Maesopsis.*

Lebacq et al. 1973 – *Krugiodendron, Ziziphus.*

Lomibao 1973c – *Alphitonia.*

Mainieri 1960 – *Colubrina, Rhamnidium.*

Messeri 1938 – *Ziziphus.*

Meylan & Butterfield 1978b – *Discaria.*

Moll & Janssonius 1906–1936 – *Ziziphus.*

(RHAMNACEAE)

Molle 1939 – *Condalia.*

Nardi Berti & Edlmann Abbate 1988 – *Maesopsis.*

Nikitin 1938 – *Frangula, Paliurus, Rhamnus* 11 spp., *Sageretia, Ziziphus.*

Niloofari 1961 – *Rhamnus, Ziziphus.*

Normand 1935 – *Maesopsis.*

Normand 1955 – *Lasiodiscus, Maesopsis.*

Normand & Paquis 1976 [1977] – *Maesopsis.*

Ogata 1975–1983 – *Ziziphus.*

Panshin & Zeeuw 1980 – *Rhamnus.*

Parsa Pajouh & Schweingruber 1985 – *Frangula.*

Paula & Alves 1980 – *Ziziphus.*

Pearson & Brown 1932 – *Ziziphus.*

Peraza Oramas & Lopez de Roma 1967 – *Rhamnus.*

Qian 1988 – *Berchemia, Berchemiella.*

Rao, B.S.S. & Rao, R.V. 1979 – *Gouania.*

Rebollar Dominguez et al. 1987 – *Karwinskia.*

Record 1926b – *Krugiodendron.*

Record 1928a – *Rhamnus.*

*Record 1939a – 14 genera.

Record & Hess 1943 – Family (13 genera).

Saint-Laurent 1928, 1934 – *Rhamnus, Ziziphus.*

Schirarend 1987 – *Krugiodendron.*

*Schirarend 1991 – 18 genera of Zizipheae.

Schirarend & Süss 1985 – *Maesopsis.*

Schweingruber 1978 – *Frangula, Rhamnus.*

Schweingruber 1990 – *Frangula, Paliurus, Rhamnus, Ziziphus.*

Shimaji & Itoh 1988 – *Hovenia, Rhamnus.*

Sudo 1959 – *Hovenia, Rhamnus.*

Sudo 1963 – *Krugiodendron, Maesopsis, Ziziphus.*

Sudo 1988 – *Alphitonia, Emmenosperma, Ziziphus.*

Tang 1973 – *Ziziphus.*

Tortorelli 1956 – *Ziziphus.*

Urling & Smith 1953 – *Krugiodendron.*

Vent et al. 1973 – *Frangula.*

Williams 1936 – *Gouania, Rhamnidium.*

Wuang 1979 – *Ziziphus.*

Yamabayashi 1938 – *Hovenia, Rhamnella, Rhamnus, Sageretia, Ziziphus.*

Yao 1988 – *Hovenia.*

(RHAMNACEAE)

Crystals

Baker 1917 – *Emmenosperma.*
Chattaway 1955 – *Ceanothus, Colubrina, Rhamnus.*
Chattaway 1956 – 10 genera.

Ecological anatomy

Baas et al. 1983 – *Rhamnus, Ziziphus.*
Baas & Schweingruber 1987 – *Frangula, Paliurus, Rhamnus, Ziziphus.*
Carlquist 1977c – *Trymalium.*
Carlquist 1985a – *Adolphia, Ceanothus, Chacaya* (= *Discaria*), *Colletia, Colubrina, Condalia, Rhamnus, Ziziphus.*
Carlquist & Hoekman 1985a – *Adolphia, Ceanothus, Colubrina, Condalia, Rhamnus, Ziziphus.*
Novruzova 1968 – *Paliurus, Rhamnus.*
Van der Graaff & Baas 1974 – *Rhamnus.*
Webber 1936a – *Ceanothus, Rhamnus.*

Helical thickenings

Meylan & Butterfield 1978a – *Discaria.*

Pits and perforation plates

Meylan & Butterfield 1974, 1975 – *Discaria.*
Ohtani & Ishida 1978a – *Hovenia, Ziziphus.*
Roig 1986 [1987] – *Discaria.*

Rays

McLean & Richardson 1973 [1974] – *Condalia.*

Tracheary elements

Ohtani 1983 – *Hovenia, Ziziphus.*

RHIZOPHORACEAE

(incl. ANISOPHYLLEACEAE)

Abbate & Cavina 1980 – *Carallia.*
Araujo & Mattos Filho 1973b – *Cassipourea, Rhizophora, Sterigmapetalum.*
Bargagli-Petrucci 1903 – *Bruguiera.*
Bascopé et al. 1959 – *Rhizophora.*
Benoist 1931 – *Cassipourea.*
Brazier & Franklin 1961 – *Cassipourea, Poga, Rhizophora.*
Burgerstein 1909 – *Rhizophora.*
Carreras 1988 – *Rhizophora.*
Carreras & Vales 1986b – *Rhizophora.*
Cheng, J.-Q. 1980 – *Carallia, Kandelia.*
Cheng, J.-Q. et al. 1992 – *Carallia, Kandelia.*

(RHIZOPHORACEAE)

Croptier & Kučera 1990 – *Cassipourea.*
Dechamps 1985 – *Cassipourea, Rhizophora.*
Desch 1954 – *Anisophyllea, Bruguiera, Carallia, Ceriops, Combretocarpus, Gynotroches, Kandelia, Pellacalyx, Rhizophora.*
Détienne & Jacquet 1983 – *Anisophyllea, Cassipourea, Rhizophora, Sterigmapetalum.*
Détienne et al. 1982 – *Cassipourea, Rhizophora.*
Edlmann Abbate & De Luca 1981 – *Rhizophora.*
Eeckhout 1951 – *Rhizophora.*
Freitas 1988 – *Anisophyllea, Polygonanthus.*
Furuno 1977 – *Bruguiera, Carallia.*
*Geh-Siew-Yin & Keng 1974 – *Anisophyllea, Carallia, Combretocarpus, Gynotroches, Pellacalyx.*
Hayashi et al. 1973 – *Bruguiera, Rhizophora.*
Hayashi & Nomura 1986 – *Carallia.*
Ilic 1991 – 10 genera.
Janssonius 1950 – Relations.
Jentsch et al. 1936–1939 – *Rhizophora.*
Kanehira 1921a – *Bruguiera, Ceriops, Rhizophora.*
Kanehira 1924 – *Carallia.*
Karstedt & Parameswaran 1976 – *Rhizophora.*
Keating & Randrianasolo 1988 – Summary of wood data.
Kribs 1928a – *Cassipourea.*
Kribs 1959 – *Carallia, Poga, Rhizophora.*
Lebacq & Dechamps 1964 – *Anisophyllea, Anopyxis, Cassipourea, Poga, Rhizophora.*
Lebacq & Dechamps 1967 – *Anisophyllea.*
Lebacq et al. 1973 – *Rhizophora.*
Lebacq & Staner 1964 – *Anopyxis, Rhizophora.*
Lecomte 1922 – *Carallia, Macarisia.*
Lecomte 1926a – *Carallia.*
López & Ortega 1989 – *Rhizophora.*
*Marco 1935 – 16 genera.
Martawijaya et al. 1989 – *Bruguiera.*
Martin 1953 – *Rhizophora.*
Metcalfe 1952b – *Anisophyllea* (young).
Moll & Janssonius 1906–1936 – *Bruguiera, Carallia, Gynotroches, Rhizophora.*

(RHIZOPHORACEAE)
Nardi Berti & Edlmann Abbate 1988 – *Poga.*
Normand 1960 – *Anisophyllea, Anopyxis, Cassipourea, Rhizophora.*
Normand & Paquis 1976 [1977] – *Anisophyllea, Anopyxis, Cassipourea, Poga, Rhizophora.*
Ogata 1975–1983 – *Bruguiera, Carallia, Ceriops, Combretocarpus, Kandelia, Rhizophora.*
Panshin 1932 – *Bruguiera, Ceriops, Rhizophora.*
Pearson & Brown 1932 – *Bruguiera, Carallia, Rhizophora.*
Pfeiffer, J.P. 1926 – *Rhizophora.*
Record & Hess 1943 – *Cassipourea, Rhizophora, Sterigmapetalum.*
Riera 1947 – *Poga.*
Souza et al. 1982 – *Rhizophora.*
Sudo 1963 – *Combretocarpus.*
Sudo 1988 – *Bruguiera, Carallia, Ceriops, Rhizophora.*
Tang 1973 – *Carallia.*
Vales & Carreras 1987 – *Rhizophora.*
*Van Vliet 1976a – 18 genera.
Wiraj Chunwarin & Damrong Sri-Aran 1974 – *Bruguiera, Carallia, Ceriops, Rhizophora.*

Crystals
Chattaway 1955 – *Crossostylis.*
Chattaway 1956 – *Anopyxis, Bruguiera, Carallia, Cassipourea, Ceriops, Combretocarpus, Rhizophora.*
Espinoza de Pernía 1987b – *Rhizophora.*

Silica
Butterfield et al. 1974 – *Gynotroches.*

RHOIPTELEACEAE (*Rhoiptelea*)

Chang 1981.
Cheng, J.-Q. 1980.
Cheng, J.-Q. et al. 1992.
Luo 1989.
Tang 1932, 1973.
Tippo 1938.
Withner 1941.
Yao 1988.

RHOPALOCARPACEAE
see SPHAEROSEPALACEAE

RORIDULACEAE

*Carlquist 1976c – *Roridula.*

ROSACEAE
(see also CHRYSOBALANACEAE)
(*Amygdalus, Cerasus* & *Pygeum* = *Prunus*, *Pourthiaea* = *Photinia*)

Anon. 1966 – *Prunus.*
Ancibor 1984 – *Polylepis.*
Baas et al. 1984 – *Crataegus, Prunus.*
Baird & Thieret 1989 – *Mespilus* (anatomy by M.H. Hils).
Barajas Morales 1980 – *Crataegus, Prunus.*
Barbosa et al. 1977–1978 – *Prunus.*
Benoist 1931 – *Prunus.*
Brazier & Franklin 1961 – *Crataegus, Malus, Prunus, Pygeum, Pyrus, Sorbus.*
Burgerstein 1898 – 20 genera of Pomoideae.
Burgerstein 1899 – *Prunus* more than 50 spp. (mostly branches).
Burgerstein 1912 – *Polylepis.*
Carvalho 1954–1955, 1956 – *Prunus.*
Cheng, C. 1985 – *Photinia, Pyrus.*
Cheng, J.-Q. 1980 – *Eriobotrya, Photinia, Prunus, Pygeum, Pyrus.*
Cheng, J.-Q. et al. 1992 – *Eriobotrya, Malus, Photinia, Prunus, Pygeum, Pyrus, Sorbus.*
Chudnoff 1956 – *Crataegus, Pyrus.*
Cristiani 1961b – *Cotoneaster, Crataegus, Pyracantha.*
Cutler et al. 1987 – 14 genera (root).
Daniel 1916 – *Malus, Pyrus, Sorbus.*
Dechamps 1985 – *Polylepis, Prunus.*
Desch 1954 – *Eriobotrya, Pygeum.*
Descole & O'Donell 1937 – *Prunus.*
Détienne & Jacquet 1983 – *Prunus.*
Détienne et al. 1982 – *Prunus.*
Doležal 1959 – *Pygeum.*
Edlmann & Monaco 1981 – *Crataegus, Malus, Prunus, Pyrus, Sorbus.*
Fabbri Tarchi 1960 – *Prunus, Pyrus, Rosa, Spiraea.*
Fahn et al. 1986 – 11 genera.
Fegel 1941 – *Prunus* (root).
Freitas 1958 – *Pygeum.*
Friedman 1978 – *Holodiscus, Osmaronia (= Oemleria), Prunus, Pyrus, Rosa, Rubus, Spiraea.*

(ROSACEAE)
Furuno 1979 – *Prunus*.
Furuno 1985, 1987 – *Malus, Prunus*.
Gabrielyan 1954 – *Sorbus* 12 spp.
Gabrielyan 1971 – *Micromeles* (= *Sorbus*), *Sorbus*.
Gabrielyan 1978 – *Sorbus*.
Greguss 1959 – 16 genera.
Grosser 1977 – *Crataegus, Prunus, Pyrus, Rosa, Sorbus*.
Gziryan 1952 – *Armeniaca* (= *Prunus*).
Hayashi 1991 – *Amelanchier, Malus, Pourthiaea, Prunus, Pyrus, Sorbus*.
Hayashi et al. 1973 – *Prunus*.
Hirai 1979–1985 – *Eriobotrya, Malus, Photinia, Pourthiaea, Prunus, Pyrus, Sorbus*.
Hofmann 1955 – *Crataegus, Prunus*.
Huber & Rouschal 1954 – *Amelanchier, Amygdalus, Cotoneaster, Sorbus*.
Ilic 1991 – *Amelanchier, Cercocarpus, Crataegus, Malus, Prunus, Pygeum, Pyrus, Sorbus*.
Jacquiot et al. 1973 – 11 genera.
Jagiella & Kurschner 1987 – *Rosa*.
Kanehira 1921a – *Cotoneaster, Eriobotrya, Malus, Photinia, Prinsepia, Prunus, Rhaphiolepis, Stranvaesia*.
Kanehira 1921b – *Amelanchier, Eriobotrya, Micromeles* (= *Sorbus*), *Photinia, Prunus, Sorbus*.
Kanehira 1924 – *Pygeum*.
Kanehira 1926 – *Amelanchier, Eriobotrya, Micromeles* (= *Sorbus*), *Photinia, Pourthiaea, Prunus, Sorbus*.
Kribs 1959 – *Cercocarpus, Prunus, Pygeum, Pyrus, Vauquelinia*.
Latorre 1979 – *Prunus*.
Lebacq 1957 – *Hagenia, Pygeum*.
Lebacq & Dechamps 1964 – *Hagenia, Pygeum*.
Lebacq et al. 1973 – *Kageneckia, Polylepis, Prunus*.
Lebedenko 1962a – *Hagenia, Pygeum*.
Lecomte 1926a – *Rhaphiolepis*.
Lotova 1958, 1960 – *Malus*.
Luo 1989 – *Prunus, Pygeum, Pyrus, Sorbus*.
Mainieri & Chimelo 1989 – *Prunus*.
Miller, H.J. 1975 – *Dryas*.
Moll & Janssonius 1906–1936 – *Eriobotrya, Photinia, Prunus, Pygeum*.

(ROSACEAE)
Mork 1946 – *Prunus, Sorbus*.
Nagy & Veress 1961 – *Sorbus*.
Niloofari 1961 – *Crataegus, Cydonia, Mespilus, Prunus, Pyrus*.
Novruzova 1964a – *Crataegus*.
Novruzova 1964c – *Cerasus*.
Novruzova & Gadzhieva 1974 – *Rosa*.
Oprea 1972 [1974] – *Amygdalus, Cerasus, Crataegus, Malus, Padus* (= *Prunus*), *Persica* (= *Prunus*), *Prunus, Pyrus, Sorbus*.
Panshin & Zeeuw 1980 – *Prunus*.
Parsa Pajouh & Schweingruber 1985 – *Crataegus, Mespilus, Prunus, Pyrus*.
Pearson & Brown 1932 – *Prunus*.
Peraza Oramas & Lopez de Roma 1967 – *Prunus*.
Pérez Mogollón 1993 – *Hesperomeles*.
Pérez Olvera et al. 1982 [1985] – *Prunus*.
Poller 1967 – *Pygeum*.
Prance 1965 – *Stylobasium* (or Stylobasiaceae).
Rancusi et al. 1987 – *Kageneckia, Quillaja*.
Record & Hess 1943 – Family (14 genera).
Riedl 1937 – *Prunus* (root).
Saiki 1982 – *Prunus*.
Saint-Laurent 1928, 1934 – *Amelanchier, Cotoneaster, Crataegus, Prunus, Pyrus, Rosa, Rubus, Sorbus*.
Schweingruber 1974 – *Amelanchier, Cotoneaster, Crataegus, Cydonia, Mespilus, Pyrus, Sorbus*.
Schweingruber 1978 – *Amelanchier, Cotoneaster, Crataegus, Cydonia, Mespilus, Prunus, Pyrus, Rosa, Sorbus*.
Schweingruber 1990 – 20 genera.
Shafranova 1968 – *Potentilla*.
Shimaji & Itoh 1982 – *Prunus*.
Shimaji & Itoh 1988 – *Pourthiaea, Prunus, Sorbus*.
Snezhkova 1977 – *Sorbus*.
Snezhkova 1979 – *Crataegus*.
Sudo 1959 – *Amelanchier, Malus, Photinia, Pourthiaea, Prunus, Pyrus, Sorbus*.
Sudo 1963 – *Cercocarpus, Pygeum*.
Suzuki et al. 1991 – *Prunus, Pyracantha, Pyrus, Rosa, Sorbaria, Sorbus*.
Tang 1973 – *Photinia, Prunus*.
Thunell & Perem 1947 – *Prunus, Pyrus*.
Tippo 1938 – Family (many genera).
Tumanyan 1947 – *Malus, Pyrus*.
Tumanyan 1949 – *Sorbus* 8 spp.

(ROSACEAE)
*Tumanyan 1950 – Pomoideae (15 genera).
Tumanyan 1954 – *Pyrus*.
Wagemann 1949 – *Kageneckia, Quillaja*.
Wagenführ & Scheiber 1974 – *Prunus, Pyrus, Sorbus*.
Wang 1966 – *Prunus*.
Wuang 1979 – *Malus, Pyrus, Sorbus*.
Yamabayashi 1938 – 11 genera.
Yao 1988 – *Pyrus*.
Yaskevich 1956 – *Amygdalus*.
Yatsenko-Khmelevsky 1954a – 20 genera.
*Zhang 1992 – 62 genera, 280 spp.
*Zhang & Baas 1992 – 30 genera, 162 spp.

Crystals
Chattaway 1955 – *Prunus, Pygeum*.
Chattaway 1956 – *Amelanchier, Cercocarpus, Crataegus, Heteromeles (= Photinia), Rhaphiolepis*.
Yatsenko-Khmelevsky 1933 – *Cerasus, Cotoneaster, Crataegus*.

Ecological anatomy
Baas 1973 – *Prunus*.
Baas et al. 1983 – *Amygdalus, Cerasus, Crataegus, Eriolobus (= Malus), Prunus, Pyrus, Rosa, Sarcopoterium*.
Baas & Schweingruber 1987 – 18 genera.
Carlquist 1985a – *Holodiscus, Kerria, Prunus, Spiraea*.
Carlquist 1985 [1986]a – *Rosa*.
Carlquist & Hoekman 1985a – 17 genera.
Lim & Soh 1991a – *Prunus*.
Novruzova 1962b – *Cerasus, Crataegus, Malus, Pyrus*.
Novruzova 1968 – 14 genera.
Webber 1936a – *Adenostoma, Amelanchier, Cercocarpus, Coleogyne, Photinia, Prunus, Purshia*.
*Zhang et al. 1992 – 62 genera.

Growth rings
Fahn 1953 – *Crataegus*.
Paolis 1950 – *Prunus*.
Trautner-Jäger 1962 – *Polylepis*.

Helical thickenings
Ohtani & Ishida 1978b – *Eriobotrya, Malus, Photinia, Pourthiaea, Prunus, Sorbus*.
Parham & Kaustinen 1973 – *Prunus*.

(ROSACEAE)
Pits and perforation plates
Meylan & Butterfield 1974 – *Rubus*.
Ohtani & Ishida 1978a -- *Eriobotrya, Malus, Photinia, Pourthiaea, Prunus, Sorbus*.

Tracheary elements
Carlquist 1988f – *Cotoneaster, Holodiscus, Prunus, Rubus, Spiraea*.
Jing et al. 1989 – *Cerasus, Malus, Sorbus*.
Ohtani 1983 – *Eriobotrya, Malus, Photinia, Pourthiaea, Prunus, Sorbus*.

RUBIACEAE
(incl. DIALYPETALANTHACEAE)
(*Anthocephalus = Breonia, Sickingia = Simira*)

Anon. 1981 (Andes) – *Calycophyllum*.
Abbate 1971a – *Adina*.
Abbate 1977 – *Adina, Gardenia*.
Aiello 1979 – *Cigarrilla, Portlandia*.
Ayensu & Bentum 1974 – *Mitragyna, Nauclea*.
Babos & Vales 1977 [1978] – *Ceratopyxis*.
Barajas Morales & León Gómez 1989 – *Exostema, Guettarda, Hintonia*.
Barbosa et al. 1977–1978 – *Rudgea*.
Bargagli-Petrucci 1903 – *Mussaendopsis, Sarcocephalus*.
Bascopé 1954 – *Cinchona*.
Benoist 1931 – *Genipa, Palicourea*.
Brazier & Franklin 1961 – *Adina, Calycophyllum, Gardenia, Mitragyna, Nauclea*.
Bridson et al. 1980 – *Phellocalyx*.
Brown 1922 – *Bobea, Coprosma, Gardenia, Morinda, Plectronia (= Canthium), Psychotria, Straussia (= Psychotria)*.
Burgerstein 1909 – *Gardenia, Hydnophytum, Ixora, Morinda, Mussaenda, Psychotria, Randia, Sarcocephalus*.
Burgerstein 1912 – *Calycophyllum, Coutarea*.
Cardoso 1961 – *Adina*.
Chalk et al. 1933 – *Mitragyna*.
Chauhan & Dayal 1987 – *Adina, Mitragyna*.
Cheng, C. 1985 – *Adina*.
Cheng, J.-Q. 1980 – 10 genera.
Cheng, J.-Q. et al. 1992 – 10 genera.
Cockrell 1942 – *Urophyllum*.
Corral Lopez 1985 – *Guettarda, Sickingia*.
Cunha Mello 1950 [1951] – *Alseis*.

(RUBIACEAE)

Cunha Mello 1967 – *Ferdinandusa.*
Cunha Mello 1971b – *Genipa.*
Dadswell & Eckersley 1935 – *Sarcocephalus.*
Darwin 1977 – *Mastixiodendron.*
Dechamps 1985 – 27 genera.
Desch 1954 – 18 genera.
Descole & O'Donell 1937 – *Basanacantha* (= *Randia*).
Détienne & Jacquet 1983 – 33 genera.
Détienne et al. 1982 – *Amaioua, Capirona, Chimarrhis, Coussarea, Duroia, Genipa, Isertia, Palicourea, Posoqueria.*
Donaldson 1984 – *Anthocephalus.*
Eeckhout 1951 – *Corynanthe, Mitragyna, Sarcocephalus.*
Ferreirinha 1955 – *Adina.*
Ferreirinha 1958 – *Nauclea.*
Fouarge & Gérard 1964 – *Aidia, Corynanthe.*
Fouarge et al. 1953 – *Mitragyna, Sarcocephalus.*
Francis 1926 – *Canthium.*
Freitas 1955 – *Sarcocephalus, Timonius.*
Freitas 1971 – *Adina.*
Freitas 1987 – *Morinda.*
Fundter & Wisse 1977 – *Adina, Mastixiodendron, Nauclea.*
Furuno 1977, 1979 – *Anthocephalus, Mastixiodendron, Mitragyna, Nauclea, Neonauclea, Timonius.*
Gaiotti de Peralta & Edlmann Abbate 1981 – *Calycophyllum.*
Giordano 1939–1940 – *Canthium, Galiniera, Gardenia.*
Grisa 1988 – *Breonia, Hymenodictyon.*
Hirai 1979–1985 – *Anthocephalus.*
*Hogeweg & Koek-Noorman 1975 – Numerical taxonomy of family.
Hoheisel et al. 1968 – *Genipa, Warszewiczia.*
Ilic 1991 – 30 genera.
Jagiella & Kurschner 1987 – *Breonadia.*
Janssonius 1950 – Relations.
Kanehira 1921a – *Chomelia, Diplospora, Gardenia, Morinda, Nauclea, Psychotria, Randia, Timonius, Wendlandia.*
Kanehira 1924 – *Neonauclea.*
Kobayashi & Sugawa 1963 – *Anthocephalus.*
Kobayashi & Sugawa 1972 – *Adina.*

(RUBIACEAE)

*Koek-Noorman 1968, 1969 – Numerous South American genera.
*Koek-Noorman 1970 – 19 genera of Cinchoneae, Coptosapelteae & Naucleeae.
*Koek-Noorman 1972 – 41 genera of Gardenieae, Ixoreae & Mussaendeae.
Koek-Noorman 1976 – *Rubia.*
*Koek-Noorman 1977 – Summary paper.
*Koek-Noorman 1980 – *Gleasonia, Henriquezia, Platycarpum.*
*Koek-Noorman & Hogeweg 1974 – Numerous genera of Vanguerieae, Cinchoneae, Condamineae & Rondeletieae.
*Koek-Noorman & Puff 1983 – 15 genera of Anthospermeae & Paederieae.
Koek-Noorman & Puff 1991 – *Paederia.*
Kribs 1928a – *Amaioua, Isertia, Palicourea, Psychotria.*
Kribs 1959 – *Adina, Calycophyllum, Corynanthe, Genipa, Mitragyna, Neonauclea, Pausinystalia, Sarcocephalus.*
Larrieu 1930 – *Mitragyna.*
Lebacq & Dechamps 1964 – 20 genera.
Lebacq & Dechamps 1967 – 14 genera.
Lebacq et al. 1973 – 29 genera.
Lebacq & Staner 1964 – *Nauclea.*
Lecomte 1922 – *Breonia, Craterispermum, Nauclea, Pyrostria, Schismatoclada.*
Lecomte 1926a – *Adina, Anthocephalus, Canthium, Randia, Wendlandia.*
Lemesle 1947c – *Cephaelis* (= *Psychotria*), *Manettia, Psychotria, Richardsonia* (= *Richardia*), *Uragoga* (= *Psychotria*).
Lemesle 1953, 1956b – *Uragoga* (= *Psychotria*).
Leroy 1975 – *Hallea, Mitragyna.*
Lomibao 1975 – *Adina, Canthium, Greeniopsis, Guettarda, Neonauclea.*
Luo 1989 – *Adina, Anthocephalus, Neonauclea, Tarenna.*
Mainieri 1960, 1978 – *Sickingia.*
Mainieri & Chimelo 1989 – *Sickingia.*
Marchiori 1987 – *Randia.*
Martawijaya et al. 1989 – *Anthocephalus.*
Meylan & Butterfield 1978b – *Coprosma.*
Milanez 1936a – *Calycophyllum.*
Moll & Janssonius 1906–1936 – 27 genera.
Monteiro & França 1971 – *Corynanthe.*
Nardi Berti & Edlmann Abbate 1988 – *Corynanthe, Mitragyna, Nauclea, Pausinystalia.*

(RUBIACEAE)

Nardi Berti & Edlmann Abbate 1992 – *Calycophyllum.*

Normand 1960 – *Canthium, Corynanthe, Gaertnera, Gardenia, Mitragyna, Morinda, Nauclea.*

Normand & Paquis 1976 [1977] – *Brenania, Canthium, Craterispermum, Gaertnera, Hallea, Hymenodictyon, Morinda, Nauclea, Pausinystalia* and briefer notes on other genera.

Ogata 1975–1983 – *Adina, Anthocephalus, Gardenia, Mastixiodendron, Nauclea, Neonauclea.*

Ortega 1958 – *Alseis, Sickingia.*

Ortega et al. 1988 – *Coffea.*

Panshin 1932 – *Scyphiphora.*

Pearson & Brown 1932 – 10 genera.

Pérez Mogollón 1993 – *Cinchona, Guettarda.*

Pérez Olvera et al. 1980 [1981] – *Alseis, Blepharidium, Exostema, Guettarda.*

Pfeiffer, J.P. 1926 – *Genipa.*

Prakash 1972 – *Coffea* (root).

Purkayastha et al. 1976 – *Mitragyna, Nauclea.*

Record 1932a – *Ladenbergia.*

Record 1932c – *Gleasonia.*

Record 1938c – *Pagamea.*

Record 1942b – *Balmea.*

Record & Garratt 1925 – *Gardenia.*

Record & Hess 1943 – Family (58 genera + *Pagamea* in Loganiaceae).

Record & Mell 1924 – *Calycophyllum, Genipa, Sickingia.*

Richter & Schmitt 1987 – *Cosmocalyx.*

Ridsdale et al. 1972 – *Versteegia.*

Riera 1947 – *Mitragyna, Sarcocephalus.*

Rogers 1981, 1984 – *Gleasonia, Henriquezia, Platycarpum.*

Rozmarin et al. 1983 – *Nauclea.*

Saint-Laurent 1928 – *Crucianella, Putoria, Rubia.*

Schmidt 1951–1952 – *Mitragyna.*

Schweingruber 1990 – *Asperula, Crucianella, Galium, Putoria, Rubia.*

Scott 1927 – *Adina.*

Sudo 1963 – *Adina, Anthocephalus, Calycophyllum, Mitragyna, Nauclea, Neonauclea, Sarcocephalus, Sickingia.*

(RUBIACEAE)

Sudo 1988 – *Anthocephalus, Antirhea, Mastixiodendron, Neonauclea, Sarcocephalus, Timonius.*

Tang 1973 – *Adina, Anthocephalus, Gardenia, Mitragyna.*

Tortorelli 1956 – *Calycophyllum.*

Tunman 1908 – *Morinda.*

Urling & Smith 1953 – *Cephalanthus.*

Vales & Babos 1977 – *Ceratopyxis.*

Vales & Süss 1985a – *Acunaeanthus, Ariadne, Neomazaea (= Mazaea).*

Vales & Süss 1985b – *Ceratopyxis, Phyllomelia.*

Wagenführ & Scheiber 1974 – *Mitragyna.*

Wang 1984–1988 – *Anthocephalus, Neonauclea.*

*Welle et al. 1983 – *Antirhea* 4 spp., *Bobea* 5, *Chomelia* 5, *Dichilanthe* 1, *Guettarda* 15, *Machaonia* 2, *Malanea* 3, *Timonius* 4.

Williams 1936 – 37 genera.

Wiraj Chunwarin & Damrong Sri-Aran 1974 – *Adina, Anthocephalus, Gardenia, Hymenodictyon, Mitragyna, Morinda.*

Yamabayashi 1938 – *Adina.*

Yao 1988 – *Adina, Anthocephalus.*

Anomalous structure

Obaton 1960 – *Mussaenda.*

Crystals

Chattaway 1955 – 12 genera.

Chattaway 1956 – *Alseis, Coffea, Randia.*

Butterfield et al. 1973 – *Hamelia, Morinda, Randia.*

Ecological anatomy

Baas & Schweingruber 1987 – *Asperula, Crucianella, Galium, Putoria, Rubia.*

Carlquist 1985 [1986]a – *Chiococca.*

Carlquist & Hoekman 1985a – *Galium.*

Den Outer & Van Veenendaal 1976 – *Canthium, Gaertnera, Morinda, Nauclea, Oxyanthus, Pavetta.*

Versteegh 1968 – *Amaracarpus.*

Webber 1936a – *Galium.*

Helical thickenings

Meylan & Butterfield 1978a – *Coprosma.*

Nair 1987 – *Meyna.*

Pits and perforation plates

Jing et al. 1988 – *Anthocephalus.*

Meylan & Butterfield 1974, 1975 – *Coprosma.*

(RUBIACEAE)

Nair & Ram 1989 – *Anthocephalus, Catunaregam, Haldina, Hymenodictyon, Meyna, Mitragyna, Morinda.*
Ohtani 1986 – *Lasianthus* (vestures).
Ohtani 1987 – *Damnacanthus* (vestures and warts).
Ohtani et al. 1983 – *Coprosma* (warts).
Rudall 1982 – *Canthium.*
Vales 1983a, b – *Acunaeanthus, Ariadne, Ceratopyxis, Neomazaea* (= *Mazaea*), *Phyllomelia.*

Septate fibres
Butterfield & Meylan 1976 – *Coprosma.*

Silica
Butterfield et al. 1974 – *Mitragyna.*

Tracheary elements
Gill et al. 1985b – *Mitragyna.*
Gill & Onuja 1984a – *Canthium, Nauclea.*
Jing et al. 1989 – *Anthocephalus, Gardenia.*

RUTACEAE
(*Fagara = Zanthoxylum, Xanthoxylum = Zanthoxylum*)

Anon. 1966 – *Phellodendron.*
Abbate & Cavina 1980 – *Chloroxylon.*
Albuquerque & Honda 1972 – *Fagara.*
Barajas Morales & León Gómez 1989 – *Esenbeckia.*
Bascopé 1954 – *Zanthoxylum.*
Bastos 1946 [1947] – *Euxylophora.*
Brazier & Franklin 1961 – *Citrus, Fagara, Fagaropsis, Flindersia.*
Brown 1922 – *Melicope, Pelea* (= *Melicope*), *Platydesma, Zanthoxylum.*
Burgerstein 1909 – *Citrus, Euodia, Micromelum.*
Burgerstein 1912 – *Zanthoxylum.*
Carreras & Pérez 1988 – *Zanthoxylum.*
Cheng, C. 1985 – *Euodia, Phellodendron.*
Cheng, J.-Q. 1980 – *Acronychia, Euodia.*
Cheng, J.-Q. et al. 1992 – *Acronychia, Euodia, Phellodendron.*
Cockrell 1935 – New genus near *Murraya* (*Burkillanthus*).
Cockrell 1942 – *Euodia, Merrillia, Micromelum, Tetractomia.*
Cozzo 1960 – *Balfourodendron.*
Cunha Mello 1950 [1951] – *Dictyoloma.*

(RUTACEAE)

Cutler et al. 1987 – *Skimmia* (root).
Dadswell & Eckersley 1934 – *Acradenia.*
Dadswell & Eckersley 1935 – *Acradenia, Flindersia, Halfordia, Phebalium.*
Dadswell & Eckersley 1938a – 11 genera.
Dechamps 1985 – *Fagara, Helietta, Zanthoxylum.*
Desch 1954 – *Acronychia, Burkillanthus, Euodia, Merrillia, Murraya, Tetractomia, Zanthoxylum.*
Détienne & Jacquet 1983 – *Adiscanthus, Balfourodendron, Euxylophora, Hortia, Spathelia, Zanthoxylum.*
Détienne et al. 1982 – *Zanthoxylum.*
Edlmann & Monaco 1981 – *Euodia, Phellodendron.*
Eeckhout 1951 – *Fagara.*
Fahn et al. 1986 – *Citrus, Ruta.*
Fouarge & Gérard 1964 – *Fagara.*
Freitas 1963 – *Aegle.*
Freitas 1987 – *Fagara.*
Fundter & Wisse 1977 – *Flindersia.*
Furuno 1977, 1979 – *Euodia, Flindersia, Geijera, Halfordia.*
Gaiotti de Peralta & Edlmann Abbate 1981 – *Zanthoxylum.*
Gasson & Cutler 1990 – *Euodia* (root).
Giordano 1939–1940 – *Clausena, Clausenopsis* (= *Fagaropsis*).
Goldblatt et al. 1985 – *Empleuridium.*
Greguss 1959 – *Citrus, Ptelea.*
Grisa 1988 – *Zanthoxylum.*
Harrar 1937 – *Flindersia* 10 spp.
Hayashi 1991 – *Phellodendron, Zanthoxylum.*
Hayashi et al. 1973 – *Merrillia.*
Hayashi & Nomura 1986 – *Chloroxylon.*
Hedayetullah & Chakravarty 1942 – *Chloroxylon, Murraya.*
Heimsch 1942 – 63 genera.
Hirai 1979–1985 – *Fagara, Phellodendron, Zanthoxylum.*
Huber & Rouschal 1954 – *Citrus.*
Ilic 1991 – 25 genera.
Jagiella & Kurschner 1987 – *Teclea.*
Janssonius 1950 – Relations.
Kaastra 1982 – *Esenbeckia, Pilocarpus.*
Kanehira 1921a – *Acronychia, Clausena, Euodia, Fagara, Murraya, Phellodendron, Skimmia, Zanthoxylum.*

(RUTACEAE)
Kanehira 1921b – *Orixa, Phellodendron, Zanthoxylum.*
Kanehira 1924 – *Murraya.*
Kanehira 1926 – *Orixa, Phellodendron.*
Kribs 1959 – 10 genera.
Lebacq 1963 – *Fagara.*
Lebacq & Dechamps 1964 – *Fagara, Vepris.*
Lebacq & Dechamps 1967 – *Fagara,* cf. *Vepris.*
Lebacq et al. 1973 – *Dictyoloma, Pilocarpus, Zanthoxylum.*
Lecomte 1922 – *Toddalia.*
Lecomte 1926a – *Acronychia, Feronia* (= *Limonia*), *Murraya.*
Leprince 1911 – *Zanthoxylum.*
Loureiro et al. 1981 – *Zanthoxylum.*
Luo 1989 – *Acronychia, Euodia.*
Mainieri 1978 – *Balfourodendron, Esenbeckia, Helietta.*
Mainieri & Chimelo 1989 – *Balfourodendron, Esenbeckia, Helietta.*
Mainieri & Steigleder 1968 – *Helietta.*
Martin 1953 – *Fagara.*
Metcalfe 1935 – *Amyris.*
Meylan & Butterfield 1978b – *Melicope.*
*Milanez 1943 – 11 genera.
Milanez 1945 – Key + *Dictyoloma.*
Moll & Janssonius 1906–1936 – 12 genera.
Mziray 1992 – *Teclea, Toddalia, Toddaliopsis, Vepris.*
Nardi Berti & Edlmann Abbate 1988 – *Fagara, Fagaropsis.*
Nardi Berti & Edlmann Abbate 1992 – *Balfourodendron, Euxylophora, Zanthoxylum.*
Nikitin 1934 – *Phellodendron.*
Normand 1955 – *Araliopsis, Fagara, Oricia.*
Normand & Paquis 1976 [1977] – *Araliopsis, Fagara, Oricia, Vepris.*
Ogata 1975–1983 – *Euodia, Flindersia.*
Ortega 1958 – *Zanthoxylum.*
Pearson & Brown 1932 – *Aegle, Atalantia, Chloroxylon, Euodia, Feronia* (= *Limonia*), *Limonia, Murraya, Zanthoxylum.*
Pereira 1933 – *Balfourodendron, Esenbeckia.*
Pereira et al. 1970 – *Hortia.*
Pérez Mogollón 1993 – *Zanthoxylum.*
Pfeiffer, J.P. 1926 – Indet.
Prakash 1972 – *Murraya, Pilocarpus* (root).

(RUTACEAE)
Purkayastha et al. 1976 – *Murraya.*
Record & Garratt 1925 – *Esenbeckia.*
*Record & Hess 1940c – 24 genera.
Record & Hess 1943 – Family (25 genera).
Record & Mell 1924 – *Amyris, Balfourodendron, ?Esenbeckia, Euxylophora, Zanthoxylum.*
Rock 1972 – *Amyris, Citrus, Zanthoxylum.*
Rozmarin et al. 1983 – *Fagara.*
Schmidt 1951–1952 – *Balfourodendron.*
Schweingruber 1990 – *Citrus, Ruta.*
Scott 1927 – *Calodendrum, Fagara, Vepris.*
Shimaji & Itoh 1988 – *Fagara, Orixa, Phellodendron.*
Stern & Brizicky 1960 – *Diomma, Sohnreyia* (both = *Spathelia*).
Sudo 1959 – *Phellodendron, Zanthoxylum.*
Sudo 1963 – *Amyris, Balfourodendron, Chloroxylon, Citrus, Euxylophora, Fagara, Flindersia, Murraya, Zanthoxylum.*
Sudo 1988 – *Euodia, Flindersia, Geijera, Halfordia.*
Sudworth & Mell 1911c – *Zanthoxylum.*
Tang 1973 – *Phellodendron, Zanthoxylum.*
Thunell & Perem 1947 – *Chloroxylon.*
Tortorelli 1956 – *Balfourodendron, Fagara, Helietta.*
Urling & Smith 1953 – *Zanthoxylum.*
Wagenführ & Scheiber 1974 – *Fagara.*
Wang 1984–1988 – *Euodia.*
Welch 1931a – *Flindersia.*
Williams 1936 – *Citrus, Dictyoloma, Erythrochiton, Zanthoxylum.*
Wiraj Chunwarin & Damrong Sri-Aran 1973 – *Murraya.*
Wuang 1979 – *Euodia.*
Yamabayashi 1938 – *Citrus, Euodia, Fagara, Phellodendron, Poncirus, Zanthoxylum.*
Yao 1988 – *Euodia, Phellodendron.*

Canals
Welch 1931b – *Flindersia.*

Crystals and silica
Baker 1917 – *Bosistoa, Flindersia.*
Bamber & Lanyon 1960 – *Medicosma, Pleiococca* (= *Acronychia*).
Chattaway 1956 – 22 genera.
Espinoza de Pernía 1987b – *Erythrochiton, Fagara, Galipea, Zanthoxylum.*
Hillis & Silva 1979 – *Chloroxylon.*

(RUTACEAE)
Butterfield et al. 1974 – *Euodia.*
Sudo et al. 1967 – *Euodia.*
Welle 1976b – *Erythrochiton, Galipea.*

Ecological anatomy
Baas et al. 1983 – *Ruta.*
Baas & Schweingruber 1987 – *Ruta.*
Carlquist 1977c – *Boronia, Chorilaena, Diplolaena, Eriostemon, Geleznowia, Phebalium.*
Carlquist 1985a – *Acradenia, Boronia, Choisya, Cneoridium, Correa, Eriostemon, Ptelea, Skimmia, Thamnosma.*
Carlquist & Hoekman 1985a – *Cneoridium, Thamnosma.*
Webber 1936a – *Cneoridium.*

Helical thickenings
Ohtani & Ishida 1978b – *Phellodendron.*

Pits and perforation plates
Meylan & Butterfield 1974 – *Melicope.*
Ohtani & Ishida 1978a – *Phellodendron, Zanthoxylum.*
Sharma et al. 1985 – *Euodia.*

Tracheary elements
Gill & Onuja 1984a – *Fagara.*
Ohtani 1983 – *Phellodendron, Zanthoxylum.*

SABIACEAE
(for *Meliosma* see MELIOSMACEAE)

Dadswell & Record 1936 – *Sabia.*
Heimsch 1942 – *Sabia.*

Ecological anatomy
Carlquist 1985 [1986]a – *Sabia.*

SACCIFOLIACEAE

Maguire & Pires 1978 – *Saccifolium.*

SALICACEAE

Anon. 1966 – *Populus.*
Abbate 1970 – *Salix.*
Acar 1973 [1974] – *Populus.*
Brazier & Franklin 1961 – *Populus, Salix.*
Burgerstein 1912 – *Salix.*
Carvalho 1954–1956 – *Populus, Salix.*
Cheng, C. 1985 – *Populus, Salix.*

(SALICACEAE)
Cheng, J.-Q. 1980 – *Populus, Salix.*
Cheng, J.-Q. et al. 1992 – *Chosenia* (= *Salix*), *Populus, Salix.*
Chudnoff 1956 – *Populus, Salix.*
Cutler et al. 1987 – *Populus, Salix* (root).
Dechamps 1985 – *Salix.*
Derviz-Sokolova 1966 – *Salix.*
Derviz-Sokolova & Katumba 1975a, b – *Salix.*
Détienne & Jacquet 1983 – *Salix.*
Detzner 1910 – *Populus, Salix* (root).
Edlmann & Monaco 1981 – *Populus, Salix.*
Fahn et al. 1986 – *Salix.*
Fegel 1941 – *Populus* (root).
Filipovici et al. 1962 – *Populus.*
Friedman 1978 – *Populus, Salix.*
Furuno 1985, 1987 – *Populus, Salix.*
Gandelová 1978 – *Salix.*
Greguss 1959 – *Populus, Salix.*
Grosser 1977 – *Populus, Salix.*
Hayashi 1991 – *Populus, Salix.*
Hejnowicz, A. 1973 – *Populus.*
Hejnowicz, A. & Z. 1956 [1957] – *Populus.*
Herrmann 1922 – *Populus, Salix.*
Hirai 1979–1985 – *Populus, Salix, Toisusu* (= *Salix*).
Ilic 1991 – *Populus, Salix.*
Jacquiot et al. 1973 – *Populus, Salix.*
Jagiella & Kurschner 1987 – *Salix.*
Kanehira 1921a – *Salix.*
Kanehira 1921b – *Populus, Salix.*
Kanehira 1926 – *Chosenia* (= *Salix*), *Populus, Salix.*
Kasir et al. 1986 – *Salix.*
Kedrov 1971 – *Populus.*
Kobayashi & Sugawa 1964 – *Populus.*
Lebedenko 1962b – *Salix.*
Li et al. 1983 – *Populus.*
Lindorf 1988 – *Populus, Salix.*
Luo 1989 – *Populus, Salix.*
Lyr & Bergmann 1960 – *Salix.*
Metcalfe, G. 1939 – *Salix.*
Meyer-Uhlenried 1958a, b – *Populus.*
Miller, H.J. 1975 – *Salix.*
Mork 1946 – *Populus, Salix.*
Nájera Angulo & López Fraile 1969 – *Populus, Salix.*
Niloofari 1961 – *Populus, Salix.*
Panshin & Zeeuw 1980 – *Populus, Salix.*
Parsa Pajouh & Schweingruber 1985 – *Populus.*

(SALICACEAE)

Pearson & Brown 1932 – *Populus, Salix.*
Penhallow 1905 – *Populus, Salix.*
Pérez Mogollón 1993 – *Salix.*
Pérez Olvera et al. 1982 [1985] – *Populus, Salix.*
Pinker & Linskens 1958 – *Populus.*
Rancusi et al. 1987 – *Salix.*
Record & Hess 1943 – Family (*Populus, Salix*).
Riedl 1937 – *Populus, Salix* (root).
Rozens 1978 – *Populus.*
Ryu & Soh 1988 – *Salix.*
Saiki 1982 – *Populus.*
Saint-Laurent 1928, 1934 – *Populus, Salix.*
Sárkány et al. 1957 – *Populus.*
Schweingruber 1978, 1990 – *Populus, Salix.*
Shimaji & Itoh 1982 – *Populus.*
Shimaji & Itoh 1988 – *Populus, Salix.*
Šimič 1964, 1964–1965, 1965 – *Populus.*
Smilga 1967 – *Populus.*
Sudo 1959 – *Populus, Salix.*
Takizawa et al. 1980 – *Populus.*
Tewfik & Al-Dawoody 1982 – *Populus.*
Thunell & Perem 1947 – *Populus, Salix.*
Tortorelli 1956 – *Salix.*
Wagemann 1949 – *Salix.*
Wagenführ & Scheiber 1974 – *Populus, Salix.*
Wałek-Czernecka 1952 – *Populus.*
Williams 1936 – *Salix.*
Wuang 1979 – *Populus, Salix.*
Yamabayashi 1938 – *Chosenia* (= *Salix*), *Populus, Salix.*
Yao 1988 – *Chosenia* (= *Salix*), *Populus, Salix.*
Yu 1948 – *Populus.*

Crystals

Clément & Janin 1973 – *Populus.*
Janin & Clément 1972 – *Populus.*
Lee 1988 – *Populus.*
Butterfield et al. 1973 – *Populus.*

Ecological anatomy

Baas et al. 1983 – *Populus, Salix.*
Baas & Schweingruber 1987 – *Populus, Salix.*
Carlquist & Hoekman 1985a – *Populus, Salix.*
Novruzova 1968 – *Populus, Salix.*

(SALICACEAE)

Growth rings

Novruzova 1963a – *Populus.*

Helical thickenings

Ohtani & Ishida 1978b – *Populus.*

Perforation plates

Ohtani & Ishida 1978a – *Populus, Salix.*

Rays

Braun 1955 – *Populus.*
Braun 1967 – *Populus, Salix.*
Braun & den Outer 1965 – *Populus, Salix.*
Braun et al. 1968 – *Populus, Salix.*
Burgerstein 1911 – *Populus, Salix.*
Chattaway 1951b – *Populus, Salix.*
Kim & Hong 1984b – *Populus, Salix.*
Leroy 1960 – *Populus, Salix.*

Tracheary elements

Jing et al. 1989 – *Populus, Salix.*
Ohtani 1983 – *Populus, Salix.*

SALVADORACEAE

Abbate 1970 – *Salvadora.*
Chudnoff 1956 – *Salvadora.*
Den Outer & Van Veenendaal 1981 – *Azima.*
Fahn et al. 1986 – *Salvadora.*
Fasolo 1941–1944 – *Dobera.*
Jagiella & Kurschner 1987 – *Dobera, Salvadora.*
Saint-Laurent 1932a – *Salvadora.*

Anomalous structure

Chalk & Chattaway 1937 – *Salvadora.*
Singh 1944 – *Salvadora.*

Ecological anatomy

Baas et al. 1983 – *Salvadora.*

SAMBUCACEAE see CAPRIFOLIACEAE

SAMYDACEAE see FLACOURTIACEAE

SANTALACEAE

(for *Okoubaka* see OCTOKNEMACEAE)

Brazier & Franklin 1961 – *Santalum.*
Brown 1922 – *Santalum.*
Burgerstein 1912 – *Acanthosyris, Iodina.*
Freitas 1955 – *Santalum.*

(SANTALACEAE)

Gagnepain & Boureau 1946 [1947], 1947 –
  Sarcopus (= *Exocarpos*).
Greguss 1959 – *Osyris*.
Huber & Rouschal 1954 – *Osyris*.
Ilic 1991 – *Acanthosyris, Exocarpos, Santalum, + Scleropyrum* (in Opiliaceae).
Kribs 1959 – *Santalum*.
Metcalfe 1935 – *Eucarya* (= *Santalum*),
  Exocarpos, Santalum.
Meylan & Butterfield 1978b – *Mida*.
Muñiz et al. 1987 – *Iodina*. [Abstr.]
Ogata 1975–1983 – *Santalum*.
Patel 1974 – *Exocarpos, Mida*.
Pearson & Brown 1932 – *Santalum*.
Record 1938a – *Acanthosyris, Cervantesia,
  Iodina, Myoschilos*.
Record & Hess 1943 – *Acanthosyris, Cervantesia, Iodina, Myoschilos*.
Saint-Laurent 1928, 1934 – *Osyris*.
Schweingruber 1990 – *Osyris*.
Stemmermann 1980 [1981] – *Santalum*.
Sudo 1963, 1988 – *Santalum*.
*Swamy 1949 – 29 genera (some twig only).
Wang 1984–1988 – *Santalum*.

Crystals

Chattaway 1956 – *Exocarpos, Santalum*.

Ecological anatomy

Baas & Schweingruber 1987 – *Osyris*.
Carlquist 1977c – *Exocarpos, Santalum*.
Carlquist 1985a – *Iodina, Myoschilos,
  Thesium*.

Helical thickenings

Nair 1987 – *Santalum*.

Pits

Meylan & Butterfield 1974 – *Mida*.

Rays

Rao, R.V. et al. 1984 – *Pyrularia, Scleropyrum*.

SAPINDACEAE

Abbate 1964 – *Aphania* (= *Lepisanthes*).
Acevedo-Rodríguez 1993 – *Serjania*.
Alves de Pinho 1966 – *Magonia*.
Babos & Borhidi 1978 – *Cupania*.
Balan Menon 1955 – *Pometia*.
Barajas Morales & León Gómez 1989 –
  Thouinia.
Barbosa et al. 1977–1978 – *Cupania*.

(SAPINDACEAE)

Brown 1922 – *Dodonaea, Sapindus*.
Burgerstein 1912 – *Allophylus, Thouinia*.
Carlquist 1978b – *Dodonaea, Thouinidium,
  Toulicia*.
Carreras & Vales 1986b – *Matayba*.
Cellai 1967 – *Dodonaea*.
Cellai 1971 – *Allophylus*.
Cheng, C. 1985 – *Litchi*.
Cheng, J.-Q. 1980 – *Amesiodendron,
  Euphoria* (= *Litchi*), *Koelreuteria, Litchi,
  Mischocarpus, Nephelium, Pometia,
  Sapindus*.
Cheng, J.-Q. et al. 1992 – Same genera as
  Cheng 1980.
Cunha Mello 1950 [1951] – *Cupania*.
Dadswell & Eckersley 1935 – *Elattostachys,
  Harpullia*.
Dechamps 1985 – *Cupania, Matayba, Pseudima, Talisia, Toulicia*.
Desch 1954 – *Guioa, Harpullia, Lepisanthes,
  Nephelium, Pometia, Tristira, Xerospermum*.
Détienne & Jacquet 1983 – *Allophylus,
  Cupania, Magonia, Matayba, Pseudima,
  Sapindus, Talisia, Toulicia, Vouarana*.
Détienne et al. 1982 – *Cupania, Matayba,
  Talisia, Toulicia, Vouarana*.
Doležal 1959 – *Pometia*.
Fouarge & Gérard 1964 – *Allophylus,
  Blighia, Eriocoelum, Majidea*.
Fouarge et al. 1953 – *Blighia*.
Francis 1926 – *Arytera, Sarcopteryx*.
Freitas 1955 – *Pometia*.
Freitas 1958 – *Ganophyllum, Schleichera*.
Fundter & Wisse 1977 – *Pometia*.
Furuno 1977, 1979 – *Ganophyllum, Pometia, Tristiropsis*.
Gasson & Cutler 1990 – *Koelreuteria* (root).
Giordano 1939 – *Allophylus*.
Greguss 1959 – *Koelreuteria, Xanthoceras*.
Hayashi 1991 – *Sapindus*.
Hayashi et al. 1973 – *Nephelium, Pometia*.
Hayashi & Nomura 1986 – *Filicium, Nephelium, Schleichera*.
Heimsch 1942 – 53 genera.
Hirai 1979–1985 – *Koelreuteria, Pometia,
  Sapindus*.
Ilic 1991 – 33 genera.
Jagiella & Kurschner 1987 – *Dodonaea*.

(SAPINDACEAE)

Kanehira 1921a – *Allophylus, Dodonaea, Koelreuteria, Nephelium, Pometia, Sapindus.*

Kanehira 1924 – *Litchi, Pometia.*

Kanehira 1926 – *Dodonaea, Nephelium, Sapindus.*

Klaassen 1992 – Nephelieae [Abstr.]

Kobayashi & Sugawa 1963 – *Pometia.*

Kribs 1928a – *Cupania, Matayba.*

Kribs 1959 – *Pometia.*

Lebacq & Dechamps 1964 – 13 genera.

Lebacq & Dechamps 1967 – 10 genera.

Lebacq et al. 1973 – *Allophylus, Cupania, Sapindus, Serjania, Talisia.*

Lecomte 1922 – *Tina.*

Lecomte 1926a – *Litchi, Nephelium, Schleichera.*

Luo 1989 – *Litchi, Nephelium, Pometia, Sapindus.*

Mainieri 1978 – *Talisia.*

Mainieri & Chimelo 1989 – *Cupania, Talisia.*

Martawijaya et al. 1986 – *Pometia.*

Martin 1953 – *Chytranthus.*

*Mennega 1972c – *Talisia* 15 spp.

Meylan & Butterfield 1978b – *Alectryon, Dodonaea.*

Moll & Janssonius 1906–1936 – 15 genera.

Nishida et al. 1966 – *Pometia.*

Normand 1955 – *Allophylus, Aphania (= Lepisanthes), Aporrhiza, Blighia, Eriocoelum, Lecaniodiscus, Majidea, Pancovia, Placodiscus.*

Normand & Paquis 1976 [1977] – 14 genera.

Ogata 1975–1983 – *Ganophyllum, Pometia, Tristiropsis.*

Patel 1975 – *Alectryon, Dodonaea.*

Paula & Alves 1989 – *Diplokeleba.*

Pearson & Brown 1932 – *Filicium, Schleichera.*

Pérez Olvera et al. 1980 [1981] – *Cupania.*

Pfeiffer, J.P. 1926 – *Matayba.*

Prakash 1972 – *Euphoria (= Litchi), Sapindus, Serjania* (root).

Purkayastha et al. 1976 – *Pometia.*

Record & Hess 1943 – Family (21 genera).

Rock 1972 – *Cardiospermum, Cupania, Dodonaea, Exothea, Hypelate, Sapindus.*

Rodriguez 1958 – *Allophylus, Athyana, Cupania, Diatenopteryx, Diplokeleba, Matayba, Melicoccus, Sapindus.*

(SAPINDACEAE)

Rogel Gomez 1982 – *Talisia.*

Saiki 1982 – *Pometia.*

Schmid 1915 – *Cupania.*

Shimaji & Itoh 1988 – *Sapindus.*

Sudo 1959 – *Sapindus.*

Sudo 1963 – *Ganophyllum, Pometia.*

Sudo 1988 – *Ganophyllum, Pometia, Tristiropsis.*

Tang 1973 – *Amesiodendron, Litchi, Mischocarpus, Nephelium, Pometia.*

Tôrres 1941 – *Dictyoneura, Pometia.*

Tortorelli 1956 – *Allophylus, Diatenopteryx, Diplokeleba, Sapindus.*

Vales & Carreras 1986 – *Matayba.*

Van der Veken 1960 – *Blighiopsis* (brief).

Wang 1984–1988 – *Pometia.*

Williams 1928 – *Dipterodendron (= Dilodendron).*

Williams 1936 – *Allophylus, Cupania, Matayba, Talisia.*

Wiraj Chunwarin & Damrong Sri-Aran 1973 – *Nephelium, Schleichera, Xerospermum.*

Yamabayashi 1938 – *Sapindus.*

Yao 1988 – *Pometia.*

Anomalous structure

Obaton 1960 – *Paullinia.*

Pfeiffer 1925 – *Serjania, Thinouia.*

Van der Walt et al. 1973 – *Paullinia.*

Crystals and silica

Baker 1917 – *Ratonia (= Matayba).*

Chattaway 1956 – 26 genera.

Espinoza de Pernía 1987b – *Cupania, Melicoccus, Sapindus, Toulicia.*

Welle 1976b – *Toulicia.*

Ecological anatomy

Barajas Morales 1985 – *Cupania, Sapindus.*

Carlquist 1985a – *Serjania.*

Carlquist 1985 [1986]a – *Cardiospermum.*

Den Outer & Van Veenendaal 1976 – *Paullinia.*

Versteegh 1968 – *Dodonaea.*

Helical thickenings

Meylan & Butterfield 1978a – *Alectryon.*

Ohtani & Ishida 1978b – *Sapindus.*

Pits and perforation plates

Meylan & Butterfield 1974, 1975 – *Alectryon, Dodonaea.*

Ohtani & Ishida 1978a – *Sapindus.*

(SAPINDACEAE)

Rays

Holden 1912 – *Sapindus*.

Record 1945 – *Matayba*.

Septate fibres

Butterfield & Meylan 1976 – *Alectryon,*
Dodonaea.

Tracheary elements

Jing et al. 1989 – *Arytera, Pometia*.

Ohtani 1983 – *Sapindus*.

SAPOTACEAE

(for *Sarcosperma* see SARCOSPERMATA-
CEAE; see also GOETZEACEAE)
(*Aningeria = Pouteria, Bassia = Madhuca,*
Bumelia = Sideroxylon, Gambeya = Chry-
sophyllum, Lucuma = Pouteria, Plancho-
nella = Pouteria)

Anon. 1981 (Andes) – *Chrysophyllum,*
Pouteria.

Anon. 1981 (Curua) – *Manilkara, Nema-*
luma (*= Pouteria*), *Pouteria, Syzygiopsis*
(*= Pouteria*).

Abbate 1973 – *Faucherea.*

Abbate & Cavina 1980 – *Manilkara, Pala-*
quium.

Ayensu 1972 – *Synsepalum.*

Ayensu & Bentum 1974 – *Tieghemella.*

Babos & Borhidi 1978 – *Mastichodendron*
(*= Sideroxylon*).

Balan Menon 1955 – *Madhuca.*

Balan Menon 1959 – *Ganua* (*= Madhuca*),
Palaquium, Payena.

Barajas Morales & Echenique-Manrique
1976 – *Pouteria.*

Barajas Morales et al. 1979 – *Manilkara.*

Barbosa et al. 1977–1978 – *Chrysophyl-*
lum, Pouteria.

Bargagli-Petrucci 1903 – *Bassia, Palaquium.*

Benoist 1931 – *Chrysophyllum, Ecclinusa,*
Manilkara, Micropholis.

Brazier & Franklin 1961 – *Achras* (*= Manil-*
kara), *Aningeria, Autranella, Mimusops,*
Palaquium, Payena.

Brown 1922 – *Sideroxylon.*

Burgerstein 1912 – *Bumelia, Chrysophyl-*
lum.

Carreras & Vales 1986b, 1987 – *Masticho-*
dendron (*= Sideroxylon*).

Cheng, C. 1985 – *Madhuca.*

(SAPOTACEAE)

Cheng, J.-Q. 1980 – *Madhuca, Pouteria.*

Cheng, J.-Q. et al. 1992 – *Eberhardtia,*
Madhuca, Sarcosperma.

Chesnais 1944a – *Eberhardtia.*

Chevalier 1932 – ?*Ecclinusa, Manilkara.*

Cockrell 1942 – *Palaquium.*

Cozzo 1951c – *Bumelia, Chrysophyllum,*
Pouteria.

Croptier & Kučera 1990 – *Chrysophyllum.*

Cunha Mello 1950 [1951] – *Sideroxylon.*

Dadswell & Eckersley 1935 – *Lucuma,*
Sideroxylon.

Dechamps 1985 – 12 genera.

Desch 1954 – *Chrysophyllum, Ganua*
(*= Madhuca*), *Lucuma, Madhuca, Mimu-*
sops, Palaquium, Payena.

Détienne & Jacquet 1983 – 21 genera.

Détienne et al. 1982 – 17 genera.

Dixon 1919 – *Baillonella, Mimusops.*

Duchaigne 1963 – *Dumoria* (*= Tieghe-*
mella).

Edlmann Abbate & De Luca 1981 – *Pala-*
quium, Pouteria.

Eeckhout 1951 – *Autranella, Chrysophyl-*
lum, Mimusops.

Enchev & Bl"skova 1979 – *Autranella,*
Tieghemella.

Flores Rodríguez 1968 – *Pouteria.*

Fouarge & Gérard 1964 – *Gambeya,*
Letestua.

Fouarge et al. 1953 – *Autranella, Chryso-*
phyllum.

Freitas 1961 – *Baillonella.*

Freitas 1987 – *Manilkara.*

Frison 1953 – *Mimusops.*

Fundter & Wisse 1977 – *Chrysophyllum,*
Manilkara, Mimusops, Palaquium,
Pouteria.

Furuno 1977, 1979 – *Chrysophyllum,*
Manilkara, Palaquium, Planchonella.

Giordano 1939–1940 – *Manilkara, Mimu-*
sops, Pouteria, Sideroxylon.

Gómez 1959 – *Pouteria.*

Grisa 1988 – *Capurodendron.*

Guridi Gomez 1978 – *Bumelia, Chryso-*
phyllum, Manilkara, Pouteria.

Hayashi et al. 1973 – *Ganua, Madhuca,*
Palaquium, Planchonella, Pouteria.

Hayashi & Nomura 1986 – *Manilkara,*
Palaquium.

Hoheisel et al. 1968 – *Pouteria.*

(SAPOTACEAE)

Honda 1971 – *Ecclinusa, Eremoluma* (= *Pouteria*), *Micropholis, Richardella* (= *Pouteria*).

Ilic 1991 – 17 genera.

Jacquiot et al. 1973 – *Argania*.

Janssonius 1950 – Relations.

Jayawardana 1932 – *Madhuca*.

Jentsch et al. 1936, 1938 – *Chrysophyllum, Mimusops*.

Kanehira 1921a – *Palaquium, Sideroxylon*.

Kanehira 1924 – *Bassia, Mimusops, Palaquium, Sideroxylon*.

Kanehira 1926 – *Palaquium, Sideroxylon*.

Kobayashi & Sugawa 1962 – *Mimusops, Palaquium*.

Kribs 1928a – *Chrysophyllum*.

Kribs 1959 – *Achras* (= *Manilkara*), *Autranella, Bassia, Bumelia, Chrysophyllum, Manilkara, Micropholis, Mimusops, Pouteria*.

*Kukachka 1978–1982 – (38 papers) Numerous neotropical genera.

Lebacq & Dechamps 1964 – 10 genera.

Lebacq & Dechamps 1967 – 11 genera.

Lebacq et al. 1973 – *Chrysophyllum, Lucuma, Manilkara, Micropholis, Mimusops, Sideroxylon*.

Lebacq & Staner 1964 – *Autranella, Manilkara*.

Lebedenko 1962a – *Aningeria*.

Lecomte 1922 – *Faucherea, Gambeya, Sideroxylon*.

Lecomte 1926a – *Bassia, Donella* (= *Chrysophyllum*), *Palaquium, Payena*.

Lepe 1959 – *Lucuma, Sideroxylon*.

Lisboa 1989a – *Glycoxylon*.

Luo 1989 – *Madhuca*.

Mainieri 1958 – *Mastichodendron* (= *Sideroxylon*).

Mainieri 1978 – *Bumelia, Chrysophyllum, Ecclinusa, Manilkara, Micropholis, Pouteria*.

Mainieri & Chimelo 1989 – *Bumelia, Chrysophyllum, Ecclinusa, Manilkara, Micropholis, Pouteria*.

Marchiori 1986b – *Pouteria*.

Martawijaya et al. 1986 – *Palaquium*.

Martawijaya et al. 1989 – *Mimusops*.

Meylan & Butterfield 1978b – *Planchonella*.

Milanez 1934 – *Mimusops*.

(SAPOTACEAE)

Moll & Janssonius 1906–1936 – *Achras* (= *Manilkara*), *Chrysophyllum, Mimusops, Palaquium, Payena, Sideroxylon*.

Nardi Berti & Edlmann Abbate 1988 – *Aningeria, Autranella, Baillonella, Gambeya, Mimusops, Tieghemella*.

Nardi Berti & Edlmann Abbate 1992 – *Manilkara, Micropholis, Pouteria*.

Normand 1960 – 13 genera.

Normand 1970 – *Aningeria, Gambeya*.

Normand & Paquis 1976 [1977] – 26 genera.

Ogata 1975–1983 – Family (*Chrysophyllum, Palaquium, Planchonella*).

Ortega 1958 – *Manilkara, Pouteria*.

Paula & Alves 1980 – *Bumelia*.

Paula & Alves 1989 – *Ragala* (= *Chrysophyllum*).

Pearson & Brown 1932 – *Bassia, Mimusops, Palaquium, Sideroxylon*.

Pereira et al. 1970 – *Manilkara*.

Pérez Mogollón 1973 – *Ecclinusa, Manilkara*.

Pérez Olvera et al. 1980 [1981] – *Dipholis* (= *Sideroxylon*), *Pouteria, Sideroxylon*.

Pfeiffer, J.P. 1926 – *Chrysophyllum, Mimusops, Pouteria, ?Sideroxylon*.

Prakash 1972 – *Mimusops, Pouteria* (root).

Purkayastha et al. 1976 – *Diploknema, Manilkara, Planchonella*.

Record 1932a – *Ecclinusa*.

*Record 1939c – 17 genera.

Record & Hess 1943 – Family (16 genera).

Record & Mell 1924 – *Bumelia, Lucuma, Mimusops, Pradosia, Sideroxylon*.

Riera 1947 – *Baillonella, Dumoria* (= *Tieghemella*), *Lecomtedoxa*.

Rozmarin et al. 1983 – *Tieghemella*.

Saiki 1982 – *Palaquium*.

Saint-Laurent 1932b – *Argania*.

Scott 1927 – *Mimusops*.

Sudo 1963 – *Autranella, Bumelia, Chrysophyllum, Manilkara, Mimusops*.

Sudo 1988 – *Burckella, Chrysophyllum, Manilkara, Palaquium, Planchonella*.

Tang 1973 – *Pouteria*.

Tomazello Filho et al. 1983 – *Manilkara, Pouteria*.

Tortorelli 1956 – *Bumelia*.

Urling & Smith 1953 – *Bumelia, Sideroxylon*.

(SAPOTACEAE)

Valente 1974 – *Ecclinusa*.
Van der Slooten 1968 – *Chrysophyllum*.
Vitalis-Brun & Mariaux 1982 – Numerical analysis of 20 genera.
Wagenführ & Scheiber 1974 – *Aningeria, Autranella, Baillonella, Dumoria.*
Wang 1984–1988 – *Chrysophyllum, Manilkara, Palaquium, Planchonella.*
Williams 1936 – *Chrysophyllum, Lucuma, Manilkara, Sideroxylon.*
Wiraj Chunwarin & Damrong Sri-Aran 1974 – *Madhuca, Manilkara, Mimusops.*
Yao 1988 – *Eberhardtia, Madhuca.*
Ziliani 1989 – *Bumelia, Chrysophyllum, Pouteria* [Abstr.]

Crystals and silica
Chattaway 1955 – *Pouteria.*
Chattaway 1956 – *Archradotypus, Chrysophyllum, Ganua* (= *Madhuca*), *Lucuma, Manilkara, Mimusops, Palaquium, Planchonella.*
Espinoza de Pernía 1987b – 22 genera.
Richter & Roth 1985 – *Aningeria, Gambeya, Gambeyobotrys* (= *Chrysophyllum*).
Scurfield et al. 1973 – *Chrysophyllum.*
Scurfield et al. 1974 – *Madhuca.*
Sudo et al. 1967 – *Madhuca, Manilkara, Palaquium, Payena.*
Welle 1976b – 20 genera.
Ziliani 1987 – *Chrysophyllum, Pouteria.*

Ecological anatomy
Barajas Morales 1985 – *Lucuma, Pouteria.*
Carlquist 1985a – *Bumelia, Madhuca, Pouteria* and others.
Worbes 1986 – *Labatia* (= *Pouteria*).

Growth rings
Détienne 1974a, 1989 – *Tieghemella.*

Helical thickenings
Nair 1987 – *Mimusops.*

Rays
Braun et al. 1967 – *Palaquium.*
Chattaway 1951b – *Chrysophyllum, Madhuca, Palaquium.*
McLean & Richardson 1973 [1974] – *Bumelia.*

Tracheary elements
Gill & Onuja 1984a – *Aningeria, Manilkara.*
Jing et al. 1989 – *Pouteria.*

SARCOLAENACEAE

*Den Outer & Schütz 1981b – *Eremolaena, Leptolaena, Pentachlaena, Perrierodendron, Rhodolaena, Sarcolaena, Schizolaena.*
Ilic 1991 – *Rhodolaena.*
Lecomte 1922 – *Leptolaena, Rhodolaena.*

SARCOSPERMATACEAE
(*Sarcosperma*)

Cheng, J.-Q. 1980.
Chesnais 1944b.
Desch 1954.
Ilic 1991.
Marco 1933.
Tang 1973.

SARGENTODOXACEAE
(*Sargentodoxa*)

Lemesle 1955a, 1956b.

Pits
Lemesle 1943, 1946a.

SARRACENIACEAE

*DeBuhr 1977 – *Darlingtonia, Heliamphora, Sarracenia* (mostly rhizomes).

Pits and perforation plates
Carlquist 1992d – *Heliamphora.*

SAURAUIACEAE see ACTINIDIACEAE

SAXIFRAGACEAE
(for *Penthorum* see PENTHORACEAE. See also ESCALLONIACEAE and HYDRANGEACEAE)

SCHISANDRACEAE

Bailey & Nast 1948 – *Kadsura, Schisandra.*
Garratt 1933b – *Kadsura, Schisandra.*
Lemesle 1933, 1953, 1956b – *Kadsura, Schisandra.*
McLaughlin 1933 – *Kadsura, Schisandra.*
Metcalfe 1987 – General survey.
Snezhkova 1986 – *Schisandra.*
Soh & Park 1985 – *Kadsura, Schisandra.*
Takahashi 1985 – *Kadsura, Schisandra.*

(SCHISANDRACEAE)

Ecological anatomy

Carlquist 1985 [1986]a – *Schisandra*.

Pits

Lemesle 1946a – *Kadsura, Schisandra*.

SCROPHULARIACEAE

Anon. 1966 – *Paulownia*.
Böcher & Lyshede 1968 – *Monttea*.
Brazier & Franklin 1961 – *Paulownia*.
Carlquist 1992c – *Calceolaria, Hebe, Paulownia, Selago, Walafrida*.
Carlquist & Hoekman 1986b – *Leucophyllum*.
Cheng, C. 1985 – *Paulownia*.
Cheng, J.-Q. 1980 – *Paulownia*.
Cheng, J.-Q. et al. 1992 – *Paulownia*.
Chiang 1964 – *Paulownia*.
Cristiani 1948 – *Monttea*.
Cutler et al. 1987 – *Hebe* (root).
Deb & Datta 1977 – 24 genera (young stems).
Edlmann & Monaco 1981 – *Paulownia*.
Gasson & Cutler 1990 – *Paulownia* (root).
Greguss 1959 – *Paulownia*.
Hayashi 1991 – *Paulownia*.
Henrickson & Flyr 1985 – *Leucophyllum*.
Hirai 1979–1985 – *Paulownia*.
Huber & Rouschal 1954 – *Paulownia*.
Ilic 1991 – *Paulownia*.
Kanehira 1921a, b, 1926 – *Paulownia*.
Lin & Wang 1991 – *Paulownia*.
Luo 1989 – *Paulownia*.
Mainieri 1978 – *Paulownia*.
Mennega 1975 – *Aragoa* [Abstr.].
Meylan & Butterfield 1978b – *Hebe*.
Michener 1981 – *Keckiella* 7 spp.
Michener 1983 – *Antirrhinum, Castilleja, Galvezia, Mimulus* 7 spp.
Michener 1986 – *Penstemon* 6 spp.
Moll & Janssonius 1906–1936 – *Wightia*.
Niloofari 1961 – *Paulownia*.
Record & Hess 1943 – Family (*Dermatocalyx* (= *Schlegelia*), *Monttea, Penstemon*).
Saiki 1982 – *Paulownia*.
Saint-Laurent 1928 – *Scrophularia*.
Schweingruber 1990 – *Antirrhinum, Digitalis, Isoplexis, Scrophularia, Veronica*.
Shimaji & Itoh 1982, 1988 – *Paulownia*.
Solereder 1915 – *Heteranthia*.

(SCROPHULARIACEAE)

Sudo 1959 – *Paulownia*.
Tang 1973 – *Paulownia*.
Wang 1965 – *Paulownia*.
Wu & Wang 1976 – *Paulownia*.
Wuang 1979 – *Paulownia*.
Yamabayashi 1938 – *Paulownia*.
Yao 1988 – *Paulownia*.

Ecological anatomy

Baas & Schweingruber 1987 – *Antirrhinum, Digitalis, Isoplexis, Scrophularia, Veronica*.
Carlquist & Hoekman 1985a – *Antirrhinum, Castilleja, Galvezia, Keckiella, Mimulus, Penstemon*.

Helical thickenings

Meylan & Butterfield 1978a – *Hebe*.
Ohtani & Ishida 1978b – *Paulownia*.

Pits and perforation plates

Meylan & Butterfield 1974, 1975 – *Hebe*.
Ohtani & Ishida 1978a – *Paulownia*.

Rays

McLean & Richardson 1973 [1974] – *Leucophyllum*.

Tracheary elements

Ohtani 1983 – *Paulownia*.

SCYPHOSTEGIACEAE (*Scyphostegia*)

Metcalfe 1956a.

SCYTOPETALACEAE

(*Scytopetalum* only unless otherwise stated)

*Carlquist 1988d – *Rhaptopetalum, Scytopetalum*.
Freitas 1987.
Lebacq & Dechamps 1964, 1967.
Metcalfe & Chalk 1950.
Normand 1955.
Normand & Paquis 1976 [1977] – *Oubanguia, Scytopetalum*.

SIMAROUBACEAE

(see also IRVINGIACEAE)

Anon. 1981 (Andes) – *Simarouba*.
Almeida 1973 [1974] – *Kirkia* (or in Meliaceae).

(SIMAROUBACEAE)
Babos & Borhidi 1978 – *Alvaradoa*.
Barajas Morales & Léon Gómez 1989 –
  Recchia.
Bastos 1946 [1947] – *Simarouba*.
Benoist 1931 – *Simaba, Simarouba*.
Brazier & Franklin 1961 – *Ailanthus, Han-*
  noa, Simarouba.
Carreras & Vales 1986b, 1987 – *Alvaradoa,*
  Simarouba.
Carvalho 1954–1955, 1956 – *Ailanthus*.
Cheng, C. 1985 – *Ailanthus*.
Cheng, J.-Q. 1980 – *Ailanthus, Picrasma*.
Cheng, J.-Q. et al. 1992 – *Ailanthus, Pi-*
  crasma.
Cockrell 1942 – *Eurycoma*.
Cutler et al. 1987 – *Ailanthus* (root).
Dechamps 1985 – *Simaba, Simarouba*.
Détienne & Jacquet 1983 – *Picramnia,*
  Quassia, Simaba, Simarouba.
Détienne et al. 1982 – *Simaba, Simarouba*.
Edlmann & Monaco 1981 – *Ailanthus*.
Fedalto et al. 1989 – *Simarouba*.
Fouarge & Gérard 1964 – *Hannoa*.
Furuno 1977, 1985, 1987 – *Ailanthus*.
Gómez 1959 – *Simarouba*.
Greguss 1959 – *Ailanthus*.
Grosser 1977 – *Ailanthus*.
Hayashi 1991 – *Picrasma*.
Heimsch 1942 – 26 genera, 45 spp.
Hirai 1979–1985 – *Ailanthus, Picrasma*.
Huber & Rouschal 1954 – *Ailanthus*.
Ilic 1991 – *Ailanthus, Picrasma, Quassia,*
  Simarouba.
Jacquiot et al. 1973 – *Ailanthus*.
Janssonius 1950 – Relations.
Kanehira 1921a, 1924 – *Ailanthus*.
Kanehira 1921b, 1926 – *Picrasma*.
Kribs 1928a, 1959 – *Simarouba*.
Lebacq 1963 – *Hannoa*.
Lebacq & Dechamps 1964 – *Hannoa*.
Lebacq & Dechamps 1967 – *Hannoa, Pier-*
  reodendron.
Lebacq et al. 1973 – *Quassia, Simarouba*.
Lecomte 1926a – *Ailanthus*.
Loesener & Solereder 1905 – *Rigiostachys*
  (= *Recchia*).
Mainieri 1958, 1962 – *Simarouba*.
Mainieri & Chimelo 1989 – *Simarouba*.
Moll & Janssonius 1906–1936 – *Ailanthus,*
  Picrasma.
Muñiz et al. 1987 – *Castela* [Abstr.].

(SIMAROUBACEAE)
Nardi Berti & Edlmann Abbate 1988 – *Gym-*
  nostemon.
Nardi Berti & Edlmann Abbate 1992 – *Sima-*
  rouba.
Niloofari 1961 – *Ailanthus*.
Normand 1950b–1960 – *Gymnostemon,*
  Hannoa, Mannia (= *Pierreodendron*).
Normand & Paquis 1976 [1977] – *Gymno-*
  stemon, Hannoa, Iridosma, Nothospon-
  dias, Odyendea, Pierreodendron.
O'Donell 1937 – *Alvaradoa, Castela, Pi-*
  craena (= *Picrasma*).
Ogata 1975–1983 – *Ailanthus*.
Paula 1979 – *Simaba, Simarouba*.
Pearson & Brown 1932 – *Ailanthus*.
Pereira et al. 1970 – *Simaba, Simarouba*.
Pérez Mogollón 1973 – *Simaba, Simarouba*.
Pérez Olvera et al. 1980 [1981] – *Simarou-*
  ba.
Pfeiffer, J.P. 1926 – *Simarouba*.
Prakash 1972 – *Picrasma* (root).
Purkayastha et al. 1976 – *Ailanthus*.
Record & Hess 1943 – Family (*Aeschrion*
  (= *Picrasma*), *Alvaradoa, Castela, Hola-*
  cantha (= *Castela*), *Picramnia, Picrolem-*
  ma, Quassia, Simaba, Simarouba).
Record & Mell 1924 – *Simarouba*.
Rock 1972 – *Simarouba*.
Saya 1961 – *Ailanthus*.
Shimaji & Itoh 1988 – *Picrasma*.
Sudo 1959 – *Ailanthus, Picrasma*.
Sudo 1963 – *Ailanthus, Simarouba*.
Sudo 1988 – *Ailanthus*.
Tang 1973 – *Ailanthus*.
Teles & Paula 1980 – *Simaba*.
Vales & Martinez 1983 – *Alvaradoa, Sima-*
  rouba.
*Webber 1936b – 19 genera (incl. *Kirkia*).
Weberling et al. 1980 – *Recchia*.
Williams 1936 – *Picramnia*.
Wiraj Chunwarin & Damrong Sri-Aran 1973
  – *Ailanthus*.
Wuang 1979 – *Ailanthus*.
Yamabayashi 1938 – *Ailanthus, Picrasma*.
Yao 1988 – *Ailanthus*.

Crystals and silica
Chattaway 1956 – *Ailanthus, Picramnia,*
  Picrasma.
Espinoza de Pernía 1987b – *Aeschrion*
  (= *Picrasma*), *Quassia, Simarouba*.

(SIMAROUBACEAE)
Scurfield et al. 1974 – *Quassia*.
Welle 1976b – *Quassia*.

Ecological anatomy
Carlquist 1985a – *Alvaradoa, Castela, Holacantha* (= *Castela*).
Carlquist & Hoekman 1985a – *Castela*.
Den Outer & Van Veenendaal 1976 – *Harrisonia*.
Ergo & Dechamps 1984 – *Simarouba*.
Van der Graaff & Baas 1974 – *Ailanthus*.
Webber 1936a – *Holacantha* (= *Castela*).

Helical thickenings
Ohtani & Ishida 1978b – *Ailanthus*.

Perforation plates
Ohtani & Ishida 1978a – *Ailanthus, Picrasma*.

Rays
Jaccard 1922 – *Ailanthus*.

Storied structure
Cozzo & Cristiani 1950 – *Castela, Picraena* (= *Picrasma*).

Tracheary elements
Ohtani 1983 – *Ailanthus, Picrasma*.

SIMMONDSIACEAE see BUXACEAE

SIPHONODONTACEAE
see CELASTRACEAE

SLADENIACEAE see THEACEAE

SOLANACEAE (incl. RETZIACEAE; for *Nolana* see NOLANACEAE)

Araujo & Sonkin 1984 – *Metternichia*.
Barbosa et al. 1977–1978 – *Solanum*.
Bascopé 1954 – *Solanum*.
Brown 1922 – *Solanum*.
Burgerstein 1909 – *Brachistus, Cestrum, Solanum*.
Burgerstein 1912 – *Acnistus, Cestrum, Grabowskia, Solanum*.
Carlquist 1986c – *Retzia*.
*Carlquist 1992b – 21 genera, 82 spp.
D'Arcy 1970 – *Brunfelsia*.
Dechamps 1985 – *Solanum*.

(SOLANACEAE)
Descole & O'Donell 1937 – *Solanum*.
Détienne & Jacquet 1983 – *Solanum*.
Fahn et al. 1986 – *Lycium, Nicotiana, Withania*.
Greguss 1959 – *Lycium*.
Ilic 1991 – *Duboisia*.
Jagiella & Kurschner 1987 – *Lycium, Withania*.
Kutuzova 1965 – *Capsicum, Lycopersicon, Physalis, Solanum*.
Mennega 1980a – *Retzia* (in Loganiaceae).
Norverto 1989 – *Lycium*.
Pérez Mogollón 1993 – *Solanum*.
Pinho et al. 1986a – *Sessea, Solanum*.
Record & Hess 1943 – Family (15 genera).
Saint-Laurent 1928, 1934 – *Lycium, Solanum, Withania*.
Schweingruber 1990 – *Lycium, Nicotiana, Solanum, Withania*.
Tang 1973 – *Solanum*.
Tortorelli 1956 – *Solanum*.
Williams 1936 – *Cestrum, Cyphomandra, Solanum*.

Anomalous structure
Bonnemain 1970 – 19 genera.

Ecological anatomy
Baas & Schweingruber 1987 – *Lycium, Solanum, Withania*.
Baas et al. 1983 – *Lycium, Nicotiana, Withania*.
Carlquist 1985a – *Grabowskia, Lycium, Solanum*.
Carlquist 1985 [1986]a – *Solanum*.
Carlquist & Hoekman 1985a – *Lycium, Solanum*.
Dadasheva 1962 – *Lycium* (stem & root).
Novruzova 1968 – *Lycium*.
Webber 1936a – *Lycium*.

SONNERATIACEAE

Bargagli-Petrucci 1903 – *Sonneratia*.
Cheng, J.-Q. 1980 – *Duabanga*.
Cheng, J.-Q. et al. 1992 – *Duabanga*.
Desch 1954 – *Duabanga, Sonneratia*.
Hayashi et al. 1973 – *Duabanga*.
Ilic 1991 – *Duabanga, Sonneratia*.
Janssonius 1950 – Relations.
Kanehira 1924 – *Sonneratia*.
Kartasujana 1977 – *Duabanga*.

(SONNERATIACEAE)

Kribs 1959 – *Sonneratia*.
Lecomte 1926a – *Duabanga* (in Lythraceae).
Luo 1989 – *Duabanga*.
Moll & Janssonius 1906–1936 – *Duabanga, Sonneratia*.
Ogata 1975–1983 – *Duabanga, Sonneratia*.
Panshin 1932 – *Sonneratia*.
Pearson & Brown 1932 – *Duabanga, Sonneratia*.
*Rao, R.V. et al. 1987b – *Duabanga, Sonneratia*.
Rao, R.V. et al. 1989 – *Sonneratia* (root).
Sudo 1963, 1988 – *Duabanga, Sonneratia*.
Tang 1973 – *Duabanga*.
Van Vliet & Baas 1984 – Relations of myrtalean families.
Venkateswarlu & Rao 1964 – *Duabanga, Sonneratia*.

Crystals

Chattaway 1956 – *Duabanga, Sonneratia*.

Pits and perforation plates

Jing et al. 1988 – *Duabanga*.
Rao, R.V. et al. 1987a – *Sonneratia*.

Tracheary elements

Jing et al. 1989 – *Duabanga*.

SPHAEROSEPALACEAE
(incl. RHOPALOCARPACEAE)

Abbate 1973 – *Rhopalocarpus*.
Boureau 1958 – *Rhopalocarpus*.
*Den Outer & Schütz 1981b – *Dialyceras, Rhopalocarpus*.
*Huard 1965 – *Dialyceras, Rhopalocarpus*.
Keating 1968 [1969] – *Rhopalocarpus*.
Leroy 1973 – *Dialyceras*.

SPHENOSTEMONACEAE

Baas 1975 – *Sphenostemon*.
Bailey & Swamy 1953 – *Idenburgia, Nouhuysia* (both = *Sphenostemon*).
Ilic 1991 – *Sphenostemon*.
Metcalfe 1956b – *Sphenostemon* (young).

Pits and perforation plates

Carlquist 1992d – *Sphenostemon*.

STACHYURACEAE (*Stachyurus*)

Hayashi 1991.
Hirai 1979–1985.
Kanehira 1921a,b.
Suzuki et al. 1991.
Tippo 1938.

STACKHOUSIACEAE (*Stackhousia*)

*Carlquist 1987f 5 spp.

STAPHYLEACEAE

Abbate 1971b – *Staphylea*.
Bascopé 1954 – *Turpinia*.
*Carlquist & Hoekman 1985b – *Euscaphis, Huertea, Staphylea, Tapiscia, Turpinia*.
Cheng, J.-Q. 1980 – *Euscaphis, Turpinia*.
Cheng, J.-Q. et al. 1992 – *Euscaphis, Turpinia*.
Dechamps 1985 – *Turpinia*.
Détienne & Jacquet 1983 – *Huertea, Turpinia*.
Greguss 1959 – *Staphylea*.
Grosser 1977 – *Staphylea*.
Hayashi 1991 – *Euscaphis*.
Heimsch 1942 – *Euscaphis, Huertea, Staphylea, Tapiscia, Turpinia*.
Hess 1950c – *Huertea*.
Ilic 1991 – *Turpinia*.
Ingle & Dadswell 1956 – *Kaernbachia* (= *Turpinia*) (in Cunoniaceae).
Kanehira 1921a – *Euscaphis, Turpinia*.
Lebacq et al. 1973 – *Turpinia*.
Lomibao 1973c – *Turpinia*.
Moll & Janssonius 1906–1936 – *Turpinia*.
Pérez Mogollón 1993 – *Turpinia*.
Record & Hess 1943 – Family (*Staphylea, Turpinia*).
Schweingruber 1990 – *Staphylea*.
Sudo 1959 – *Euscaphis*.
Williams 1936 – *Turpinia*.
Wu & Wang 1976 – *Turpinia*.
Yamabayashi 1938 – *Euscaphis, Staphylea*.
Yao 1988 – *Tapiscia*.

Ecological anatomy

Baas & Schweingruber 1987 – *Staphylea*.
Versteegh 1968 – *Turpinia*.

Helical thickenings

Ohtani & Ishida 1978b – *Euscaphis*.

(STAPHYLEACEAE)

Perforation plates

Ohtani & Ishida 1978a – *Euscaphis*.

Rays

Holden 1912 – *Staphylea*.

Tracheary elements

Ohtani 1983 – *Euscaphis*.

STEGNOSPERMATACEAE

(*Stegnosperma*)

*Bedell 1980 [1981].

Anomalous structure

Horak 1981.

STERCULIACEAE (*Cistanthera* = *Nesogordonia, Tarrietia* = *Heritiera*)

Anon. 1955–1959 – *Cola*.
Anon. 1977b – *Mansonia*.
Anon. 1981 (Curua) – *Sterculia*.
Abbate & Cenerini 1976 – *Sterculia*.
Arbo 1981 – *Rayleya*.
Ayensu & Bentum 1974 – *Nesogordonia, Tarrietia, Triplochiton*.
Babos & Borhidi 1981 – *Guazuma*.
Balan Menon 1959 – *Tarrietia*.
Barajas Morales & León Gómez 1989 – *Guazuma*.
Bargagli-Petrucci 1903 – *Heritiera, Sterculia*.
Benoist 1931 – *Sterculia*.
Brazier & Franklin 1961 – *Argyrodendron* (= *Heritiera*), *Mansonia, Nesogordonia, Pterospermum, Pterygota, Sterculia, Tarrietia, Triplochiton*.
Burgerstein 1909 – *Commersonia, Kleinhovia, Melochia, Theobroma*.
Carreras & Vales 1986b, 1987 – *Guazuma*.
Cellai 1971 – *Sterculia*.
Chalk et al. 1933 – *Cistanthera*.
*Chattaway 1932 – *Brachychiton, Cola, Firmiana, Heritiera, Pterocymbium, Pterygota, Sterculia, Tarrietia*.
*Chattaway 1937 – 12 genera.
Cheng, C. 1985 – *Pterospermum*.
Cheng, J.-Q. 1980 – *Eriolaena, Firmiana, Pterospermum, Reevesia, Sterculia, Tarrietia*.
Cheng, J.-Q. et al. 1992 – Same genera as Cheng 1980.

(STERCULIACEAE)

Chowdhury & Ghosh 1956 – *Mansonia*.
Cockrell 1942 – *Commersonia, Pterocymbium, Scaphium*.
Croptier & Kučera 1990 – *Dombeya*.
Cuatrecasas 1964 – *Theobroma*.
Dadswell & Eckersley 1935 – *Brachychiton, Tarrietia*.
Dechamps 1985 – *Guazuma, Herrania, Pterygota, Sterculia*.
Den Outer & Schütz 1981b – 16 genera for comparison with Sarcolaenaceae and Rhopalocarpaceae.
Desch 1954 – *Heritiera, Pterocymbium, Pterospermum, Scaphium, Sterculia, Tarrietia*.
Détienne & Jacquet 1983 – *Guazuma, Pterygota, Sterculia, Theobroma*.
Détienne et al. 1982 – *Guazuma, Sterculia, Theobroma*.
Dixon 1919 – *Tarrietia*.
Dorr & Barnett 1989 – *Melochia*.
Eeckhout 1951 – *Cistanthera, Triplochiton*.
Fasolo 1941–1944 – *Dombeya*.
Fedalto et al. 1989 – *Sterculia*.
Ferreirinha 1955 – *Sterculia*.
Ferreirinha & Reis 1969 – *Nesogordonia*.
Fouarge & Gérard 1964 – *Nesogordonia, Sterculia*.
Freitas 1955 – *Sterculia*.
Freitas 1958 – *Pterospermum*.
Frison 1953 – *Cistanthera*.
Fundter & Wisse 1977 – *Pterygota, Sterculia*.
Furuno 1977, 1979 – *Heritiera, Pterocymbium, Pterygota, Sterculia*.
Gill & Onuja 1983a – *Mansonia, Nesogordonia, Pterygota, Sterculia, Triplochiton*.
Giordano 1939–1940 – *Dombeya*.
Gottwald & Richter 1984 – *Pterygota*.
Hayashi 1991 – *Firmiana*.
Hayashi et al. 1973 – *Heritiera, Pterospermum, Scaphium*.
Hayashi & Nomura 1986 – *Pterospermum*.
Hess 1950c – *Chiranthodendron* (or Bombacaceae).
Hirai 1979–1985 – *Firmiana*.
Hoheisel et al. 1968 – *Sterculia*.
Huynh-Long 1968 – *Tarrietia*.
Ilic 1991 – 18 genera.
Jagiella & Kurschner 1987 – *Melhania*.

(STERCULIACEAE)

Janssonius 1950 – Relations.

Jentsch et al. 1936 – *Pterygota, Sterculia, Triplochiton.*

Kanehira 1921a – *Heritiera, Kleinhovia, Pterospermum, Reevesia, Sterculia.*

Kanehira 1921b – *Firmiana.*

Kanehira 1924 – *Heritiera, Pterocymbium, Pterospermum, Sterculia, Tarrietia.*

Kanehira 1926 – *Firmiana, Heritiera.*

Kobayashi & Sugawa 1966a – *Pterocymbium, Tarrietia.*

Kribs 1928a – *Sterculia.*

Kribs 1959 – *Cistanthera, Cola, Guazuma, Mansonia, Sterculia, Tarrietia, Triplochiton.*

Lebacq & Dechamps 1964 – *Cola, Dombeya, Nesogordonia, Pterygota, Sterculia, Tarrietia, Triplochiton.*

Lebacq & Dechamps 1967 – *Cola, Pterygota, Sterculia.*

Lebacq et al. 1973 – *Guazuma, Pterygota, Sterculia, Theobroma.*

Lecomte 1922 – *Dombeya, Sterculia.*

Lecomte 1926a – *Commersonia, Pterospermum, Sterculia.*

Lim & Soh 1991b – *Firmiana.*

Lomibao 1978 – *Heritiera.*

Luo 1989 – *Eriolaena, Firmiana, Pterospermum, Sterculia.*

Mainieri 1962 – *Sterculia.*

Manchester 1979 – *Triplochiton* (and fossils).

Manchester 1980 – *Pterospermum* (and fossils).

Martawijaya et al. 1986 – *Heritiera.*

Martawijaya et al. 1989 – *Pterospermum.*

Martin 1953 – *Cola.*

Metcalfe 1933 – *Mansonia.*

Moll & Janssonius 1906–1936 – 10 genera.

Monteiro & Frade 1960 – *Sterculia.*

Nardi Berti & Edlmann Abbate 1988 – *Eribroma* (= *Sterculia*), *Heritiera, Mansonia, Nesogordonia, Pterygota, Sterculia, Triplochiton.*

Normand 1955 – *Cola, Hildegardia, Mansonia, Nesogordonia, Pterygota, Sterculia, Tarrietia, Triplochiton.*

Normand & Paquis 1976 [1977] – *Cola, Eribroma* (= *Sterculia*), *Mansonia, Nesogordonia, Pterygota, Sterculia, Tarrietia, Triplochiton.*

(STERCULIACEAE)

Ogata 1975–1983 – *Argyrodendron* (= *Heritiera*), *Heritiera, Kleinhovia, Pterocymbium, Pterospermum, Pterygota, Scaphium, Sterculia, Tarrietia.*

Panshin 1932 – *Heritiera.*

Pearson & Brown 1932 – *Eriolaena, Heritiera, Pterospermum, Sterculia.*

Pérez Mogollón 1973 – *Sterculia.*

Pérez Olvera et al. 1980 [1981] – *Guazuma.*

Prakash 1972 – *Theobroma* (root).

Purkayastha et al. 1976 – *Pterocymbium.*

Record 1929a – *Mansonia, Triplochiton.*

Record & Hess 1943 – Family (*Basiloxylon* (= *Pterygota*), *Buettneria* (= *Byttneria*), *Fremontia* (= *Fremontodendron*), *Guazuma, Helicteres, Sterculia, Theobroma, Waltheria*).

Robyns et al. 1977 – *Commersonia, Maxwellia, Nesogordonia.*

Rogel Gomez 1982 – *Chiranthodendron* (or in Bombacaceae).

Rozmarin et al. 1983 – *Triplochiton.*

Saiki 1982 – *Pterocymbium.*

Schmidt 1951–1952 – *Cistanthera, Tarrietia, Triplochiton.*

Schultz & Wollheim 1962 – *Brachychiton, Guazuma.*

Solheim 1987 – *Reevesia* (incl. *Veeresia*; also fossils).

Sudo 1959 – *Firmiana.*

Sudo 1963 – *Argyrodendron* (= *Heritiera*), *Kleinhovia, Mansonia, Nesogordonia* (in Tiliaceae), *Pterocymbium, Pterospermum, Tarrietia, Triplochiton.*

Sudo 1988 – *Firmiana, Heritiera, Kleinhovia, Pterocymbium, Pterygota, Sterculia.*

Sugawa 1968c – *Tarrietia.*

Tabirih & Seehann 1981 – *Triplochiton.*

Tang 1973 – *Pterospermum, Sterculia.*

Tang 1992a – *Melhania.*

Tang 1992b – *Corchoropsis* (or Tiliaceae).

Tang 1993 – *Paradombeya.*

Tôrres 1941 – *Sterculia.*

Wagenführ 1990 – *Heritiera.*

Wagenführ & Scheiber 1974 – *Mansonia, Pterygota, Sterculia, Tarrietia, Triplochiton.*

Wang 1984–1988 – *Heritiera, Pterocymbium, Sterculia, Tarrietia.*

Williams 1936 – *Guazuma, Sterculia, Theobroma.*

(STERCULIACEAE)
Wiraj Chunwarin & Damrong Sri-Aran
1973 – *Heritiera, Pterospermum, Pterygota, Sterculia, Tarrietia.*
Wuang 1979 – *Firmiana.*
Zamuco 1967 – *Sterculia.*

Crystals
Baker 1917 – *Tarrietia.*
Chattaway 1955 – *Pterocymbium, Sterculia.*
Chattaway 1956 – 13 genera.
Espinoza de Pernía 1987b – *Guazuma, Sterculia.*
Meniado et al. 1970 – *Heritiera, Kleinhovia, Pterospermum, Sterculia, Tarrietia.*

Ecological anatomy
Carlquist 1977c – *Guichenotia, Lasiopetalum.*
Carlquist & Hoekman 1985a – *Fremontodendron.*
Den Outer & Van Veenendaal 1976 – *Sterculia.*

Growth rings
Détienne 1975b – *Mansonia.*
Détienne 1989 – *Mansonia, Tarrietia, Triplochiton.*
Détienne & Mariaux 1975 – *Tarrietia.*
Détienne & Mariaux 1976 – *Triplochiton.*

Helical thickenings
Nair 1987 – *Sterculia.*
Ohtani & Ishida 1978b – *Firmiana.*

Perforation plates
Ohtani & Ishida 1978a – *Firmiana.*

Rays
Braun et al. 1967 – *Sterculia.*
Chattaway 1933a – Malvales: general.
Chattaway 1933b – 26 genera.

Silica
Scurfield et al. 1974 – *Scaphium.*
Sudo et al. 1967 – *Heritiera, Tarrietia.*
Sugawa et al. 1993 – *Argyrodendron* (= *Heritiera*), *Heritiera, Tarrietia* [Abstr.].

Storied structure
Cozzo & Cristiani 1950 – *Guazuma, Sterculia.*

Tracheary elements
Jing et al. 1989 – *Pterospermum.*
Ohtani 1983 – *Firmiana.*

(STERCULIACEAE)
Xylem parenchyma
Lowe 1962 – *Triplochiton.*

STILBACEAE

*Carlquist 1986c – *Campylostachys, Eurylobium, Euthystachys, Stilbe, Xeroplana.*
Ecological anatomy
Carlquist 1985a – *Stilbe.*

STRASBURGERIACEAE
(*Strasburgeria*)

*Dickison 1981.

STYLIDIACEAE (*Stylidium*)

Carlquist 1981b.

Anomalous structure
Mullenders 1947.

STYLOBASIACEAE (*Stylobasium*)

Carlquist 1978b.
Prance 1965.

Ecological anatomy
Carlquist 1985a.

STYLOCERATACEAE see BUXACEAE

STYRACACEAE

Baas et al. 1984 – *Styrax.*
Cheng, C. 1985 – *Alniphyllum.*
Cheng, J.-Q. 1980 – *Alniphyllum, Huodendron, Melliodendron, Pterostyrax, Rehderodendron, Styrax.*
Cheng, J.-Q. et al. 1992 – Same genera as Cheng 1980.
Chudnoff 1956 – *Styrax.*
Cutler et al. 1987 – *Styrax* (root).
Dechamps 1985 – *Styrax.*
Desch 1954 – *Styrax.*
Détienne & Jacquet 1983 – *Styrax.*
*Dickison & Phend 1985 – *Alniphyllum, Bruinsmia, Halesia, Huodendron, Melliodendron, Pterostyrax, Rehderodendron, Sinojackia, Styrax.*
Edlmann & Monaco 1981 – *Styrax.*

(STYRACACEAE)

Fahn et al. 1986 – *Styrax.*
Furuno 1979 – *Bruinsmia.*
Gasson & Cutler 1990 – *Halesia* (root).
Hayashi 1991 – *Pterostyrax, Styrax.*
Hirai 1979–1985 – *Pterostyrax, Styrax.*
Ilic 1991 – *Bruinsmia, Halesia, Styrax.*
Inokuma et al. 1953 – *Alniphyllum, Halesia, Pterostyrax, Sinojackia, Styrax.*
Janssonius 1950 – Relations.
Kanehira 1921a – *Alniphyllum, Styrax.*
Kanehira 1921b – *Pterostyrax, Styrax.*
Kanehira 1926 – *Alniphyllum, Pterostyrax, Styrax.*
Luo 1989 – *Alniphyllum, Styrax.*
Moll & Janssonius 1906–1936 – *Bruinsmia, Styrax.*
Pérez Olvera & Corral Lopez 1980 – *Styrax.*
Record & Hess 1943 – Family (*Halesia, Pamphilia, Styrax*).
Schweingruber 1990 – *Styrax.*
Shimaji & Itoh 1988 – *Pterostyrax, Styrax.*
Sudo 1959 – *Pterostyrax, Styrax.*
Sudo 1988 – *Bruinsmia.*
Tang 1973 – *Alniphyllum, Huodendron, Melliodendron, Rehderodendron, Styrax.*
Tortorelli 1956 – *Styrax.*
Tortorelli & Castiglioni 1949 – *Styrax.*
Yamabayashi 1938 – *Styrax.*
Yao 1988 – *Alniphyllum, Huodendron, Styrax.*

Crystals

Chattaway 1956 – *Styrax.*

Ecological anatomy

Baas & Schweingruber 1987 – *Styrax.*
Baas et al. 1983 – *Styrax.*
Carlquist & Hoekman 1985a – *Styrax.*
Van der Graaff & Baas 1974 – *Styrax.*
Versteegh 1968 – *Bruinsmia.*

Perforation plates

Ohtani & Ishida 1978a – *Pterostyrax, Styrax.*

Silica

Espinoza de Pernía 1987b – *Styrax.*
Scurfield et al. 1974 – *Styrax.*
Welle 1976b – *Styrax.*

Tracheary elements

Ohtani 1983 – *Pterostyrax, Styrax.*

SURIANACEAE

Gutzwiller 1961 – *Suriana.*
Loesener & Solereder 1905 – *Rigiostachys* (= *Recchia*) (or in Simaroubaceae).
Record & Hess 1943 – *Suriana.*
Record & Mell 1924 – *Suriana.*
Rock 1972 – *Suriana.*
Webber 1936b – *Cadellia, Guilfoylia, Suriana.*
Weberling et al. 1980 – *Cadellia, Recchia* (in Simaroubaceae).

Crystals

Chattaway 1956 – *Cadellia.*

Rays

Chattaway 1951b – *Guilfoylia* (in Simaroubaceae).

SYMPLOCACEAE (*Symplocos*)

Carreras & Vales 1986b.
Cheng, J.-Q. 1980.
Cheng, J.-Q. et al. 1992.
Dadswell & Eckersley 1935.
Dechamps 1985.
Desch 1954.
Détienne & Jacquet 1983.
Hayashi 1991.
Hirai 1979–1985.
Ilic 1991.
Janssonius 1950 – Relations.
Kanehira 1921a, b, 1926.
Lecomte 1926a.
Luo 1989.
Mainieri 1958.
Moll & Janssonius 1906–1936.
Norverto 1993.
Pérez Mogollón 1993.
Record & Hess 1943.
Shimaji & Itoh 1982, 1988.
Sudo 1959.
Suzuki et al. 1991.
Tang 1973.
Vales & Carreras 1987.
*Van den Oever et al. 1981 – 31 spp.
Wu & Wang 1976.
Yamabayashi 1938.
*Yamauchi 1979 – *Dicalyx* 5 spp., *Palura* 3 spp. (both split from *Symplocos*).
Yao 1988.

(SYMPLOCACEAE)
Ecological anatomy
Baas 1973.
Versteegh 1968.

Helical thickenings
Ohtani & Ishida 1978b.

Perforation plates
Ohtani & Ishida 1978a.

Tracheary elements
Ohtani 1983.

TAMARICACEAE

Brunner 1908 [1909] – *Hololachna, Myri-caria, Reaumuria, Tamarix.*
Chudnoff 1956 – *Tamarix.*
Cutler et al. 1987 – *Tamarix* (root).
Fahn 1958 – *Tamarix.*
Fahn & Sarnat 1963 – *Reaumuria.*
Fahn et al. 1986 – *Reaumuria, Tamarix.*
Greguss 1959 – *Myricaria, Tamarix.*
Huber & Rouschal 1954 – *Myricaria, Tamarix.*
Ilic 1991 – *Tamarix.*
Jacquiot et al. 1973 – *Tamarix.*
Jagiella & Kurschner 1987 – *Tamarix.*
Mele 1972 – *Myricaria.*
Messeri 1938 – *Tamarix.*
Niloufari 1977 – *Tamarix.*
Pearson & Brown 1932 – *Tamarix.*
Saint-Laurent 1928, 1932a, 1934 – *Tamarix.*
Schweingruber 1990 – *Myricaria, Tamarix.*
Sudo 1963 – *Tamarix.*
Trabut 1926 – *Tamarix.*

Ecological anatomy
Baas & Schweingruber 1987 – *Myricaria, Tamarix.*
Baas et al. 1983 – *Reaumuria, Tamarix.*
Novruzova 1968 – *Reaumuria, Tamarix.*

Storied structure
Cozzo & Cristiani 1950 – *Tamarix.*

TEPUIANTHACEAE (*Tepuianthus*)

Maguire & Steyermark 1981 – (wood by C. de Zeeuw).

TETRACENTRACEAE (*Tetracentron*)

Bailey & Nast 1945b.
Bailey & Thompson 1918.
Chen, G. 1989.
Cheng, J.-Q. 1980.
Cheng, J.-Q. et al. 1992.
Gasson & Cutler 1990 – (root).
Gupta 1934.
Lemesle 1963a.
Luo 1989.
McLaughlin 1933.
Tang 1973.
Thompson & Bailey 1916.
Wuang 1979.
Yao 1988.
Zheng & Gao 1990.

Pits
Lemesle 1946a.

Tracheary elements
Suzuki, Joshi et al. 1991.

TETRAMELACEAE see DATISCACEAE

TETRAMERISTACEAE
(*Tetramerista* only unless otherwise stated)

Balan Menon 1955.
Baretta-Kuipers 1976 – Relationships.
Brazier & Franklin 1961.
Decker 1966.
Hayashi et al. 1973.
Ilic 1991.
Kobayashi & Sugawa 1966a.
Maguire et al. 1972 – *Pentamerista, Tetramerista.*
Ogata 1975–1983.
Sudo 1963.
Vestal 1937 – (in Theaceae).

Crystals
Chattaway 1955.

THEACEAE (see BONNETIACEAE or GUTTIFERAE for *Ploiarium*)
(*Stewartia* is spelt *Stuartia* as in Brummitt 1992)

Baretta-Kuipers 1976 – Comparison with Bonnetiaceae.
Bascopé 1954 – *Laplacea, Ternstroemia.*

(THEACEAE)
Benoist 1931 – *Laplacea*.
Burgerstein 1909 – *Eurya*.
Cheng, C. 1985 – *Schima*.
Cheng, J.-Q. 1980 – 10 genera.
Cheng, J.-Q. et al. 1992 – 10 genera.
Chiang 1964 – *Schima*.
Cockrell 1942 – *Eurya*.
Cutler et al. 1987 – *Camellia* (root).
Dechamps 1985 – *Freziera, Laplacea, Ternstroemia*.
*Deng & Baas 1990 – 15 genera incl. *Sladenia*.
*Deng & Baas 1991 – *Archboldiodendron, Balthasaria, Ficalhoa, Franklinia, Freziera, Visnea*, plus notes on 10 other genera.
Desch 1954 – *Adinandra, Anneslea, Gordonia, Schima, Ternstroemia*.
Détienne & Jacquet 1983 – *Freziera, Laplacea, Ternstroemia*.
Détienne et al. 1982 – *Laplacea, Ternstroemia*.
Edlmann & Monaco 1981 – *Camellia, Stuartia*.
Furuno 1979 – *Adinandra*.
Gasson & Cutler 1990 – *Stuartia* (root).
Hayashi 1991 – *Camellia, Cleyera, Eurya, Stuartia, Ternstroemia*.
Hayashi et al. 1973 – *Adinandra, Gordonia, Schima*.
Herat & Theobald 1977 [1978] – *Adinandra, Eurya, Gordonia, Ternstroemia*.
Hirai 1979–1985 – *Camellia, Cleyera, Eurya, Stuartia, Ternstroemia*.
Ilic 1991 – *Eurya, Gordonia, Schima, Ternstroemia*.
Kanehira 1921a – *Adinandra, Anneslea, Cleyera, Eurya, Gordonia, Schima, Ternstroemia, Thea* (= *Camellia*).
Kanehira 1921b – *Camellia, Cleyera, Eurya, Stuartia, Ternstroemia*.
Kanehira 1926 – *Camellia, Cleyera, Eurya, Schima, Stuartia, Ternstroemia*.
*Keng 1962 – Wood of 21 genera, over 80 spp. (incl. *Sladenia*).
Kribs 1959 – *Schima*.
Lebacq & Dechamps 1964 – *Ficalhoa* (in Ericaceae).
Lechner 1914 – *Sladenia* (twig).
Lecomte 1926a – *Anneslea, Ternstroemia*.
Luo 1989 – *Schima, Sladenia, Ternstroemia*.

(THEACEAE)
Martawijaya et al. 1989 – *Schima*.
Moll & Janssonius 1906–1936 – *Adinandra, Camellia, Eurya, Gordonia, Haemocharis* (= *Laplacea*), *Pyrenaria, Schima, Ternstroemia*.
Ogata 1975–1983 – *Schima*.
Pearson & Brown 1932 – *Schima*.
Peraza Oramas & Lopez de Roma 1967 – *Visnea*.
Pérez Mogollón 1993 – *Freziera, Laplacea*.
Pérez Olvera et al. 1982 [1985] – *Eurya, Ternstroemia*.
*Record 1942a – *Eurya, Franklinia, Gordonia, Laplacea, Stuartia, Ternstroemia*. (See also Pellicieraceae.)
Record & Hess 1943 – Family (genera as for Record 1942a).
Shimaji & Itoh 1982 – *Camellia, Cleyera*.
Shimaji & Itoh 1988 – *Camellia, Cleyera, Eurya, Stuartia*.
Soh & Sun 1986 – *Camellia, Cleyera, Eurya, Stuartia, Ternstroemia, Thea*.
Sudo 1959 – *Camellia, Cleyera, Eurya, Stuartia, Ternstroemia*.
Sudo 1963 – *Schima*.
Sudo 1988 – *Adinandra, Gordonia*.
Suzuki et al. 1991 – *Camellia, Eurya, Schima*.
Tang 1973 – *Adinandra, Anneslea, Camellia, Hartia* (= *Stuartia*), *Schima*.
Van der Slooten 1968 – *Cleyera*.
Vestal 1937 – Family (15 genera, incl. Bonnetiaceae).
Williams 1936 – *Ternstroemia*.
Wu & Wang 1976 – *Adinandra, Gordonia, Schima, Tutcheria*.
Xie & Mo 1987 – *Apterosperma*.
Xie et al. 1987 – *Camellia*.
Xu et al. 1989 – *Camellia*.
Yamabayashi 1938 – *Camellia, Eurya, Freziera, Stuartia, Taonabo* (= *Ternstroemia*).
Yamauchi 1980 – *Stuartia*.
Yao 1988 – *Adinandra, Anneslea, Schima, Ternstroemia*.

Crystals
Chattaway 1956 – *Gordonia, Schima*.

Ecological anatomy
Van der Graaff & Baas 1974 – *Eurya, Gordonia*.

(THEACEAE)
Versteegh 1968 – *Gordonia, Pyrenaria, Ternstroemia.*

Helical thickenings
Ohtani & Ishida 1978b – *Camellia, Cleyera, Eurya, Stuartia, Ternstroemia.*

Perforation plates
Ohtani & Ishida 1978a – Same genera as Ohtani & Ishida 1978b.

Silica
Espinoza de Pernía 1987b – *Ternstroemia.*
Welle 1976b – *Ternstroemia.*

Tracheary elements
Jing et al. 1989 – *Schima.*
Ohtani 1983 – Same genera as Ohtani & Ishida 1978b.

THEOPHRASTACEAE

Barajas Morales & León Gómez 1989 – *Jacquinia.*
Dechamps 1985 – *Clavija.*
Détienne & Jacquet 1983 – *Clavija, Jacquinia.*
Kribs 1959 – *Jacquinia.*
Record & Hess 1943 – Family (*Clavija, Jacquinia, Theophrasta*).
Williams 1936 – *Clavija* (in Myrsinaceae).

Crystals
Chattaway 1956 – *Jacquinia.*

Silica
Espinoza de Pernía 1987b – *Clavija.*
Welle 1976b – *Clavija.*

THYMELAEACEAE
(see also GONYSTYLACEAE)

Bandoni & O'Donell 1939 – *Ovidia.*
Brown 1922 – *Wikstroemia.*
Burgerstein 1909 – *Phaleria, Wikstroemia.*
Cheng, J.-Q. 1980 – *Aquilaria.*
Cheng, J.-Q. et al. 1992 – *Aquilaria.*
Choquette 1926 – *Dirca.*
Cutler et al. 1987 – *Daphne* (root).
Desch 1954 – *Aquilaria.*
Fahn & Sarnat 1963 – *Thymelaea.*
Fahn et al. 1986 – *Thymelaea.*
Giordano 1940 – *Lasiosiphon* (= *Gnidia*).
Gorczyńska 1955, 1958 – *Daphne.*

(THYMELAEACEAE)
Greguss 1959 – *Daphne, Thymelaea.*
Grosser 1977 – *Daphne.*
*Hamaya 1959 – *Daphne, Daphnimorpha, Diplomorpha* (= *Wikstroemia*), *Edgeworthia, Wikstroemia.*
Hayashi 1991 – *Edgeworthia.*
Hayashi et al. 1973 – *Aquilaria.*
Ilic 1991 – *Amyxa* (under Gonystylaceae), *Aquilaria, Microsemma* (= *Lethedon*).
Janssonius 1950 – Relations.
Kanehira 1921a – *Daphne, Wikstroemia.*
Lebacq et al. 1973 – *Schoenobiblus.*
Lecomte 1926a – *Aquilaria, Rhamnoneuron, Wikstroemia.*
Luo 1989 – *Aquilaria.*
Luxova 1992 – *Daphne.*
Metcalfe 1933 – *Aquilaria.*
Miller, R.B. 1975 – *Lethedon* (in Flacourtiaceae).
Moll & Janssonius 1906–1936 – *Phaleria, Wikstroemia.*
Ogata 1975–1983 – *Aquilaria.*
Pearson & Brown 1932 – *Aquilaria.*
Rao & Dayal 1992 – *Aquilaria.*
Record & Hess 1943 – Family (*Daphnopsis, Dirca, Lagetta, Lasiadenia, Ovidia, Schoenobiblus*).
Saint-Laurent 1928, 1934 – *Daphne, Thymelaea.*
Saya 1957 – *Daphne.*
Schweingruber 1978 – *Daphne.*
Schweingruber 1990 – *Daphne, Thymelaea.*
Sudo 1959 – *Edgeworthia.*
Sudo 1963 – *Aquilaria.*
Sugawa 1968c – *Aquilaria.*
Tang 1973 – *Aquilaria.*
Van Vliet & Baas 1984 – Relations of myrtalean families.
Williams 1936 – *Schoenobiblus.*

Anomalous structure
Chalk & Chattaway 1937 – Family (*Aquilaria, Gyrinops*).
Joshi 1935 – *Stellera.*
Lashevski 1925 [1926] – *Daphne.*
Léandri 1928 – *Daphne.*
Léandri 1931 – *Gnidia.*

Crystals
Chattaway 1955 – *Pimelea.*

(THYMELAEACEAE)

Ecological anatomy
Baas & Schweingruber 1987 – *Daphne,*
Thymelaea.
Baas et al. 1983 – *Thymelaea.*
Carlquist 1977c – *Pimelea.*
Carlquist 1985a – *Daphne, Dirca, Gnidia,*
Ovidia, Pimelea, Wikstroemia.

Helical thickenings
Meylan & Butterfield 1978a – *Pimelea.*
Ohtani & Ishida 1978b – *Daphne.*

Pits and perforation plates
Dute et al. 1990 – *Daphne.*
Ohtani & Ishida 1976, 1978a – *Daphne.*

Tracheary elements
Ohtani 1983 – *Daphne.*

TICODENDRACEAE

*Carlquist 1991a – *Ticodendron.*

TILIACEAE (for *Cistanthera* (= *Neso-*
gordonia) see STERCULIACEAE)

Anon. 1966 – *Tilia.*
Anon. 1981 (Andes) – *Apeiba.*
Abbate 1963, 1964 – *Grewia.*
Abbate 1977 – *Berrya.*
Babos & Borhidi 1978 – *Luehea.*
Balan Menon 1959 – *Pentace.*
Bamps et al. 1977 – *Westphalina.*
Barajas Morales & León Gómez 1989 –
Heliocarpus.
Bargagli-Petrucci 1903 – *Berrya, Brown-*
lowia.
Benoist 1931 – *Apeiba.*
Brazier & Franklin 1961 – *Pentace, Tilia.*
Carvalho 1954–1956 – *Tilia.*
Cebrat 1991 – *Tilia.*
Chattaway 1934 – *Grewia, Microcos.*
Cheng, C. 1985 – *Burretiodendron, Tilia.*
Cheng, J.-Q. 1980 – *Burretiodendron,*
Colona, Microcos, Tilia.
Cheng, J.-Q. et al. 1992 – Same genera as
Cheng 1980.
Corral Lopez 1985 – *Luehea.*
Cutler et al. 1987 – *Tilia* (root).
Datta, A. K. & Saha 1960 – *Corchorus*
(young).

(TILIACEAE)

Datta, R. M. & Roy 1964 – *Corchorus*
(young).
Dechamps 1985 – *Apeiba, Christiana,*
Heliocarpus, Lueheopsis, Mollia.
Den Outer & Schütz 1981a – *Apeiba.*
Den Outer & Schütz 1981b – Many genera
for comparison with Sarcolaenaceae etc.
Desch 1954 – *Grewia, Microcos, Pentace,*
Schoutenia, Trichospermum.
Détienne & Jacquet 1983 – *Apeiba, Hassel-*
tia (or in Flacourtiaceae), *Heliocarpus,*
Luehea, Lueheopsis, Mollia, Muntingia,
Prockia (or in Flacourtiaceae).
Détienne et al. 1982 – *Apeiba, Lueheopsis.*
Dixon 1919 – *Pentace.*
Edlmann & Monaco 1981 – *Tilia.*
Eeckhout 1951 – *Tilia.*
Fahn et al. 1986 – *Grewia.*
Fasolo 1941–1944 – *Grewia.*
Fegel 1941 – *Tilia* (root).
Freudweiler 1933 – *Grewia.*
Furuno 1985, 1987 – *Tilia.*
Greguss 1959 – *Tilia.*
Grosser 1977 – *Tilia.*
Hayashi 1991 – *Tilia.*
Hayashi et al. 1973 – *Grewia, Pentace.*
Hayashi & Nomura 1986 – *Berrya, Grewia.*
Hirai 1979–1985 – *Tilia.*
Hoheisel et al. 1968 – *Apeiba.*
Hyde 1925 – *Apeiba, Heliocarpus.*
Ilic 1991 – 11 genera.
Jacquiot et al. 1973 – *Tilia.*
Jagiella & Kurschner 1987 – *Grewia.*
Janssonius 1950 – Relations.
Jayawardana 1932 – *Berrya, Pityranthe.*
Kanehira 1921a – *Grewia.*
Kanehira 1921b – *Tilia.*
Kanehira 1924 – *Grewia.*
Kanehira 1926 – *Tilia.*
Krempl 1963 – *Tilia.*
Kribs 1928a – *Mollia.*
Kribs 1959 – *Grewia, Hasseltiopsis* (or in
Flacourtiaceae), *Luehea, Pentace, Tilia.*
*Kukachka & Rees 1943 – 35 genera.
Lebacq & Dechamps 1964 – *Desplatsia,*
Diplanthemum (= *Duboscia*), *Glyphaea,*
Grewia.
Lebacq & Dechamps 1967 – *Desplatsia,*
Grewia.
Lebacq et al. 1973 – *Apeiba, Heliocarpus,*
Luehea, Mollia, Muntingia.

(TILIACEAE)

Lecomte 1922 – *Grewia.*
Lecomte 1926a – *Columbia* (= *Colona*),
  Pentace.
Lim & Soh 1991b – *Grewia, Tilia.*
Lomibao 1973c – *Trichospermum.*
Luo 1989 – *Burretiodendron, Tilia.*
Mainieri 1978 – *Hydrogaster, Luehea.*
Mainieri & Chimelo 1989 – *Hydrogaster,*
  Luehea.
Meylan & Butterfield 1978b – *Entelea.*
Moll & Janssonius 1906–1936 – *Berrya,*
  Columbia (= *Colona*), *Grewia, Pentace,*
  Schoutenia, Trichospermum.
Mork 1946 – *Tilia.*
Nájera Angulo & López Fraile 1969 – *Tilia.*
Niloofari 1961 – *Tilia.*
Normand 1955 – *Christiana, Desplatsia,*
  Duboscia, Glyphaea.
Normand & Paquis 1976 [1977] – *Christi-*
  ana, Desplatsia, Duboscia, Glyphaea,
  Grewia.
Novruzova 1962a – *Tilia.*
Ogata 1975–1983 – *Microcos, Pentace.*
Ortega et al. 1988 – *Heliocarpus.*
Panshin & Zeeuw 1980 – *Tilia.*
Parsa Pajouh & Schweingruber 1985 – *Tilia.*
Patel 1988 – *Entelea.*
Pearson & Brown 1932 – *Berrya, Grewia,*
  Pentace.
Pereira 1933 – *Luehea.*
Pérez Mogollón 1973 – *Apeiba.*
Pérez Olvera et al. 1980 [1981] – *Belotia*
  (= *Trichospermum*), *Carpodiptera.*
Pérez Olvera et al. 1982 [1985] – *Tilia.*
Record 1927a – *Mollia.*
Record & Hess 1943 – Family (11 genera).
Record & Mell 1924 – *Luehea.*
Riedl 1937 – *Tilia* (root).
Saiki 1982 – *Tilia.*
Schultz & Wollheim 1962 – *Luehea.*
Schweingruber 1978, 1990 – *Tilia.*
Shimaji & Itoh 1982, 1988 – *Tilia.*
Silva 1991 – *Heliocarpus.*
Sudo 1959 – *Tilia.*
Sudo 1963 – *Diplodiscus, Grewia, Pentace.*
Sudo 1988 – *Microcos.*
Tang 1973 – *Burretiodendron.*
Tang 1992b – *Corchoropsis* (or Sterc100-
  ceae).
Thunell & Perem 1947 – *Tilia.*
Tortorelli 1956 – *Luehea.*

(TILIACEAE)

Wagenführ & Scheiber 1974 – *Nesogor-*
  donia, Tilia.
Williams 1928 – *Goethalsia.*
Williams 1936 – *Apeiba, Heliocarpus,*
  Luehea, Mollia, Muntingia.
Wiraj Chunwarin & Damrong Sri-Aran
  1973 – *Berrya, Pentace, Schoutenia.*
Wuang 1979 – *Tilia.*
Yamabayashi 1938 – *Grewia, Tilia.*
Yao 1988 – *Tilia.*

Crystals and silica
Chattaway 1956 – *Actinophora* (= *Schou-*
  tenia), *Colona, Diplodiscus, Grewia,*
  Luehea, Microcos, Pentace, Schoutenia,
  Trichospermum.
Espinoza de Pernía 1987b – *Apeiba, Goet-*
  halsia, Heliocarpus, Luehea.
Meniado et al. 1970 – *Colona.*
Scurfield et al. 1974 – *Brownlowia.*
Welle 1976b – *Luehea.*

Ecological anatomy
Baas & Schweingruber 1987 – *Tilia.*
Baas et al. 1983 – *Grewia.*
Barajas Morales 1985 – *Belotia* (= *Tricho-*
  spermum).
Den Outer & Van Veenendaal 1976 – *Chris-*
  tiana.
Novruzova 1968 – *Tilia.*

Helical thickenings
Nair 1987 – *Grewia.*
Ohtani & Ishida 1978b – *Tilia.*
Parham & Kaustinen 1973 – *Tilia.*

Pits and perforation plates
Meylan & Butterfield 1974 – *Entelea.*
Ohtani & Ishida 1978a – *Tilia.*

Rays
Chattaway 1933a – Malvales: general.

Storied structure
Cozzo & Cristiani 1950 – *Heliocarpus,*
  Luehea, Muntingia.
Włoch & Szendera 1989 – *Tilia.*

Tracheary elements
Fukazawa & Ohtani 1982 – *Tilia.*
Jing et al. 1989 – *Tilia.*
Ohtani 1983 – *Tilia.*

TORRICELLIACEAE (*Torricellia*)

Li & Chao 1954 – (in Cornaceae).
Purkayastha & Bahadur 1977 – (brief).
Suzuki et al. 1991.

TOVARIACEAE (*Tovaria*)

*Carlquist 1985b.

TREMANDRACEAE

*Carlquist 1977b – *Platytheca, Tetratheca,
Tremandra*.
Heimsch 1942 – *Tetratheca, Tremandra*.

Ecological anatomy
Carlquist 1985a – *Platytheca*.

TRIGONIACEAE (incl. EUPHRONIACEAE)

Desch 1954 – *Trigoniastrum*.
Détienne & Jacquet 1983 – *Euphronia* (in
Verbenaceae).
Espinoza de Pernía 1989 – *Euphronia*.
Heimsch 1942 – *Lightia* (= *Euphronia*),
Trigonia, Trigoniastrum.
Lleras 1978 – *Humbertiodendron, Trigonia,
Trigoniastrum* (young, brief).
Record & Hess 1943 – Family (*Euphronia,
Trigonia*).

TRIMENIACEAE
(for *Xymalos* see MONIMIACEAE)

*Carlquist 1984e *Piptocalyx* (= *Trimenia*),
Trimenia.
Ilic 1991 – *Trimenia*.
Lemesle & Pichard 1954 – *Trimenia*.
Metcalfe 1987 – General survey.
Money et al. 1950 – *Piptocalyx* (= *Trime-
nia*), *Trimenia*.

Ecological anatomy
Versteegh 1968 – *Trimenia*.

TROCHODENDRACEAE
(*Trochodendron*)

Bailey 1944b.
Bailey & Nast 1945b.
Bailey & Thompson 1918.
Chen, G. 1989.

(TROCHODENDRACEAE)
Cheng, J.-Q. 1980.
Cheng, J.-Q. et al. 1992.
Chiang 1962.
Gupta 1934.
Hayashi 1991.
Hirai 1979–1985.
Ilic 1991.
Kanehira 1921a, b, 1926.
Lemesle 1953, 1963a.
McLaughlin 1933.
Nast & Bailey 1946.
Saiki 1982.
Shimaji & Itoh 1982.
Sudo 1959.
Takahashi 1985.
Thompson & Bailey 1916.
Wu & Wang 1976.
Yang 1981.

Pits
Lemesle 1946a.

TURNERACEAE

Record 1927c – *Erblichia*.
Record & Hess 1943 – *Erblichia, Turnera*.

Ecological anatomy
Carlquist 1985a – *Turnera*.

UAPACACEAE see EUPHORBIACEAE

ULMACEAE
(for *Barbeya* see BARBEYACEAE)

Anon. 1966 – *Ulmus, Zelkova*.
Abbate & Cavina 1980 – *Holoptelea*.
Abbate & Cenerini 1976 – *Celtis, Holo-
ptelea*.
Ayensu & Bentum 1974 – *Celtis*.
Barajas Morales et al. 1979 – *Ampelocera,
Mirandaceltis* (= *Aphananthe*).
Brazier & Franklin 1961 – *Celtis, Holo-
ptelea, Phyllostylon, Ulmus, Zelkova*.
Burgerstein 1909 – *Gironniera, Trema*.
Burgerstein 1912 – *Celtis, Phyllostylon,
Trema*.
Carreras & Vales 1986b – *Celtis*.
Carvalho 1954–1956 – *Celtis, Ulmus*.
Chalk et al. 1933 – *Holoptelea*.
Chang 1981 – *Aphananthe*.

(ULMACEAE)

Cheng, C. 1985 – *Celtis, Ulmus, Zelkova.*

Cheng, J.-Q. 1980 – *Aphananthe, Celtis, Gironniera, Pteroceltis, Trema, Ulmus, Zelkova.*

Cheng, J.-Q. et al. 1992 – Same genera as Cheng 1980.

Chiang 1962 – *Zelkova.*

Chudnoff 1956 – *Celtis, Ulmus.*

Clarke 1930 – *Ulmus.*

Cox 1941 – *Celtis.*

Cutler et al. 1987 – *Ulmus, Zelkova* (root).

Dadswell & Eckersley 1935 – *Aphananthe.*

Dechamps 1985 – *Ampelocera, Trema.*

Desch 1954 – *Gironniera, Trema.*

Détienne & Jacquet 1983 – *Ampelocera, Celtis, Trema.*

Détienne et al. 1982 – *Ampelocera, Trema.*

Duchaigne 1966 – *Ulmus.*

Edlmann & Monaco 1981 – *Celtis, Hemiptelea, Ulmus, Zelkova.*

Fahn et al. 1986 – *Celtis, Ulmus.*

Fegel 1941 – *Ulmus* (root).

Ferreirinha 1955 – *Celtis.*

Fouarge & Gérard 1964 – *Holoptelea.*

Freitas 1987 – *Celtis.*

Fundter & Wisse 1977 – *Celtis.*

Furuno 1979 – *Celtis.*

Furuno 1985, 1987 – *Celtis, Ulmus.*

Gasson & Cutler 1990 – *Celtis* (root).

Giordano 1939 – *Celtis.*

Gómez 1959 – *Ampelocera.*

Greguss 1959 – *Celtis, Ulmus, Zelkova.*

Grosser 1977 – *Celtis, Ulmus.*

Grumbles 1941 – *Celtis.*

Hayashi 1991 – *Aphananthe, Celtis, Ulmus, Zelkova.*

Hayashi & Nomura 1986 – *Holoptelea.*

Hirai 1979–1985 – *Aphananthe, Celtis, Ulmus, Zelkova.*

Huber & Rouschal 1954 – *Zelkova.*

Ilic 1991 – *Ampelocera, Aphananthe, Celtis, Gironniera, Holoptelea, Trema, Ulmus, Zelkova.*

Jaccard 1914 – *Ulmus* (root).

Jacquiot et al. 1973 – *Celtis, Ulmus, Zelkova.*

Janssonius 1932 – *Gironniera.*

Kachroo & Bhat 1982 – *Celtis, Trema, Ulmus.*

Kanehira 1921a – *Celtis, Trema, Ulmus, Zelkova.*

(ULMACEAE)

Kanehira 1921b – *Aphananthe, Celtis.*

Kanehira 1926 – *Abelicea (= Zelkova), Aphananthe, Celtis, Hemiptelea, Trema, Ulmus.*

Kribs 1959 – *Celtis, Phyllostylon, Trema.*

Lebacq 1955 – *Celtis, Holoptelea, Trema.*

Lebacq & Dechamps 1964 – *Celtis, Holoptelea, Trema.*

Lebacq & Dechamps 1967 – *Celtis, Trema.*

Lebacq et al. 1973 – *Celtis, Trema.*

Lebedenko 1962a – *Celtis.*

Lecomte 1922 – *Trema.*

Lecomte 1926a – *Gironniera.*

Lepe 1959 – *Ampelocera.*

Leroy 1946 – *Aphananthe, Gironniera.*

Luo 1989 – *Celtis, Trema, Ulmus, Zelkova.*

Milanez 1937 – *Ampelocera.*

Minaki et al. 1988 – *Hemiptelea* (also fossils).

Moll & Janssonius 1906–1936 – *Celtis, Gironniera, Parasponia, Trema.*

Monteiro & Frade 1960 – *Celtis.*

Monteiro & França 1971 – *Celtis.*

Mork 1946 – *Ulmus.*

Moseley 1973 [1974] – Relations.

Nájera Angulo & López Fraile 1969 – *Ulmus.*

Nardi Berti & Edlmann Abbate 1988 – *Celtis.*

Niloofari 1961 – *Ulmus, Zelkova.*

Normand 1950b – *Celtis, Chaetachme, Holoptelea, Trema.*

Normand & Paquis 1976 [1977] – *Celtis, Holoptelea, Trema.*

Ocloo & Laing 1991 – *Celtis.*

Ogata 1975–1983 – *Celtis.*

Ortega et al. 1988 – *Trema.*

Palandzhyan 1953 – *Celtis, Holoptelea, Planera, Pteroceltis, Ulmus, Zelkova* + notes from literature on 7 other genera.

Panshin & Zeeuw 1980 – *Celtis, Ulmus.*

Parsa Pajouh & Schweingruber 1985 – *Ulmus, Zelkova.*

Pearson & Brown 1932 – *Celtis, Holoptelea, Ulmus.*

Pérez Olvera et al. 1980 [1981] – *Ampelocera.*

Record & Garratt 1925 – *Phyllostylon.*

Record & Hess 1943 – Family (*Ampelocera, Celtis, Chaetoptelea (= Ulmus), Momisia (= Celtis), Phyllostylon, Planera, Trema, Ulmus*).

(ULMACEAE)

Record & Mell 1924 – *Celtis, Phyllostylon*.
Riedl 1937 – *Ulmus* (root).
Saiki 1982 – *Aphananthe, Ulmus, Zelkova*.
Saint-Laurent 1928, 1934 – *Celtis, Ulmus*.
Şanli 1981 – *Ulmus*.
Schweingruber 1978 – *Ulmus*.
Schweingruber 1990 – *Celtis, Ulmus*.
Scott 1927 – *Celtis*.
Senkevich 1977 – *Ulmus*.
Shimaji & Itoh 1982, 1988 – *Aphananthe,
Celtis, Ulmus, Zelkova*.
Stern & Sweitzer 1972 – *Trema*.
Suciu 1960 – *Ulmus*.
Sudo 1959 – *Aphananthe, Celtis, Ulmus,
Zelkova*.
Sudo 1963 – *Celtis, Phyllostylon, Trema*.
Sudo 1988 – *Celtis*.
*Sweitzer 1971 – 18 genera.
Tang 1973 – *Celtis, Gironniera, Ulmus,
Zelkova*.
Thunell & Perem 1947 – *Ulmus*.
Tippo 1938 – Family (9 genera).
Tortorelli 1956 – *Celtis, Phyllostylon*.
Vales & Carreras 1987 – *Celtis*.
Wagenführ & Scheiber 1974 – *Ulmus*.
Wang 1966 – *Zelkova*.
Wang 1984–1988 – *Celtis*.
Wheeler et al. 1989 – *Celtis* 6 spp., *Ulmus*
6 spp.
Williams 1936 – *Trema*.
Wu & Wang 1976 – *Celtis, Trema, Zelkova*.
Wuang 1979 – *Ulmus, Zelkova*.
Yamabayashi 1938 – *Aphananthe, Celtis,
Hemiptelea* (= *Zelkova*), *Ulmus, Zelkova*.
Yao 1988 – *Aphananthe, Celtis, Pteroceltis,
Ulmus*.
Yatsenko-Khemelevsky 1954a – *Celtis,
Planera, Pteroceltis, Ulmus, Zelkova*.
*Zhong et al. 1992 – *Aphananthe, Celtis,
Gironniera, Hemiptelea, Pteroceltis,
Trema, Ulmus, Zelkova*.

Crystals
Chattaway 1955 – *Celtis*.
Chattaway 1956 – *Ampelocera, Aphananthe,
Celtis, Phyllostylon, Ulmus, Zelkova*.
Meniado et al. 1970 – *Celtis*.

Ecological anatomy
Baas & Schweingruber 1987 – *Celtis,
Ulmus*.
Baas et al. 1983 – *Ulmus*.

(ULMACEAE)

Carlquist 1985a – *Celtis, Ulmus*.
Carlquist & Hoekman 1985a – *Celtis*.
Den Outer & Van Veenendaal 1976 – *Trema*.
Enchev 1961 – *Ulmus*.
Lim & Soh 1991a – *Zelkova*.
Novruzova 1962d – *Ulmus*.
Novruzova 1968 – *Celtis, Ulmus, Zelkova*.

Helical thickenings
Ohtani & Ishida 1978b – *Aphananthe, Celtis,
Ulmus, Zelkova*.
Parham & Kaustinen 1973 – *Celtis, Ulmus*.

Pits and perforation plates
Dute & Rushing 1990 – *Celtis, Ulmus*.
Ohtani & Ishida 1978a – Same genera as
Ohtani & Ishida 1978b.

Rays
Schmidt 1922 – *Ulmus*.

Silica
Scurfield et al. 1974 – *Gironniera*.

Storied structure
Cozzo & Cristiani 1950 – *Phyllostylon*.

Tracheary elements
Gill & Onuja 1984a – *Holoptelea*.
Gill et al. 1985b – *Trema*.
Jing et al. 1989 – *Aphananthe, Trema*.
Ohtani 1983 – Same genera as Ohtani &
Ishida 1978b above.

UMBELLIFERAE

Abbate 1963 – *Steganotaenia*.
Carlquist 1962a – *Foeniculum*.
Cellai 1967 – *Heteromorpha*.
Dechamps 1977 – *Steganotaenia*.
Greguss 1959 – *Bupleurum*.
Lemesle 1956c – *Eryngium*.
Lemesle 1958b – *Peucedanum*.
Lemesle & Rousseau 1959 – *Peucedanum*.
Messeri 1938 – *Pityranthus* (= *Pituranthos*).
*Rodríguez 1957a – 22 genera.
Rodríguez 1957b – *Arracacia, Daucus,
Foeniculum, Sanicula*.
Rodríguez 1971 – Relations of Umbellulales.
Saint-Laurent 1928, 1934 – *Bupleurum*.
Saint-Laurent 1932a – *Pituranthos*.
Schweingruber 1990 – *Bupleurum, Melano-
selinum*.

(UMBELLIFERAE)

Anomalous structure

Ancibor 1986 [1987] – *Mulinum*.
Bonomo et al. 1978 – *Athamanta*.

Ecological anatomy

Baas & Schweingruber 1987 – *Bupleurum, Melanoselinum*.

Tracheary elements

Lemesle 1951 – *Gymnophyton, Hydrocotyle, Siebera* (= *Platysace*)*, Trachymene, Xanthosia*.
Lemesle 1952 – *Bupleurum, Heteromorpha*.
Lemesle 1958a – *Bupleurum, Heteromorpha, Pituranthos*.

URTICACEAE

(for CECROPIACEAE see MORACEAE)

*Bonsen & Welle 1984 – 21 genera.
Brown 1922 – *Pipturus*.
Burgerstein 1909 – *Laportea, Leucosyke*.
Cockrell 1942 – *Villebrunea* (= *Oreocnide*).
Ilic 1991 – *Gyrotaenia, Leucosyke, Pipturus*.
Janssonius 1950 – Relations.
Kanehira 1921a – *Debregeasia, Maoutia, Pipturus*.
Moll & Janssonius 1906–1936 – *Laportea, Leucosyke, Maoutia, Pipturus, Villebrunea* (= *Oreocnide*).
Pearson & Brown 1932 – *Boehmeria*.
Record & Hess 1943 – Family (*Myriocarpa, Urera*).
Silva 1991 – *Urera*.
Sudo 1963 – *Boehmeria*.
Tippo 1938 – Family (12 genera).
Williams 1936 – *Boehmeria, Myriocarpa, Urera*.

Anomalous structure

Chalk & Chattaway 1937 – Family (*Laportea, Myriocarpa, Touchardia, Urera*).
Obaton 1960 – *Urera*.

Crystals

Chattaway 1955 – *Boehmeria, Pipturus*.
Chattaway 1956 – *Pipturus*.

Rays

Chattaway 1951b – *Pipturus*.

Storied structure

Cozzo & Cristiani 1950 – *Urera*.

VACCINIACEAE see ERICACEAE

VALERIANACEAE

*Carlquist 1983d – *Centranthus, Patrinia, Valeriana*.
*Lörcher 1990 – *Belonanthus, Centranthus, Patrinia, Phyllactis, Stangea, Valeriana*.
Lörcher & Weberling 1984 – *Valeriana* 10 spp.
Lörcher & Weberling 1985 – *Valeriana* 2 spp.

Anomalous structure

Lörcher & Weberling 1982 – *Aretiastrum, Belonanthus, Phyllactis, Stangea, Valeriana*.

VERBENACEAE (incl. AVICENNIACEAE; see also DICRASTYLIDACEAE)

(*Nyctanthes* is indexed both here and under OLEACEAE)

Abbate 1977 – *Tectona*.
Akachuku & Burley 1979 – *Gmelina*.
Baas et al. 1988 – *Nyctanthes*.
Baker 1915 – *Avicennia*.
Bargagli-Petrucci 1903 – *Vitex*.
Bascopé et al. 1959 – *Avicennia*.
Brazier & Franklin 1961 – *Avicennia, Gmelina, Tectona*.
Burgerstein 1909 – *Clerodendrum, Premna, Stachytarpheta*.
Carreras 1988 – *Avicennia*.
Carreras et al. 1989 – *Avicennia, Gmelina, Petitia, Tectona, Vitex*.
Carreras & Pérez 1988 – *Vitex*.
Carreras & Vales 1986b – *Avicennia, Gmelina, Tectona*.
Cellai 1967 – *Avicennia*.
Cheng, C. 1985 – *Gmelina, Tectona*.
Cheng, J.-Q. 1980 – *Gmelina, Tectona, Vitex*.
Cheng, J.-Q. et al. 1992 – *Gmelina, Tectona, Vitex*.
Chowdhury 1953 – *Gmelina*.
Cockrell 1942 – *Callicarpa, Premna, Vitex*.
Cunha Mello 1950 [1951] – *Vitex*.
Dadswell & Eckersley 1935 – *Gmelina, Vitex*.
D'Arcy & Keating 1973 – *Lithophytum* (= *Plocosperma*) (or in Loganiaceae).

(VERBENACEAE)

Das 1984a – *Avicennia, Callicarpa, Gmelina, Premna, Tectona, Vitex.*
Dechamps 1979 – *Avicennia.*
Dechamps 1985 – *Aegiphila, Citharexylum, Lippia, Vitex.*
Desch 1954 – *Avicennia, Callicarpa, Clerodendrum, Gmelina, Peronema, Premna, Vitex.*
Détienne & Jacquet 1983 – *Aegiphila, Avicennia, Citharexylum, Vitex.*
Détienne et al. 1982 – *Avicennia, Vitex.*
Donaldson 1984 – *Tectona.*
Fahn et al. 1986 – *Avicennia, Vitex.*
Fouarge et al. 1953 – *Vitex.*
Francis 1928 – *Gmelina.*
Freitas 1958 – *Tectona, Vitex.*
Freitas 1963, 1973 [1974] – *Tectona.*
Frison 1948a – *Avicennia.*
Fundter & Wisse 1977 – *Vitex.*
Furuno 1977 – *Avicennia, Gmelina, Tectona, Teijsmanniodendron, Vitex.*
Gaiotti de Peralta & Edlmann Abbate 1981 – *Vitex.*
Garratt 1924 – *Vitex.*
Gottwald & Noack 1965 [1966] – *Vitex.*
Gottwald & Parameswaran 1980 – *Tectona.*
Greguss 1959 – *Vitex.*
Hayashi 1991 – *Clerodendrum.*
Hayashi et al. 1973 – *Avicennia, Tectona, Vitex.*
Hayashi & Nomura 1986 – *Vitex.*
Heim 1971 – *Vitex.*
Hirai 1979–1985 – *Tectona.*
Hofmann 1955 – *Vitex.*
Ilic 1991 – 12 genera.
Jagiella & Kurschner 1987 – *Avicennia.*
Janssonius 1950 – Relations.
Kanehira 1921a – *Avicennia, Callicarpa, Clerodendrum, Premna, Vitex.*
Kanehira 1921b – *Clerodendrum.*
Kanehira 1924 – *Avicennia, Tectona, Vitex.*
Kanehira 1926 – *Clerodendrum, Vitex.*
Kiew & Baas 1984 – *Nyctanthes.*
Kobayashi & Sugawa 1963 – *Tectona.*
Kribs 1959 – *Avicennia, Gmelina, Petitia, Tectona, Vitex.*
Krishnamurthy & Sigamani 1987 – *Avicennia.*
Kundu & De 1968 [1969] – *Clerodendrum, Nyctanthes, Tectona.*

(VERBENACEAE)

Lamb 1968 – *Gmelina.*
Lebacq & Dechamps 1964 – *Tectona, Vitex.*
Lebacq & Dechamps 1967 – *Vitex.*
Lebacq et al. 1973 – *Aegiphila, Avicennia, Lippia, Vitex.*
Lecomte 1922 – *Tectona, Vitex.*
Lecomte 1926a – *Avicennia, Tectona, Vitex.*
Lomibao & Salva 1972 – *Vitex.*
López & Ortega 1989 – *Avicennia.*
Luo 1989 – *Gmelina, Tectona, Vitex.*
Martawijaya et al. 1986 – *Peronema, Tectona.*
Meylan & Butterfield 1978b – *Avicennia, Vitex.*
Moll & Janssonius 1906–1936 – *Avicennia, Geunsia (= Callicarpa), Gmelina, Premna, Tectona, Vitex.*
Nardi Berti & Edlmann Abbate 1988 – *Vitex.*
Normand 1931 – *Gmelina.*
Normand 1960 – *Avicennia, Gmelina, Tectona, Vitex.*
Normand & Paquis 1976 [1977] – *Avicennia, Gmelina, Premna, Tectona, Vitex.*
Ogata 1975–1983 – *Avicennia, Gmelina, Peronema, Tectona, Teijsmanniodendron, Vitex.*
Ortega 1958 – *Vitex.*
Panshin 1932 – *Avicennia.*
Patel 1974 – *Teucridium, Vitex.*
Pearson & Brown 1932 – *Callicarpa, Gmelina, Tectona, Vitex.*
Pereira 1933 – *Vitex.*
Pérez Olvera et al. 1980 [1981] – *Vitex.*
Pfeiffer 1951 – *Aegiphila, Citharexylum, Clerodendrum, Duranta, Lantana, Lippia, Vitex.*
Prakash 1972 – *Citharexylum, Tectona* (root).
Rancusi et al. 1987 – *Rhaphithamnus.*
Record 1932a – *Vitex.*
*Record & Hess 1941a – 13 genera.
Record & Hess 1943 – *Avicennia* + family (18 genera).
Record & Mell 1924 – *Avicennia, Petitia, Vitex.*
Saiki 1982 – *Tectona.*
Schweingruber 1990 – *Vitex.*
Shimaji & Itoh 1988 – *Callicarpa, Clerodendrum.*
Sudo 1959 – *Clerodendrum.*

(VERBENACEAE)

Sudo 1963 – *Avicennia, Gmelina, Peronema, Premna, Tectona, Vitex.*
Sudo 1988 – *Avicennia, Gmelina, Tectona, Teijsmanniodendron, Vitex.*
Tang 1973 – *Gmelina, Tectona, Vitex.*
Urling & Smith 1953 – *Avicennia.*
Wagenführ & Scheiber 1974 – *Tectona.*
Wang 1984–1988 – *Gmelina, Tectona, Vitex.*
Welle & Détienne 1988 – *Aegiphila, Avicennia, Citharexylum, Cornutia, Petrea, Vitex.*
Williams 1936 – *Aegiphila, Callicarpa, Lippia, Vitex.*
Wiraj Chunwarin & Damrong Sri-Aran 1974 – *Avicennia, Gmelina, Premna, Tectona, Vitex.*
Yamabayashi 1938 – *Callicarpa, Clerodendrum.*

Anomalous structure

Chalk & Chattaway 1937 – *Avicennia.*
Majumdar 1941 – *Nyctanthes.*
Mathews & Rao 1986 – *Avicennia.*
Studholme & Philipson 1966 – *Avicennia.*
Zamski 1979 – *Avicennia.*

Crystals and silica

Chattaway 1955 – *Avicennia, Gmelina, Premna, Vitex.*
Chattaway 1956 – *Avicennia, Vitex.*
Espinoza de Pernía 1987b – *Aegiphila, Vitex.*
Hillis & Silva 1979 – *Tectona.*
Meniado et al. 1970 – *Premna, Vitex.*
Scurfield et al. 1973 – *Avicennia, Gmelina, Vitex.*
Scurfield et al. 1974 – *Teijsmanniodendron.*
Sharma 1971 – *Tectona.*
Welle 1976b – *Vitex.*

Ecological anatomy

Baas & Schweingruber 1987 – *Vitex.*
Baas et al. 1983 – *Avicennia, Vitex.*
Barajas Morales 1985 – *Citharexylum.*
Carlquist 1985a – *Lantana, Lippia.*
Carlquist & Hoekman 1985a – *Lippia.*
Lim & Soh 1991a – *Callicarpa.*
Worbes 1986 – *Vitex.*

Growth rings

Détienne 1989 – *Tectona.*
Geiger 1915 – *Tectona.*

(VERBENACEAE)

Helical thickenings

Meylan & Butterfield 1978a – *Vitex.*
Nair 1987 – *Tectona.*

Pits, warts and perforation plates

Gomes et al. 1989 – *Citharexylum.*
Mathew & Shah 1982 – 18 genera.
Mathew & Shah 1983 – 13 genera.
Meylan & Butterfield 1974, 1975 – *Avicennia, Vitex.*
Ohtani & Ishida 1978a – *Clerodendrum.*
Ohtani et al. 1989 – *Gmelina.*

Septate fibres

Butterfield & Meylan 1976 – *Vitex.*

Tracheary elements

Gill & Onuja 1984a – *Gmelina, Tectona.*
Jing et al. 1989 – *Callicarpa, Gmelina, Vitex.*
Murthy et al. 1978 – 11 genera + *Nyctanthes.*
Ohtani 1983 – *Clerodendrum.*

VIOLACEAE

Araujo & Mattos Filho 1978a – *Amphirrhox.*
Araujo & Mattos Filho 1978b – *Leonia.*
Araujo & Mattos Filho 1980 – *Rinorea* 7 spp.
Dechamps 1985 – *Amphirrhox, Leonia, Paypayrola, Rinorea.*
Détienne & Jacquet 1983 – *Amphirrhox, Hybanthus, Leonia, Paypayrola, Rinorea.*
Détienne et al. 1982 – *Paypayrola, Rinorea.*
Ilic 1991 – *Leonia, Rinorea.*
Kribs 1928a – *Paypayrola.*
Lebacq & Dechamps 1964, 1967 – *Rinorea.*
Mainieri & Chimelo 1989 – *Rinorea.*
Meylan & Butterfield 1978b – *Melicytus.*
Moll & Janssonius 1906–1936 – *Alsodeia* (= *Rinorea*).
Normand 1958 – *Decorsella.*
Normand 1960 – *Decorsella, Rinorea.*
Normand & Paquis 1976 [1977] – *Rinorea.*
Pfeiffer, J.P. 1926 – *Paypayrola.*
Record & Hess 1943 – Family (*Amphirrhox, Anchietea, Gloeospermum, Hybanthus, Leonia, Paypayrola, Rinorea, Rinoreocarpus*).
*Taylor 1972 – 12 genera.
Williams 1936 – *Gloeospermum, Leonia, Paypayrola, Rinorea.*

(VIOLACEAE)

Ecological anatomy
Barajas Morales 1985 – *Orthion*.
Carlquist 1974 – *Viola* (p. 395).
Carlquist 1977c – *Hybanthus*.
Carlquist 1985a – *Agation* (= *Agatea*), *Hybanthus*, *Hymenanthera* (= *Melicytus*).

Helical thickenings
Meylan & Butterfield 1978a – *Hymenanthera* (= *Melicytus*), *Melicytus*.

Pits
Meylan & Butterfield 1974 – *Melicytus*.

Septate fibres
Butterfield & Meylan 1976 – *Hymenanthera* (= *Melicytus*), *Melicytus*.

VITACEAE (for *Leea* see LEEACEAE)

Adkinson 1913 – *Ampelopsis, Cissus, Vitis*.
Cutler et al. 1987 – *Ampelopsis, Parthenocissus, Vitis* (root).
Fahn et al. 1986 – *Vitis*.
Greguss 1959 – *Parthenocissus, Vitis*.
Grosser 1977 – *Vitis*.
Hegedüs 1970 – *Vitis*.
Ilic 1991 – *Parthenocissus, Vitis*.
Record & Hess 1943 – *Vitis*.
Saint-Laurent 1928, 1934 – *Vitis*.
Schweingruber 1978, 1990 – *Vitis*.
Shimaji & Itoh 1988 – *Vitis*.
Snezhkova 1986 – *Parthenocissus, Vitis*.
Thunell & Perem 1947 – *Vitis*.

Anomalous structure
D'Ambroggio de Argueso 1982 – *Cissus*.
La Riviere 1921 – *Vitis*.
Obaton 1960 – *Cissus*.
Van der Walt et al. 1969 – *Cyphostemma*.

Ecological anatomy
Baas & Schweingruber 1987 – *Vitis*.
Carlquist 1985 [1986]a – *Parthenocissus, Vitis*.
Carlquist & Hoekman 1985a – *Vitis*.

Septate fibres
Plank & Wolkinger 1976 – *Vitis*.

VIVIANIACEAE (*Viviania*)

*Carlquist 1985 [1986]b – 3 spp. (or in Geraniaceae).

VOCHYSIACEAE
(for *Euphronia* see TRIGONIACEAE)

Anon. 1981 (Andes) – *Erisma, Vochysia*.
Anon. 1981 (Curua) – *Qualea, Vochysia*.
Alves de Pinho 1966 – *Qualea, Vochysia*.
Alves de Pinho 1969 – *Qualea*.
Barajas Morales et al. 1979 – *Vochysia*.
Barbosa et al. 1977–1978 – *Qualea*.
Benoist 1931 – *Erisma, Qualea, Vochysia*.
Brazier & Franklin 1961 – *Qualea, Vochysia*.
Dechamps 1985 – *Erisma, Qualea, Vochysia*.
Détienne & Jacquet 1983 – *Callisthene, Erisma, Qualea, Ruizterania, Salvertia, Vochysia*.
Détienne et al. 1982 – *Erisma, Qualea, Ruizterania, Vochysia*.
Gill & Ogunlowo 1988 – *Vochysia*.
Heimsch 1942 – *Erisma, Qualea, Salvertia, Vochysia*.
Honda 1970 – *Vochysia*.
Ilic 1991 – *Erisma, Qualea, Vochysia*.
Kribs 1928a – *Vochysia*.
Kribs 1959 – *Qualea, Vochysia*.
Latorre et al. 1975 – *Vochysia*.
Lebacq 1963 – *Erismadelphus*.
Lebacq & Dechamps 1964 – *Erismadelphus*.
Lebacq et al. 1973 – *Qualea, Vochysia*.
Lebacq & Staner 1964 – *Qualea*.
Lopes et al. 1983 – *Qualea*.
Loureiro & Silva 1977 – *Qualea*.
Mainieri 1962 – *Qualea, Vochysia*.
Mainieri 1978 – *Erisma*.
Mainieri & Chimelo 1989 – *Erisma, Ruizterania, Vochysia*.
Mattos Filho 1960–1961 – *Vochysia*.
Mattos Filho & Rizzini 1978 – *Vochysia*.
Nardi Berti & Edlmann Abbate 1992 – *Erisma, Qualea, Vochysia*.
Normand 1966, 1967 – *Erisma, Qualea, Vochysia*.
Normand 1977 – *Vochysia*.
Normand & Paquis 1976 [1977] – *Erismadelphus*.
Paula 1972b – *Salvertia*.
Paula 1979 – *Erisma, Salvertia, Vochysia*.
Paula 1981 – *Callisthene, Qualea, Vochysia*.
Pérez Mogollón 1973 – *Erisma, Qualea, Vochysia*.
Pérez Olvera et al. 1980 [1981] – *Vochysia*.

(VOCHYSIACEAE)

Pfeiffer, J.P. 1926 – *Erisma, Qualea, Vochysia.*

*Quirk 1980 – *Callisthene, Erisma, Erismadelphus, Qualea, Salvertia, Vochysia* (56 spp. in all).

Record & Hess 1943 – Family (*Erisma, Qualea, Salvertia, Vochysia*).

Record & Mell 1924 – *Vochysia.*

Schmidt 1951–1952 – *Vochysia.*

Sudo 1963 – *Qualea, Vochysia.*

Teles & Paula 1980 – *Erisma, Vochysia.*

Van der Slooten et al. 1962 – *Qualea.*

Wagenführ & Scheiber 1974 – *Vochysia.*

Williams 1936 – *Vochysia.*

Anomalous structure

Chalk & Chattaway 1937 – *Erisma.*

Crystals and silica

Espinoza de Pernía 1987b – *Qualea, Ruizterania.*

Welle 1976b – *Qualea.*

WINTERACEAE

(*Belliolum* and *Bubbia* = *Zygogynum*)

Bailey 1944b – *Belliolum, Drimys, Pseudowintera, Zygogynum.*

Bailey & Nast 1945a – Family summary.

Bailey & Thompson 1918 – *Drimys.*

Brazier & Franklin 1961 – *Drimys.*

Carlquist 1981 [1982] – *Zygogynum.*

Carlquist 1982d – *Exospermum.*

Carlquist 1983a – *Belliolum* 4 spp.

Carlquist 1983b – *Bubbia* 7 spp.

Carlquist 1988e – *Drimys* 4 spp.

*Carlquist 1989c – *Tasmannia* (= *Drimys*), family summary and key to 8 genera.

Cunha Mello 1950 [1951] – *Drimys.*

Gupta 1934 – *Drimys, Zygogynum.*

Ilic 1991 – *Drimys, Zygogynum.*

Jeffrey & Cole 1916 – *Drimys.*

Lebacq et al. 1973 – *Drimys.*

McLaughlin 1933 – *Drimys, Zygogynum.*

Metcalfe 1987 – General survey.

Meylan & Butterfield 1978b – *Pseudowintera.*

Nardi Berti & Edlmann Abbate 1992 – *Drimys.*

Patel 1974 – *Pseudowintera.*

Rancusi et al. 1987 – *Drimys.*

Record & Hess 1943 – *Drimys.*

(WINTERACEAE)

Record & Mell 1924 – *Drimys.*

Schultz et al. 1964 – *Drimys.*

Takahashi 1985 – *Belliolum, Drimys, Tasmannia* (= *Drimys*).

Thompson & Bailey 1916 – *Drimys.*

Tortorelli 1944 [1945], 1956 – *Drimys.*

Van der Slooten 1968 – *Drimys.*

Van der Slooten et al. 1970 – *Drimys.*

Wagemann 1949 – *Drimys.*

Ecological anatomy

Versteegh 1968 – *Drimys.*

Pits

Greguss 1982 – *Drimys.*

Meylan & Butterfield 1974 – *Pseudowintera.*

XANTHOPHYLLACEAE

see POLYGALACEAE

ZYGOPHYLLACEAE

(incl. BALANITACEAE)

Böcher & Lyshede 1968 – *Bulnesia.*

Brazier & Franklin 1961 – *Bulnesia, Guaiacum.*

Burgerstein 1912 – *Bulnesia.*

Chudnoff 1956 – *Balanites, Nitraria.*

Cozzo 1946c – *Plectrocarpa.*

Cozzo 1948 – *Bulnesia, Larrea, Plectrocarpa, Porlieria.*

Dechamps 1985 – *Guaiacum.*

Fahn & Sarnat 1963 – *Zygophyllum.*

Fahn et al. 1986 – *Balanites, Fagonia, Nitraria, Zygophyllum.*

Fasolo 1939–1940 – *Balanites.*

Heimsch 1942 – *Balanites, Bulnesia, Guaiacum, Larrea, Porlieria, Sericodes.*

Ilic 1991 – *Bulnesia, Guaiacum, Porlieria.*

Jagiella & Kurschner 1987 – *Balanites, Nitraria.*

Kobayashi & Sugawa 1963 – *Bulnesia, Guaiacum.*

Kribs 1959 – *Bulnesia, Guaiacum.*

Lebacq 1963 – *Balanites.*

Lebacq & Dechamps 1964, 1967 – *Balanites.*

Messeri 1938 – *Nitraria.*

Nardi Berti & Edlmann Abbate 1992 – *Bulnesia, Guaiacum.*

Normand 1950b–1960 – *Balanites* (in Simaroubaceae).

(ZYGOPHYLLACEAE)
Normand & Paquis 1976 [1977] – *Balanites*.
Parameswaran & Conrad 1982 – *Balanites*.
Record 1921b – *Bulnesia, Guaiacum, Porlieria*.
Record & Hess 1943 – Family (*Bulnesia, Guaiacum, Larrea, Porlieria*).
Record & Mell 1924 – *Guaiacum*.
Saiki 1982 – *Guaiacum*.
Saint-Laurent 1928, 1934 – *Nitraria*.
Saint-Laurent 1932a – *Balanites, Fagonia, Nitraria, Zygophyllum*.
Schmid 1915 – *Bulnesia*.
Schmidt 1951–1952 – *Guaiacum*.
Schweingruber 1990 – *Fagonia, Zygophyllum*.
Senni 1905 – *Balanites*.
Sheahan & Cutler 1993 – 19 genera (young stems).
Sudo 1963 – *Bulnesia, Guaiacum*.
Tortorelli 1956 – *Bulnesia*.
Vasilevskaya & Petrov 1964 – *Tetraena*.
Vasilevskaya & Trubochkina 1963 – *Nitraria, Tetraena, Zygophyllum*.
Wagemann 1949 – *Porlieria*.

(ZYGOPHYLLACEAE)
Wagenführ & Scheiber 1974 – *Guaiacum*.
Wei 1991 – *Tetraena, Zygophyllum*.

Crystals
Chattaway 1956 – *Bulnesia*.
Espinoza de Pernía 1987b – *Bulnesia*.

Ecological anatomy
Baas & Schweingruber 1987 – *Fagonia, Zygophyllum*.
Baas et al. 1983 – *Balanites, Fagonia, Nitraria, Zygophyllum*.
Carlquist 1985a – *Balanites, Fagonia, Larrea*, etc.
Carlquist & Hoekman 1985a – *Fagonia, Larrea*.
Novruzova 1968 – *Nitraria*.
Webber 1936a – *Larrea*.

Storied structure
Cozzo & Cristiani 1950 – *Bulnesia, Larrea, Plectrocarpa, Porlieria*.

GENUS INCERTAE SEDIS

Goldberg & Nelson 1989 – *Haptanthus*.

REFERENCES

Anon. 1954. Monographie de l'Azobé (Lophira procera A. Chev.). Centre tech. For. trop.: Nogent-sur-Marne. 80 pp.

Anon. 1955–1959. Essências florestais da Guiné portuguesa. Jard. Mus. agric. Ultramar, Min. Ultramar: Lisbon. 16 parts.

Anon. 1961. Differentiation of Red Lauan (Shorea negrosensis Foxw.) and Tangile (S. polysperma (Blco.) Merr.). Tech. Note For. Prod. Res. Inst. Philipp. No. 23: 4 pp.

Anon. 1963. Essências florestais do Maiombe Português-Angola. 1. Gossweilerodendron balsamiferum (Vermoes) Harms (Tola branca). Jard. Mus. agric. Ultramar, Min. Ultramar: Lisbon. 23 pp. [Eng. summ.]

Anon. 1966. Japanese timbers. Wood Technological Association of Japan. 101 pp. [Jap. only.]

Anon. 1967. Essências florestais do Maiombe Português-Angola. 2. Polyalthia suaveolens Engl. et Diels, var. suaveolens J. Paiva (Muamba preta). Jard. Mus. agric. Ultramar, Min. Ultramar: Lisbon. 21 pp.

Anon. 1968. Fichas tecnologicas. Las principales maderas commerciales del mondo: Notolaea (Olea) excelsa; Rhamnus glandulosa. Bol. Inform. téc. Asoc. Invest. Téc. Ind. Madera, Madrid 6 (29): 29–36. [For. Abstr. 30 (1969) No. 1195.]

Anon. 1977a. Identification of tropical woods, 20–25. Mokuzai Kogyo (Wood Industr.) 32 (1): 31–32; (2): 25–26; (3): 29–30; (4): 23–24; (5): 27–28; (6): 23–24. [Jap. only.]

Anon. 1977b. Bété. Bois For. Trop., No. 171: 31–44.

Anon. 1981. Descripcion general y anatomica de 105 maderas del grupo andino. Proyectos Andinos de Desarrollo Tecnológico en el area de los Recursos Forestales Tropicales (PADT-REFORT). Junta del Acuerdo de Cartagena, Paseo de la Republica y Av. Aramburu, Casilla Postal 3237, Lima, Peru. 442 pp.

Anon. 1981. Madeiras da Reserva florestal de Curuá-Una, Estado do Pará. Caracterização anatomica, propriedades gerais e aplicações. Superint. Desen. Amazonia & Inst. Pesq. tec. Est. São Paulo: Belem. 118 pp.

Anon. 1985. Studies on the wood properties of native hardwoods of major importance. (II) Wood properties of 3 species of the genus Carpinus. Res. Rep. For. Res. Inst., Korea, No. 32: 88–110. [Korean; Eng. summ.]

Abbate, M.L.E. 1963; 1964; 1970. Atlante micrografico dei legni dell'Africa orientale. Cartello III, Tav. 25–36 (1963). Cartello IV, Tav. 37–48 (1964). Cartella VI, Tav. 61–72 (1970). Firenze.

Abbate, M.L.E. 1971a. Caratteristiche anatomiche e fisico-mecchaniche di alcuni legni del Madagascar. Contrib. sci.-prat. migl. Conos. Util. Legno 15 (33): 7–27. [Eng. summ.]

Abbate, M.L.E. 1971b. Caratteristiche anatomiche e fisico-mecchaniche di legni di Staphylea pinnata. Ital. for. mont. 26 (1): 23–26. [Eng. summ.]

Abbate, M.L.E. 1973. Caratteristiche anatomiche e fisico-mecchaniche di alcuni legni del Madagascar. II. Contrib. sci.-prat. migl. Conos. Util. Legno 17 (39): 7–33. [Eng. summ.]

Abbate, M.L.E. 1977. Caratteristiche anatomiche, fisiche e di lavorazione di 22 specie legnose provenienti dalla Thailandia. Contrib. sci.-prat. migl. Conos. Util. Legno 21 (54): 75 pp. [Eng. summ.]

Abbate, M.L.E. & Cavina, V. 1980. Caratteristiche anatomiche, fisiche e di lavorazione di 13 specie provenienti da Ceylon (Srylanka). Contrib. sci.-prat. migl. Conos. Util. Legno 27: 65–109. [Eng. summ.]

Abbate, M.L.E. & Cenerini, M. 1976. Caratteristiche anatomiche e fisico-mecchaniche di alcuni legni provenienti dalla Costa d'Avorio. Contrib. sci.-prat. migl. Conos. Util. Legno 20 (53): 47–63. [Eng. summ.]

Abbe, L.B. & Abbe, E.C. 1971. The vessel member of Myrica esculenta Buch.-Ham. J. Minn. Acad. Sci. 37: 72–76.

Acar, O. 1973 [1974]. Anatomical and technological properties of the wood of Populus euphratica Oliv. Yillik. Bull. Kavak. Hizli. Gelisen Orman Agaclari Arastirme Enst. 8, 1–175. [Turk.; Eng. summ.] [For. Abstr. 37 (1976) no. 4719.]

Acevedo-Rodríguez, P. 1993. Systematics of Serjania. 1. A revision of Serjania Sect. Platycoccum. Mem. N.Y. bot. Gard. 67: 1–93.

Acuña, P.I. & Flores, E.M. 1987. Estructura de la madera de Stryphnodendron excelsum Harms (Leguminosae, Mimosoideae). Revta. Biol. trop., Costa Rica 35(1): 107–112. [Eng. summ.]

Adams, J.E. 1949. Studies in the comparative anatomy of the Cornaceae. J. Elisha Mitchell Sci. Soc. 65: 218–244.

Adamson, R.S. 1934. Anomalous secondary thickening in Compositae. Ann. Bot. 48: 505–514.

Adamson, R.S. 1937. Anomalous secondary thickening in Osteospermum. Trans. roy. Soc. S. Afr. 24: 303–312.

Adkinson, J. 1913. Some features of the anatomy of the Vitaceae. Ann. Bot. 27: 133–139 + Plate 15.

Agarwal, S.P. & Chauhan, L. 1988. On the structure and identification of Eucalyptus species. Indian For. 114: 145–151.

Aiello, A. 1979. A reexamination of Portlandia (Rubiaceae) and associated taxa. J. Arnold Arbor. 60: 38–126.

Akachuku, A.E. & Burley, J. 1979. Variation of wood anatomy of Gmelina arborea Roxb. in Nigerian plantations. IAWA Bull. 1979/4: 94–99.

Albuquerque, B.W.P. de & Honda, M. 1972. Rutaceae nova da Amazonia. Acta Amazonica 2(2): 49–54.

Aldridge, A.E. 1978. Anatomy and evolution in the Macaronesian Sonchus subgenus Dendrosonchus (Compositae: Lactuceae). Bot. J. Linn. Soc. 76: 249–285.

Aldridge, A.E. 1981. Anatomy and evolution in Macaronesian Echium (Boraginaceae). Plant Syst. Evol. 138: 9–22.

Alekseeva, A.I. 1962a. Distinguishing features of the anatomical structure of Betula verrucosa forma carelica Soc. Nauch. Dokl. Vyssh. Shk., biol. Nauki (1): 123–128. [Russ.]

Alekseeva, A.I. 1962b. Diagnostic characteristics of the wood of the Karelian birch. Izvest. Vyssh. Ucheb. Zaved., Lesn. Zh. 5 (3): 33–37 [Russ.]. Referat. Zh., Biol. (1963) No. 7V128 (Transl.).

Alencar, J. da C., Fernandes, N.P. & Loureiro, A.A. 1981. Desenvolvimento do arvores nativas em ensaios de especies. 2. Jacareuba (Calophyllum angulare A.C. Smith). Acta Amazonica 11: 357–370.

Alfaroa, U.M.E. & Mesa, M.A. 1979. El origin morfologico del floema intraxilar en Nolanaceas y la posicion sistematica de esta familia. Bol. Soc. argent. Bot. 18: 123–126.

Alfonso, V.A. & Richter, H.G. 1991. Wood and bark anatomy of Buchenavia Eichl. (Combretaceae). IAWA Bull. n.s. 12: 123–141.

Almeida, D.G. de 1947. Note on a Cordia wood from eastern Brazil. Trop. Woods 89: 48–52.

Almeida, D.G. de 1951. Dalbergia frutescens (Vell.) Britton. "Sebastiao de Arruda". Arq. Serv. Florestal, Rio de Janeiro 5: 15–34. [Eng. summ.]

Almeida M. da G.C. de 1973 [1974]. Contribuição para o estudo de algumas essências florestais de Moçambique. Revta Cienc. agron., A 6: 29–59. [Eng. summ.]

Alves de Pinho, R. 1966. Contribuição ao estudo anatômico do lenho secundário de árvores da flora dos Cerrados. I. An. Acad. bras. Cienc., 38: Supl. 113–124.

Alves de Pinho, R. 1968. Estudo anatômico do lenho secundário de tres especies florestais do estado de São Paulo. Brasil. Arq. Bot. Est. S. Paulo II, 4: 137–140.

Alves de Pinho, R. 1969. Contribuição ao estudo anatômico do lenho secundário de árvores da flora dos Cerrados. II. São Paulo. Brasil. Arq. Bot. Est. S. Paulo II, 4: 229–235.

Alves de Pinho, R. & Camargo, T.M. 1979. Contribuição ao estudo anatômico do lenho secundário de árvores da flora dos Cerrados. III. São Paulo. Brasil. Hoehnea 8: 1–9.

Amaldi, P. 1929. Osservazioni sull'anatomia del legno secondario dell'Olea chrysophylla. Nuovo G. bot. ital. (NS) 36: 282–299.

America, W.M. 1974. Wood of the 'Palosapis' group. Forpride Digest 3: 67–68.

America, W.M. & Meniado, J.A. 1975. Anatomy and differentiation of the woods of Pahudia and Intsia (Leguminosae). Forpride Digest 4: 71–72.

Amos, G.L. 1951. Some siliceous timbers of British Guiana. Caribbean Forester 12: 133–137.

Amos, G.L. 1952. Silica in timbers. CSIRO Australia, Bull. No. 267: 55 pp.

Amos, G.L. & Dadswell, H.E. 1948. Siliceous inclusions in wood in relation to marine borer resistance. Jl. CSIRO Aust. 21 (3): 190–196.

Ancibor, E. 1984. Estructura de la madera de Polylepis tomentella Wedd. (Rosaceae). Physis, C, 42 (102): 23–28.

Ancibor, E. 1986 [1987]. Ontogenia de la arquitectura del eje en Mulinum spinosum (Cav.) Persoon. Parodiana 4: 187–193. [Eng. summ.]

Anderson, L.C. 1963 [1964]. Studies on Petradoria (Compositae): anatomy, cytology, taxonomy. Trans. Kansas Acad. Sci. 66: 632–684.

Anderson, L.C. 1972. Studies on Bigelowia (Asteraceae), II. Xylary comparisons, woodiness, and paedomorphosis. J. Arnold Arbor. 53: 499–514.

Anderson, L.C. 1974. A study of systematic wood anatomy in Cannabis. Bot. Mus. Leafl. Harvard Univ. 24: 29–36.

Anderson, L.C. 1983. Chrysothamnus eremobius (Asteraceae): a new species from Nevada. Brittonia 35: 23–27.

Anderson, L.C. & Weberg, P.S. 1974. The anatomy and taxonomy of Vanclevea (Asteraceae). Great Basin Nat. 34: 151–160.

Araujo, P.A.M. 1962–1965. Contribuição ao conhecimento da madeira de Plathymenia foliosa Benth. (Leg. Mim.). Arq. Jard. bot. Rio de Janeiro 18: 9–15.

Araujo, P.A.M. 1968. Bibliografia sôbre anatomia das madeiras. Anu. bras. Econ. flor., Inst. Nac. Pinho 19 (19): 243–332.

Araujo, P.A. de M. & Mattos Filho, A. de 1965. Contribuição ao conhecimento da madeira de Xylopia brasiliensis Spreng. Arq. Jard. bot. Rio de Janeiro 18: 269–276. [Eng. summ.]

Araujo, P.A. de M. & Mattos Filho, A. de 1973a. Estrutura das madeiras de Caryocaraceae. Arq. Jard. bot. Rio de Janeiro 19: 5–47.

Araujo, P.A. de M. & Mattos Filho, A. de 1973b. Estrutura das madeiras de Rhizophoraceae. Arq. Jard. bot. Rio de Janeiro 19: 133–147.

Araujo, P.A. de M. & Mattos Filho, A. de 1973c. Estrutura das madeiras brasileiras de angiospermas dicotiledôneas (X). Monimiaceae (Siparuna bifida (Poepp. & Endl.) A. DC.). Brasil Florestal 4 (14): 41–45. [Eng. summ.]

Araujo, P.A. de M. & Mattos Filho, A. de 1973d. Estrutura da madeira de Goupia glabra Aubl. (Goupiaceae). Arq. Jard. bot. Rio de Janeiro 19: 149–153.

Araujo, P.A. de M. & Mattos Filho, A. de 1973e. Estrutura da madeira de Campnosperma gummifera (Benth.) L. March. (Anacardiaceae). Arq. Jard. bot. Rio de Janeiro 19: 171–176.

Araujo, P.A. de M. & Mattos Filho, A. de 1973–1977 [1977]. Estrutura das madeiras brasileiras de angiospermas dicotiledôneas (XI). Momimiaceae (Bracteanthus glycycarpus Ducke). Arq. Jard. bot. Rio de Janeiro 20: 15–20. [Eng. summ.] Also in: Brasil Florestal 4 (16): 35–39; 1973.

Araujo, P.A. de M. & Mattos Filho, A. de 1974a. Estrutura das madeiras brasileiras de angiospermas dicotiledôneas (V). Aquifoliaceae. Rodriguésia 27 (39): 25–51. [Eng. summ.] (VI). Cyrillaceae (Cyrilla antillana Michx.). Ibid.: 53–60. (VII). Proteaceae (Panopsis sessilifolia (Rich.) Sandw.). Ibid.: 61–69. (VIII). Proteaceae (Panopsis rubescens (Polh.) Pittier). Ibid.: 71–83. (IX). Piperaceae (Piper aduncum L.). Ibid.: 85–93. (X). Monimiaceae (Siparuna bifida (Poepp. & Endl.) A. DC.). Ibid.: 153–162.

Araujo, P. A. de M. & Mattos Filho, A. de 1974b. Estrutura das madeiras brasileiras de angiospermas dicotiledôneas (XII). Monimiaceae (Mollinedia iomalla Perkins). Brasil Florestal 5 (18): 57–50. (XIII). Icacinaceae (Dendrobangia boliviana Rusby). Ibid. (19): 49–54. [Eng. summ.]

Araujo, P. A. de M. & Mattos Filho, A. de 1975. Estrutura das madeiras brasileiras de angiospermas dicotiledôneas (XIV). Icacinaceae (Discophora guianensis Miers). Brasil Florestal 6 (22): 40–44. (XV). Icacinaceae (Emmotum holosericeum Ducke). Ibid. (24): 53–57. [Eng. summ.]

Araujo, P. A. de M. & Mattos Filho, A. de 1976. Estrutura das madeiras brasileiras de angiospermas dicotiledôneas (XVI). (Poraqueiba guianensis Aubl.). Brasil Florestal 7 (25): 45–49. [Eng. summ.] (XVII). Icacinaceae (Villaresia megaphylla Miers). Ibid. (26): 36–41. [Eng. summ.]

Araujo, P. A. de M. & Mattos Filho, A. de 1977. Estrutura das madeiras brasileiras de angiospermas dicotiledôneas (XVIII). Dilleniaceae (Curatella americana L.). Rodriguésia 29 (42): 233–245.

Araujo, P. A. de M. & Mattos Filho, A. de 1978a. Estrutura das madeiras brasileiras de angiospermas dicotiledôneas (XIX). Violaceae (Amphirrox longifolia (St.-Hil.) Spreng. e A. surinamensis Eichl.). Arq. Jard. bot. Rio de Janeiro 22: 29–46. [Eng. summ.]

Araujo, P. A. de M. & Mattos Filho, A. de 1978b. Estrutura das madeiras brasileiras de angiospermas dicotiledôneas (XX). Violaceae (Leonia cymosa Mart. e L. glycycarpa Ruiz e Pav.). Rodriguésia 30 (46): 7–22. [Eng. summ.]

Araujo, P. A. de M. & Mattos Filho, A. de 1980. Estrutura das madeiras brasileiras de angiospermas dicotiledôneas (XXII). Violaceae (Rinorea Aubl.). Rodriguésia 32 (54): 125–159.

Araujo, P. A. de M. & Mattos Filho, A. de 1981 [1982]a. Estrutura das madeiras brasileiras de angiospermas dicotiledôneas (XXIII). Cunoniaceae (Belangera Camb.). Arq. Jard. bot. Rio de Janeiro 25: 5–24.

Araujo, P. A. de M. & Mattos Filho, A. de 1981 [1982]b. Estrutura das madeiras brasileiras de angiospermas dicotiledôneas (XXIV). Cunoniaceae (Weinmannia Linn.). Rodriguésia 33 (56): 117–133.

Araujo, P. A. de M. & Mattos Filho, A. de 1982 [1983]. Estrutura das madeiras brasileiras de dicotiledôneas (XXV). Clethraceae (Clethra Linn.). Arq. Jard. bot. Rio de Janeira 26: 5–26.

Araujo, P. A. de M. & Mattos Filho, A. de 1984. Estrutura das madeiras brasileiras de dicotiledôneas (XXVI). Euphorbiaceae. Rodriguésia 36 (59): 25–39.

Araujo, P. A. de M. & Mattos Filho, A. de 1985. Estrutura das madeiras brasileiras de dicotiledôneas (XXVII). Humiriaceae. Rodriguésia 37 (62): 91–114.

Araujo, P. A. de M. & Sonkin, L. C. 1984. Estrutura de Metternichia princips Mikan (Solanaceae). Rodriguésia 36 (58): 85–88. [Eng. summ.]

Arbo, M. M. 1981. Anatomia de tallo y hoja de Rayleya bahiensis Cristobal (Sterculiaceae). Bonplandia 5 (9): 52–62. [Eng. summ.]

Archer, R. H. & Van Wyk, A. E. 1993. Wood structure and generic status of some southern African Cassinoideae (Celastraceae). IAWA Jl. 14: 373–389.

Armando Rondon, J. & Hernandez Gil, R. 1987. Estudio anatómico de la hoja y madera de Alnus acuminata. Pittieria 16: 5–26.

Armstrong, J. E. & Wilson, T. K. 1980. Wood anatomy of Horsfieldia (Myristicaceae). IAWA Bull. n. s. 1: 121–129.

Arnaez, E. & Flores, E. 1988. Caracteristicas de la madera de Cedrela odorata L. (cedro amargo, Meliaceae) en Costa Rica. Rev. Biol. trop. 36: 67–74. [Eng. summ.]

Artsikhovskii, V. [Arzikhovskii, V.] 1928. Growth of the saxaul (Arthrophytum) and the structure of its trunk. Tr. Prikl. Bot. Genet. Selek. 19 (4): 289–358. [Russ.; Eng. summ.]

Aubréville, A., Besson, A., Berengier, E., Collardet, J., Normand, D. & Petitpas, J. 1947. L'Iroko. Bois For. Trop. 1: 34–52.

Ayensu, E.S. 1972. Morphology and anatomy of Synsepalum dulcificum (Sapotaceae). Bot. J. Linn. Soc. 65: 179–187.

Ayensu, E.S. & Bentum, A. 1974. Commercial timbers of West Africa. Smithsonian Contrib. Bot., No. 14: 1–69.

Ayensu, E.S. & Stern, W.L. 1964. Systematic anatomy and ontogeny of the stem in Passifloraceae. Contrib. U.S. Nat. Herb. 34 (3): 45–72.

Aymard, M. 1968 [1969]. Le xylème secondaire chez Lysimachia punctata L. Bull. Soc. bot. Fr. 115: 187–196.

Baagøe, J. 1974. The genus Guizotia (Compositae). A taxonomic revision. Bot. Tidsskr. 69: 1–39.

Baas, P. 1969. Comparative anatomy of Platanus kerrii Gagnep. Bot. J. Linn. Soc. 62: 413–421.

Baas, P. 1970. Anatomical contributions to plant taxonomy I. Floral and vegetative anatomy of Eliaea from Madagascar and Cratoxylum from Indo-Malesia (Guttiferae). Blumea 18: 369–391.

Baas, P. 1972a. Anatomical contributions to plant taxonomy II. The affinities of Hua Pierre and Afrostyrax Perkins et Gilg. Blumea 20: 161–192.

Baas, P. 1972b. The vegetative anatomy of Kostermansia malayana Soegeng. Reinwardtia 8: 335–344.

Baas, P. 1973. The wood anatomical range in Ilex (Aquifoliaceae) and its ecological and phylogenetic significance. Blumea 21: 193–258.

Baas, P. 1975. Vegetative anatomy and the affinities of Aquifoliaceae, Sphenostemon, Phelline, and Oncotheca. Blumea 22: 311–407.

Baas, P. 1976. Some functional and adaptive aspects of vessel member morphology. In: Wood structure in biological and technological research (eds. Baas, P., Bolton, A.J. & Catling, D.M.): 157–181. Leiden Botanical Series No. 3. Leiden Univ. Press.

Baas, P. 1977. The peculiar wood structure of Leptospermum crassipes Lehm. (Myrtaceae). IAWA Bull. 1977/2: 25–30.

Baas, P. 1979a. The peculiar wood structure of Vaccinium lucidum (Bl.) Miq. (Ericaceae). IAWA Bull. 1979/1: 11–16.

Baas, P. 1979b. The anatomy of Alzatea Ruiz & Pav. (Myrtales). Acta bot. neerl. 28: 156–158.

Baas, P. 1980. Reliability and citation of wood specimens. IAWA Bull. n.s. 1: 72.

Baas, P. 1982. Systematic, phylogenetic, and ecological wood anatomy – history and perspectives. In: New perspectives in wood anatomy (ed. Baas, P.): 23–58. Martinus Nijhoff/ Dr W. Junk: The Hague, etc.

Baas, P. 1984a. Vegetative anatomy and taxonomy of Berberidopsis and Streptothamnus (Flacourtiaceae). Blumea 30: 39–44.

Baas, P. 1984b. Vegetative anatomy and the taxonomic status of Ilex collina and Nemopanthus (Aquifoliaceae). J. Arnold Arbor. 65: 243–250.

Baas, P. 1986a. Terminology of imperforate tracheary elements – in defence of libriform fibres with minutely bordered pits. IAWA Bull. n.s. 7: 82–86.

Baas, P. 1986b. Wood anatomy of Lythraceae – additional genera (Capuronia, Galpinia, Haitia, Orias, and Pleurophora). Ann. Missouri bot. Gard. 73: 810–819.

Baas, P. 1990. Ecological trends in the wood anatomy and their biological significance. In: Anatomy of European woods, by F.H. Schweingruber: 739–764. Verlag Paul Haupt: Bern & Stuttgart.

Baas, P. & Carlquist, S. 1985. A comparison of the ecological wood anatomy of the floras of southern California and Israel. IAWA Bull. n.s. 6: 349–353.

Baas, P., Esser, P.M. & Van der Westen, M.E.T. 1988. Wood anatomy of the Oleaceae. IAWA Bull. n.s. 9: 103–182.

Baas, P., Geesink, R., Van Heel, W.A. & Muller, J. 1979. The affinities of Plagiopteron suaveolens Griff. (Plagiopteraceae). Grana 18: 69–89.

Baas, P. & Gregory, M. 1985. A survey of oil cells in the dicotyledons with comments on their replacement by and joint occurrence with mucilage cells. Israel J. Bot. 34: 167–186.

Baas, P., Lee, C.-L., Zhang, X.Y., Cui, K.-M. & Deng, Y.F. 1984. Some effects of dwarf growth on wood structure. IAWA Bull. n.s. 5: 45–63.

Baas, P. & Schweingruber, F.H. 1987. Ecological trends in the wood anatomy of trees, shrubs and climbers from Europe. IAWA Bull. n.s. 8: 245–274.

Baas, P. & Vetter, R.E. (eds.) 1989. Growth rings in tropical trees. IAWA Bull. n.s. 10: 95–174.

Baas, P. & Werker, E. 1981. A new record of vestured pits in Cistaceae. IAWA Bull. n.s. 2: 41–42.

Baas, P., Werker, E. & Fahn, A. 1983. Some ecological trends in vessel characters. IAWA Bull. n.s. 4: 141–159.

Baas, P. & Zhang, X. 1986. Wood anatomy of trees and shrubs from China. I. Oleaceae. IAWA Bull. n.s. 7: 195–220.

Baas, P. & Zweypfenning, R.C.V.J. 1979. Wood anatomy of the Lythraceae. Acta bot. neerl. 28: 117–155.

Babos, K. 1980 [1981]. Összehasonlító xylotómiai vizsgálatok Quercus cerris var. cerris Loud. és Quercus cerris var. austriaca (Willd.) Loud. egyedeken. [Comparative xylotomic examinations of Quercus cerris var. cerris Loud. and Quercus cerris var. austriaca (Willd.) Loud.]. Bot. Közlem. 67: 173–178. [Eng. summ.].

Babos, K., Bermudez, I.R. & Cumana, L.J.C. 1981; 1982; 1983. Xylotomic examination of some Venezuelan Capparis species, I. Acta bot. Acad. sci. hung. 27: 295–308 (1981). II. Ibid. 28 (1–2): 1–14 (1982). III. Ibid. 29: 217–229 (1983).

Babos, K., Bermudez, I.R. & Cumana, L.J.C. 1984; 1987. Xylotomic examinations of some Venezuelan species of the Capparidaceae I. Acta bot. hung. 30: 333–340 (1984). II. Ibid. 33: 325–331 (1987).

Babos, K. & Borhidi, A. 1978; 1981. Xylotomic study of some woody plant species from Cuba, I, II, III. Acta bot. Acad. sci. hung. 24: 15–40, 235–261 (1978); 27 (1–2): 1–14 (1981).

Babos, K. & Cumana, L.J.C. 1988. Xylotomical examinations of some Venezuelan tree species (Caesalpiniaceae I). Acta bot. hung. 34 (1–2): 243–256.

Babos, K. & Vales, M. 1977 [1978]. Négy kubai endemikus fafaj xylotómai vizsgálata. [Xylotomic study of four endemic species from Cuba]. Bot. Közlem. 64: 179–181.

Bahadur, K.N. 1988. Monograph on the genus Toona (Meliaceae). Bishen Singh Mahendra Pal Singh: Dehra Dun, India. 251 pp.

Bailey, D.C. 1980. Anomalous growth and vegetative anatomy of Simmondsia chinensis. Amer. J. Bot. 67: 147–161.

Bailey, I.W. 1910. Notes on the wood structure of the Betulaceae and Fagaceae. For. Quart. 8: 178–185.

Bailey, I.W. 1912. The evolutionary history of the foliar ray in the wood of the dicotyledons: and its phylogenetic significance. Ann. Bot. 26: 647–661.

Bailey, I.W. 1933. The cambium and its derivative tissues: VIII. Structure, distribution and diagnostic significance of vestured pits in dicotyledons. J. Arnold Arbor. 14: 259–273.

Bailey, I.W. 1944a. The development of vessels in angiosperms and its significance in morphological research. Amer. J. Bot. 31: 421–428.

Bailey, I.W. 1944b. The comparative morphology of the Winteraceae. III. Wood. J. Arnold Arbor. 25: 97–103.

Bailey, I.W. 1951. The use and abuse of anatomical data in the study of phylogeny and classification. Phytomorphology 1: 67–69.

Bailey, I.W. 1953. Evolution of the tracheary tissue of land plants. Amer. J. Bot. 40: 4–8.

Bailey, I.W. 1957a. The potentialities and limitations of wood anatomy in the study of the phylogeny and classification of angiosperms. J. Arnold Arbor. 38: 243–254.

Bailey, I.W. 1957b. Additional notes on the vesselless dicotyledon, Amborella trichopoda Baill. J. Arnold Arbor. 38: 374–378.

Bailey, I.W. 1962. Comparative anatomy of the leaf-bearing Cactaceae, VI. The xylem of Pereskia sacharosa and Pereskia aculeata. J. Arnold Arbor. 43: 376–388.

Bailey, I.W. 1963. Comparative anatomy of the leaf-bearing Cactaceae, VII. The xylem of the Pereskias from Peru and Bolivia. J. Arnold Arbor. 44: 127–137. VIII. The xylem of Pereskias from southern Mexico and Central America. Ibid.: 211–221. IX. The xylem of Pereskia grandifolia and Pereskia bleo. Ibid.: 222–231. X. The xylem of Pereskia colombiana, Pereskia guamacho, Pereskia cubensis, and Pereskia portulacifolia. Ibid.: 390–401.

Bailey, I.W. 1964. Comparative anatomy of the leaf-bearing Cactaceae, XI. The xylem of Pereskiopsis and Quiabentia. J. Arnold Arbor. 45: 140–157.

Bailey, I.W. 1966. The significance of the reduction of vessels in the Cactaceae. J. Arnold Arbor. 47: 288–292.

Bailey, I.W. & Howard, R.A. 1941. The comparative morphology of the Icacinaceae. I. Anatomy of the node and internode. J. Arnold Arbor. 22: 125–132 + 4 plates. II. Vessels. Ibid.: 171–187 + 6 plates. III. Imperforate tracheary elements and xylem parenchyma. Ibid.: 432–442 + 3 plates. IV. Rays of the secondary xylem. Ibid.: 556–568 + 4 plates.

Bailey, I.W. & Nast, C.G. 1945a. The comparative morphology of the Winteraceae. VII. Summary and conclusions. J. Arnold Arbor. 26: 37–47.

Bailey, I.W. & Nast, C.G. 1945b. Morphology and relationships of Trochodendron and Tetracentron, I. Stem, root, and leaf. J. Arnold Arbor. 26: 143–154.

Bailey, I.W. Nast, C.G. 1948. Morphology and relationships of Illicium, Schizandra and Kadsura I: Stem and leaf. J. Arnold Arbor. 29: 77–89.

Bailey, I.W., Nast, C.G. & Smith, A.C. 1943. The family Himantandraceae. J. Arnold Arbor. 24: 190–206.

Bailey, I.W. & Smith, A.C. 1942. Degeneriaceae, a new family of flowering plants from Fiji. J. Arnold Arbor. 23: 356–365.

Bailey, I.W. & Swamy, B.G.L. 1948. Amborella trichopoda Baill., a new morphological type of vesselless dicotyledon. J. Arnold Arbor. 29: 245–253.

Bailey, I.W. & Swamy, B.G.L. 1949. Morphology and relationships of Austrobaileya. J. Arnold Arbor. 30: 211–226.

Bailey, I.W. & Swamy, B.G.L. 1953. The morphology and relationships of Idenburgia and Nouhuysia. J. Arnold Arbor. 34: 77–87.

Bailey, I.W. & Thompson, W.P. 1918. Additional notes upon the angiosperms Tetracentron, Trochodendron, and Drimys, in which vessels are absent from the wood. Ann. Bot. 32: 503–512 + Plate 16.

Baird, J.R. & Thieret, J.W. 1989. The medlar (Mespilus germanica, Rosaceae) from antiquity to obscurity. Econ. Bot. 43: 328–372.

Baird, M.M. 1915. Anatomy of Platanus occidentalis. Kansas Univ. Sci. Bull. 9: 281–290.

Baird, W.V. & Blackwell, W.H. 1980. Secondary growth in the axis of Halogeton glomeratus (Bieb.) Meyer (Chenopodiaceae). Bot. Gaz. 141: 269–276.

Baker, R.T. 1915. The Australian grey mangrove. J. Proc. roy. Soc. N.S. Wales 49: 257–281.

Baker, R.T. 1917. On the occurrence of crystals in some Australian timbers. J. Proc. roy. Soc. N.S. Wales 51: 435–444.

Baker, R.T. 1919. On the technology and anatomy of some silky oak timbers. J. Proc. roy. Soc. N.S. Wales 52: 363–76.

Balan Menon, P.K. 1955. The wood anatomy of Malayan timbers. Commercial timbers. 1. Heavy hardwoods. 2. Medium hardwoods. Res. Pamph. For. Dept. Malaya 18: 1–16.

Balan Menon, P.K. 1956. Siliceous timbers of Malaya. Malayan For. Rec. No. 19: 1–55.

Balan Menon, P.K. 1959. The wood anatomy of Malayan timbers. Commercial timbers (cont.) 3. Light hardwoods. Res. Pamph. For. Dept. Malaya 27: 1–30.

Balan Menon, P.K. 1960. Anomalous structure of Gonystylus. J. Inst. Wood Sci., No. 6: 47–54.

Balan Menon, P.K. 1965. Guide to distribution of silica in Malayan woods. Malayan Forester 28: 284–288.

Bamber, R.K. 1974. Fibre types in the wood of Euphorbiaceae. Austral. J. Bot. 22: 629–634.

Bamber, R.K. 1984. Wood anatomy of some Australian rainforest vines. Proc. Pacific Regional Wood Anatomy Conf., Tsukuba, Japan, 1984: 58–60.

Bamber, R.K. & Lanyon, J.W. 1960. Silica deposition in several woods of New South Wales. Trop. Woods 113: 48–53.

Bamps, P., Robyns, A., Dechamps, R. & Nilsson, S. 1977. Westphalina macrocarpa gen. et sp. nov. (Tiliaceae) du Guatemala. Bull. Jard. bot. natn. Belg. 47: 183–189.

Bancroft, H. 1934. New material of Monotes kerstingii from the Gold Coast. Kew Bull. 1934: 233–237.

Bancroft, H. 1935a. Material of Marquesia acuminata from Northern Rhodesia. Kew Bull. 1935: 559–568.

Bancroft, H. 1935b. The wood anatomy of representative members of the Monotoideae. Amer. J. Bot. 22: 717–739.

Bandoni, A.J. & O'Donell, C.A. 1939. La anatomía de la Timeleácea Ovidia pillo-pillo, planta medicinal de los Andes patagónicos. Physis 15: 377–385.

Bandyopadhyaya, M. & Dutta, P.C. 1986 [1988]. Comparative anatomy of different species of Plumeria. Bull. bot. Soc. Bengal 40: 59–66.

Banks, C.H. & Kromhout, C.P. 1966. Notes on the timber of Burkea africana Hook., with particular reference to material from South West Africa. Forestry S. Afr., No. 7: 17–29.

Bannan, M.W. 1943. Wood structure of Ryania. Amer. J. Bot. 30: 351–355.

Barajas Morales, J. 1980. Anatomía de maderas de México, No. 3. Diez especies del bosque caducifolio de las cercanías de Xalapa, Veracruz, México. Biotica, Méx. 5: 23–40.

Barajas Morales, J. 1981. Description and notes on the wood anatomy of Boraginaceae from western Mexico. IAWA Bull. n.s. 2: 61–67.

Barajas Morales, J. 1983 [1984]. Detalles ultraestructurales de la madera de algunas Boraginaceae de Mexico. Bol. Soc. bot. Mex. 45: 3–14.

Barajas Morales, J. 1985. Wood structural differences between trees of two tropical forests in Mexico. IAWA Bull. n.s. 6: 355–364.

Barajas Morales, J. & Echenique-Manrique, R. 1976. Anatomía de maderas de México. 1. 12 especies de Valisco y Veracruz. Biotica, Méx. 1 (2): 29–70.

Barajas Morales, J. & León Gómez, C. 1989. Anatomía de maderas de México, especies de una selva baja caducifolia. Univ. nac. autón. México, Inst. Biol. Publ. espec. No. 1: 126 pp. + 36 plates.

Barajas Morales, J., Rebollar Domínguez, S. & Echenique-Manrique, R. 1979. Anatomía de maderas de México. No. 2. Veinte especies de la Selva Lacandona. Biotica, Méx. 4: 163–193. [Eng. summ.]

Barbosa, O. 1981–1982. Características estruturais do lenho de Copaifera langsdorfii Desf. e Copaifera lucens Dwyer. Silvicultura, São Paulo 15/16: 23–36. [Eng. summ.]

Barbosa, O., Baitello, J.B., Mainieri, C., Montagna, R.G. & Negreiros, O.C. de 1977–1978. Identificação e fenologia de espécies arbóreas da Serra da Cantareira (São Paulo). Silvicultura, São Paulo 11/12: 1–86.

Barbosa, O. & Gurgel Filho, O. do A. 1982. Estudo dos elementos anatômicos do lenho de Copaifera langsdorfii Desf. Silvicultura, São Paulo 16A: 312–317. [Eng. summ.]

Barefoot, A.C. & Hankins, F.W. 1982. Identification of modern and Tertiary woods. Clarendon Press: Oxford. 189 pp.

Baretta-Kuipers, T. 1972. Some remarks on the wood structure of Pinzona and allied genera of the subfamily Tetraceroideae (Dilleniaceae). Acta bot. neerl. 21: 573–577.

Baretta-Kuipers, T. 1973. Some aspects of wood-anatomical research in the genus Inga (Mimosaceae) from the Guianas and especially Suriname. Acta bot. neerl. 22: 193–205.

Baretta-Kuipers, T. 1976. Comparative wood anatomy of Bonnetiaceae, Theaceae and Guttiferae. In: Wood structure in biological and technological research (eds. Baas, P., Bolton, A.J. & Catling, D.M.): 76–101. Leiden Botanical Series No. 3. Leiden Univ. Press.

Baretta-Kuipers, T. 1978. Aspects of wood anatomy in Leguminosae, with special reference to the Pithecellobium complex (Mimosaceae). Acta bot. neerl. 27: 139. [Abstr.]

Baretta-Kuipers, T. 1979. Wood anatomy of Archidendron F. v. Mueller, Mimosoideae, Leguminosae. IAWA Bull. 1979/2-3: 47–50.

Baretta-Kuipers, T. 1981. Wood anatomy of Leguminosae: its relevance to taxonomy. In: Advances in legume systematics 2 (eds. Polhill, R.M. & Raven, P.H.): 677–705. Royal Botanic Gardens: Kew.

Baretta-Kuipers, T. 1982. Wood structure of the genus Erythrina. Allertonia 3 (1): 53–69.

Bargagli-Petrucci, G. 1903. Sulla struttura dei legnami raccolti in Borneo dal Dott. O. Beccari. Malpighia 17: 280–371 + Plates IV–XV.

Bargagli-Petrucci, G. 1904. Osservazioni anatomico-sistematiche sulle Bombacee. Nuovo G. bot. ital. 11: 407–415.

Barghoorn, A.W. & Renteira, M. 1967. Estudio anatomico y fisico-mecanico del cagui (Caryocar costarricense Donn. Sm.). Inst. Forest. Latino-Amer. Invest. Capac. Merida Venez. 24: 35–57.

Barghoorn, E.S. 1940; 1941. The ontogenetic development and phylogenetic specialization of rays in the xylem of dicotyledons I. The primitive ray structure. Amer. J. Bot. 27: 918–928 (1940). II. Modification of the multiseriate and uniseriate rays. Ibid. 28: 273–282 (1941). III. The elimination of rays. Bull. Torrey bot. Cl. 68: 317–325 (1941).

Barreto, L.S. 1967. Madeiras de Moçambique. Estrutura do lenho (1a série). Rev. Est. Gerais Univ. Moçambique, Lourenço Marques (sér. II) 4: 59–183.

Barykina, R.P. 1971. Morphologico-anatomical studies of Berberis vulgaris f. atropurpurea Rgl. and Berberis thunbergii DC. in connection with problem of transformation of life forms in family Berberidaceae. In: Morfologiia Tsvetkovykh Rastenii: 95–126. [Russ.]

Barykina, R.P. & Gulanyan, T.A. 1976. Ontomorphogenesis of shrubby Paeonia L. representatives: I. P. suffruticosa Andr. Vest. mosk. Univ., ser. 6, Biol. Pochvov. 31 (6): 45–55. [Russ.; Eng. summ.]

Barykina, R.P. & Gulanyan, T.A. 1978. Ontomorphogenesis of shrubby representatives of the genus Paeonia L.: II. P. lutea Franch. and P. delavayi Franch. Vest. mosk. Univ., ser. 16, Biol. (2): 64–76. [Russ.; Eng. summ.] Also: Moscow Univ. biol. Sci. Bull. 33 (2): 48–56 [Eng. transl.]

Barykina, R.P. & Kudryashev, L.V. 1973. Anatomical study of hypoarctic shrubs Betula exilis Sukacz. and Betula nana L. Bot. Zh. SSSR 58: 421–428. [Russ. only.]

Bascopé V., F. 1954. Estudios estructurales de ciertas maderas de los bosques del valle de la Mucuy, cerca de Mérida. Bol. Ingen. for. Univ. Los Andes 1 (3): 20–26; (4): 11–18; (5): 8–15.

Bascopé, F., Bernardi, A.L., Jorgensen, R.N., Hueck, K. & Lamprecht, H. 1959. Descripciones de arboles forestales No. 5. Los manglares en America. Inst. Forest. Latinoamer. Invest. Capac., Merida: 52 pp. + 16 plates.

Bascopé, F., Bernardi, A.L., Lamprecht, H. & Martinez E., P. 1957. Descripciones de arboles forestales No. 2. El genero Cedrela en America. Inst. Forest. Latinoamer. Invest. Capac.: 25 pp.

Basson, P.W. & Bierhorst, D.W. 1967. An analysis of differential lateral growth in the stem of Bauhinia surinamensis. Bull. Torrey bot. Cl. 94: 404–411.

Bastos, A. de M. 1946 [1947]. As madeiras do Pará. Caracteres gerais e caracteres anatômicos. Arq. Serv. Florestal, Rio de Janeiro 2 (2): 157–182.

Bastos, A. de M. 1952. Contribuição para o conhecimento dendrologico das especies do genero Centrolobium. Arq. Serv. Florestal, Rio de Janeiro 6: 125–186.

Bausch, J. 1938. A revision of the Eucryphiaceae. Kew Bull. 317–349.

Beck, G.F. 1945. Nyssa woods of the Pacific northwest mid-Tertiary. Northwest Science 19 (1): 11–13.

Becking, W. 1960. A summary of information on Aucoumea klaineana. For. Abstr. 21: 1–6, 163–172.

Bedell, H.G. 1980 [1981]. A taxonomic and morphological re-evaluation of Stegnospermaceae (Caryophyllales). Syst. Bot. 5: 419–431.

Benoist, R. 1927. Sur les bois de quelques Annonacées americaines. Bull. Soc. bot. Fr. 74: 281–285.

Benoist, R. 1931. Les bois de la Guyane française. Arch. Bot. Caen, Mém. 5 (1): 1–292.

Berg, C.C., Akkermans, R.W.A.P. & Van Heusden, E.C.H. 1990. Cecropiaceae: Coussapoa and Pourouma, with an introduction to the family. Flora Neotropica Mon. 51: 1–208.

Berger, L.G. den 1922. Inleiding tot de herkenning van hout in de praktijk. Meded. Proefst. Boschw. Batavia, No. 7: 55 pp.

Berger, L.G. den 1928. Beiträge zur Kenntnis der Anatomie des sekundären Holzes der Niederländisch Indischen Baumarten. I. Bull. Jard. bot. Buitenzorg 9: 223–248.

Berkel, A. 1955. A summary of the anatomical structure of the wood of Liquidambar orientalis Mill. Istanb. Univ. Orman Fak. Derg. A, 5 (1–2): 1–18.

Berndt, J. 1963. Badania anatomiczne drewna krajowych gatunków rodzaju Betula L. [Anatomical studies of the wood of the native species of genus Betula L.] Stud. Soc. Sci. Torun., sect. D. 6: 155–204. [Eng. summ.]

Berndt, J. 1979. Anatomia i kariologia. In: Brzozy Betula L. (ed. Białobok, S.): 83–104. [Monografie popularnonaukowe 7.] Polska Akad. Nauk., Inst. Dendrol., Warsaw. [Eng. summ.]

Berry, P.E., Stein, B.A., Carlquist, S. & Nowicke, E. 1988. Fuchsia pachyrrhiza (Onagraceae), a tuberous new species and section of Fuchsia from western Peru. Syst. Bot. 13: 483–492.

Besson, A. 1946. Richesse en cendres et teneur en silice des bois tropicaux. Agron. trop. 1: 44–56.

Bhambie, S., Joshi, M.C. & Gupta, M.L. 1977. Anatomical studies on certain members of Aizoaceae. Proc. Indian Acad. Sci., B, 85: 399–406.

Bhargava, H.R. 1932. Contribution to the morphology of Boerhavia repanda. J. Indian bot. Soc. 11: 303–326 + 4 plates.

Bhat, K.M. 1983. A note on aggregate rays of Betula species. IAWA Bull. n.s. 4: 183–185.

Bhat, K.M. & Kärkkäinen, M. 1980. Distinguishing between Betula pendula and Betula pubescens on the basis of wood anatomy. Silva fenn. 14: 294–304.

Bhat, K.M. & Kärkkäinen, M. 1981a. Wood anatomy and physical properties of wood and bark in Betula tortuosa Ledeb. Silva fenn. 15 (2): 148–155.

Bhat, K.M. & Kärkkäinen, M. 1981b. Variation in structure and selected properties of Finnish birch wood: II. Observations on the anatomy of root wood. Silva fenn. 15: 180–189. IV. Fibre and vessel length in branches, stems and roots. Ibid.: 10–17.

Bhat, K.M. & Kärkkäinen, M. 1982. Wood anatomy and physical properties of the wood and bark in Betula nana growing in Finland. Silva fenn. 16 (1): 1–10.

Bhat, R.B., Inamdar, J.A. & Weber, D.J. 1990. Phylogeny of Hibiscus as interpreted from vessel elements. Angew. Bot. 64: 113–121.

Bhattacharyya, P. 1975. The xylem anatomy of the section Callianche Yuncker (Cuscutaceae Dumortier). Bull. bot. Soc. Bengal 29: 43–47.

Bhattacharyya, P.K. 1988 [1990]. The vascular cambia of dodder and its allies. Bull. bot. Surv. India 30: 149–155.

Bianchi, A.T.J. 1934. The resistance of some Netherlands East Indian timbers against the attack of shipworm (teredo). Proc. 5th Pacific Sci Congr., Canada: 3903–3906.

Bierhorst, D.W. 1960. Observations on tracheary elements. Phytomorphology 10: 249–305.

Biondi, E. & Baldoni, M. 1984. A contribution to the knowledge of Betula aetnensis Rafin. through an anatomic and morphometric study of its wood. Webbia 38: 623–637.

Bisen, S.S. & Sharma, B. 1985. An unusual vessel perforation plate in Cordia myxa L. (Boraginaceae). IAWA Bull. n.s. 6: 163–164.

Bissing, D.R. 1982. Variation in qualitative anatomical features of the xylem of selected dicotyledonous woods in relation to water availability. Bull. Torrey bot. Cl. 109: 371–384.

Blake, S.T. 1972. Idiospermum (Idiospermaceae), a new genus and family for Calycanthus australiensis. Contrib. Queensland Herb. No. 12: 1–37.

Blesa Rodriguez, A.C., Caballero-Ruano, A. & Jimenez Parrondo, M.S. 1979. Estudio anatomico-fisiologico del leño de las Crasulaceas en relacion con el habitat. An. Edafol. Agrobiol. 38: 2169–2179.

Blunden, G., Aye Kyi & Jewers, K. 1974. The comparative stem and root anatomy of Goniothalamus andersonii, G. macrophyllus, G. malayanus and G. velutinus (Annonaceae) from the peat swamps of Sarawak. Bot. J. Linn. Soc. 68: 209–225.

Böcher, T.W. 1971. Anatomical studies in cottonthorn, Tetradymia axillaris A. Nels. Nat. canad. 98: 225–249.

Böcher, T.W. & Lyshede, O.B. 1968. Anatomical studies in xerophytic apophyllous plants. I. Monttea aphylla, Bulnesia retama and Bredemeyera colletioides. Biol. Skr. Dan. Vid. Selsk. 16(3): 1–44.

Bogdanova, T.L. 1971. Microscopic structure of woody liana Polygonum baldshuanicum Rgl. Dokl. mosk. sel'khoz. Akad. K.A. Timiryazeva 161: 291–295. [Russ.]

Bokhari, M.H. 1982. Anatomical studies of a new Limonium from Iran. Notes roy. bot. Gard. Edinb. 40: 93–98.

Bokhari, M.H. & Hedge, I.C. 1975. Anatomical characters in Capparis spinosa and its allies. Notes roy. bot. Gard. Edinb. 34: 231–240.

Bokhari, M.H. & Wendelbo, P. 1978. On anatomy, adaptations to xerophytism and taxonomy of Anabasis inclusive Esfandiaria (Chenopodiaceae). Bot. Notiser 131: 279–292.

Boland, D.J. & Kleinig, D.A. 1983 [1984]. Eucalyptus wilcoxii (Myrtaceae), a new species from south-eastern New South Wales. Brunonia 6: 241–250.

Bonde, S.D. & Upadhye, A.S. 1989. Contribution to the wood anatomy of Tinospora sinensis (Lour.) Merrill in relation with T. cordifolia Miers. Ancient Sci. Life 9: 80–85.

Bonnemain, J.-L. 1970. Histogénèse du phloème interne et du phloème inclus des Solanacées. Rev. gén. Bot. 77: 5–51.

Bonomo, R., Colombo, P. & Princiotta, R. 1978. Athamanta sicula L. in Sicilia: aspetti morfologici e struttura anomala del rizoma. Naturalista siciliano, ser. IV, 2: 135–147.

Bonsen, K.J.M. & Kučera, L.J. 1990. Vessel occlusions in plants: morphological, functional and evolutionary aspects. IAWA Bull. n.s. 11: 393–399.

Bonsen, K. & Welle, B.J.H. ter 1983. Comparative leaf and wood anatomy of the Cecropiaceae (Urticales). Bull. Mus. natn. Hist. nat., Paris, B, Adansonia, sér. 4, 5: 151–177.

Bonsen, K.J.M. & Welle, B.J.H. ter 1984. Systematic wood anatomy and affinities of the Urticaceae. Bot. Jb. 105: 49–71.

Borges Flörsheim, S.M. & Barbosa, O. 1983–1985. Anatomia do lenho das Lauráceas da Serra da Cantareira. I. Cryptocarya. Silvicultura, São Paulo 17–19: 9–16. [Eng. summ.]

Bosshard, H.H. 1974, 1975. Holzkunde. 3 vols. Birkhäuser Verlag: Basel & Stuttgart. 224, 312, & 286 pp.

Bosshard, H.H. 1982, 1984. Holzkunde. 3 vols. Birkhäuser Verlag: Basel. 2nd edn.

Botelho, E.A. 1951. Fichas anatomicas de especies vegetais brasileiras. Bol. INT, Rio de Janeiro 2: 65–71.

Botosso, P.C. & Gomes, A.V. 1982. Radial vessels and series of perforated ray cells in Annonaceae. IAWA Bull. n.s. 3: 39–44.

Boulton, E.H.B. & Price, T.J. 1931. Notes on Iroko (Chlorophora excelsa). Trop. Woods 28: 4–7.

Boureau, E. 1958. Contribution à l'étude anatomique des espèces actuelles de Ropalocarpaceae. Bull. Mus. natn. Hist. nat., Paris, sér. 2, 30: 213–221.

Boureau, E. 1960. Bois hétéroxylé et évolution. Mém. Soc. bot. fr. 41–49.

Boureau, E. & Marguerier, J. 1985 [1986]. L'origine et l'évolution du xylème chez les Trachéo-phytes. G. bot. ital. 119: 89–149.

Bramwell, D. 1976 [1977]. The systematic position of the genus Bosea L. (Amaranthaceae). Bot. macaronesica, No. 2: 19–24.

Brandão, N. 1954. Contribuição ao estudo anatomico do sabia. Agronomia, Rio de Janeiro 13 (1): 85–90.

Braun, H.J. 1955. Beiträge zur Entwicklungsgeschichte der Markstrahlen. In: Vergleichend-anatomische Untersuchungen aus dem forstbotanischen Institut München (ed. Huber, B.). Bot. Stud. 4: 73–131. Gustav Fischer: Jena.

Braun, H.J. 1963. Die Organisation des Stammes von Bäumen und Sträuchern. Wissenschaft-liche Verlagsgesellschaft m.b.H., Stuttgart. 162 pp.

Braun, H.J. 1967. Entwicklung und Bau der Holzstrahlen unter dem Aspekt der Kontakt-Iso-lations-Differenzierung gegenüber dem Hydrosystem. I. Das Prinzip der Kontakt-Isolations-Differenzierung. Holzforschung 21: 33–37. [Eng. summ.]

Braun, H.J. 1970. Funktionelle Histologie der sekundären Sprossachse. I. Das Holz. [Handb. Pflanzenanat. IX.1.] Borntraeger: Berlin & Stuttgart. 190 pp.

Braun, H.J. & Den Outer, R.W. 1965. Die unterschiedlichen Beziehungen der Holzstrahlen zum Hydrosystem als wesentliches Differenzierungsprinzip. I. Die einschichtigen Strahlen und die durch Verschmelzung aus ihnen entstehenden mehrschichtigen Strahlen. Zeit. Bot. 52: 539–571. [Eng. summ., p. 565.]

Braun, H.J. & Wolkinger, F. 1970. Zur funktionellen Anatomie des axialen Holzparenchyms und Vorschläge zur Reform seiner Terminologie. Holzforschung 24: 19–26.

Braun, H.J., Wolkinger, F. & Böhme, H. 1967; 1968. Entwicklung und Bau der Holzstrahlen unter dem Aspekt der Kontakt-Isolations-Differenzierung gegenüber dem Hydrosystem. II. Die Typen der Kontakt-Holzstrahlen. Holzforschung 21: 145–153 (1967). III. Die Typen der Kontakt-Isolations-Holzstrahlen und der Isolations-Holzstrahlen. Ibid. 22: 53–60 (1968). IV. Die Organisation der Holzstrahlen. Ibid.: 153–157 (1968). [Eng. summ.]

Braun, K. 1900. Beiträge zur Anatomie der Adansonia digitata L. Diss.: Basel.

Brazier, J.D. 1957–1958 [1959]. Pseudosindora palustris Sym. An account of its timber and anatomical evidence for its taxonomic status. Proc. Linn. Soc., Lond. 170: 178–184.

Brazier, J.D. 1958. The anatomy of some timbers formerly included in Piptadenia. Trop. Woods 108: 46–64.

Brazier, J.D. 1968. The contribution of wood anatomy to taxonomy. Proc. Linn. Soc., Lond. 179: 271–274.

Brazier, J.D. 1976. Observations on some anatomical features used in identification and taxon-omy. In: Wood structure in biological and technological research (eds. Baas, P., Bolton, A.J. & Catling, D.M.): 102–106. Leiden Botanical Series No. 3. Leiden University Press.

Brazier, J.D. 1979. Classifying the Dipterocarpaceae: the wood technologist's view. Mém. Mus. natn. Hist. nat., Paris, B (NS) 26: 76–80.

Brazier, J.D. & Franklin, G.L. 1961. Identification of hardwoods. A microscope key. For. Prod. Res. Bull., No. 46: 96 pp. HMSO: London. See also Miles 1978 for photographs.

Bricker, J.S. 1991. A revision of the genus Crinodendron (Elaeocarpaceae). Syst. Bot. 16: 77–88.

Bridgwater, S.D. & Baas, P. 1978. Wood anatomy of the Punicaceae. IAWA Bull. 1978/1: 3–6.

Bridgwater, S. & Baas, P. 1982. Wood anatomy of Xanthophyllum Roxb. IAWA Bull. n.s. 3: 115–125.

Bridson, D., Gasson, P. & Robbrecht, E. 1980. Phellocalyx, a new tropical African genus in Rubiaceae (Gardenieae). Kew Bull. 35: 315–321.

Briggs, B.G., Hyland, B.P.M. & Johnson, L.A.S. 1975. Sphalmium, a distinctive new genus of Proteaceae from North Queensland. Aust. J. Bot. 23: 165–172.

Brindha, P., Sasikala, E. & Kundu, A.B. 1990. Contribution to the pharmacognostic anatomy of the root wood of Oroxylum indicum Vent. (Syonaka). Indian Drugs 28: 120–123.

Brizicky, G.K. 1960. A new species of Paramachaerium from Panama. Trop. Woods 112: 58–64.

Brook, P.J. 1951. Vegetative anatomy of Carpodetus serratus Forst. Trans. roy. Soc. N.Zealand 79: 276–285.

Brown, F.B.H. 1922. The secondary xylem of Hawaiian trees. Occ. Pap. B.P. Bishop Mus. 8 (6): 217–371.

Brown, F.B.H. 1928. Cornaceae and allies in the Marquesas and neighboring islands. B.P. Bishop Mus., Bull. 52: 1–22.

Brown, H.P. & Panshin, A.J. 1940. Commercial timbers of the United States. McGraw-Hill: New York. 554 pp. [Panshin & Zeeuw 1980 indexed.]

Brummitt, R.K. 1992. Vascular plant families and genera. Royal Botanic Gardens, Kew. 804 pp.

Brunner, C. 1908 [1909]. Beiträge zur vergleichenden Anatomie der Tamaricaceen. Jb. Hamburg wiss. Anst. 26, Beiheft 3: 89–162.

Brush, W.D. 1917. Distinguishing characters of North American sycamore woods. Bot. Gaz. 64: 480–496.

Burgerstein, A. 1898. Xylotomisch-systematische Studien über die Gattungen der Pomaceen. Jahresber. k.k. Staatsgym. Wien. 35 pp.

Burgerstein, A. 1899. Beiträge zur Xylotomie der Pruneen. Verh. k.k. zool.-bot. Ges. Wien 49: 28–32.

Burgerstein, A. 1909. Anatomische Untersuchungen samoanischer Hölzer. Denkschr. Akad. Wiss. Wien, math.-nat. Kl. 84: 456–514.

Burgerstein, A. 1911. Diagnostische Merkmale der Markstrahlen von Populus und Salix. Ber. dt. bot. Ges. 29: 679–684.

Burgerstein, A. 1912. Anatomische Untersuchungen argentinischer Hölzer des K.K. naturhistorischen Hofmuseums in Wien. Ann. k.k. naturh. Hofmuseums Wien 26: 1–36.

Burgess, P.F. 1965. Silica in Sabah timbers. Malayan Forester 28: 223–229.

Burkart, A. 1947. Leguminosas nuevas o criticas II. Darwiniana 7: 504–540.

Burtt, B.L. & Dickison, W.C. 1975. The morphology and relationships of Seemannaralia (Araliaceae). Notes roy. bot. Gard. Edinb. 33: 449–464.

Burtt Davy, J. 1928. African "Sandaleen" wood. Trop. Woods 17: 15–17.

Butnik, A.A. 1983. A characteristic of anomalous (polycambial) types of secondary thickening in axilial organs of the Chenopodiaceae species. Bot. Zh. SSSR 68: 572–580. [Russ.; Eng. summ.] + 1 plate.

Butterfield, B.G. & Meylan, B.A. 1976. The occurrence of septate fibres in some New Zealand woods. N.Z. Jl. Bot. 14: 123–130.

Butterfield, B.G. & Meylan, B.A. 1979. Observations of trabeculae in New Zealand woods. Wood Sci. Technol. 13: 59–65.

Butterfield, B.G. & Meylan, B.A. 1980. Three-dimensional structure of wood. An ultrastructural approach. Chapman & Hall: London, New York. 2nd edn. 103 pp.

Butterfield, B.G., Philipson, W.R., Meylan, B.A. & Ohtani, J. 1984. Comparative morphology of the vessel elements in the woods of Pseudopanax C.Koch (Araliaceae). N.Z. Jl. Bot. 22: 509–514.

Caballé, G. 1993. Liana structure, function and selection: a comparative study of xylem cylinders of tropical rainforest species in Africa and America. Bot. J. Linn. Soc. 113: 41–60.

Cai, S.S. & Su, Z.H. 1978. Quantitative anatomy of the wood of Casuarina equisetifolia L. Res. Paper No. 56, For. Res. Inst. Guangdong Prov. 10 pp. [Chin.; Eng. summ. & captions.]

Callejas, R. 1986. Taxonomic revision of Piper subgenus Ottonia (Piperaceae). PhD thesis: City Univ. of New York. 416 pp. Univ. Microfilms Intn.: Ann Arbor.

Cambini, A. 1960. Micrografia comparata dei legni del genere Castanea. Ann. Accad. ital. Sci. for. 9: 17–41.

Cambini, A. 1967a. Micrografia comparata dei legni del genere Quercus. Contrib. sci.-prat. migl. Conos. Util. Legno, Firenze 10, No. 19: 7–49. [Eng. summ.]

Cambini, A. 1967b. Riconoscimento microscopico del legno delle querce italiane. Contrib. sci.-prat. migl. Conos. Util. Legno, Firenze 10, No. 20: 51–69.

Camus, A. 1936–1954. Les Chênes. 3 vols. Lechevalier: Paris.

Canessa, E. 1989. Descripcion anatomica de la madera de camibar Copaifera camibar Poveda, Zamora & Sanchez. Brenesia 31: 113–115.

Canright, J.E. 1955. The comparative morphology and relationships of the Magnoliaceae. IV. Wood and nodal anatomy. J. Arnold Arbor. 36: 119–140.

Cao, W.-H. & Zhang, X.-Y. 1991. The secondary xylem anatomy of 6 desert plants of Caragana. Acta bot. sin. 33: 181–187. [Chin.; Eng. summ.] + 2 plates.

Cardoso, J.G.A. 1960; 1961. Madeiras de Moçambique. I–VIII. Publ. Serv. Agric. Flor., Lourenço Marques, sér. A, Nos. 3–8 (1960); 11–12 (1961). [Eng. summ.]

Cardoso, J.G.A. 1966; 1968; 1969. Madeiras de Moçambique XIV. Albizzia versicolor. Publicações, Moçambique, sér. A, No. 19: 57 pp. (1966). XV. Pterocarpus angolensis. Ibid., No. 22: 54 pp. (1968). XIX. Cordyla africana. Ibid., No. 23: 55 pp. (1969).

Cardoso, J.G.A. & Cardoso, M. del J.A. 1960? [n.d.]. Estudo comparativo dos caracteres histologicos de uma amostra de madeira com os da Afzelia quangensis Welw. Suspeita da existencia em Moçambique de Afzelia africana Smith. Publ. Serv. Agric., Moçambique, sér. A, No. 2: 9 pp.

Carlquist, S. 1957a. The genus Fitchia (Compositae). Univ. Calif. Publ. Bot. 29 (1): 1–144.

Carlquist, S. 1957b. Wood anatomy of Mutisieae (Compositae). Trop. Woods 106: 29–45.

Carlquist, S. 1958a. Wood anatomy of Heliantheae (Compositae). Trop. Woods 108: 1–30.

Carlquist, S. 1958b. The woods and flora of the Florida Keys. Compositae. Trop. Woods 109: 1–37.

Carlquist, S. 1958c. Anatomy and systematic position of Centaurodendron and Yunquea (Compositae). Brittonia 10: 78–93.

Carlquist, S. 1959a. Studies on Madinae: anatomy, cytology, and evolutionary relationships. Aliso 4: 171–236.

Carlquist, S. 1959b. Wood anatomy of Helenieae (Compositae). Trop. Woods 111: 19–39.

Carlquist, S. 1960a. Wood anatomy of Cichorieae (Compositae). Trop. Woods 112: 65–91.

Carlquist, S. 1960b. Wood anatomy of Astereae (Compositae). Trop. Woods 113: 54–84.

Carlquist, S. 1961. Wood anatomy of Inuleae (Compositae). Aliso 5: 21–37.

Carlquist, S. 1962a. A theory of paedomorphosis in dicotyledonous woods. Phytomorphology 12: 30–45.

Carlquist, S. 1962b. Wood anatomy of Senecioneae (Compositae). Aliso 5: 123–146.

Carlquist, S. 1964a. Morphology and relationships of Lactoridaceae. Aliso 5: 421–435.

Carlquist, S. 1964b. Wood anatomy of Vernonieae (Compositae). Aliso 5: 451–467.

Carlquist, S. 1965a. Wood anatomy of Cynareae (Compositae). Aliso 6 (1): 13–24.

Carlquist, S. 1965b. Wood anatomy of Eupatorieae (Compositae). Aliso 6 (1): 89–103.

Carlquist, S. 1966a. Wood anatomy of Anthemideae, Ambrosieae, Calenduleae, and Arctotideae (Compositae). Aliso 6 (2): 1–23.

Carlquist, S. 1966b. Wood anatomy of Compositae: a summary, with comments on factors controlling wood evolution. Aliso 6 (2): 25–44.

Carlquist, S. 1969a. Wood anatomy of Lobelioideae (Campanulaceae). Biotropica 1: 47–72.

Carlquist, S. 1969b. Wood anatomy of Goodeniaceae and the problem of insular woodiness. Ann. Missouri bot. Gard. 56: 358–390.

Carlquist, S. 1970a. Wood anatomy of Echium (Boraginaceae). Aliso 7: 183–199.

Carlquist, S. 1970b. Wood anatomy of Hawaiian, Macaronesian, and other species of Euphorbia. In: New research in plant anatomy (eds. Robson, N.K.B., Cutler, D.F. & Gregory, M.). Bot. J. Linn. Soc. 63, Suppl. 1: 181–193. Academic Press.

Carlquist, S. 1970 [1971]. Wood anatomy of insular species of Plantago and the problem of raylessness. Bull. Torrey bot. Cl. 97: 353–361.

Carlquist, S. 1971. Wood anatomy of Macaronesian and other Brassicaceae. Aliso 7: 365–384.

Carlquist, S. 1974. Island biology. Columbia University Press: New York & London. 660 pp.

Carlquist, S. 1975a. Ecological strategies of xylem evolution. Univ. California Press: Berkeley, Los Angeles, London, 259 pp.

Carlquist, S. 1975b. Wood anatomy of Onagraceae, with notes on alternative modes of photosynthate movement in dicotyledon woods. Ann. Missouri bot. Gard. 62: 386–424.

Carlquist, S. 1975c. Wood anatomy and relationships of Geissolomataceae. Bull. Torrey bot. Cl. 102: 128–134.

Carlquist, S. 1976a. Wood anatomy of Myrothamnus flabellifolia (Myrothamnaceae) and the problem of multiperforate perforation plates. J. Arnold Arbor. 57: 119–126.

Carlquist, S. 1976b. Wood anatomy of Byblidaceae. Bot. Gaz. 137: 35–38.

Carlquist, S. 1976c. Wood anatomy of Roridulaceae: ecological and phylogenetic implications. Amer. J. Bot. 63: 1003–1008.

Carlquist, S. 1976d. Tribal interrelationships and phylogeny of the Asteraceae. Aliso 8: 465–492.

Carlquist, S. 1977a. Wood anatomy of Grubbiaceae. Jl. S. Afr. Bot. 43: 129–144.

Carlquist, S. 1977b. Wood anatomy of Tremandraceae: phylogenetic and ecological implications. Amer. J. Bot. 64: 704–713.

Carlquist, S. 1977c. Ecological factors in wood evolution: a floristic approach. Amer. J. Bot. 64: 887–896.

Carlquist, S. 1977 [1978]. Wood anatomy of Onagraceae: additional species and concepts. Ann. Missouri bot. Gard. 64: 627–637.

Carlquist, S. 1978a. Wood anatomy of Bruniaceae: correlations with ecology, phylogeny, and organography. Aliso 9: 323–364.

Carlquist, S. 1978b. Wood anatomy and relationships of Bataceae, Gyrostemonaceae, and Stylobasiaceae. Allertonia 1 (5): 297–330.

Carlquist, S. 1980a. Further concepts in ecological wood anatomy, with comments on recent work in wood anatomy and evolution. Aliso 9: 499–553.

Carlquist, S. 1980b. Anatomy and systematics of Balanopaceae. Allertonia 2: 191–246.

Carlquist, S. 1981a. Wood anatomy of Pittosporaceae. Allertonia 2: 355–392.

Carlquist, S. 1981b. Types of cambial activity and wood anatomy of Stylidium (Stylidiaceae). Amer. J. Bot. 68: 778–785.

Carlquist, S. 1981c. Wood anatomy of Cephalotaceae. IAWA Bull. n.s. 2: 175–178.

Carlquist, S. 1981d. Wood anatomy of Nepenthaceae. Bull. Torrey bot. Cl. 108: 324–330.

Carlquist, S. 1981e. Wood anatomy of Chloanthaceae (Dicrastylidaceae). Aliso 10: 19–34.

Carlquist, S. 1981 [1982]. Wood anatomy of Zygogynum (Winteraceae); field observations. Bull. Mus. natn. Hist. nat., Paris, Adansonia, sér. 4, 3: 281–292.

Carlquist, S. 1982a. Wood anatomy of Daphniphyllaceae: ecological and phylogenetic considerations, review of pittosporalean families. Brittonia 34: 252–266.

Carlquist, S. 1982b. Wood anatomy of Dipsacaceae. Taxon 31: 443–450.

Carlquist, S. 1982c. Wood anatomy of Buxaceae: correlations with ecology and phylogeny. Flora 172: 463–491.

Carlquist, S. 1982d. Exospermum stipitatum (Winteraceae): observations on wood, leaves, flowers, pollen, and fruit. Aliso 10: 277–289.

Carlquist, S. 1982e. Wood and bark anatomy of Scalesia (Asteraceae). Aliso 10: 301–312.

Carlquist, S. 1982f. Wood anatomy of Illicium (Illiciaceae): phylogenetic, ecological, and functional interpretations. Amer. J. Bot. 69: 1587–1598.

Carlquist, S. 1982 [1983]. Wood anatomy of Onagraceae: further species; root anatomy; significance of vestured pits and allied structures in dicotyledons. Ann. Missouri bot. Gard. 69: 755–769.

Carlquist, S. 1983a. Wood anatomy of Belliolum (Winteraceae) and a note on flowering. J. Arnold Arbor. 64: 161–169.

Carlquist, S. 1983b. Wood anatomy of Bubbia (Winteraceae), with comments on origin of vessels in dicotyledons. Amer. J. Bot. 70: 578–590.

Carlquist, S. 1983c. Observations on the vegetative anatomy of Crepidiastrum and Dendrocacalia (Asteraceae). Aliso 10: 383–395.

Carlquist, S. 1983d. Wood anatomy of Calyceraceae and Valerianaceae, with comments on aberrant perforation plates in predominantly herbaceous groups of dicotyledons. Aliso 10: 413–425.

Carlquist, S. 1983e. Wood anatomy of Calycanthaceae: ecological and systematic implications. Aliso 10: 427–441.

Carlquist, S. 1984a. Vessel grouping in dicotyledon wood: significance and relationship to imperforate tracheary elements. Aliso 10: 505–525.

Carlquist, S. 1984b. Wood anatomy of some Gentianaceae: systematic and ecological conclusions. Aliso 10: 573–582.

Carlquist, S. 1984c. Wood anatomy of Loasaceae with relation to systematics, habit, and ecology. Aliso 10: 583–602.

Carlquist, S. 1984d. Wood and stem anatomy of Bergia suffruticosa: relationships of Elatinaceae and broader significance of vascular tracheids, vasicentric tracheids, and fibriform vessel elements. Ann. Missouri bot. Gard. 71: 232–242.

Carlquist, S. 1984e. Wood anatomy of Trimeniaceae. Pl. Syst. Evol. 144: 103–118.

Carlquist, S. 1984f. Wood and stem anatomy of Lardizabalaceae, with comments on the vining habit, ecology and systematics. Bot. J. Linn. Soc. 88: 257–277.

Carlquist, S. 1984 [1985]a. Wood anatomy and relationships of Pentaphylacaceae: significance of vessel features. Phytomorphology 34: 84–90.

Carlquist, S. 1984 [1985]b. Wood anatomy of Malesherbiaceae. Phytomorphology 34: 180–190.

Carlquist, S. 1985a. Vasicentric tracheids as a drought survival mechanism in the woody flora of southern California and similar regions; review of vasicentric tracheids. Aliso 11: 37–68.

Carlquist, S. 1985b. Vegetative anatomy and familial placement of Tovaria. Aliso 11: 69–76.

Carlquist, S. 1985c. Wood and stem anatomy of Misodendraceae: systematic and ecological conclusions. Brittonia 37: 58–75.

Carlquist, S. 1985d. Wood anatomy of Begoniaceae, with comments on raylessness, paedomorphosis, relationships, vessel diameter, and ecology. Bull. Torrey bot. Cl. 112: 59–69.

Carlquist, S. 1985e. Wood anatomy of Coriariaceae: phylogenetic and ecological implications. Syst. Bot. 10: 174–183.

Carlquist, S. 1985 [1986]a. Observations on functional wood histology of vines and lianas: vessel dimorphism, tracheids, vasicentric tracheids, narrow vessels, and parenchyma. Aliso 11: 139–157.

Carlquist, S. 1985 [1986]b. Wood anatomy and familial status of Viviania. Aliso 11: 159–165.

Carlquist, S. 1986a. Terminology of imperforate tracheary elements. IAWA Bull. n.s. 7: 75–81.

Carlquist, S. 1986b. Terminology of imperforate tracheary elements: a reply. IAWA Bull. n.s. 7: 168–170.

Carlquist, S. 1986c. Wood anatomy of Stilbaceae and Retziaceae: ecological and systematic implications. Aliso 11: 299–316.

Carlquist, S. 1987a. Diagonal and tangential vessel aggregations in wood: function and relationship to vasicentric tracheids. Aliso 11: 451–462.

Carlquist, S. 1987b. Wood anatomy of Nolanaceae. Aliso 11: 463–471.

Carlquist, S. 1987c. Wood anatomy of Martyniaceae and Pedaliaceae. Aliso 11: 473–483.

Carlquist, S. 1987d. Wood anatomy of Plakothira (Loasaceae). Aliso 11: 563–569.

Carlquist, S. 1987e. Pliocene Nothofagus wood from the transantarctic mountains. Aliso 11: 571–583.

Carlquist, S. 1987f. Wood anatomy and relationships of Stackhousiaceae. Bot. Jb. 108: 473–480.

Carlquist, S. 1987g. Presence of vessels in wood of Sarcandra (Chloranthaceae); comments on vessel origins in angiosperms. Amer. J. Bot. 74: 1765–1771.

Carlquist, S. 1987 [1988]. Wood anatomy of noteworthy species of Ludwigia (Onagraceae) with relation to ecology and systematics. Ann. Missouri bot. Gard. 74: 889–896.

Carlquist, S. 1988a. Comparative wood anatomy. Systematic, ecological, and evolutionary aspects of dicotyledon wood. Springer-Verlag: Berlin, etc. 436 pp.

Carlquist, S. 1988b. Wood anatomy and relationships of Duckeodendraceae and Goetzeaceae. IAWA Bull. n.s. 9: 3–12.

Carlquist, S. 1988c. Wood anatomy of Cneoraceae: ecology, relationships, and generic definition. Aliso 12: 7–16.

Carlquist, S. 1988d. Wood anatomy of Scytopetalaceae. Aliso 12: 63–76.

Carlquist, S. 1988e. Wood anatomy of Drimys s.s. (Winteraceae). Aliso 12: 81–95.

Carlquist, S. 1988f. Tracheid dimorphism: a new pathway in evolution of imperforate tracheary elements. Aliso 12: 103–118.

Carlquist, S. 1989a. Adaptive wood anatomy of chaparral shrubs. In: The California chaparral: Paradigms reexamined (ed. Keeley, S.C.): 25–35. Nat. Hist. Mus. Los Angeles, Sci. ser. No. 34.

Carlquist, S. 1989b. Wood anatomy of Cercidium (Fabaceae), with emphasis on vessel wall sculpture. Aliso 12: 235–255.

Carlquist, S. 1989c. Wood anatomy of Tasmannia; summary of wood anatomy of Winteraceae. Aliso 12: 257–275.

Carlquist, S. 1989d. Wood anatomy and relationships of Montinia. Aliso 12: 369–378.

Carlquist, S. 1989e. Wood and bark anatomy of Degeneria. Aliso 12: 485–495.

Carlquist, S. 1989f. Wood and bark anatomy of Empetraceae; comments on paedomorphosis in woods of certain small shrubs. Aliso 12: 497–515.

Carlquist, S. 1990a. Wood anatomy of Ascarina (Chloranthaceae) and the tracheid-vessel element transition. Aliso 12: 667–684.

Carlquist, S. 1990b. Wood anatomy and relationships of Lactoridaceae. Amer. J. Bot. 77: 1498–1505.

Carlquist, S. 1991a. Wood and bark anatomy of Ticodendron: comments on relationships. Ann. Missouri bot. Gard. 78: 96–104.

Carlquist, S. 1991b. Anatomy of vine and liana stems: a review and synthesis. In: The biology of vines (eds. Putz, F.E. & Mooney, H.A.): 53–71. Cambridge Univ. Press: Cambridge.

Carlquist, S. 1992a. Wood anatomy and stem of Chloranthus; summary of wood anatomy of Chloranthaceae, with comments on relationships, vessellessness, and the origin of monocotyledons. IAWA Bull. n.s. 13: 3–16.

Carlquist, S. 1992b. Wood anatomy of Solanaceae: a survey. Allertonia 6 (4): 279–326.

Carlquist, S. 1992c. Wood anatomy of sympetalous dicotyledon families: a summary, with comments on systematic relationships and evolution of the woody habit. Ann. Missouri bot. Gard. 79: 303–332.

Carlquist, S. 1992d. Pit membrane remnants in perforation plates of primitive dicotyledons and their significance. Amer. J. Bot. 79: 660–672.

Carlquist, S. 1992e. Vegetative anatomy and relationships of Eupomatiaceae. Bull. Torrey bot. Cl. 119: 167–180.

Carlquist, S. 1992f. Wood anatomy of Lamiaceae. A survey: with comments on vascular and vasicentric tracheids. Aliso 13: 309–338.

Carlquist, S. 1992g. Wood anatomy of selected Cucurbitaceae and its relationship to habit and systematics. Nordic J. Bot. 12: 347–355.

Carlquist, S. 1992h. Wood anatomy of insular and mainland Caryophyllaceae. IAWA Bull. n.s. 13: 242. [Abstr.]

Carlquist, S. 1992i. Wood anatomy of Hedyosmum (Chloranthaceae) and the tracheid-vessel element transition. Aliso 13 (3): 447–462.

Carlquist, S. 1993. Wood and bark anatomy of Aristolochiaceae; systematic and habital correlations. IAWA Jl. 14: 341–357.

Carlquist, S. & Debuhr, L. 1977. Wood anatomy of Penaeaceae (Myrtales): comparative, phylogenetic and ecological implications. Bot. J. Linn. Soc. 75: 211–227.

Carlquist, S. & Eckhart, V.M. 1982. Wood anatomy of Darwiniothamnus, Lecocarpus, and Macraea (Asteraceae). Aliso 10: 291–300.

Carlquist, S. & Eckhart, V.M. 1984. Wood anatomy of Hydrophyllaceae. II. Genera other than Eriodictyon, with comments on parenchyma bands containing vessels with large pits. Aliso 10: 527–546.

Carlquist, S., Eckhart, V.M. & Michener, D.C. 1983. Wood anatomy of Hydrophyllaceae. I. Eriodictyon. Aliso 10: 397–412.

Carlquist, S., Eckhart, V.M. & Michener, D.C. 1984. Wood anatomy of Polemoniaceae. Aliso 10: 547–572.

Carlquist, S. & Grant, M.L. 1963. Studies in Fitchia (Compositae): novelties from the Society Islands; anatomical studies. Pacific Sci. 17: 282–298.

Carlquist, S. & Hanson, M.A. 1991. Wood and stem anatomy of Convolvulaceae: a survey. Aliso 13: 51–94.

Carlquist, S. & Hoekman, D.A. 1985a. Ecological wood anatomy of the woody southern Californian flora. IAWA Bull. n.s. 6: 319–347.

Carlquist, S. & Hoekman, D.A. 1985b. Wood anatomy of Staphyleaceae: ecology, statistical correlations, and systematics. Flora 177: 195–216.

Carlquist, S. & Hoekman, D.A. 1986a. Wood anatomy of Gesneriaceae. Aliso 11: 279–297.

Carlquist, S. & Hoekman, D.A. 1986b. Wood anatomy of Myoporaceae: ecological and systematic considerations. Aliso 11: 317–334.

Carlquist, S. & Raven, P.H. 1966. The systematics and anatomy of Gongylocarpus (Onagraceae). Amer. J. Bot. 53: 378–390.

Carlquist, S. & Zona, S. 1988a. Wood anatomy of Acanthaceae: a survey. Aliso 12: 201–227.

Carlquist, S. & Zona, S. 1988b. Wood anatomy of Papaveraceae, with comments on vessel restriction patterns. IAWA Bull. n.s. 9: 253–267.

Carpenter, C.S. & Dickison, W.C. 1976. The morphology and relationships of Oncotheca balansae. Bot. Gaz. 137: 141–153.

Carreras, R. 1988. Caracteres anatómicos de la madera de especies típicas de manglares. Consideraciones ecologicas. Rev. for. Baracoa 18 (1): 7–16. [Eng. summ.]

Carreras, R., Dechamps, R. & Avella, T. 1989. Estructura tridimensional de la madera de cinco especies de Verbenaceas representadas en Cuba. Revta for. Baracoa 19 (2): 67–84. [Eng. summ.]

Carreras, R. & Pérez, E. 1982. Estudio anatómico de la madera de Swietenia mahagoni, Swietenia macrophylla y su F1. Rev. for. Baracoa 12 (2): 5–27.

Carreras, R. & Pérez, E. 1988. Descripción anatómica de la madera de ocho especies forestales. Rev. for. Baracoa 18 (1): 17–37. [Eng. summ.]

Carreras, R. & Vales, M.A. 1986a. Estudio comparativo de la madera de Bucida L. (Combretaceae). Acta bot. hung. 32: 247–253.

Carreras, R. & Vales, M.A. 1986b. Atlas anatómico de maderas de Cuba. 1. Instituto de Botánica, Academia de Ciencias de Cuba: Havanna. 79 pp.

Carreras, R. & Vales, M.A. 1987. Anatomía de maderas de Cuba II. Revta. Jard. bot. nac., Univ. La Habana 8 (1): 21–32.

Carvalho, A. de 1954–1955; 1956. Madeiras de folhosas. Contribuição para o seu estudo e identificação. Bol. Soc. Port. Cienc. nat. 20 (sér. 2, 5): 54–69; 21 (sér. 2, 6): 1–188.

Cassens, D.L. 1980. Vestured pits in the New World Pithecellobium (sensu lato). IAWA Bull. n.s. 1: 59–64.

Cassens, D.L. & Miller, R.B. 1981. Wood anatomy of the New World Pithecellobium (sensu lato). J. Arnold Arbor. 62: 1–44.

Castiglioni, J.A. 1962. El leño secondario de las especies argentinas de Nectandra. Rev. Invest. For. B. Aires 3 (1): 1–15 + 5 plates.

Cavaco, A. 1954. A anatomia do lenho e a identificação de madeiras. Port. Acta Biol. B 4: 253–317.

Cebrat, J. 1991. Anatomia i embriologia. In: Lipy. Tilia cordata Mill., Tilia platyphyllos Scop. (ed. Białobok, S.): 57–84 + plates I-XIV. Polska Akad. Nauk, Inst. Dendrol.: Poznan. [Pol.; Eng. summ.]

Cellai, G.C. 1967; 1971. Atlante micrografico dei legni dell'Africa orientale. Cartella V, Tav. 49–60 (1967). Cartella VII, Tav. 73–84 (1971). Firenze.

Chakroun, S. 1983. Etude structurale en microscopie électronique à balayage des formations secondaires (bois et liber) d'Olea europaea L. Flora 173: 255–264.

Chalk, L. 1933. Multiperforate plates in vessels, with special reference to the Bignoniaceae. Forestry 7: 16–25.

Chalk, L. 1937. The phylogenetic value of certain anatomical features of dicotyledonous woods. Ann. Bot. (NS) 1: 409–428.

Chalk, L. 1944. On the taxonomic value of the anatomical structure of the vegetative organs of the dicotyledons. 2. The taxonomic value of wood anatomy. Proc. Linn. Soc., Lond. 155: 3214–3218.

Chalk, L. 1970. Short fibres with clearly defined intrusive growth, with special reference to Fraxinus. In: New research in plant anatomy (eds. Robson, N.K.B., Cutler, D.F. & Gregory, M.). Academic Press. Bot. J. Linn. Soc. 63, suppl. 1: 163–168.

Chalk, L. & Chattaway, M.M. 1933. Perforated ray cells. Proc. Roy. Soc., Lond., B, 113: 82–92.

Chalk, L. & Chattaway, M.M. 1935. Factors affecting dimensional variations of vessel members. Trop. Woods 41: 17–37.

Chalk, L. & Chattaway, M.M. 1937. Identification of woods with included phloem. Trop. Woods 50: 1–31.

Chalk, L., Chattaway, M.M., Davy, J.B., Laughton, F.S. & Scott, M.H. 1935. Forest trees and timbers of the British Empire. III. Fifteen South African high forest timber trees. Clarendon Press: Oxford. 103 pp.

Chalk, L., Davy, J.B. & Desch, H.E. 1932. Forest trees and timbers of the British Empire. I. Some East African Coniferae and Leguminosae. Imp. For. Inst.: Oxford. 68 pp.

Chalk, L., Davy, J.B., Desch, H.E. & Hoyle, A.C. 1933. Forest trees and timbers of the British Empire. II. Twenty West African timber trees. Clarendon Press: Oxford. 108 pp.

Chalk, L. & Murthy, L.S.V. 1963. Radial strands of phloem in the wood of jongkong, Dactylocladus stenostachys Oliv. in Sarawak. Comm. For. Rev. 42: 291–292.

Chang, C.T. 1974. Wood anatomy of Tsoongiodendron odorum Chun. Acta bot. sin. 16: 156–160. [Chin.; full Eng. summ.]

Chang, C. 1982. Wood anatomy of the new genus Manglietiastrum Law of Magnoliaceae from China in relation to allied genera. Acta bot. yunnan. 4: 279–288. [Chin.; Eng. summ. & captions.]

Chang, C.Y. 1981. Morphology of the family Rhoipteleaceae in relation to its systematic position. Acta phytotax. sin. 19: 168–178 + Plates 1–3. [Chin.; Eng. summ.]

Chattaway, M.M. 1931. Variations in vessel pattern in a single trunk of Entandrophragma cylindricum (Sprague). Empire For. J. 10: 263–265.

Chattaway, M.M. 1932. The wood of the Sterculiaceae. I. Specialisation of the vertical wood parenchyma within the subfamily Sterculieae. New Phytol. 31: 119–132.

Chattaway, M.M. 1933a. Tile-cells in the rays of the Malvales. New Phytol. 32: 261–273.

Chattaway, M.M. 1933b. Ray development in the Sterculiaceae. Forestry 7: 93–108.

Chattaway, M.M. 1934. Anatomical evidence that Grewia and Microcos are distinct genera. Trop. Woods 38: 9–11.

Chattaway, M.M. 1937. The wood anatomy of the family Sterculiaceae. Phil. Trans. Roy. Soc., Lond. B, 228: 313–366.

Chattaway, M.M. 1948a. The wood anatomy of the Proteaceae. Aust. J. Sci. Res. B, 1: 279–302.

Chattaway, M.M. 1948b. Note on the vascular tissue in the rays of Banksia. Counc. Sci. Indust. Res. J. 21: 275–278.

Chattaway, M.M. 1949. The development of tyloses and secretion of gum in heartwood formation. Aust. J. Sci. Res. B, 2: 227–240.

Chattaway, M.M. 1951a. The development of horizontal canals in rays. Aust. J. Sci. Res. B, 4: 1–11.

Chattaway, M.M. 1951b. Morphological and functional variations in the rays of pored timbers. Aust. J. Sci. Res. B, 4: 12–27.

Chattaway, M.M. 1955; 1956. Crystals in woody tissues; Part I. Trop. Woods 102: 55–74 (1955). Part II. Trop. Woods 104: 100–124 (1956).

Chauhan, L. & Dayal, R. 1985. Wood anatomy of Indian Albizias. IAWA Bull. n.s. 6: 213–218.

Chauhan, L. & Dayal, R. 1987. On the diagnostic value of some anatomical features in the identification of Adina Salisb. and Mitragyna Korth. J. Timber Develop. Assn. India 33 (3): 18–24.

Chauhan, L. & Dayal, R. 1990. Some structural differences in the wood of Boswellia serrata Roxb., Garuga pinnata Roxb., Lannea coromandelica Merr. and Spondias pinnata Kurz. Indian For. 116: 455–458.

Chauhan, L. & Dayal, R. 1992. Wood anatomy of Indian species of Michelia with particular reference of their identification. Indian For. 118: 922–928.

Chehaibar, T. & Grether, R. 1990. Anatomía de la madera de algunas especies del género Mimosa (Leguminosae). Bol. Soc. bot. Mex. 50: 3–17.

Chen, B. 1985. Studies on Magnolia coco (Lour.) DC. Acta sci. nat. Univ. Sunyatseni 24 (3): 82–88. [Chin.; Eng. summ.]

Chen, B. 1989. Wood anatomy of 8 species in Manglietia Bl. from Yunnan. Acta sci. nat. Univ. Sunyatseni 28 (4): 81–85. [Chin.; Eng. summ.]

Chen, B.L., Baas, P., Wheeler, E.A. & Wu, S.M. 1993. Wood anatomy of trees and shrubs from China. VI. Magnoliaceae. IAWA Jl. 14: 391–412.

Chen, C.L. 1957. Xylem anatomy of Strophanthus (Apocynaceae). Trop. Woods 107: 84–91.

Chen, G. 1989. A study on plant Trochodendrales. Acta sci. nat. Univ. Sunyatseni 28 (3): 73–79. [Chin.; Eng. summ.]

Chen, L.-H. & Huang, T.-C. 1986. Anatomical study of leaf and stem of Formosan Pittosporum, as an ecological implication. Taiwania 31: 41–64. [Eng.]

Cheng, C. (ed.) 1985. Wood science. Chinese Forestry Publications: Beijing. 1379 pp. [Chin.]

Cheng, J.-Q. 1980. Chinese tropical and subtropical timbers, their distinction, properties and application. 621 pp. + 163 plates. [Title page and text in Chinese only.]

Cheng, J.-Q., Yang, J.-J. & Liu, P. 1992. Anatomy and properties of Chinese woods. China Forestry Publ. House, Beijing. 820 pp. + 196 plates. [Title page and text in Chinese only.]

Chesnais, F. 1941. De l'ancienneté du genre Actinidia et de sa parenté avec les Magnoliaceae. Bull. Mus. natn. Hist. nat., Paris, sér. 2, 13: 202–206.

Chesnais, F. 1943. Recherches sur l'anatomie du genre Hoplestigma Pierre. Bull. Mus. natn. Hist. nat., Paris, sér. 2, 15: 226–230.

Chesnais, F. 1944a. Anatomie du système végétatif du genre Eberhardtia H. Lec. Bull. Mus. natn. Hist. nat., Paris, sér. 2, 16: 142–147.

Chesnais, F. 1944b. Etude anatomique du genre Sarcosperma Hook. f. (Sarcospermacées). Bull. Mus. natn. Hist. nat., Paris, sér. 2, 16: 514–518.

Chevalier, A. 1927. Note sur l'Erica arborea et sur l'emploi de ses souches dans la fabrication des pipes. Rev. Bot. appl. 7: 649–656, 739–752.

Chevalier, A. 1928. Revision des Acacias du Nord, de l'Ouest et du Centre africain. IV. Le bois des Acacias. Rev. Bot. appl. 8: 648–650.

Chevalier, A. 1932. Les vrais et les faux balatas. Rev. Bot. appl. Agric. trop. 12: 261–282, 347–358. [See pp. 351–354.]

Chevalier, A. & Normand, D. 1931. Quelques Légumineuses de la Côte d'Ivoire à bois utilisable. Rev. Bot. appl. Agric. trop. 11: 397–409, 569–577.

Chiang, F.-C. 1962; 1964. Studies on the anatomical structure and identification of the commercial timbers in Taiwan (1). Bull. Taiwan For. Res. Inst., No. 81: 24 pp. (1962). (2). Ibid., No. 95: 25 pp. (1964). [Chin. & Eng.]

Chiba, M. 1989. Wood anatomy and identification of the family Dipterocarpaceae in Sabah. For. Res. Centre, Sabah, FRC Publ. No. 57, 186 pp. [Also numbered FRC Publ. No. 6/89.] [For. Abstr. 52 (1991) No. 8933.]

Choquette, L. 1926. Contribution à l'étude du Dirca palustris L. ou "bois du plomb". Trav. Lab. Mat. méd. Paris 17 (4): 95 pp.

Chowdhury, K.A. 1936. Terminal and initial parenchyma cells in the wood of Terminalia tomentosa W. & A. New Phytol. 35: 351–358.

Chowdhury, K.A. 1938 [1939], 1939 [1940]. The formation of growth rings in Indian trees. I, II. Indian For. Rec. (NS) Utilization 2 (1): 1–39 + 8 plates (1939); 2 (2): 41–57 + 4 plates (1940).

Chowdhury, K.A. 1940. The formation of growth rings in Indian trees. III. A study of the effect of locality. Indian For. Rec. (NS) Utilization 2: 59–75 + 2 plates.

Chowdhury, K.A. 1953. The role of initial parenchyma in the transformation of the structure diffuse-porous to ring-porous in the secondary xylem of the genus Gmelina Linn. Proc. Nat. Inst. Sci. India 19: 361–369.

Chowdhury, K.A. 1964. Growth rings in tropical trees and taxonomy. J. Indian bot. Soc. 43: 334–342.

Chowdhury, K.A. & Ghosh, S.S. 1956. Aid of anatomy in the discovery of Mansonia dipikae Purkayastha. Indian For. 82: 444–448. Also in: Indian For. Rec. (NS) Wood Anat. 1: 97–101; 1956.

Chu, F.F.-T. 1974. Anatomical features of the dipterocarp timbers of Sarawak. Gard. Bull., Singapore 27: 95–119.

Chudnoff, M. 1956. Minute anatomy and identification of the woods of Israel. Ilanoth (3): 37–52.

Chun, S.K. & Lee, W.Y. 1989. Systematic studies on the Korean Rhamnaceae. Res. Bull. Exp. For. Kangweon natn. Univ. 9: 63–65. [Kor.; Eng. summ.]

Ciampi, C. 1951. Evoluzione della cerchia legnosa in Castanea sativa Mill. Nuovo G. bot. ital. (NS) 58: 271–292 + plates V–VII.

Clarke, S.H. 1930. Home grown timbers. Their anatomical structure and its relation to physical properties. Elm. For. Prod. Res. Bull. No. 7: 27 pp.

Clément, A. & Janin, G. 1973. Etude complementaire de la présence de cristaux de carbonate de calcium dans le bois des peupliers: Existence de cinq zones fonctionnelles reconnues à partir de leurs teneurs en phosphore. Annls Sci. for. 30: 63–81.

Cockrell, R.A. 1935. The wood anatomy of the north Sumatran "Djeroek oetan", a supposed new genus of Rutaceae allied to Murraya. Pap. Michigan Acad. Sci. 20: 33–36.

Cockrell, R.A. 1941. A comparative study of the wood structure of several South American species of Strychnos. Amer. J. Bot. 28: 32–41.

Cockrell, R.A. 1942. An anatomical study of eighty Sumatran woods. Univ. Mich. Microfilm Publ. 384: 1–317.

Cockrell, R.A. & Monachino, J. 1947. Supplementary notes on Cockrell's study of the wood structure of Strychnos. Amer. J. Bot. 34: 44.

Coimbra Filho, A.F. 1950. Contribuição ao estudo dos jacarandás do gênero Machaerium. Anu. bras. Econ. flor. 3 (3): 345–352.

Coimbra Filho, A.F. & Mattos Filho, A. de 1953. Ensaios e apontamentos sobre a urucurana. [Tests and observations on Hieronyma alchorneoides.] Anu. bras. Econ. flor., Inst. nac. Pinho, No. 6: 188–195. [Eng. summ.]

Coineau, Y. & Duchaigne, A. 1967. Contribution à l'étude du liber inclus chez l'Oenothera biennis L. C.R. 91(e) Congr. natn. Soc. sav. Rennes 1966, III: 107–117.

Collardet, J. 1929a. Okoumé (Aucoumea klaineana Pierre). Trop. Woods 17: 1–5.

Collardet, J. 1929b. Bossé (Guarea cedrata). Trop. Woods 20: 10–14.

Coode, M.J.E. 1969. Manual of the forest trees of Papua and New Guinea. Part 1 (revised issue). Combretaceae. Divn. of Botany, Dept. of Forests: Lae, New Guinea. 86 pp.

Coradin, V.T.R., Marchiori, J.N.C. & Muniz, G.I.B. de 1992. Estudo anatomico da madeira de Brachynema ramiflorum Benth. (Olacaceae). Arq. Jard. bot. Rio de Janeiro 31: 79–85.

Core, H.A., Côté, W.A. & Day, A.C. 1979. Wood structure and identification. [Syracuse wood science series 6.] Syracuse Univ. Press. 2nd edn. 182 pp.

Corothie, H. 1960. Anatomía de la madera de seis géneros de las Anacardiaceas. Rev. For. Venez. 3(3–4): 9–31.

Corothie, H. 1961a. Anatomía de la madera de dos géneros de las Acanthaceas. Rev. For. Venez. 4(5): 7–15.

Corothie, H. 1961b. Anatomía de la madera del género Achatocarpus (Achatocarpaceae). Rev. For. Venez. 4(5): 17–19.

Corral López, G. 1981. Anatomía de la madera de siete especies del género Quercus. Bol. téc. Inst. nac. Invest. for. México, No. 72: 55 pp.

Corral López, M.G. 1985. Características anatómicas de la madera de once especies tropicales. Bol. téc. Inst. nac. Invest. for., México, No. 127: 66 pp.

Coster, C. 1927; 1928. Zur Anatomie und Physiologie der Zuwachszonen- und Jahresringbildung in den Tropen. Ann. Jard. bot. Buitenzorg 37: 49–160 (1927); 38: 1–114 (1928).

Côté, W.A. & Day, A.C. 1962. Vestured pits – fine structure and apparent relationship with warts. Tappi 45: 906–910.

Coulaud, J. 1988. Une nouvelle approche des caractères quantitatifs du bois des Loganiacées. Annls. Sci. nat., Bot., sér. 13, 9: 37–44.

Coulaud, J. 1989. Comparaison de quelques Loganiacées à l'aide des caractères quantitatifs et qualitatifs de l'anatomie du bois. Can. J. Bot. 67: 872–878.

Cowan, R.S. 1979. Harleyodendron, a new genus of Leguminosae (Swartzieae). Brittonia 31: 72–78.

Cox, H.T. 1948a. Studies in the comparative anatomy of the Ericales. I. Ericaceae – subfamily Rhododendroideae. Amer. Midl. Nat. 39: 220–245.

Cox, H.T. 1948b. Studies in the comparative anatomy of the Ericales. II. Ericaceae – subfamily Arbutoideae. Amer. Midl. Nat. 40: 493–516.

Cox, M.J. 1941. The comparative anatomy of the secondary xylem of five American species of Celtis. Amer. Midl. Nat. 25: 348–357.

Cozzo, D. 1944; 1945. La estructura estratificada del leño de Capparis salicifolia Gris. Ingen. Agron. 6: 151–153 (1944). Also: Min. Agric. nac. Direc. For., Buenos Aires, Publ. téc. no. 3: 1–5 (1945).

Cozzo, D. 1946a. Relacion anatomica entre la estructura del leño de las especies argentinas de Capparis y Atamisquea. Lilloa 12: 29–37.

Cozzo, D. 1946b. Anatomía comparada de las maderas argentinas del genero Erythrina L. Darwiniana 7: 175–184.

Cozzo, D. 1946c. Estructura leñosa estratificada en el género Plectrocarpa (Zigofilaceas). Rev. argent. Agron. 13: 286–292. [Eng. summ.]

Cozzo, D. 1946d. Los géneros de fanerógamas argentinas con radios leñosos altos en su leño secundario. Rev. argent. Agron. 13: 207–230.

Cozzo, D. 1947. Anatomía del leño secundario de Tricomaria usillo Gill. ex H. et A. Lilloa 13: 17–21.

Cozzo, D. 1948. Anatomía del leño secundario de las especies argentinas de la tribu Zygophyl-leae (Zigofilaceas). Rev. Inst. nac. Invest. Ci. nat. "Bernardino Rivadavia", Ci. Bot. 1 (3): 57–85. [Eng. summ.]

Cozzo, D. 1949a. Estructura leñosa estratificada no registrada en géneros de leguminosas argentinas. Lilloa 16: 63–95.

Cozzo, D. 1949b. Estudio anatómico sobre la posición sistemática de algunos géneros argentinos de leguminosas papilionoideas. Lilloa 16: 97–124.

Cozzo, D. 1950. Anatomía del leño secundario de las leguminosas papilionoideas argentinas silvestres y cultivadas. Rev. Inst. nac. Invest. Ci. nat. "Bernardino Rivadavia", Ci. Bot. 1 (7): 223–361 + 31 plates.

Cozzo, D. 1951a. Claves para el reconocimiento anatómico del leño secundario de las leguminosas argentinas. Rev. argent. Agron. 18: 78–97.

Cozzo, D. 1951b. Anatomía del leño secundario de las leguminosas mimosoideas y caesalpinoideas argentinas silvestres y cultivadas. Rev. Mus. argent. Ci. nat. "Bernardino Rivadavia", Ci. Bot. 2: 63–146.

Cozzo, D. 1951c. Investigaciones anatómicas en maderas de Sapotáceas argentinas. Rev. Mus. argent. Ci. nat. "Bernardino Rivadavia", Ci. Bot. 2: 263–290.

Cozzo, D. 1952. Estratificación del leño secundario en el género Cyclolobium Bentham. Rev. argent. Agron. 19: 143–146.

Cozzo, D. 1953. The structure and diagnostic significance of crateriform bordered pits in the vessels of Cercidium. J. Arnold Arbor. 34: 187–190. Also: Puntuaciones craterimorfas en los vasos de Cercidium. Rev. argent. Agron. 20: 126–129.

Cozzo, D. 1954. Filogenia de los tipos de estructura leñosa estratificada. Rev. argent. Agron. 21: 196–214.

Cozzo, D. 1960. Una particular anomalia anatómica que sirve a la identificacion de la madera del 'guatambu' blanco (Balfourodendron riedelianum (Engl.) Engl.). Rev. for. argent. 4 (3): 81–84.

Cozzo, D. 1976. Interpretación del grado evolutivo de la estructura estratificada del leño de una población de Sesbania punicea. Darwiniana 20: 469–475.

Cozzo, D. & Cristiani, L.Q. 1946. Anatomía del leño de Cyclolepis genistoides Don. Arch. Farm. Bioquim. Tucuman 3 (1): 121–125.

Cozzo, D. & Cristiani, L.Q. 1950. Los generos de fanerogamas argentinas con estructura leñosa estratificada. Rev. Inst. nac. Invest. Ci. nat. "Bernardino Rivadavia", Ci. Bot. 1 (8): 363–405.

Cozzo, D. & Rodriguez, E.M. 1959. Anatomía comparada de la madera de 14 especies de Eucalyptus cultivadas en la Argentina. Rev. Fac. Agron., Buenos Aires 14: 416–444. [Eng. summ.]

Crespo, J.H. 1973. La madera de Pereskia conzattii Britton y Rose. Cact. Sucul. mex. 18 (2): 31–36. [Eng. summ.]

Cristiani, L.Q. 1948. Anatomía del leño secundario de las especies argentinas del genero Monttea. Comun. Inst. nac. Cienc. nat., Bot. 1: 6 pp.

Cristiani, L.Q. 1961a. Anatomía del leño secundario de las Caparidáceas argentinas. Rev. Inst. munic. bot., Buenos Aires 1: 39–55.

Cristiani, L.Q. 1961b. Diferenciación de los géneros Cotoneaster, Crataegus y Pyracantha por la anatomia del leño secundario. Rev. Inst. munic. bot., Buenos Aires 1: 57–60.

Croptier, S. & Kučera, L.J. 1990. Description anatomique de 20 espèces ligneuses croissant au Rwanda. Inst. Sci. Agron. Rwanda (ISAR), Dept. For., Butare, Rwanda & Dept. Biol. Technol. Wood, Inst. For. Wood Sci., ETH: Zurich. 46 pp.

Cuatrecasas, J. 1964. Cacao and its allies. A taxonomic revision of the genus Theobroma. Contrib. U.S. Nat. Herb. 35 (6): 379–605.

Cuatrecasas, J. 1970. Brunelliaceae. Flora Neotropica Mon., No. 2: 189 pp.

Cumbie, B.G. 1960. Anatomical studies on the Leguminosae. Trop. Woods 113: 1–47.

Cumbie, B.G. 1967. Developmental changes in the vascular cambium in Leitneria floridana. Amer. J. Bot. 54: 414–424.

Cumbie, B.G. 1983. Developmental changes in the wood of Bocconia vulcanica Donn. Smith. IAWA Bull. n.s. 4: 131–140.

Cumbie, B.G. & Mertz, D. 1962. Xylem anatomy of Sophora (Leguminosae) in relation to habit. Amer. J. Bot. 49: 33–40.

Cumming, N.M. 1925. Notes on strand plants. I. Atriplex babingtonii, Woods. Trans. Proc. bot. Soc. Edinb. 29: 171–185.

Cunha Mello, E. 1950 [1951]. Estudo dendrologico de essencias florestais do Parque Nacional de Itatiáia e os caracteres anatomicos de seus lenhos. Bol. Parque nac. Itatiáia 2: 172 pp.

Cunha Mello, E. 1954. Contribuição ao estudo do Louro Pardo, Cordia trichotoma (Vell.) Johnst. Arg. Serv. Florestal, Rio de Janeiro 8: 1–44.

Cunha Mello, E. 1967. Estudo anatômico das madeiras dos gêneros 1) Enterolobium Mart., 2) Zeyheria Mart., 3) Kielmeyera Mart., 4) Ferdinandusa Pohl, 5) Caryocar Linn. Anu. bras. Econ. flor., Inst. Nac. Pinho 18 (18): 227–269.

Cunha Mello, E. 1970. Estudo anatômico das madeiras do gênero Caryocar Linn. Brasil Florestal 1 (2): 54–62.

Cunha Mello, E. 1971a. Estudo dendrológico e determinação das características físicas e mecânicas da bicuíba, Virola bicuhyba (Schott) Warb. Brasil Florestal 2 (5): 21–26.

Cunha Mello, E. 1971b. Estudo dendrológico e determinação das características físicas e mecânicas do Genipapo, Genipa americana L. Brasil Florestal 2 (8): 17–21.

Cunha Mello, E. 1972. Contribuição para o estudo de algumas espécies de Jacarandas. Brasil Florestal 3 (9): 45–53.

Cunha Mello, E. 1976. Contribuição para o estudo do Jacatirao. Brasil Florestal 7 (26): 42–48.

Cutler, D.F. 1964. Anatomy of vegetative organs of Trigonobalanus Forman (Fagaceae). Kew Bull. 17: 401–409.

Cutler, D.F. 1968. Anatomical notes on Givotia gosai A.R. Sm. Kew Bull. 22: 507–511.

Cutler, D.F. 1969. The vegetative anatomy of Acacia albida Del. Kew Bull. 23: 203–208.

Cutler, D.F. 1976. Variation in root wood anatomy. In: Wood structure in biological and technological research (eds. Baas, P., Bolton, A.J. & Catling, D.M.): 143–156. Leiden Botanical Series No. 3. Leiden Univ. Press.

Cutler, D.F., Rudall, P.J., Gasson, P.E. & Gale, R.M.O. 1987. Root identification manual of trees and shrubs. A guide to the anatomy of roots of trees and shrubs hardy in Britain and Northern Europe. Chapman & Hall: London. 245 pp.

Dadasheva, Sh.G. 1962. Some features of the structure of the axial organs of desert and semi-desert shrubs. Dokl. Akad. Nauk SSSR 147: 974–976. [Russ. only.]

Dadswell, H.E. 1972. The anatomy of eucalypt woods. Div. Appl. Chem. Tech. Paper, C.S.I.R., Australia: No. 66: 1–28.

Dadswell, H.E. & Burnell, M. 1932. Methods for the identification of the coloured woods of the genus Eucalyptus. C.S.I.R. Bull. No. 67; Divn. For. Prod., Melbourne, Tech. Pap. No. 5: 50 pp. + 34 plates.

Dadswell, H.E., Burnell, M. & Eckersley, A.M. 1934. Methods for the identification of the light-coloured woods of the genus Eucalyptus. C.S.I.R., Bull. No. 78; Divn. For. Prod., Melbourne, Tech. Paper No. 12: 60 pp. + 35 plates.

Dadswell, H.E. & Eckersley, A.M. 1934. A note on the wood structure of Acradenia frankliniae Kipp. Jl. C.S.I.R., Melbourne 7: 39–42.

Dadswell, H.E. & Eckersley, A.M. 1935. The identification of the principal commercial Australian timbers other than eucalypts. C.S.I.R. Bull. No. 90; Divn. For. Prod., Melbourne, Tech. Paper No. 16: 103 pp.

Dadswell, H.E. & Eckersley, A.M. 1938a. The wood structure of some Australian Rutaceae with methods for their identification. C.S.I.R. Bull. No. 114; Tech. Pap. For. Prod. Res. Aust., No. 25: 32 pp.

Dadswell, H.E. & Eckersley, A.M. 1938b. The wood structure of some Australian Cunoniaceae with methods for their identification. C.S.I.R. Bull. No. 119; Tech. Pap. For. Prod. Res. Aust., No. 27: 23 pp.

Dadswell, H.E. & Eckersley, A.M. 1940. The wood anatomy of some Australian Lauraceae with methods for their identification. C.S.I.R. Bull. No. 132; Tech. Pap. For. Prod. Res. Aust., No. 34: 48 pp.

Dadswell, H.E. & Ellis, D.J. 1939. The wood anatomy of some Australian Meliaceae with methods for their identification. C.S.I.R. Bull. No. 124; Tech. Pap. For. Prod. Res. Aust., No. 31: 20 pp.

Dadswell, H.E. & Ingle, H.D. 1947. The wood anatomy of the Myrtaceae. I. A note on the genera Eugenia, Syzygium, Acmena, and Cleistocalyx. Trop. Woods 90 : 1–7.

Dadswell, H.E. & Ingle, H.D. 1948. The anatomy of timbers of the South-west Pacific area I. Anacardiaceae. Aust. J. Sci. Res., ser. B, 1: 391–415.

Dadswell, H.E. & Ingle, H.D. 1951. Wood anatomy in the genus Eucalyptopsis White. J. Arnold Arbor. 32: 150–151.

Dadswell, H.E. & Ingle, H.D. 1954. The wood anatomy of New Guinea Nothofagus Bl. Aust. J. Bot. 2: 141–153.

Dadswell, H.E. & Record, S.J. 1936. Identification of woods with conspicuous rays. Trop. Woods 48: 1–30.

Dahlgren, R. & Van Wyk, A.E. 1988. Structures and relationships of families endemic to or centered in southern Africa. Mon. Syst. Bot. Missouri bot. Gard. 25: 1–94.

Dahms, K.G. 1989. Das Holzportrait. Echtes oder amerikanisches Mahagoni (Swietenia macrophylla King, Familie Meliaceen). Holz Roh- u. Werkst. 47: 1–6. [Eng. summ.]

D'Ambroggio de Argüeso, A. 1982. Estudio anatómico de los tallos de las especies argentinas de Cissus (Vitaceae). Bol. Soc. argent. Bot. 20: 241–254.

Daniel, J. 1916. Influence du mode de vie sur la structure secondaire des dicotylédones. Croissance et âge des plantes. Librairie Générale de l'Enseignement: Paris.

D'Arcy, W.G. 1970. Solanaceae studies. I. Ann. Missouri bot. Gard. 57: 258–263.

D'Arcy, W.G. & Keating, R.C. 1973. The affinities of Lithophytum: a transfer from Solanaceae to Verbenaceae. Brittonia 25: 213–225.

Dariev, A.S. & Valichek, P. 1980. On the delimitation of the closely related species Gossypium klotzschianum and G. davidsonii. Bot. Zh. SSSR 65: 1161–1169. [Russ. only.]

Darwin, S.P. 1977. The genus Mastixiodendron (Rubiaceae). J. Arnold Arbor. 58: 349–381.

Das, D.K. 1970a. An anatomical study of Jam (Syzygium spp.) timbers of East Pakistan. Bull. Wood Anat. ser., For. Res. Inst., East Pakistan [Bangladesh], No. 1: 16 pp.

Das, D.K. 1970b. The anatomy of Gurjan (Dipterocarpus spp.) timbers of East Pakistan. Bull. Wood Anat. ser., For. Res. Inst.: East Pakistan [Bangladesh], No. 2: 13 pp.

Das, D.K. 1970c. Anatomy of garjan (Dipterocarpus spp.) timbers of East Pakistan. Sci. Indus. 7: 177–186.

Das, D.K. 1976a. An anatomical study of Jarul (Lagerstroemia spp.) timber of Bangladesh. Bull. (Wood Anat. ser.) For. Res. Inst., Bangladesh, No. 3: 12 pp.

Das, D.K. 1976b. The anatomy of dipterocarp woods of Bangladesh. Bull. (Wood Anat. ser.) For. Res. Inst., Bangladesh, No. 4: 25 pp.

Das, D.K. 1984a. Wood anatomy of some timbers of Verbenaceae of Bangladesh. Bull. (Wood Anat. ser.) For. Res. Inst., Bangladesh, No. 6: 28 pp.

Das, D.K. 1984b. Wood anatomy of some timbers of Anacardiaceae of Bangladesh. Bull. (Wood Anat. ser.) For. Res. Inst., Bangladesh, No. 8: 31 pp. + plates.

Dassanayake, M.D. & Paranavithana, S. 1976. Eccentric secondary thickening in stems of Bougainvillea. Ceylon J. Sci. biol. Sci. 12 (1): 9–13.

Datta, A.K. & Saha, S.B. 1960. Wood anatomy of the genus Corchorus (jute). Indian Agric. 4 (11): 129–134.

Datta, P.C. & Deb, A. 1968a. Secondary xylem, floral traces and phylogeny of common Indian species of Rumex. Beitr. Biol. Pfl. 45: 69–90.

Datta, P.C. & Deb, A. 1968b. East Indian cytotypes of Adhatoda vasica Nees. Their wood characters compared. Broteria, ser. Ci. nat. 37: 143–153.

Datta, P.C. & Ghosh, P.K. 1983. Wood character changes in Strychnos nux-vomica Linn. II. Vigour, height, age and season. Flora 174: 153–158.

Datta, P.C. & Ghosh, P.K. 1984a. Wood character changes in Strychnos nux-vomica L. III. Flowering and non-flowering trees compared. Flora 175: 427–433.

Datta, P.C. & Ghosh, P.K. 1984b. Wood anatomy and phylogeny of Dalbergieae. In: Proc. Symp. Evolutionary Botany and Biostratigraphy, Univ. Calcutta 1979 (eds. Sharma, A.K., Mitra, G.C. & Banerjee, M.): 221–236. Today & Tomorrow's Printers & Publ.: New Delhi.

Datta, P.C. & Maiti, R.K. 1968. Wood microscopy of Galegeae (Papilionaceae). Bull. bot. Soc. Bengal 22: 137–141.

Datta, P.C. & Maiti, R.K. 1971a. Relationships of Justicieae (Acanthaceae) based on wood microscopy. Castanea 36: 54–61.

Datta, P.C. & Maiti, R.K. 1971b. Relationships of Plumiereae (Apocynaceae) II. Based on wood microscopy. Bull. bot. Soc. Bengal 25: 55–61.

Datta, P.C. & Saha, N. 1971 [1972]. Secondary xylem of Phaseoleae (Fabaceae). Acta bot. hung. 17: 347–359.

Datta, P.C. & Samanta, P. 1983. Wood anatomy of some Indo-Malayan Meliaceae. J. Indian bot. Soc. 62: 185–203.

Datta, R.M. & Roy, K. 1964. Wood anatomy of a few species of Corchorus (jute). Bull. bot. Soc. Bengal 18 (1–2): 17–20.

Davidson, C. 1976. Anatomy of xylem and phloem of the Datiscaceae. Contr. Sci. nat. Hist. Mus. Los Angeles County, No. 280: 28 pp.

Davtyan, A. 1950. Comparative anatomical study of woody wild and cultivated species of Elae-agnus in the Caucasus. Trud. bot. Inst. Akad. Nauk arm. SSR 7: 133–144. [Russ.]

Dayal, R. & Rao, R.V. 1983. A note on the occurrence of radial vessels in Combretum lati-folium Bl. Indian For. 109: 848.

Dayal, R., Rao, R.V. & Sharma, B. 1984. Perforated ray cells in woods of Indian Myrsinaceae and Loganiaceae. IAWA Bull. n.s. 5: 225–228.

Deb, A. & Datta, P.C. 1977. Interrelations of Scrophulariaceae based on secondary xylem of common Indian species. J. Indian bot. Soc. 56: 149–164.

DeBuhr, L.E. 1977. Wood anatomy of the Sarraceniaceae; ecological and evolutionary implica-tions. Pl. Syst. Evol. 128: 159–169.

DeBuhr, L.E. 1978. Wood anatomy of Forsellesia (Glossopetalon) and Crossosoma (Crosso-somataceae, Rosales). Aliso 9: 179–184.

Dechamps, R. 1971. Confirmation de la synonymie de Strychnos stuhlmannii Gilg et de S. potatorum L.f. par l'étude anatomique du bois. Bull. Jard. bot. natn. Belg. 41: 287–288.

Dechamps, R. 1977. Comparaison anatomique d'une espèce fossile arborescente d'Afrique à Steganotaenia araliacea (Ombellifère). Bull. Jard. bot. natn. Belg. 47: 473–482.

Dechamps, R. 1979; 1980; 1985. Etude anatomique de bois d'Amérique du Sud. I. Acanthaceae à Lecythidaceae. Ann. Mus. roy. Afr. Cent., Tervuren, sér. IN-8, Sci. econ., No 10: 332 pp. (1979). II. Leguminosae. Ibid., No. 11: 229 pp. (1980). III. Linaceae à Quinaceae. Ibid., No. 14: 471 pp. (1985). [Really Linaceae to Zygophyllaceae.]

Dechamps, R., Mosango, M. & Robbrecht, E. 1985. Etudes systématiques sur les Hymeno-cardiaceae d'Afrique: la morphologie du pollen et l'anatomie du bois. Bull. Jard. bot. natn. Belg. 55: 473–485.

Decker, J.M. 1966. Wood anatomy and phylogeny of Luxemburgeieae (Ochnaceae). Phyto-morphology 16: 39–55.

De Filice Mastelloni, M. 1960. Andamento dell'accrescimento del legno in Ceratonia siliqua L. Nuovo G. bot. ital. 67: 363–376. [Eng. summ.]

Deng, L. & Baas, P. 1990. Wood anatomy of trees and shrubs from China. II. Theaceae. IAWA Bull. n.s. 11: 337–378.

Deng, L. & Baas, P. 1991. The wood anatomy of the Theaceae. IAWA Bull. n.s. 12: 333–353.

Deng, L. & Zhang, X.-Y. 1989. The ecological wood anatomy of the lilac (Syringa oblata var. giraldii Rehd.) in Taibai mountain. Acta bot. sin. 31: 95–102. [Chin.; Eng. summ.] + 1 plate.

Den Outer, R.W. 1985. Wood anatomy of Buxus madagascarica Baill. Acta bot. neerl. 34: 111–113.

Den Outer, R.W. & Schütz, P.R. 1981a. Wood anatomy of Apeiba (Tiliaceae). IAWA Bull. n.s. 2: 187–92.

Den Outer, R.W. & Schütz, P.R. 1981b. Wood anatomy of some Sarcolaenaceae and Rhopalocarpaceae and their systematic position. Meded. Landbouwhogesch. Wageningen 81 (8): 1–25.

Den Outer, R.W. & Van Veenendaal, W.L.H. 1976. Variation in wood anatomy of species with a distribution covering both rain forest and savanna areas of the Ivory Coast, West Africa. In: Wood structure in biological and technological research (eds. Baas, P., Bolton, A.J. & Catling, D.M.): 182–195. Leiden Botanical Ser. No. 3. Leiden Univ. Press.

Den Outer, R.W. & Van Veenendaal, W.L.H. 1980. Wood and bark anatomy of Alluaudia (Didiereaceae) from Madagascar. IAWA Bull. n.s. 1: 133–139.

Den Outer, R.W. & Van Veenendaal, W.L.H. 1981. Wood and bark anatomy of Azima tetracantha Lam. (Salvadoraceae) with description of its included phloem. Acta bot. neerl. 30: 199–207.

Den Outer, R.W. & Van Veenendaal, W.L.H. 1982. Wood anatomy of Tambourissa (Monimiaceae) from Madagascar. Acta bot. neerl. 31: 265–274.

Den Outer, R.W. & Van Veenendaal, W.L.H. 1983. Wood anatomy of Uncarina leandrii H. Humb. (Pedaliaceae) and its relation to Bignoniaceae. IAWA Bull. n.s. 4: 53–59.

Den Outer, R.W. & Van Veenendaal, W.L.H. 1989. Wood anatomy. In: The Connaraceae. A taxonomic study with emphasis on Africa (ed. Breteler, F.J.): 78–101. Agric. Univ. Wageningen Pap. 89 (6): 403 pp.

Den Outer, R.W. & Van Veenendaal, W.L.H. 1992. Wood anatomy of the Baphia group (Leguminosae). IAWA Bull. n.s. 13: 135–149.

Derviz-Sokolova, T.G. 1966. Anatomo-morphological structure of Salix polaris Wahlb. and S. phlebophylla Anderss. Byull. mosk. Obshch. Ispyt. Prir., Otdel. biol. 71 (2): 28–38. [Russ. only.]

Derviz-Sokolova, T.G. & Katumba, A.K.S. 1975a. On the anatomical structure of Salix reticulata L., as a representative of the subgenus Chamaetia Dum. Byull. mosk. Obshch. Ispyt. Prir., Otdel. biol. 80 (4): 126–132. [Russ.]

Derviz-Sokolova, T.G. & Katumba, A.K.S. 1975b. Anatomical characteristics of Salix rotundifolia Trautv. as a representative of the shrub willows of the subgenus Chamaetia (Dum.) Nasarov. Nauch. Dokl. vyssh. Shk., biol. Nauki 18 (9): 61–6. [Russ.]

Desch, H.E. 1932. Anatomical variation in the wood of some dicotyledonous trees. New Phytol. 31: 73–118.

Desch, H.E. 1941. Dipterocarp timbers of the Malay Peninsula. Malayan For. Rec., No. 14: 171 pp.

Desch, H.E. 1954. Manual of Malayan timbers. Malayan For. Rec., No. 15 (vol. II): 329–762.

Desch, H.E. & Symington, C.F. 1936. Commercial timbers of the Malay Peninsula. I. The genus Shorea. Malayan For. Rec., No. 12: 73 pp.

Descole, H.R. & O'Donell, C.A. 1937. Estudios anatómicos en el leño de plantas tucumanas. Lilloa 1: 75–93.

Descole, H.R. & O'Donell, C.A. 1938. La disposición estratificada de los elementos leñosos en la Cascaronia astragalina. Lilloa 2: 23–30.

Détienne, P. 1974a. Nature et périodicité des cernes dans le bois de makoré (Tieghemella heckelii Pierre). Centre tech. For. trop.: Nogent-sur-Marne. 14 pp.

Détienne, P. 1974b. Nature et périodicité des cernes dans le bois de padouk (Pterocarpus soyauxii Taub.). Centre tech. For. trop.: Nogent-sur-Marne. 11 pp.

Détienne, P. 1975a. Nature et périodicité des cernes dans le bois de doussié (Afzelia sp.). Centre tech. For. trop.: Nogent-sur-Marne. 17 pp.

Détienne, P. 1975b. Nature et périodicité des cernes dans le bois de bété (Mansonia altissima A. Chev.). Centre tech. For. trop.: Nogent-sur-Marne. 26 pp.

Détienne, P. 1976a. Particularités de structure du bois dans un okoumé cannelé. Centre tech. For. trop.: Nogent-sur-Marne. 22 pp.

Détienne, P. 1976b. Nature et périodicité des cernes dans le bois d'iroko (Chlorophora excelsa Benth. & Hook.). Centre tech. For. trop.: Nogent-sur-Marne. 26 pp.

Détienne, P. 1980. Le bois de Moronobea coccinea Aubl. Analogies et différences avec le manil et le parcouri. Bois For. Trop., No. 194: 29–33.

Détienne, P. 1988. Cours illustré d'anatomie des bois. Centre tech. For. trop., Nogent-sur-Marne. 47 pp.

Détienne, P. 1989. Appearance and periodicity of growth rings in some tropical woods. IAWA Bull. n.s. 10: 123–132.

Détienne, P. 1991. Anatomie du bois de Balgoya pacifica (Polygalaceae) de Nouvelle-Calédonie. Bull. Mus. natn. Hist. nat., Paris, sér. 4, B, Adansonia 13: 17–20.

Détienne, P. & Jacquet, P. 1983. Atlas d'identification des bois de l'Amazonie et des régions voisines. Centre tech. For. trop.: Nogent-sur-Marne. 640 pp.

Détienne, P., Jacquet, P. & Mariaux, A. 1982. Manuel d'identification des bois tropicaux. 3. Guyane française. Centre tech. For. trop.: Nogent-sur-Marne. 315 pp.

Détienne, P., Loureiro, A.A. & Jacquet, P. 1983. Estudo anatômico do lenho da família Bombacaceae da America. Acta Amazonica 13: 831–867. [Eng. summ.]

Détienne, P. & Mariaux, A. 1975. Nature et périodicité des cernes dans le bois de Niangon. Bois For. Trop., No. 159: 29–37.

Détienne, P. & Mariaux, A. 1976. Nature et périodicité des cernes dans le bois de samba. Bois For. Trop., No. 169: 29–35.

Détienne, P. & Mariaux, A. 1977. Nature et périodicité des cernes dans les bois rouges de Méliacées africaines. Bois For. Trop., No. 175: 52–61.

Détienne, P. & Thiel, J. 1988 [1989]. Monographie des wapas de Guyane Française. Bois For. Trop., No. 216: 43–68.

Détienne, P. & Welle, B.J.H. ter 1989. Wood and timber. In: Flora of the Guianas. 88. Caesalpiniaceae p.p. (by Cowan, R.S. & Lindeman, J.C.): 123–149. Koeltz Scientific Books: Koenigstein.

Detzner, H. 1910. Beiträge zur vergleichenden Anatomie der Amentaceen-Wurzeln mit Rücksicht auf die Systematik. Diss.: Univ. Göttingen. 61 pp. W.F. Kaestner: Göttingen.

Dhar, N. & Purkayastha, S.K. 1973. Variation in silica content of the wood in Lannea coromandelica (Houtt.) Merr. J. Indian Acad. Wood Sci. 4: 13–21.

Díaz-Vaz, J.E. 1987a. Anatomía de madera de Nothofagus dombeyi (Mirbel) Oerstedt. Bosque 8 (1): 63–65.

Díaz-Vaz, J.E. 1987b. Anatomía de madera de Nothofagus alpina (P. et E.) Oerstedt. Bosque 8 (2): 143–145.

Díaz-Vaz, J.E. 1988a. Anatomía de madera de Laurelia phillipiana Looser. Bosque 9 (1): 65–67.

Díaz-Vaz, J.E. 1988b. Anatomía de madera de Laurelia sempervirens (R. et Pav.) Tul. Bosque 9 (2): 123–124.

Dickison, W.C. 1967. Comparative morphological studies in Dilleniaceae, I. Wood anatomy. J. Arnold Arbor. 48: 1–29.

Dickison, W.C. 1972. Anatomical studies in the Connaraceae. II. Wood anatomy. J. Elisha Mitchell Sci. Soc. 88: 120–136.

Dickison, W.C. 1975 [1976]. The bases of angiosperm phylogeny: vegetative anatomy. Ann. Missouri bot. Gard. 62: 590–620.

Dickison, W.C. 1977. Wood anatomy of Weinmannia (Cunoniaceae). Bull. Torrey bot. Cl. 104: 12–23.

Dickison, W.C. 1978. Comparative anatomy of Eucryphiaceae. Amer. J. Bot. 65: 722–735.

Dickison, W.C. 1979. A note on the wood anatomy of Dillenia (Dilleniaceae). IAWA Bull. 1979/2-3: 57–60.

Dickison, W.C. 1980. Comparative wood anatomy and evolution of the Cunoniaceae. Allertonia 2: 281–321.

Dickison, W.C. 1981. Contributions to the morphology and anatomy of Strasburgeria and a discussion of the taxonomic position of the Strasburgeriaceae. Brittonia 33: 564–580.

Dickison, W.C. 1982. Vegetative anatomy of Oncotheca macrocarpa, a newly described species of Oncothecaceae. Bull. Mus. natn. Hist. nat., Paris, ser. 4, Adansonia 4: 177–181.

Dickison, W.C. 1984. On the occurrence of silica grains in woods of Hibbertia (Dilleniaceae). IAWA Bull. n.s. 5: 341–343.

Dickison, W.C. 1986. Wood anatomy and affinities of the Alseuosmiaceae. Syst. Bot. 11: 214–221.

Dickison, W.C. 1988. Xylem anatomy of Diegodendron humbertii. IAWA Bull. n.s. 9: 332–336.

Dickison, W.C. 1989a. Steps toward the natural system of the dicotyledons: vegetative anatomy. Aliso 12: 555–566.

Dickison, W.C. 1989b. Comparisons of primitive Rosidae and Hamamelidae. In: Evolution, systematics, and fossil history of the Hamamelidae. Vol. 1: Introduction and "Lower" Hamamelidae (eds. Crane, P.R. & Blackmore, S.): 47–73. Clarendon Press: Oxford.

Dickison, W.C. 1990. The morphology and relationships of Medusagyne (Medusagynaceae). Pl. Syst. Evol. 171: 27–55.

Dickison, W.C. & Baas, P. 1977. The morphology and relationships of Paracryphia (Paracryphiaceae). Blumea 23: 417–438.

Dickison, W.C. & Miller, R.B. 1993. Morphology and anatomy of the malagasy genus Physena (Physenaceae), with a discussion of the relationships of the genus. Bull. Mus. natn. Hist. nat., Paris, sér. 4, B, Adansonia 15: 85–106.

Dickison, W.C. & Phend, K.D. 1985. Wood anatomy of the Styracaceae: evolutionary and ecological considerations. IAWA Bull. n.s. 6: 3–22.

Dickison, W.C., Rury, P.M. & Stebbins, G.L. 1978. Xylem anatomy of Hibbertia (Dilleniaceae) in relation to ecology and evolution. J. Arnold Arbor. 59: 32–49.

Dickison, W.C. & Sweitzer, E.M. 1970. The morphology and relationships of Barbeya oleoides. Amer. J. Bot. 57: 468–476.

Diehl, G.A. 1935. A study of the Lecythidaceae. Trop. Woods 43: 1–15.

Diettert, R.A. 1938. The morphology of Artemisia tridentata Nutt. Lloydia 1: 3–74.

Dixon, H.H. 1919. Mahogany, and the recognition of some of the different kinds by their microscopic characteristics. Notes Bot. School, Dublin 3 (1): 3–58. Also: Sci. Proc. Roy. Dublin Soc. (NS) Vol. 15 (1918).

Dobbins, D.R. 1971. Studies on the anomalous cambial activity in Doxantha unguis-cati (Bignoniaceae). II. A case of differential production of secondary tissues. Amer. J. Bot. 58: 697–705.

Dobbins, D.R. 1981. Anomalous secondary growth in lianas of the Bignoniaceae is correlated with the vascular pattern. Amer. J. Bot. 68: 142–144.

Doležal, J. 1959. Xylotomický rozbor a technické vlastnosti některých vietnamských drev. [Analysis of wood anatomy and physical and mechanical properties of some Vietnam woods.] Drev. Výskum 4 (2): 173–190 + 55 photos. [Eng. summ.]

Donaldson, L.A. 1984. Wood anatomy of five exotic hardwoods grown in Western Samoa. N.Z. Jl. for. Sci. 14: 305–318.

Dong, Z. & Baas, P. 1993. Wood anatomy of trees and shrubs from China. V. Anacardiaceae. IAWA Jl. 14: 87–102.

Donoso, C. & Landrum, L.R. 1979. Nothofagus leoni Espinosa, a natural hybrid between Nothofagus obliqua (Mirb.) Oerst. and Nothofagus glauca (Phil.) Krasser. N.Z. Jl. Bot. 17: 353–360.

Dorr, L.J. & Barnett, L.C. 1989. A revision of Melochia section Physodium (Sterculiaceae) from Mexico. Brittonia 41: 404–423.

Dörries, W. 1912. Bemerkungen über anomales Dickenwachstum der Lianen nebst einer Bestimmungstabelle nach den Stammen der Göttinger Sammlung. Jber. naturhist. Ges. Hannover 60/61: 83–98.

Dos Santos, G. & Miller, R.B. 1992. Wood anatomy of Tecomeae. In: Flora Neotropica Mon. 25 (II) Bignoniaceae II (Tribe Tecomeae) by A.H. Gentry: 336–358.

Dressler, R.L. 1957. The genus Pedilanthus (Euphorbiaceae). Contrib. Gray Herb. Harv. Univ., No. 182: 1–188.

Duchaigne, A. 1951. L'ontogénie du phloème intraxylémien dans la tige de Lebrunia bushaie Staner (Guttifères). C.R. Acad. Sci., Paris 232: 646–648.

Duchaigne, A. 1963. Sur l'anatomie de makoré. C.R. 87 Congr. natn. Soc. sav., Poitiers, 1962, Sect. Sci.: 889–893.

Duchaigne, A. 1966. Sur les particularités histologiques de l'Ulmus campestris L. C.R. 90 Congr. natn. Soc. sav., Nice II, 1965: 305–315.

Duchaigne, A. & Chalard, A. du 1951. Nouveau complement à la connaissance du Distephania involucrata Gagnepain (Saxifragacée d'Indo-Chine). Bull. Soc. bot. Fr. 98: 106–108.

Duchaigne, A. & Chalard, A. du 1952. Contribution à l'étude du Polyosma aulacocarpha Gagnepain (nouvelle Saxifragacée indochinoise). Bull. Soc. bot. Fr. 99: 278–281.

Duchaigne, A. & Chalard, A. du 1955. Contribution à l'étude du Polyosma turfosa Gagnep. et du Polyosma nhatrangensis Gagnep. (nouvelles Saxifragacées indochinoises). Bull. Soc. bot. Fr. 102: 1–6.

Duchaigne, A. & Chalard, A. du 1956. Contribution à l'étude des nouvelles espèces indochinoises de Polyosma (Saxifragacées au sens large, Escalloniacées des nouvelles classifications) (fin). Bull. Soc. bot. Fr. 103: 582–586.

Duchesne, F. 1930. Etude sur les bois de trois Meliacées du Congo Belge. Rev. Zool. Bot. Afr. 19: 131–149.

Duchesne, F. 1932. La structure du bois de l'arbre à vernis (Kela). Rev. Zool. Bot. Afr. 23: 46–51.

Dugand, A. 1962. La madera de Uribea tamarindoides (Leguminosae–Lotoideae–Sophoreae). Mutisia, No. 27: 13–16.

Dupéron, J. 1979. Contribution à l'étude de Boswellia sacra: anatomie de la plantule et de la tige agée. Bull. Mus. natn. Hist. nat., Paris, sér. 4, B, 1: 171–189.

Dupéron, J. 1988. Les bois fossiles de Juglandaceae: inventaire et révision. Rev. Palaeobot. Palynol. 53: 251–282.

Dute, R.R. & Rushing, A.E. 1987. Pit pairs with tori in the wood of Osmanthus americanus (Oleaceae). IAWA Bull. n.s. 8: 237–244.

Dute, R.R. & Rushing, A.E. 1990. Torus structure and development in the woods of Ulmus alata Michx., Celtis laevigata Willd., and Celtis occidentalis L. IAWA Bull. n.s. 11: 71–83.

Dute, R.R., Rushing, A.E. & Perry, J.W. 1990. Torus structure and development in species of Daphne. IAWA Bull. n.s. 11: 401–412.

Dutt, B.S.M., Rao, P.S.P. & Rai, B.H. 1978. A study of the secondary xylem of Moringa concanensis Nimmo with discussion on the relationships and the systematic status of Moringaceae. J. Indian Acad. Wood Sci. 9 (2): 111–119.

Duvigneaud, P., Staquet, J. & Dewit, J. 1952. Contribution à l'étude anatomique des rameaux chez les Sections africaines du genre Strychnos. Bull. Soc. roy. bot. belg. 85: 39–67.

Eames, A.J. 1910. On the origin of the broad ray in Quercus. Bot. Gaz. 49: 161–167.

Ebel, F. & Kästner, A. 1973. Morphologisch-anatomische Beobachtungen an einigen kubanischen Asteraceen-Sippen, insbesondere an Senecio plumbeus Griseb. s.l. und Senecio rivalis Greenm. Flora 162: 191–205.

Edlmann, M.L. & Monaco, S. del. 1981. Atlante micrografico di 110 specie legnose della Corea. Contrib. sci.-prat. migl. Conos. Util. Legno 28: 99 pp.

Edlmann Abbate, M.L. & De Luca, L. 1981. Caratteristiche anatomiche e proprietà di dieci specie legnose provenienti dalle Filippine. Rivta Agric. subtrop. trop. 75 (1): 37–77.

Eeckhout, L.-E. 1951. Structuur en gebruik van de Kongolese houtsoorten. Bull. agric. Congo belge 42: 675–718. [French summ.]

Efe, A. 1987. Liquidambar orientalis Mill. (sığala ağaci) in morfolojik ve palinolojik özellikleri üzerine araştırmalar. [Studies on the morphological and palynological characteristics of Liquidambar orientalis Mill. in Turkey.] Istanb. Univ. Orman Fak. Derg., ser. A, 37 (2): 84–114. [Full Eng. summ.]

Eggeling, W.J. & Harris, C.M. 1939. Forest trees and timbers of the British Empire. IV. Fifteen Uganda timbers. Clarendon Press: Oxford. 120 pp.

Eimunjeze, V.E. 1976. A revision of Hemandradenia Stapf (Connaraceae). Meded. Landbouwhogesch. Wageningen 76 (9): 1–34.

Eliasson, U. 1971. Studies in Galapagos plants. X. The genus Lecocarpus Decaisne. Svensk bot. Tidskr. 65: 245–277.

Eliasson, U. 1974. Studies in Galapagos plants. XIV. The genus Scalesia Arn. Opera bot., Lund, No. 36: 1–117.

El-Oqlah, A.A. 1984. The taxonomical study of the macro- and micro-morphological characteristics of indigenous Pistacia L. taxa in Jordan. Istanb. Univ. Orman Fak. Derg., ser. A, 34 (2): 166–186.

El-Osta, M.L.M., El-Lakany, M.H. & Megahed, M.M. 1981. Anatomical characteristics of some Casuarina species grown in Egypt. IAWA Bull. n.s. 2: 95–98.

Enchev, E. 1961. Der Einfluss des Wuchsgebietes und des Standortes auf den anatomischen Aufbau und die physikalisch-mechanischen Eigenschaften des Holzes von Feldulmen (Ulmus campestris L.). Drev. Výskum 6 (1): 1–17.

Enchev, E.A. & Bl"skova, G. 1979. Alteration in the anatomic elements of the wood along the stem radius of makoré (Tieghemella heckelii Pierre) and mukulungu (Autranella congolensis A. Chev.). Gorsk. Nauka 16 (2): 71–79. [Bulg.; Eng. summ.]

Enchev, E., Bl"skova, G. & Tsvetanova, A. 1986. Aufbau und Eigenschaften des Dau- und Krabak-Holzes. Nauch. Trud. Mekh. tekh. Drves., Vissh Lesotek. Inst., Sofiya 30: 91–100. [Bulg.; Germ. summ.]

Erak, S. 1971. Height, width and frequency of rays in Corylus colurna. Pregled nauch. Rad. Inform., Zavod Techn. Drveta 8 (2): 19–24. [Serbo-Croat; Germ. summ.]

Erak, S. 1972. Anatomical structure and nominal density of wood of Corylus colurna. Pregled Zavod Techn. Drveta, Sarajevo 9 (1): 33–44. [Serbo-Croat; Eng. summ.]

Erak, S. 1974. Some anatomical characteristics of beech wood in Bosnia. Pregled Zavod Techn. Drveta, Sarajevo (1/2): 53–59. [Serbo-Croat; Germ. summ.] [For. Abstr. 33 (1972) No. 1390.]

Erdtman, G., Leins, P., Melville, R. & Metcalfe, C.R. 1969. On the relationships of Emblingia. Bot. J. Linn. Soc. 62: 169–186.

Erdtman, G. & Metcalfe, C.R. 1963. Affinities of certain genera incertae sedis suggested by pollen morphology and vegetative anatomy. Kew Bull. 17: 249–256.

Ergo, A.B. & Dechamps, R. 1984. Influence du milieu sur l'anatomie du bois de Simarouba glauca DC. (aire américaine d'origine et aire d'introduction en Afrique). Centre Inform. appl. Dev. Agric. trop.: Tervuren, Belgium. 100 pp.

Esau, K. & Cheadle, V.I. 1969. Secondary growth in Bougainvillea. Ann. Bot. (NS) 33: 807–819.

Esdorn, I. & Zohm, G. 1961. Die afrikanischen Alstonia-Arten unter besonderer Berücksichtigung des Holzes. Flora, Jena 150: 318–331.

Espinoza de Pernía, N. 1987a. Estudio xilologico de algunas especies de Cedrela y Toona. Pittieria 14: 5–32.

Espinoza de Pernía, N. 1987b. Cristales y sílice en maderas dicotiledóneas de Latinoamérica. Pittieria 15: 13–65.

Espinoza de Pernía, N. 1989. Estudio xilologico del genero Euphronia. Pittieria 18: 57–61.

Espinoza de Pernía, N. & Miller, R.B. 1991. Adapting the IAWA list of microscopic features for hardwood identification to DELTA. IAWA Bull. n.s. 12: 34–50.

Etienne, R. 1919. Etude anatomique de la famille des Epacridées. Thèse: Toulouse. 222 pp. E. Arrault et Cie: Tours.

Eyde, R.H. & Olson, S.L. 1983. The dead trees of Ilha da Trinidade. Bartonia, No. 49: 32–51.

Fabbri Tarchi, A.M. 1960. Micrografia comparata dei legni di alcune Rosaceae. Ann. Accad. ital. Sci. forest. 9: 57–116. Also: Pubbl. Ist. bot. Univ. Firenze Erb. colon. (NS) 6, No. 155 (1960–1963).

Fahn, A. 1953. Annual wood ring development in maquis trees of Israel. Palest. J. Bot., Jerusalem ser. 6: 1–26.

Fahn, A. 1955. The development of the growth ring in wood of Quercus infectoria and Pistacia lentiscus in the hill region of Israel. Trop. Woods 101: 52–59.

Fahn, A. 1958. Xylem structure and annual rhythm of development in trees and shrubs of the desert I. Tamarix aphylla, T. jordanis var. negevensis, T. gallica var. maris-martui. Trop. Woods 109: 81–94.

Fahn, A. 1959. Xylem structure and annual rhythm of development in trees and shrubs of the desert. II. Acacia tortilis and A. raddiana. Bull. Res. Counc. Israel D, Bot. 7: 23–28. III. Eucalyptus camaldulensis and Acacia cyanophylla. Ibid.: 122–131.

Fahn, A. 1979. Secretory tissues in plants. Academic Press: London, etc. 302 pp.

Fahn, A. 1985. The development of the secondary body in plants with interxylary phloem. In: Xylorama (ed. Kučera, L.J.): 58–67. Birkhäuser Verlag: Basel, etc.

Fahn, A. & Leshem, B. 1963. Wood fibres with living protoplasts. New Phytol. 62: 91–98.

Fahn, A. & Sarnat, C. 1963. Xylem structure and annual rhythm of development in trees and shrubs of the desert. IV. Shrubs. Bull. Res. Counc. Israel, D, Bot. 11: 198–209.

Fahn, A. & Shchori, Y. 1967 [1968]. The organization of the secondary conducting tissues in some species of the Chenopodiaceae. Phytomorphology 17: 147–154.

Fahn, A., Werker, E. & Baas, P. 1986. Wood anatomy and identification of trees and shrubs from Israel and adjacent regions. Israel Academy of Sciences: Jerusalem. 221 pp. + 82 plates.

Falcão, W.F. de A. 1968. Contribuição ao conhecimento anatômico da espécie Persea americana Miller. Anu. bras. Econ. flor., Inst. nac. Pinho 19: 179–194.

Falcão, W.F. de A. 1969. Anatomia da castanha mineira (Salacia brachypoda (Miers) Peyr). Atas. Soc. Biol. Rio de Janeiro 12: 233–236.

Falcão, W.F. de A., Alencastro, F.M.M.R. de & Lima Correia, I. de 1973. Notas sôbre a anatomia e morfologia da espécie Polygala paniculata L. Arq. Jard. bot. Rio de Janeiro 19: 281–294.

Fanshawe, D.B. 1947. Studies of the trees of British Guiana. I. Crabwood (Carapa guianensis). Trop. Woods 90: 30–40.

Fasolo, U. 1939–1940; 1941–1944. Atlante micrografico dei legni dell'Africa orientale italiana. Cartello I, Tav 1–12 (1939–1940). Cartello II, Tav 13–24 (1941–1944). Firenze.

Fedalto, L.C. 1982. Estudo anatômico do lenho de Bixa arborea Huber. Acta Amazonica 12: 389–399. [Eng. summ.]

Fedalto, L.C., Mendes, I. da C.A. & Coradin, V.T.R. 1989. Madeiras da Amazonia. Descrição do lenho de 40 especies ocorrentes na Floresta Nacional do Tapajos. Inst. Bras. meio Ambiente Recurs. nat. Renov. IBAMA, Brasilia. 156 pp.

Fegel, A.C. 1941. Comparative anatomy and varying physical properties of trunk, branch and root wood in certain northeastern trees. Tech. Publ. N.Y. St. Coll. For., No. 55: 1–20.

Ferguson, C.W. 1964. Annual rings in big sagebrush. Papers Lab. Tree-ring Research No.1, Univ. Arizona Press, Tucson. 95 pp.

Ferreirinha, M.P. 1955. Catálogo das madeiras de Moçambique. I. Mem. Junta Invest. Ultramar, sér. Bot. 2: 131 pp.

Ferreirinha, M.P. 1956. Madeiras do ultramar português. Garcia de Orta 4: 95–96.

Ferreirinha, M.P. 1958. Identificação de uma madeira angolana – Morus lactea (Sim) Mildbr. Garcia de Orta 6: 283–300. [Eng. summ.] [Incl. Enantia, Nauclea.]

Ferreirinha, M.P. 1962. Madeiras de Angola. 2a série. Garcia de Orta 10: 113–123.

Ferreirinha, M.P. & Reis, J.E.B. Dos 1969. Madeiras de Angola. 3a série. Garcia de Orta 17: 289–297.

Filipovici, J. et al. 1962. Lemnul de plop. Structura şi proprietăti. Lucr. ştiinţ. Inst. Polit. Brasov (Fac. Industr. Lemn.) 1: 107–155. [Rumanian; Germ. summ.]

Fisher, J.B. 1980. The vegetative and reproductive structure of papaya (Carica papaya). Lyonia 1: 191–208.

Flamigni, A. 1948. L'arbre "Bonkenyama", Morus mesozygia Stapf. Bull. agric. Congo belge 39: 593–600.

Flint, E.M. 1918. Structure of wood in blueberry and huckleberry. Bot. Gaz. 65: 556–559.

Flores Rodríguez, L.J. 1968. Caracteristicas anatomicas, fisicas y mecanicas de la madera de tres especies del estado de Campeche. Bol. téc. Inst. nac. Invest. for. Méx. 24: 1–13. [Eng. summ.]

Fonseca, F.M. de A. 1971. Qualificação tecnológica de madeiras de eucalipto. Contribuição para o estudo macroscópico, microscópico, físico e mecânico da madeira de algumas espécies de eucaliptos cultivados em Angola. Publ. Inst. Invest. agron. Angola, sér. Cien., No. 20: 72 pp. [Eng. summ.]

Fontella Pereira, J., Valente, M. da C. & Alencastro, F.M.M.R. de 1971. Contribuição ao estudo das Asclepiadaceae brasileiras V. Estudo taxonômico e anatômico de Oxypetalum banksii Roem. et Schult. Rodriguésia 26: 261–281. [Eng. summ.]

Ford, J. 1984. Vessel characteristics of the wood of some Australian species of Acacia in relation to habitat. Proc. Pacific Regional Wood Anatomy Conf., Tsukuba, Japan, 1984: 156–158.

Foreman, D.B. 1987. Notes on the wood anatomy of Idiospermum australiense (Idiospermaceae). Muelleria 6: 329–333.

Foreman, D.B. 1988. Wood anatomy of Idiospermum australiense (Diels) S.T. Blake. In: The ecology of Australia's wet tropics (ed. Kitching, R.): 281. [Proc. Ecol. Soc. Aust. 15.] Surrey Beatty & Sons: Chipping Norton, N.S.W., Australia.

Forman, L.L., Brandham, P.E., Harley, M.M. & Lawrence, T.J. 1989. Beiselia mexicana (Burseraceae) and its affinities. Kew Bull. 44: 1–31.

Forman, L.L. & Cutler, D.F. 1967. Additional notes on Trigonobalanus Forman (Fagaceae). Kew Bull. 21: 331–334.

Forsaith, C.C. 1920. Anatomical reduction in some alpine plants. Ecology 1: 124–135.

Fouarge, J. & Gérard, G. 1964. Bois du Mayumbe. Publ. Inst. nat. Etude agr. Congo: Bruxelles. 579 pp.

Fouarge, J., Gérard, G. & Sacré, E. 1953. Bois du Congo. Publ. Inst. nat. Etude agr. Congo: Bruxelles. 424 pp.

Foulger, A.N., Vimmerstedt, J.P. & Eichar, C. 1975. Stem anatomy of 30 year old yellow-poplar. Forest Sci. 21: 23–33.

Francis, W.D. 1926. The development of the corrugated stems of some Eastern Australian trees. Proc. roy. Soc. Queensland 38: 62–76.

Francis, W.D. 1928. Features of the vegetative anatomy of the Australian white beech (Gmelina leichhardtii). Proc. Linn. Soc. N. S. Wales 53: 474–484.

Franco, R.-P. 1990. The genus Hyeronima (Euphorbiaceae) in South America. Bot. Jb. 111: 297–346.

Franklin, T. 1952. O Cumaru das Caatingas (Amburana cearensis (Fr. All.) A.C. Smith). Arq. Serv. Florestal, Rio de Janeiro 6: 1–124. [Eng. summ.]

Freitas, J.A. de 1988. Estudo anatômico das madeiras dos gêneros Anisophyllea R. Brown ex Sabine e Polygonanthus Ducke (Rhizophoraceae). Acta Amazonica 18(1–2): 117–132. [Eng. summ.]

Freitas, M.C.P.G. de 1955; 1958. Estudo das madeiras de Timor I. Mem. Min. Ultramar, Junta Invest. Ultramar, sér. Bot. III: 74 pp. (1955). II. Ibid., sér. 2, 5: 89 pp. (1958).

Freitas, M.C.P.G. de 1961. Madeiras de Angola. 1a série. Garcia de Orta 9: 699–712.

Freitas, M.C.P.G. de 1963. Madeiras da India Portuguesa. Mem. Junta Invest. Ultramar, Lisboa, sér. 2, No. 47: 93 pp.

Freitas, M.C.P.G. de 1971. Características anatómicas, físicas e mecânicas das madeiras de Moçambique: I. Revta Ciênc. agron., sér. B, 4: 125–182. [Eng. summ.]

Freitas, M.C.P.G. de 1973 [1974]. Contribuição para o estudo das madeiras exóticas em Moçambique. I. Revta Ciênc. agron., sér. A, 6: 3–28. [Eng. summ.]

Freitas, M.C.P.G. de 1986. Madeiras de Moçambique. Características anatómicas, físicas e mecânicas. Centro Estudos tecnologia florestal Inst. Invest. Cient. trop.: Lisboa. 52 pp.

Freitas, M.C.P.G. de 1987. Madeiras de São Tomé. Características anatómicas e físicas. Centro Estudos tecnologia florestal Inst. Invest. Cient. trop.: Lisboa. 119 pp.

Freitas, M.C.P.G. de & Oliveira, J.S. 1969. Le bois de "Chanfuta" (Afzelia cuanzensis Welw.) du Mozambique. Rev. Cienc. Agron., sér. B, 2(2): 3–36.

Freitas, M.C.P.G. de, Oliveira, J.F. dos Santos et al. 1968. Umbila (Pterocarpus angolensis) madeira de Moçambique. Revta Ciênc. agron., Lourenco Marques, sér. A, 1: 199–236. [Eng. summ.]

Freudweiler, R. 1933. Sur quelques drogues d'Indochine. Trav. Lab. Mat. méd., Paris 24(6): 30 pp.

Friedman, J. 1978. Wood identification by microscopic examination. A guide for the archae- ologist on the northwest coast of North America. British Columbia Provincial Museum. Heritage Record No. 5: 84 pp.

Fries, R.E. 1906. Morphologisch-anatomische Notizen über zwei südamerikanische Lianen. Botaniska Studier till. F.R. Kjellman: 89–101. Upsala.

Frison, E. 1942. De la présence de corpuscules siliceux dans les bois tropicaux en général et en particulier dans le bois du Parinari glabra Oliv. et du Dialium klainei Pierre. Utilisation de ces bois en construction maritime. Bull. agric. Congo belge 33: 91–105.

Frison, E. 1948a. De la structure microscopique du bois de l'Avicennia africana P. Beauv. Bull. agric. Congo belge 39: 587–592.

Frison, E. 1948b. De la présence d'amidon dans le lumen des fibres du bois. Bull. agric. Congo belge 39: 869–874.

Frison, E. 1950. Structure du bois de bushaie, Lebrunia bushaie Staner – Guttiferae. Valeur industrielle et possibilités d'emploi. Bull. agric. Congo belge 41: 715–730; 1087.

Frison, E. 1953. Kondo-findo & Makoré. Bull. agric. Congo belge 44: 511–520.

Frost, F.H. 1930; 1931. Specialization in secondary xylem of dicotyledons. I. Origin of vessels. II. The evolution of the end wall of the vessel segment. III. Specialization of the lateral wall of the vessel segment. Bot. Gaz. 89: 67–94 (1930); 90: 198–212 (1930); 91: 88–96 (1931).

Fujii, T. 1986–1993. Wood architecture, Nos. 1–28. Research Forum for Wood Architecture, Sakamoto Lab., Univ. Tokyo. [Back cover of each issue; Jap. only.]

Fujii, T. 1988. Structure of latex and tanniferous tubes in tropical hardwoods. Bull. Forest. For. Prod. Res. Inst. (Japan), No. 352: 113–118 + 12 plates.

Fujii, T. & Baas, P. 1992. Vessel characters of the Sophora group (Leguminosae). In: Proc. 2nd Pacific Regional Wood Anat. Conf. (eds. Rojo, J. et al.): 135–149. Forpridecom: Laguna.

Fukazawa, K. & Ohtani, J. 1982. Within-a-tree variation of wood element size in Tilia japonica. IAWA Bull. n.s. 3: 201–206.

Fukuda, Y. 1967. Anatomical study of the internal phloem in the stems of dicotyledons, with special reference to its histogenesis. J. Fac. Sci. Univ. Tokyo, Sect. III, 9: 313–375.

Fundter, J.M. & Wisse, J.H. 1977. 40 belangrijke houtsoorten uit Indonesisch Nieuw Guinea (Irian Jaya) met de anatomische en technische kenmerken. Meded. Landbouwhogesch. Wageningen 77 (9): 1–223.

Furlow, J.J. 1979. The systematics of the American species of Alnus (Betulaceae). Rhodora 81: 1–121; 151–248.

Furst, G.G. 1965. Changes in anatomical structure of Carica papaya L. during the process of ontogeny. Byull. Glav. Bot. Sada 60: 67–77. [Russ. only.]

Furuno, T. 1977; 1979. Anatomy of Papua New Guinea woods. Res. Rep. Foreign Wood, Shimane Univ. No. 6: 192 pp., 104 plates (1977). [Jap.; Eng. captions]. No. 8: 148 pp. (1979). [Jap.; Eng. summ.]

Furuno, T. 1985. Anatomy of North American woods. An atlas of light and scanning electron micrographs. I. Hardwoods. Studies of the San'in Region, Research Data and Source Material, No. 1. Center for Studies of San'in Region, Shimane Univ., Japan. 151 pp. [Jap.; Eng. summ.]

Furuno, T. 1987. Anatomical features of North American hardwoods. Studies of the San'in Region, Forest Resources, Center for Studies of San'in Region, Shimane Univ., No. 3: 37–52. [Jap.; Eng. summ.]

Furuno, T. & Saiki, H. 1974. Anatomical characteristics of tropical woods. Res. Rep. Foreign Wood, Shimane Univ. No. 3: 39–119. [Jap.; Eng. summ.]

Gabrielyan, E.Ts. 1954. The wood structure of the chief Caucasian species of Sorbus. Izv. Akad. Nauk arm. SSR 7 (4): 73–79. [Russ.]

Gabrielyan, E.Ts. 1971. Wood structure of the western Asiatic species of the genus Sorbus L. Biol. Zh. arm. SSR 24 (2): 45–53. [Russ.]

Gabrielyan, E.Ts. 1978. Ryabiny (Sorbus L.) zapadnoi Azii i Gimalaev. Akad. Nauk arm. SSR: Erevan. 264 pp. [Eng. summ. 233–240.]

Gagnepain, F. & Boureau, E. 1946 [1947]. Une nouvelle famille de Gymnospermes: les Sarcopodacées. Bull. Soc. bot. Fr. 93: 313–320.

Gagnepain, F. & Boureau, E. 1947. Nouvelles considerations systématiques à propos du Sarcopus aberrans Gagnepain. Bull. Soc. bot. Fr. 94: 182–185.

Gaiotti de Peralta, C. & Edlmann Abbate, M.L. 1981. Caratteristiche anatomiche ed usi di 25 specie legnose provenienti dalla Repubblica di Panama. Rivta Agric. subtrop. trop. 75: 325–379.

Gajvoronskij, V.G. [Gayvoronsky, V.G.] 1969. The Kamchatka plane. Dokl. Akad. Nauk SSSR 184: 945–948. [Russ.]

Gale, R. 1982. Some pitfalls in wood identification, with reference to Nothofagus. IAWA Bull. n.s. 3: 179–184.

Gandelová, L. 1978. Anatomická stavba dřeva u vybraných druhů křovitých vrb vyšších poloh. [The anatomical structure of xylem in selected willow species of the shrubby growth habit at higher elevations.] Čas. Slez. Muz., Dendrol., ser. C, 27: 159–172. [Eng. summ.]

Gardner, R.O. 1978. Systematic notes on the Alseuosmiaceae. Blumea 24: 138–142.

Garratt, G.A. 1924. Some New Zealand woods. N.Z. State For. Serv., Professional Paper No. 1: 56 pp.

Garratt, G.A. 1931. Philippine Dao (Dracontomelum dao). Trop. Woods 27: 1–11.

Garratt, G.A. 1933a. Systematic anatomy of the woods of the Myristicaceae. Trop. Woods 35: 6–48.

Garratt, G.A. 1933b. Bearing of wood anatomy on the relationships of the Myristicaceae. Trop. Woods 36: 20–44.

Garratt, G.A. 1934. Systematic anatomy of the woods of the Monimiaceae. Trop. Woods 39: 18–44.

Garratt, G.A. 1936. The wood of Symphonia globulifera. Trop. Woods 45: 1–15.

Gasson, P. 1979. The identification of eight woody genera of the Caprifoliaceae by selected features of their root anatomy. Bot. J. Linn. Soc. 78: 267–284.

Gasson, P. 1987. Some implications of anatomical variations in the wood of pedunculate oak (Quercus robur L.), including comparisons with common beech (Fagus sylvatica L.). IAWA Bull. n.s. 8: 149–166.

Gasson, P. 1993. Wood anatomy of Swartzieae and related caesalpinioid and papilionoid legumes. Abstr. XV intn. Bot. Congr., Yokohama: 3.5.4-3 [Abstr.]

Gasson, P. & Cheek, M. 1992. The wood anatomy of Pseudobersama mossambicensis and Trichilia capitata (Meliaceae) compared. Kew Bull. 47: 753–758.

Gasson, P. & Cutler, D.F. 1990. Root anatomy of 17 genera growing in the British Isles. IAWA Bull. n.s. 11: 3–46.

Gasson, P. & Dobbins, D.R. 1991. Wood anatomy of the Bignoniaceae, with a comparison of trees and lianas. IAWA Bull. n.s. 12: 389–417.

Gattuso, M.A. & Gattuso, S.J. 1985. Study of the development of the unusual growth in the stem of Chenopodium ambrosioides L. (Chenopodiaceae). Physis, C, 42 (105): 53–56.

Geh-Siew-Yin & Keng, H. 1974. Morphological studies on some inland Rhizophoraceae. Gard. Bull., Singapore 27: 183–220.

Geiger, F. 1915. Anatomische Untersuchungen über die Jahresringbildung von Tectona grandis. Jb. wiss. Bot. 55: 521–607.

Gencsi, L. 1976 [1977]. Change of anatomical characteristics in Quercus cerris from pith to bark. Erdesz. Faipari Egy Tud. Kozl. (1): 85–89. [Hung.]

Gérard, A. 1917. Recherches sur la spécification histologique de différents bois de Madagascar, avec étude comparative des principaux bois industriels d'Europe. Lons-Le-Saunier. 160 pp. Also in: Trav. Lab. Mat. méd., Paris 11 (1917–19) [1920] (1): 160 pp.

Gerry, E. 1914. Tylosis: their occurrence and practical significance in some American woods. J. agric. Res. 1: 445–469 + 10 plates.

Ghelmeziu, N. 1958. Lemnul de cătină de rîu (Hippophae rhamnoides L., fam. Eleagnaceae). Revta Pădurilor, No. 5: 267–272.

Ghosh, S.S. & Purkayastha, S.K. 1960a. Characteristic arrangement of septate fibres in the wood of Averrhoa sp. Sci. Cult. 25: 690–691.

Ghosh, S.S. & Purkayastha, S.K. 1960b. Anatomical studies on the resiniferous system in Boswellia serrata Roxb. Indian For. 86: 684–695.

Ghosh, S.S. & Shahi, R. 1961. Taggar wood and its Indian substitute. Indian For. 87: 119–123.

Ghouse, A.K.M. & Yunus, M. 1974. A new record on the occurrence of stratified cambium in the family Mimosaceae. Geobios, Jodhpur 1: 138.

Gibson, A.C. 1973. Comparative anatomy of secondary xylem in Cactoideae (Cactaceae). Biotropica 5: 29–65.

Gibson, A.C. 1977a. Vegetative anatomy of Maihuenia (Cactaceae) with some theoretical discussions of ontogenetic changes in xylem cell types. Bull. Torrey bot. Cl. 104: 35–48.

Gibson, A.C. 1977b. Wood anatomy of Opuntias with cylindrical to globular stems. Bot. Gaz. 138: 334–351.

Gibson, A.C. 1978a. Woody anatomy of Platyopuntias. Aliso 9: 279–307.

Gibson, A.C. 1978b. Dimorphism of secondary xylem in two species of cacti. Flora 167: 403–408.

Gibson, A.C. 1978c. Rayless secondary xylem of Halophytum. Bull. Torrey bot. Cl. 105: 39–44.

Gibson, A.C. 1979. Anatomy of Koeberlinia and Canotia revisited. Madroño 26: 1–12.

Gibson, A.C. 1980. Wood anatomy of Thornea, including some comparisons with other Hypericaceae. IAWA Bull. n.s. 1: 87–92.

Gibson, A.C. 1981. Vegetative anatomy of Pachycormus (Anacardiaceae). Bot. J. Linn. Soc. 83: 273–284.

Giebel, K.P. & Dickison, W.C. 1976. Wood anatomy of Clethraceae. J. Elisha Mitchell sci. Soc. 92: 17–26.

Giger, E. 1913. Linnaea borealis L., eine monographische Studie. Beih. bot. Zbl. 30 (II): 1–78.

Gil, R.H. [= Hernández Gil, R.] 1989. Ritmicidad en el crecimiento de Vallea stipularis L. Pittieria 18: 44–56. [Eng. summ.]

Gilbert, S.G. 1940. Evolutionary significance of ring porosity in woody angiosperms. Bot. Gaz. 102: 105–120.

Gill, L.S., Karatela, Y.Y., Lamina, B.L. & Husaini, S.W.H. 1985a. Cytology and histomorphology of Moringa oleifera Lam. (Moringaceae). Feddes Repert. 96: 299–305.

Gill, L.S., Lamina, B.L. & Karatela, Y.Y. 1985b. Histomorphological studies of the tracheary elements and the economic potentials of some tropical hardwoods. Sylvatrop 10 (2): 119–141.

Gill, L.S. & Ogunlowo, C.O. 1986. Histomorphology of the tracheary elements of some leguminous woods. J. Timber Develop. Assn. India 32 (2): 31–38.

Gill, L.S. & Ogunlowo, C.O. 1988. Histomorphology of the tracheary elements of some tropical hardwoods. J. Timber Develop. Assn. India 34 (1): 42–52.

Gill, L.S. & Onuja, J.E. 1983a. Tracheary elements in some commercial woods (Sterculiaceae) from Nigeria. J. Indian Acad. Wood Sci. 14 (1): 53–58.

Gill, L.S. & Onuja, J.E. 1983b. Tracheary characteristics of some euphorbiaceous woods of Nigeria. Sylvatrop 8 (2-4): 139–144.

Gill, L.S. & Onuja, J.E. 1984a. A comparative study of the tracheary elements of some commercial hardwoods of Nigeria. Feddes Repert. 95: 645–655.

Gill, L.S. & Onuja, J.E. 1984b. A comparative study of the tracheary elements of some ornamental and fruit trees from Nigeria. Feddes Repert. 95: 657–662.

Gill, L.S. & Onuja, J.E. 1984c. Tracheary characteristics of some Nigerian Terminalia spp. Feddes Repert. 95: 355–358.

Gill, L.S. & Onuja, J.E. 1984d. Tracheary elements of some Nigerian woods (Meliaceae). J. Indian Acad. Wood Sci. 15 (2): 65–69.

Gill, L.S., Onuja, J.E. & Husaini, S.W.H. 1983. Observations on the tracheary elements of some Nigerian leguminous woods. Legume Res. 6: 9–17.

Gilles, M. 1905. Etude morphologique et anatomique du sablier (Hura crepitans L.). Ann. Inst. colon. Marseille, sér. 2, 3: 51–120.

Giordano, G. 1939; 1940. Cenni monografici sulle piante forestale e sui legnami dell'A.O.I. Riv. for. ital. 1: 183–188, 238–244, 447–454, 554–560, 597–606 (1939). 2: 32–36, 96–104, 250–258 (1940).

Giraud, B. 1977a. Statistical analysis of wood structure variation as related to distance from the pith in Entandrophragma utile (Meliaceae). IAWA Bull. 1977/4: 71–75.

Giraud, B. 1977b. Variation des caractères anatomiques d'un bois de Méliacée: dimensions des rayons ligneux. Adansonia, sér. 2, 17: 97–106.

Giraud, B. 1979. Corrélation entre la répartition du parenchyme ligneux vertical et la surface vasculaire dans un bois de Meliaceae. Adansonia, sér. 2, 19: 87–92.

Giraud, B. 1980. Correlation between wood anatomical characters in Entandrophragma utile (Meliaceae). IAWA Bull. n.s. 1: 73–75.

Giraud, B. 1981. Structure des perforations des éléments de vaisseaux dans le genre Hieronyma Allem. (Euphorbiaceae). Bull. Mus. natn. Hist. nat., Paris, sér. 4, B, Adansonia 3: 95–104.

Giraud, B. 1983. Les cellules perforées des rayons ligneux chez les Euphorbiacées. Bull. Mus. natn. Hist. nat., Paris, sér. 4, B, Adansonia 5: 213–221.

Giraud, B. 1985. Xylologie et évolution chez les Euphorbiacées arborescentes. Comité Trav. Hist. Sci., Bull. Sect. Sci. 8: 33–46.

Gleason, H.A. & Panshin, A.J. 1936. Swietenia krukovii, a new species of mahogany from Brazil. Amer. J. Bot. 23: 21–26.

Goldberg, A. & Nelson, S.-C. 1989. Haptanthus, a new dicotyledonous genus from Honduras. Syst. Bot. 14: 16–19.

Goldblatt, P., Tobe, H., Carlquist, S. & Patel, V.C. 1985. Familial position of the Cape genus Empleuridium. Ann. Missouri bot. Gard. 72: 167–183.

Gomes, A.V. 1984. Wood structure of Sclerocarya caffra Sond. (Anacardiaceae). Proc. Pacific Regional Wood Anatomy Conf., Tsukuba, Japan, 1984: 147–149.

Gomes, A.V., Teixeira, L.L., Schaitza, E.G. & Hofmeister, R.M. 1989. Perforation plates in vessels of Citharexylum myrianthum Cham. (Verbenaceae). IAWA Bull. n.s. 10: 27–34.

Gomes, J.I. 1982. A madeira de Cordia goeldiana Huber. Bol. Pesq. EMBRAPA Cent. Pesq. Agropec. Trop. Umido, No. 45: 16 pp. [Eng. summ.]

Gomes, J.I. 1983. Indícios de hibridação natural entre Hevea brasiliensis (H.B.K.) Muell. Arg. e H. camargoana Pires com base na anatomia da madeira. Bol. Pesq. EMBRAPA 52: 5–24.

Gomes, J.I. & Silva, E.M.S. da 1992 [1993]. Estudo anatômico da madeira do gênero Hevea. Bol. Mus. para. Emílio Goeldi, Bot. 8 (1): 3–44. [Eng. summ.]

Gómez L., B. 1959. Estructura anatómica e histológica de un grupo de 21 especies del bosque chiapaneco. Vol. II. Inst. Mex. Invest. Tec. 199 pp.

Gómez-Vázquez, B.G. & Engleman, E.M. 1983. Wood anatomy of Bursera longipes and Bursera copallifera. IAWA Bull. n.s. 4: 207–212.

Gomide, J.L., Kutscha, N.P., Shottafer, J.E. & Zabel, L.W. 1972. Kraft pulping and fiber characteristics of five Brazilian woods. Wood & Fiber 4: 158–169.

Gonzales, E.V. 1976 [1978]. Identification of white crystals from narra (Pterocarpus indicus Willd) wood. Philipp. J. Sci. 105: 223–233.

Gonzalez, M.E., Van der Slooten, H.J. & Richter, H.G. 1971. Maderas latinoamericanas. VII. Calophyllum brasiliense, Couratari panamensis, Dendropanax arboreum y Bombacopsis sessilis. Turrialba 21: 466–477.

Gorczyńska, J. 1955. O właściwe wykorzystanie wawrzynka wilczełyko (Daphne mezereum L.). [For a proper use of the Mezereon (Daphne mezereum L.).] Roczn. Sekc. Dendrol. pol. Tow. bot. 10: 325–351. [Eng. summ.]

Gorczyńska, J. 1958. Dalsze badania nad rodzajem Daphne (D. cheorum L. i D. caucasica Pall). Roczn. Sekc. Dendrol. pol. Tow. bot. 12: 121–149. [Germ. summ.]

Gorczyński, T. 1951. Badania anatomiczno-porównawcze nad drewnem buka zwyczajnego (Fagus sylvatica L.). Roczn. Sekc. Dendrol. pol. Tow. bot. 7: 3–114. [Eng. summ.]

Gottwald, H.P.J. 1968. L'identification et l'appellation des bois de "Lauan" et de "Meranti". Bois For. Trop., No. 121: 35–45.

Gottwald, H.P.J. 1972. Tyloses in fiber tracheids. Wood Sci. Technol. 6: 121–127.

Gottwald, H. 1977. The anatomy of secondary xylem and the classification of ancient dicotyledons. Pl. Syst. Evol., Suppl. 1: 111–121.

Gottwald, H. 1980a. 'Louro preto' – found to be the first silica-bearing Cordia (Cordia glabrata, Boraginaceae). IAWA Bull. n.s. 1: 55–58.

Gottwald, H. 1980b. Tropical hardwoods containing resins. Congr. Assn. Tech. int. Bois trop., Libreville, Gabon. 22 pp. [For. Prod. Abstr. 4 (1981) No. 864.]

Gottwald, H. 1982. First description of the wood anatomy of Antrophora, Lepidocordia and Pteleocarpa (Boraginaceae). IAWA Bull. n.s. 3: 161–165.

Gottwald, H. 1983a. Hochwertige Austauschhölzer der Gattung Cordia. Holz-Zbl. 109: 1228 + 3 plates.

Gottwald, H. 1983b. Wood anatomical studies of Boraginaceae (s.l.) I. Cordioideae. IAWA Bull. n.s. 4: 161–178.

Gottwald, H., Knigge, W., Noack, D. & Sachtler, M. 1968. Anatomische und physikalisch-technologische Untersuchungen an vier liberianischen Holzarten. Mitt. Bundesforsch. Anst. Forst Holzwirtsch. Hamburg No. 67: 48 pp.

Gottwald, H. & Noack, D. 1965 [1966]. Anatomische und physikalisch-technologische Untersuchungen an Holzarten der Republik Sudan. Mitt. Bundesforsch. Anst. Forst Holzwirtsch. Hamburg No. 64: 51 pp.

Gottwald, H. & Noack, D. 1968. Movingui. Distemonanthus benthamianus Baill. Caesalpiniaceae. Westafrika. Holz Roh- u. Werkst. 26: 355–356.

Gottwald, H. & Noack, D. 1972. Rotes Meranti. Red Meranti. Verschiedene Arten der Untergattung Rubroshorea der Gattung Shorea. Dipterocarpaceae. Holz Roh- u. Werkst. 30: 33–40.

Gottwald, H. & Parameswaran, N. 1964. Vielfache Gefässdurchbrechungen in der Familie Dipterocarpaceae. Zeit. Bot. 52: 321–334. [Eng. summ.]

Gottwald, H. & Parameswaran, N. 1966a. Das sekundäre Xylem der Familie Dipterocarpaceae, anatomische Untersuchungen zur Taxonomie und Phylogenie. Bot. Jb. 85: 410–508.

Gottwald, H. & Parameswaran, N. 1966b. On the taxonomic status of Vateria seychellarum Dyer based on anatomical evidence. Taxon 15: 184–186.

Gottwald, H. & Parameswaran, N. 1967. Beiträge zur Anatomie und Systematik der Quiinaceae. Bot. Jb. 87: 361–381.

Gottwald, H. & Parameswaran, N. 1968. Das sekundäre Xylem und die systematische Stellung der Ancistrocladaceae und Dioncophyllaceae. Bot. Jb. 88: 49–69. [Eng. summ.]

Gottwald, H. & Parameswaran, N. 1980. Anatomy of wood and bark of Tectona (Verbenaceae) in relation to taxonomy. Bot. Jb. 101: 363–384.

Gottwald, H. & Richter, H.G. 1984. Koto (Pterygota)-Hölzer dreier Erdteile. Holz-Zbl. 110: 2242–2243.

Gottwald, H. & Schwab, E. 1975. Kosipo. Entandrophragma candollei Harms (= E. ferrugineum A. Chev.). Meliaceae. Holz Roh- u. Werkst. 33: 37–44.

Gottwald, H. & Schwab, E. 1978. Ovengkol. Guibourtia ehie (A. Chev.) J. Léonard (= Copaifera ehie A. Chev.). Caesalpiniaceae. Holz Roh- u. Werkst. 36: 323–330.

Gottwald, H., Schwab, E. & Willeitner, H. 1982. Lenga. Nothofagus pumilio (Poepp. & Endl.) Krasser. Fagaceae. Holz Roh- u. Werkst. 40: 19–27.

Gourlay, I.D. & Kanowski, P.J. 1991. Marginal parenchyma bands and crystalliferous chains as indicators of age in African Acacia species. IAWA Bull. n.s. 12: 187–194.

Gouwentak, C.A. 1935. Macroscopical and anatomical characters of the wood of Eucalyptus globulus Labill. and E. rostrata Schl. Meded. Landbouwhoogesch. Wageningen 39 (3): 1–17.

Graham, S.A., Baas, P. & Tobe, H. 1987. Lourtella, a new genus of Lythraceae from Peru. Syst. Bot. 12: 519–533.

Graham, S.A. & Lorence, D.H. 1978. The rediscovery of Tetrataxis Hooker fil. (Lythraceae). Bot. J. Linn. Soc. 76: 71–82.

Graham, S.A., Tobe, H. & Baas, P. 1986. Koehneria, a new genus of Lythraceae from Madagascar. Ann. Missouri bot. Gard. 73: 788–809.

Greene, E.C. 1932. Santa Maria: a neotropical timber of the genus Calophyllum. Trop. Woods 30: 9–16.

Gregory, M. 1980. Wood identification: an annotated bibliography. IAWA Bull. n.s. 1: 3–41.

Gregory, M. & Baas, P. 1989. A survey of mucilage cells in vegetative organs of the dicotyledons. Israel J. Bot. 38: 125–174.

Greguss, P. 1959. Holzanatomie der europäischen Laubhölzer und Sträucher. Akadémiai Kiadó, Budapest. 2nd edn. 330 pp. + 303 plates.

Greguss, P. 1979. Polyphyletic origin of angiosperms in the light of xylotomy. Acta biol. szeged. 25 (1–2): 17–31.

Greguss, P. 1982. Phylogenetic importance of the xylotomy and geographical distribution of homoxylic Drimys winteri and Drimys colorata (2). Acta biol. szeged. 28: 41–52.

Grisa, E. 1988. Anatomie ligneuse de 24 espèces feuillues de la côte ouest de Madagascar. Fiche Technique, Centre de Formation Professionelle Forestière de Morondava: No. 16: 113 pp.

Groom, P. 1911. The evolution of the annual ring and medullary rays of Quercus. Ann. Bot. 25: 985–1003.

Groom, P. 1912. The medullary rays of Fagaceae. Ann. Bot. 26: 1124–1125.

Groom, P. 1926. Excretory systems in the secondary xylem of Meliaceae. Ann. Bot. 40: 631–649.

Gros, J.P. 1991. Xylotomie d'Acacia tristis Welw. ex Oliv., Mimosaceae. Rev. Cytol. Biol. vég., Bot. 14: 117–126.

Gros, J.P. 1992. Xylotomie d'Albizia coriaria Welw. ex Oliv., Mimosaceae. Rev. Cytol. Biol. vég., Bot. 15: 51–63.

Grosser, D. 1977. Die Hölzer Mitteleuropas. Ein mikrophotographischer Lehratlas. Springer-Verlag: Berlin. 208 pp.

Grosser, D. 1983; 1984; 1985. Mikrophotographische Reihe: Mediterrane und nahöstliche Hölzer – Tafel 1. Ficus carica L. Moraceae. Holzforschung 37: 327–330 (1983). – Tafel 2. Ficus sycomorus L., Moraceae. Ibid. 38: 55–59 (1984). – Tafel 4. Arbutus unedo L. und A. andrachne L., Ericaceae. Ibid. 39: 189–194 (1985).

Grotta, A.S. 1961. Contribuição ao estudo morfológico e anatômico de Buddleia brasiliensis Jacq. Loganiaceae. Anais Fac. Farm. Odont. Univ. S. Paulo 18: 5–23. [Eng. summ.]

Groulez, J. & Wood, P.J. 1984. Terminalia superba. Monographie. Centre tech. For. trop.: Nogent-sur-Marne. 85 pp.

Groulez, J. & Wood, P.J. 1985. Terminalia superba. A monograph. Centre tech. For. trop.: Nogent-sur-Marne & Commonw. For. Inst.: Oxford. 77 pp. [Eng. edn.]

Grumbles, T.L. 1941. The comparative anatomy of the secondary xylem of four oriental species of Celtis. Lloydia 4: 145–152.

Grundwag, M. & Werker, E. 1976. Comparative wood anatomy as an aid to identification of Pistacia L. species. Israel J. Bot. 25: 152–167.

Guédès, M. 1979. Magnolioid island plants and angiosperm evolution. In: Plants and islands (ed. D. Bramwell): 307–328. Academic Press: London, New York, etc.

Gupta, K.M. 1934. On the wood anatomy and theoretical significance of homoxylous angiosperms. J. Indian bot. Soc. 13: 71–101.

Guridi Gomez, L.I. 1978. Estudio comparativo de la anatomia de la madera de algunas Sapotaceas mexicanas. Ciencia Forestal 3 (11): 13–34.

Gutzwiller, M.-A. 1961. Die phylogenetische Stellung von Suriana maritima L. Bot. Jb. 81: 1–49.

Gziryan, M. 1950. The wood of ashes. Trud. bot. Inst. Akad. Nauk arm. SSR 7: 105–132. [Russ.]

Gziryan, M. 1952. Structure of bark and wood of apricot. Izv. Akad. Nauk arm. SSR 5 (8): 71–82. [Russ.]

Gziryan, M. 1953. The wood of planes. Izv. Akad. Nauk arm. SSR 6 (5): 75–80. [Russ.]

Hafić, V. 1958. Crveni hrast – Quercus borealis Michx. (Anatomska gradca i neka tehnička svojstva.) [The anatomical structure and some technical properties of Quercus borealis Michx. wood.] Sumarstvo 11: 186–190. [Serb.; Eng. summ.]

Hall, J.W. 1952. The comparative anatomy and phylogeny of the Betulaceae. Bot. Gaz. 113: 235–270.

Hallé, N. & Wilde, J.J.F.E. de 1978. Trichostephanus acuminatus Gilg (Flacourtiacées), une approche biosystématique. Adansonia, sér. 2, 18: 167–182.

Hamaya, T. 1959. Dendrological studies of the Japanese and some foreign genera of the Thymelaeaceae. Anatomical and phylogenetic studies. Bull. Tokyo Univ. For. 55: 1–80. [Eng.]

Hamet, R. 1912. Sur le développement des formations médullaires des Greenovia. Annls. Sci. nat., Bot., sér. 9, 15: 253–256.

Hamet, R. 1925. Sur les formations cribro-vasculaires médullaires de deux Crassulacées. C.R. Acad. Sci., Paris 180: 1424–1425.

Handa, T. 1932. Über die sukzessiven Holzbastringe von Pueraria triloba Makino und Wistaria floribunda DC. Bot. Mag., Tokyo 46: 13–22. [Jap.; Germ. summ.]

Handa, T. 1936a. Abnormal vascular bundle in the stem of Campsis grandiflora K. Schum. Jap. J. Bot. 8: 47–58.

Handa, T. 1936b. Anatomical observations on the internal cambium of the stem in Marsdenia tomentosa Morr. et Decne. Jap. J. Bot. 8: 59–64.

Handa, T. 1937. Anomalous secondary growth in Bauhinia japonica Maxim. Jap. J. Bot. 9: 37–53.

Handa, T. 1938. Anomalous secondary growth in the axis of Bauhinia championi Benth. Jap. J. Bot. 9: 303–311.

Handa, T. 1940. Anomalous secondary growth in the axis of Lophopyxis pentaptera (K. Schum.) Engler. Bot. Mag., Tokyo 54: 41–47. [Eng.]

Hanson, H.C. & Brenke, B. 1936. Seasonal development of growth layers in Fraxinus campestris and Acer saccharinum. Bot. Gaz. 82: 286–305.

Harms, H. 1940. Meliaceae. In: Die natürlichen Pflanzenfamilien by Engler, A. & Prantl, K. 2nd edn. 19B (1): 1–183. W. Engelmann: Leipzig.

Harrar, E.S. 1937. Notes on the genus Flindersia R. Br. and the systematic anatomy of the important flindersian timbers indigenous to Queensland. J. Elisha Mitchell Sci. Soc. 53: 282–291.

Harrar, E.S. 1946. Note on starch grains in septate fiber-tracheids. Trop. Woods 85: 1–9.

Hart, H. 't & Koek-Noorman, J. 1989. The origin of the woody Sedoideae (Crassulaceae). Taxon 38: 535–544.

Harvey-Gibson, R.J. 1911. Note on the synonymy and histological characters of East London Boxwood (Gonioma kamassi, E. Mey.). Biochem. J. 6: 127–129.

Harvey-Gibson, R.J. & Horsman, E. 1919. Contributions towards a knowledge of the anatomy of the lower dicotyledons. II. The anatomy of the stem of the Berberidaceae. Trans. roy. Soc. Edinb. 52: 501–515 + 1 plate.

Harzmann, L.-J., Koch, H. & Wagenführ, R. 1975. Über Eigenschaften des Holzes von Illicium verum aus der demokratischen Republik Vietnam. Wiss. Z. tech. Univ. Dresden 24: 263–268.

Haskins, M.L. & Hayden, W.J. 1987. Anatomy and affinities of Penthorum. Amer. J. Bot. 74: 164–177.

Hayashi, S. 1991. Micrographic atlas of Japanese woods. Wood Research Institute: Kyoto Univ. 23 plates + 147 plates. [Jap. only, except for Latin names.]

Hayashi, S., Kishima, T., Lau, L.C., Wong, T.M. & Balan Menon, P.K. 1973. Micrographic atlas of southeast Asian timber. Div. Wood Biology, Wood Res. Inst., Kyoto Univ. 207 pp.

Hayashi, S. & Nomura, T. 1986. Anatomy and properties of tropical woods. Manual IV. Anatomy of 31 Sri Lanka wood species. Wood Res. Tech. Notes, No. 22: 112–144. [Jap. only.]

Hayden, W.J. 1977. Comparative anatomy and systematics of Picrodendron, genus incertae sedis. J. Arnold Arbor. 58: 257–279.

Hayden, W.J. 1992. Wood anatomy and relationships of Australasian Oldfieldioideae (Euphorbiaceae). IAWA Bull. n.s. 13: 243–244. [Abstr.]

Hayden, W.J. & Brandt, D.S. 1984. Wood anatomy and relationships of Neowawraea (Euphorbiaceae). Syst. Bot. 9: 458–466.

Hayden, W.J. & Hayden, S.M. 1984. Woody anatomy and relationships of Betula uber. Castanea 49: 26–30.

Hayden, W.J., Simmons, M.P. & Swanson, L.J. 1993. Wood anatomy of Amanoa (Euphorbiaceae). IAWA Jl. 14: 205–213.

Hedayetullah, S. & Chakravarty, A.K. 1942. A contribution to the wood anatomy of the Meliaceae and Rutaceae occurring in Bengal. J. Dept. Sci. Calcutta Univ. 1 (3): 1–20.

Hegedüs, A. 1970. Xylotomic studies on vine. Acta agron. Acad. Sci. hung. 19: 1–16.

Heim, J. 1971. Notions d'anatomie des bois et application à quelques espèces ligneuses récoltées aux Baléares en 1965. Nat. belg. 52: 505–543.

Heimsch, C. 1940. Wood anatomy and pollen morphology of Rhus and allied genera. J. Arnold Arbor. 21: 279–291.

Heimsch, C. 1942. Comparative anatomy of the secondary xylem in the 'Gruinales' and 'Terebinthales' of Wettstein with reference to taxonomic grouping. Lilloa 8: 83–198.

Heimsch, C. & Tschabold, E.E. 1972. Xylem studies in the Linaceae. Bot. Gaz. 133: 242–253.

Heimsch, C. & Wetmore, R.H. 1939. The significance of wood anatomy in the taxonomy of the Juglandaceae. Amer. J. Bot. 26: 651–660.

Heintzelman, C.E. & Howard, R.A. 1948. The comparative morphology of the Icacinaceae. V. The pubescence and the crystals. Amer. J. Bot. 35: 42–52.

Hejazi, R., Sabeti, H., Tabatabai, M., Niloofari, P. & Soleymani, P. 1961. Study on Iranian Iron Wood (Parrotia persica D.C.). Bull. Coll. Agric. Univ. Teheran No. 22: 72 pp. [Pers.; Eng. summ.]

Hejnowicz, A. 1973. Anatomia, embriologia i kariologia topoli. In: Topole. Populus L. (ed. Białobok, S.): 145–183. Polska Akad. Nauk, Zakład dendrol. Arbor. Kórn., Warsaw. 517 pp. [Eng. summ.]

Hejnowicz, A. 1980. Anatomia, embriologia i kariologia. In: Olsze. Alnus Mill. (ed. Białobok, S.): 73–97. Polska Akad. Nauk Inst. Dendrol.: Warsaw. [Eng. summ.]

Hejnowicz, A. 1990. Anatomia, embriologia i kariologia. In: Buk zwyczajny, Fagus sylvatica L. (ed. Białobok, S.): 75–96. Polska Akad. Nauk, Inst. Dendrol.: Warsaw. [Eng. summ.]

Hejnowicz, A. & Hejnowicz, Z. 1956 [1957]. Badania anatomiczne nad drewnem topoli. [Wood anatomy of the Populus.] Arbor. Kórn. 2: 195–218. [Eng. summ.]

Hemsley, J.H. & Verdcourt, B. 1956. Viridivia suberosa J.H. Hemsley et Verdcourt. Tabula 3555. Hooker's Icones Plantarum 36: 4 pp.

Henrickson, J. 1969. The succulent Fouquierias. Cact. Succ. J. (U.S.) 41: 178–184.

Henrickson, J. 1976. Marshalljohnstonia, a new genus (Asteraceae) with a rosette-shrub growth habit from Mexico. Syst. Bot. 1: 169–180.

Henrickson, J. & Flyr, L.D. 1985. Systematics of Leucophyllum and Eremogeton (Scrophulariaceae). Sida 11: 107–172.

Herat, T.R. & Theobald, W.L. 1977 [1978]. Comparative studies of vegetative anatomy in the Theaceae of Sri Lanka. Bot. J. Linn. Soc. 75: 375–386.

Heringer, E.P. & Paula, J.E. de 1974. Anatomia da madeira de Apuleia leiocarpa (Vog.) Macbride (Apuleia praecox Mart.) e Apuleia molaris Spruce (Leguminosae). VII. Cerrado 6 (23): 26–29.

Heringer, E.P. & Paula, J.E. de 1976. Anatomia do lenho secundário de Annona glabra L. (Annonaceae), algumas propriedades fisicas da madeira e análise crítica da grafia do gênero. Acta Amazonica 6: 423–432. [Eng. summ.]

Heringer, E.P. & Paula, J.E. de 1977. Estudo comparativo da anatomia da madeira e da folha, e do grão de pólen de Anacardium curatellifolium A. St. Hil. (Anacardiaceae) do Cerrado do Centro-Oeste do Brasil. Trab. XXVI Congr. nac. Bot., Rio de Janeiro 1975: 231–238.

Heringer, E.P., Rizzini, C.T. & Mattos Filho, A. de 1987. Taxionomia e anatomia do lenho de Dalbergia hortensis Her., Rizz. e Mattos (Leguminosae-Papilionatae). Revta. bras. Biol. 47: 633–640. [Eng. summ.]

Hernandez Camacho, J., Lozano, C.-G. & Henao, S.-J.E. 1980. Hallazgo del genero Trigonobalanus Forman, 1962 (Fagaceae) en el neotropico. II. Caldasia 13, No. 61: 9–43 [Eng. summ.]

Herrmann, H. 1922. Vergleichende Holzanatomie der Pappeln und Baumweiden. Bot. Archiv 2: 35–56, 79–112.

Hess, R.W. 1936. Occurrence of raphides in wood. Trop. Woods 46: 22–31.

Hess, R.W. 1946a; 1948. Keys to American woods (cont.). XVII. Woods with vasicentric tracheids. XVIII. Fibers with spiral thickenings. XIX. Special fibers in parenchyma-like arrangement. XX. Woods with unilaterally paratracheal parenchyma. Trop. Woods 85: 11–19 (1946). XXI. Parenchyma in numerous concentric bands. Ibid. 94: 29–52 (1948). [For I-XVI see Record, S.J.]

Hess, R.W. 1946b. Identification of New World timbers. I. Trop. Woods 86: 14–25. – II. Ibid. 87: 11–34; 88: 12–13. - III. Ibid. 88: 13–30.

Hess, R.W. 1950a. Classification of wood parenchyma in dicotyledons. Trop. Woods 96: 1–20.

Hess, R.W. 1950b. Identification of Swietenia and Carapa. Trop. Woods 96: 47–50.

Hess, R.W. 1950c. New genera of American woods. Trop. Woods 96: 50–55.

Heubl, G.R., Gaviria, J.C. & Wanner, G. 1990. A contribution to the taxonomy and evolution of Cordia (Boraginaceae) and allied genera. Chromosome numbers, pollen morphology and crystal pattern in wood. Bot. Jb. 112: 129–165.

Hill, J.F. 1983. Relationship among vessel diameter, vessel frequency, and spacing of parenchyma bands in wood of Carya tomentosa Nutt., Mockernut Hickory. Amer. J. Bot. 70: 934–939.

Hill, T.G. 1901. On the anatomy of the stem of Dalbergia paniculata Roxb. Ann. Bot. 15: 183–186.

Hillis, W.E. & Silva, D. de 1979. Inorganic extraneous constituents of wood. Holzforschung 33: 47–53.

Hils, M.H., Dickison, W.C., Lucansky, T.W. & Stern, W.L. 1988. Comparative anatomy and systematics of woody Saxifragaceae: Tetracarpaea. Amer. J. Bot. 75: 1687–1700.

Hirai, S. 1979–1985. Encyclopedia of the woods. Kanae-shobou, Tokyo, Nos. 1–24. [Jap. only.]

Hirata, T., Saiki, H. & Harada, H. 1972. Observations of crystals and silica inclusions in parenchyma cells of certain tropical woods by scanning electron microscope. Bull. Kyoto Univ. For. 44: 194–205. [Jap.; Eng. summ.]

Hjelmqvist, H. 1963. Some notes on Nothofagus from New Guinea and New Caledonia. Bot. Notiser 116: 225–237.

Ho, T.-H. 1949. Anatomy of the wood of Manglietia moto Dandy, with special reference to its vessel members. Bot. Bull. Acad. sin. 3: 126–133.

Ho, T.-H. 1985. A note of wood structure of Castanopsis longzhouica. Guihaia 5: 188. [Chin. only.]

Hoar, C.S. 1916. The anatomy and phylogenetic position of the Betulaceae. Amer. J. Bot. 3: 415–435.

Hofmann, E. 1955. Über die Anatomie einiger Hölzer der Quarnero-Insel Cherso. Zbl. Ges. Forstw. 74: 98–110.

Hogeweg, P. & Koek-Noorman, J. 1975. Wood anatomical classification using iterative character weighting. Acta bot. neerl. 24: 269–283.

Hoheisel, H., Karstedt, P. & Londoño, A. 1968. Determinación de los usos probables de algunas maderas de Colombia en base a los ensayos de propiedades físicas y mecánicas. Inst. Forest. Latinoamer. Invest. Capac., Merida. 77 pp.

Holbrook, N.M. & Putz, F.E. 1992. Secondary thickening in stems of Jacaratia (Caricaceae). Amer. J. Bot., Suppl.: 34–35. [Abstr.]

Holden, R. 1912. Some features in the anatomy of the Sapindales. Bot. Gaz. 53: 50–58.

Holdheide, W. 1955. Über das abnorme Dickenwachstum der Hainbuche (Carpinus betulus L.) und die Rolle der falschen Markstrahlen. In: Vergleichend-anatomische Untersuchungen aus dem forstbotanischen Institut München (ed. Huber, B.): 132–164. [Bot. Stud. 4.] Gustav Fischer: Jena.

Holz, D. & Bruckner, K. 1959. Über gemeinsame und unterschiedliche Eigenschaften von Stiel, Trauben- und Roteichenholz. Holzforsch. Holzverwert. 11 (4): 88–99.

Honda, M. 1970. Contribuição ao estudo do lenho do gênero Vochysia da Amazônia brasileira. I. Vochysia guianensis Aubl., V. obscura Warm. e V. inundata Ducke. Inst. nac. Pesq. Amazônia, Bol. Pesq. florest. No. 5: 1–15. II. Vochysia maxima Ducke, V. vismiifolia Spruce ex Warm. e V. rufa Mart. Ibid. No. 16: 1–11.

Honda, M. 1971. Contribuição ao estudo anatomico do lenho de cinco Sapotaceae de Amazônia. Acta Amazonica 1 (3): 71–83. [Eng. summ.]

Honda, M. 1971 [1972]. Madeiras "Ucuuba." I. Virola divergens Ducke e V. multinervia Ducke. Acta Amazonica 1 (2): 79–83.

Hooks, R.A. 1966. A taxonomical investigation into the comparative anatomy of the genus Terminalia; family Combretaceae. J. Inst. Wood Sci. 17: 7–26.

Horak, K.E. 1981. Anomalous secondary thickening in Stegnosperma (Phytolaccaceae). Bull. Torrey bot. Cl. 108: 189–197.

Horton, J.H. 1960. The wood anatomy of Delopyrum, Dentoceras, Polygonella, and Thysanella (Polygonaceae). ASB Bull. 7 (2): 29–30. [Abstr.]

Horton, J.H. 1963. A taxonomic revision of Polygonella (Polygonaceae). Brittonia 15: 177–203.

Hu, S.-Y. 1967. The evolution and distribution of the species of Aquifoliaceae in the Pacific area (1). J. Jap. Bot. 42: 13–27. [Eng.]

Huang, G. 1986. Comparative anatomical studies on the woods of Hamamelidaceae in China. Acta sci. nat. Univ. Sunyatseni (1): 22–28. [Chin.; brief Eng. summ.]

Huang, G.-L. & Lee, C.-L. 1982. Anatomical studies of Chunia wood. Acta bot. sin. 24: 506–511. [Chin.; Eng. summ.]

Huang, T.-C. 1965. Monograph of Daphniphyllum (1). Taiwania No. 11 (special issue): 57–98.

Huard, J. 1965. Anatomie des Rhopalocarpacées. Adansonia (Paris) 5: 103–123.

Huber, B. 1951. Mikroskopische Untersuchungen von Hölzern. In: Handbuch der Mikroskopie in der Technik (ed. Freund, H.). V (1): 79–192. Umschau Verlag: Frankfurt.

Huber, B. 1970. Lichtmikroskopische Untersuchungen von Hölzern, besonders die Bestimmung ihrer systematischen Zugehörigkeit. In: Handbuch der Mikroskopie in der Technik (ed. Freund, H.). V (1): 37–108. Umschau Verlag: Frankfurt. 2nd edn.

Huber, B., Holdheide, W. & Raack, K. 1941. Zur Frage der Unterscheidbarkeit des Holzes von Stiel- und Traubeneiche. Holz Roh- u. Werkst. 4: 373–380.

Huber, B. & Mägdefrau, K. 1953. Zur Phylogenie des heterogenen Markstrahlbaues. Ber. dt. bot. Ges. 66: 117–123.

Huber, B. & Rouschal, C. 1954. Mikrophotographischer Atlas mediterraner Hölzer. Fritz Haller Verlag: Berlin-Grunewald. 107 pp.

Huber, F. & Keller, R. 1993. Variabilité de la constitution anatomique d'accroissements annuels de chênes indigènes. Acta bot. gallica 140: 383–388.

Huber, H. 1963. Die Verwandtschaftsverhältnisse der Rosifloren. Mitt. bot. Staatssamml. München 5: 1–48.

Hummel, F.C. 1946. The formation of growth rings in Entandrophragma macrophyllum A. Chev. and Khaya grandifoliola C. DC. Empire For. Rev. 25: 103–107.

Humphrey, R.R. 1935. A study of Idria columnaris and Fouquiera splendens. Amer. J. Bot. 22: 184–206.

Huynh-Long, V. 1968. Contribution à l'étude du bois de Tarrietia cochinchinensis Pierre. Bull. Soc. roy. Bot. Belg. 101: 303–320.

Huynh-Long, V. 1969. Contribution à l'étude du bois d'Hopea odorata Roxburg. Bull. Soc. roy. Bot. Belg. 102: 305–316.

Huynh-Long, V. & Homès, J. 1969. Hopea pierrei Hance (Dipterocarpaceae): étude botanique et anatomie du bois. Bull. Soc. roy. Bot. Belg. 102: 101–106.

Hyde, K.C. 1925. Tropical light weight woods. Bot. Gaz. 79: 380–411.

IAWA 1964. Multilingual glossary of terms used in wood anatomy. Committee on Nomenclature, I.A.W.A. 186 pp. [Eng., French, Germ., Ital., Port., Span., Serbo-Croat.]

IAWA Committee 1981. Standard list of characters suitable for computerized hardwood identification. IAWA Bull. n.s. 2: 99–145.

Ilic, J. 1987. The CSIRO family key for hardwood identification. CSIRO, Divn. Wood Technology, Tech. Paper No. 8: 171 pp. CSIRO: Australia. [Also distributed by Brill: Leiden.] Associated software available from CSIRO.

Ilic, J. 1991. CSIRO atlas of hardwoods. Springer-Verlag: Berlin, etc. 525 pp.

Ilic, J. 1993. Computer aided wood identification using CSIROID. IAWA Jl. 14: 333–340.

Ingle, H.D. 1956. A note on the wood anatomy of the genus Corynocarpus. Trop. Woods 105: 8–12.

Ingle, H.D. & Dadswell, H.E. 1953; 1956. The anatomy of the timbers of the south-west Pacific area. II. Apocynaceae and Annonaceae. Aust. J. Bot. 1: 1–26. III. Myrtaceae. Ibid.: 353–401 (1953). IV. Cunoniaceae, Davidsoniaceae and Eucryphiaceae. Ibid. 4: 125–152 (1956).

Inokuma, T. & Shimaji, K. 1950. Dendrological and wood anatomical notes on Yukunoki (Cladrastis shikokiana Makino) and Fujiki (Platyosprion platycarpum Maximowicz). Bull. Tokyo Univ. Forests 38: 125–138. [Jap.; Eng. summ.]

Inokuma, T., Shimaji, K. & Sudo, S. 1953. The wood anatomical characters of Styracaceae in Japan. Bull. Tokyo Univ. Forests 45: 181–201. [Jap.; Eng. summ.]

Iqbal, M. (ed.) 1990. The vascular cambium. Research Studies Press: Taunton. 246 pp.

Ito, M. & Kishima, T. 1951. Studies on the tyloses – their occurrence in the domestic wood. Wood Res. Rev. 3: 44–55. [Jap.; Eng. summ.]

Izumoto, Y. & Hayashi, S. 1990. Identification system of wood assisted by microcomputer II. Mem. Osaka Kyoiku Univ., ser. III, 39(1): 87–102. [Jap.]

Jaccard, P. 1914. Structure anatomique de racines hypertendues. Rev. gén. Bot. 25bis: 359–372.

Jaccard, P. 1922. Nombre et dimensions des rayons medullaires chez Ailanthus glandulosa. Bull. Soc. vaud. Sci. nat. 54: 253–262.

Jacquiot, C., Trenard, Y. & Dirol, D. 1973. Atlas d'anatomie des bois des angiospermes (essences feuillues). 2 vols. Cent. Tech. Bois: Paris. 175 pp. + 72 plates. [French & Eng. text.]

Jagiella, C. & Kurschner, H. 1987. Atlas der Hölzer Saudi Arabiens. Beih. Tübinger Atlas des vorderen Orients, ser. A, No. 20: 176 pp. Ludwig Reichert Verlag: Wiesbaden.

Jain, D.K. 1984. Development of primary and secondary vascular systems in stem of Adenocalymna alliaceum Miers. Acta bot. indica 12: 26–34.

Jain, D.K. & Singh, V. 1980. Studies in Bignoniaceae. VII. Wood anatomy. Proc. Indian Acad. Sci., Pl. Sci. 89: 443–456.

James, C.F. & Ingle, H.D. 1956. The anatomy of the timbers of the south-west Pacific area. V. Flacourtiaceae. Aust. J. Bot. 4: 200–215.

Jane, F.W. revised by Wilson, K. & White, D.J.B. 1970. The structure of wood. 2nd edn. A. & C. Black: London. 478 pp.

Janin, G. & Clément, A. 1972. Mise en evidence de cristaux de carbonate de calcium dans le bois des peupliers. Consequences sur la répartition des ions mineraux liée à la duraminisation. Annls. Sci. for. 29: 67–105.

Janssonius, H.H. 1914. Mikrographie einiger technisch wichtigen Holzarten aus Surinam. Verh. k. Akad. Wet. Amsterdam 18(2): 1–50.

Janssonius, H.H. 1926. Mucilage cells and oil cells in the woods of the Lauraceae. Trop. Woods 6: 3–4.

Janssonius, H.H. 1929. A contribution to the natural classification of the Euphorbiaceae. Trop. Woods 19: 8–10.

Janssonius, H.H. 1931. Die Verteilung des stockwerkartigen Aufbaues im Holz der Dikotylen. Rec. Trav. bot. néerl. 28: 97–106. [Eng. summ. in Trop. Woods 28: 49; 1931.]

Janssonius, H.H. 1932. Note on the wood of the genus Gironniera. Trop. Woods 29: 28–29.

Janssonius, H.H. 1940. Anatomische Bestimmungstabelle für die Javanischen Hölzer. E.J. Brill: Leiden. 240 pp.

Janssonius, H.H. 1950. Wood-anatomy and relationship. Taxonomic notes in connection with the key to Javanese woods. Blumea 6: 407–461. The variability of the wood-anatomy in large and small genera. Ibid.: 462–464. The vessels in the wood of Javan mangrove trees. Ibid.: 465–469.

Janssonius, H.H. 1952. Key to the Javanese woods on the basis of anatomical features. E.J. Brill: Leiden. 244 pp.

Jay, B.A. 1936. The anatomy of some lauraceous scent-yielding woods known as "Medang". Kew Bull.: 66–72.

Jayawardana, C.P. 1932. The anatomical structure of certain Ceylon woods. Ann. roy. Bot. Gard. Peradeniya 11: 307–317.

Jeffrey, E.C. & Cole, R.D. 1916. Experimental investigations on the genus Drimys. Ann. Bot. 30: 359–368.

Jenkin, C.C. 1962. Evidence from wood anatomy on whether Ptaeroxylon and Vavaea are correctly placed in the Rutaceae. Rep. Imp. For. Inst., Oxford (1960/1): 24.

Jentsch, F. et al. 1936; 1938; 1939. Beschreibung tropischer Hölzer aus dem Urwalde Kameruns. Z. Weltforstwirtschaft 3: 110–120; 235–246; 331–341; 497–506 (1936). Ibid. 4: 35–45; 515–524 (1936). Kolonial. forst. Mitt. 1: 235–245 (1938). Ibid. 1: 425–432 (1939).

Jimenez, M.S., Caballero, A. & Morales, D. 1978 [1979]. Contribucion al estudio anatomico de las euforbias canarias. Parte vegetativa. Vieraea 8 (1): 31–48. [Eng. summ.]

Jing, W., Ohtani, J. & Fukazawa, K. 1988. SEM observations on vestured pits in some Yunnan hardwoods. Res. Bull. Coll. exp. For. Hokkaido Univ. 45: 789–809. [Eng.]

Jing, W., Ohtani, J. & Fukazawa, K. 1989. SEM observations on the vessel wall modifications in Yunnan hardwoods. Res. Bull. Coll. exp. For. Hokkaido Univ. 46: 847–939. [Jap.; Eng. summ.]

Johnson, C.T. 1984. The wood anatomy of Leptospermum Forst. (Myrtaceae). Aust. J. Bot. 32: 323–337.

Johnson, L.A.S. & Briggs, B.G. 1975. On the Proteaceae – the evolution and classification of a southern family. Bot. J. Linn. Soc. 70: 83–182.

Johnston, D.R. 1952. The anatomy of some species of Tabebuia. Timb. News Sawm. Eng. 60: 337–338; 382–383.

Joshi, A.C. 1931. Anomalous secondary thickening in the stem of Rumex dentatus L. J. Indian Bot. Soc. 10: 209–212.

Joshi, A.C. 1935. Secondary thickening in the stem and root of Stellera chamaejasmae Linn. Proc. Indian Acad. Sci. B, 2: 424–436.

Joshi, A.C. 1937. Some salient points in the evolution of the secondary vascular cylinder of Amarantaceae and Chenopodiaceae. Amer. J. Bot. 24: 3–9.

Joshi, L. 1986. Comparative anatomy of branch wood of some temperate species of Nepalese Fagaceae. J. Phytogeog. Taxon. 34: 81–86. [Eng.]

Joshi, L. 1987. Branch wood anatomy of some Nepelese [Nepalese] Ficus species. J. Pl. Anat. Morph. 4: 163–176.

Joshi, L. 1988. Comparative branch wood anatomy of some Nepalese Moraceae. J. Phytogeog. Taxon. 36: 76–82. [Eng.]

Joshi, L. & Suzuki, M. 1992. Wood anatomy of Nepalese Betulaceae. In: Proc. 2nd Pacific Regional Wood Anat. Conf. 1989 (eds. Rojo, J.P., Aday, J.U., Barile, E.R., Araral, R.K. & America, W.M.): 151–157. For. Prod. Dev. Inst.: College, Laguna, Philippines.

Joshi, P.C. 1936. Anatomy of the vegetative parts of two Tibetan Caryophyllaceae – Arenaria musciformis Wall. and Thylacospermum rupifragum Schrenk. Proc. Indian Acad. Sci. B, 4: 52–65.

Kaastra, R.C. 1982. Pilocarpinae (Rutaceae). Flora Neotropica Mon., No. 33: 1–198.

Kachroo, P. & Bhat, M.M. 1982. The stem anatomy in taxonomy of Urticales. J. Econ. Taxon. Bot. 3: 633–644.

Kalinkov, V. 1961. Anatomicen stroez na darvesinata na blaguna (Quercus conferta Kit.). [Anatomical structure of wood of Quercus conferta Kit.] Nauch. Trud. Lesoteh. Inst., Sofija 9: 99–113. [Bulg.; Germ. summ.]

Kalinkov, V. & Shipchanov, I. 1976. Anatomischer Holzaufbau einiger Eichen. Gorsk. Nauka 13 (5): 21–35. [Bulg.; Germ. summ.]

Kanehira, R. 1921a. Anatomical characters and identification of Formosan woods. Govt. of Formosa. Taihoku. 317 pp. + 50 plates. [Eng.]

Kanehira, R. 1921b. Identification of the important Japanese woods by anatomical characters. Govt. of Formosa: Taihoku. 104 pp. + 9 plates. [Eng.]

Kanehira, R. 1924. Identification of Philippine woods by anatomical characters. Govt. Res. Inst: Taihoku, Formosa. 73 pp. [Eng.]

Kanehira, R. 1926. Anatomical characters and identification of the important woods of the Japanese Empire. Dept. For., Govt. Res. Inst., Taihoku, Formosa, Rep. No. 4: 297 pp. [Jap.]

Kanehira, R., Yatsutake, K. & Shigematsu, M. 1933. On light-weight woods. J. For. Soc. Japan 15: 601–615. [Jap.]

Karstedt, P. & Parameswaran, N. 1976. Beitrag zur Anatomie und Systematik der atlantischen Rhizophora-Arten. Bot. Jb. 97: 317–338.

Kartasujana, I. 1977. Struktur anatomi kayu benuang laki (Duabanga moluccana Bl.). Lembaran Penelitian, Lembaga Penelitian Hasil Hutan, Indonesia, No. 12: 5 pp. [Indonesian; Eng. summ.]

Kasapligil, B. 1962. An anatomical study of the secondary tissues in roots and stems of Umbellularia californica Nutt. and Laurus nobilis L. Madroño 16: 205–224.

Kasesalu, A. 1968. The anatomical structure of birch wood. Tr. Est. Sel'skokhoz. Akad. Sb. Nauch. 50: 210–224. [Estonian; Germ. summ.]

Kasir, W.A., Mahmoud, A.M. & Al-Kittani, M.M. 1986. Study on some anatomical properties of Salix acmophylla Boiss. and Salix alba L. growing in Iraq. Iraqi J. agric. Sci. Zanco 4 (3): 149–158. [Arabic; Eng. summ.]

Kästner, A. 1979; 1985. Beiträge zur Wuchsformanalyse und systematischen Gliederung von Teucrium L. II. Anatomie der Sprosse und Blätter. Flora 168: 431–467 (1979). IV. Wuchsformen und Verbreitung von Arten der Sektion Isotriodon. Flora 176: 73–93 (1985).

Kauffmann Fidalgo, M.E.P. 1955. Contribuição ao estudo de Lonchocarpus discolor Huber 1901. Arq. Serv. Florestal, Rio de Janeiro 9: 179–259.

Kawamura, Y. 1984. On the dimensions and the distributional number of rays in wood of 'arakashi' (Quercus glauca Thunb.) and 'mizunara' (Q. crispula Fisch.). Bull. Niigata Univ. For., No. 17: 55–64. [Jap.; Eng. summ.]

Kawamura, Y. 1987. Studies on the rays in members of the genus Quercus. Mem. Fac. Agric. Niigata Univ., No. 24: 108 pp. [Jap.; Eng. summ.]

Kaya, Z. 1991 [1993]. Delice (Olea europea var. oleaster L.) ile aşili zeytin (Olea europea var. sativa Lehr.) arasinda anatomik ve palinolojik ayricaliklar. Istanb. Univ. Orman Fak. Derg., ser. A, 41 (2): 132–148. [Eng. summ.]

Kazmi, S.M.H., Dayal, R. & Singh, R. 1989; 1990. Wood anatomy of exotics grown in India. 4. Casuarina Adans. (Casuarinaceae). 5. Acacia auriculiformis A. Cunn. ex Benth. (Leguminosae). J. Timber Develop. Assn. India 35 (4): 11–15 (1989); 36 (2): 5–9 (1990).

Kazmi, S.M.H. & Singh, R. 1988; 1989; 1992. Wood anatomy of exotics grown in India. 1. Hevea brasiliensis Muell. Arg. (Euphorbiaceae). 2. Leucaena leucocephala (Lam.) de Wit (Leguminosae). 3. Prosopis juliflora (Sw.) DC. (Leguminosae). J. Timber Develop. Assn. India 34 (2): 18–21 (1988); 35 (2): 47–50 (1989); 38 (1): 39–42 (1992).

Keating, R.C. 1968 [1969]. Comparative morphology of Cochlospermaceae. I. Synopsis of the family and wood anatomy. Phytomorphology 18: 379–392.

Keating, R.C. & Randrianasolo, V. 1988. The contribution of leaf architecture and wood anatomy to classification of the Rhizophoraceae and Anisophylleaceae. Ann. Missouri bot. Gard. 75: 1343–1368.

Kedrov, G.B. 1971. On the structure and certain functions of the living system of woody plants. In: Morfologii tsvetkovykh rastenii: 135–156. [Russ.]

Keefe, J.M. & Moseley, M.F. 1978. Wood anatomy and phylogeny of Paeonia Section Moutan. J. Arnold Arbor. 59: 274–297.

Keng, H. 1962. Comparative morphological studies in the Theaceae. Univ. Calif. Publ. Bot. 33: 269–384.

Kiew, R. & Baas, P. 1984. Nyctanthes is a member of the Oleaceae. Proc. Indian Acad. Sci., Pl. Sci. 93: 349–358.

Kim, J.K. & Hong, B.W. 1984a. Studies on anatomical properties of Forsythia in Korea. Wood Sci. Technol., Korea 12 (4): 31–35.

Kim, J.K. & Hong, B.W. 1984b. Studies on the ray parenchyma of Salicaceae in Korea. J. Korean for. Soc., No. 65: 74–79. [Korean; Eng. summ.]

Kim, S.I. & Yang, C.S. 1988. Studies on wood structure and fibre characteristics of Lespedeza species. J. Korean Wood Sci. Technol. 16 (1): 9–20. [Korean; Eng. summ.]

Kirchoff, B.K. & Fahn, A. 1984. Initiation and structure of the secondary vascular system in Phytolacca dioica (Phytolaccaceae). Can. J. Bot. 62: 2580–2586.

Klaassen, R.K.W.M. 1992. Comparative wood anatomy of the Nephelieae (Sapindaceae). IAWA Bull. n.s. 13: 256–257. [Abstr.]

Kobayashi, Y. 1949. Anatomical characters of 'Sakudara' wood, Hachido Island. Bull. Govt. For. Exp. Sta., Meguro, No. 42: 27–31. [Jap; Eng. summ.]

Kobayashi, Y. 1952. Identification of Japanese alder woods. I. Properties of wood rays. Bull. Govt. For. Exp. Sta., Meguro, No. 52: 181–197. [Jap.; Eng. summ.]

Kobayashi, Y. 1966. Anatomy of eight species of Cambodian woods. Bull. Govt. For. Exp. Sta., Meguro, No. 190: 13–31. [Jap.; Eng. summ.]

Kobayashi, Y. 1967. Identification and anatomy of Kapur woods grown in North Borneo (Sabah). Bull. Govt. For. Exp. Sta., Meguro, No. 197: 44–66. [Jap.; Eng. summ.]

Kobayashi, Y. 1968. Identification and anatomical characters of Bangkirai and White meranti woods grown in Kalimantan. Bull. Govt. For. Exp. Sta., Meguro, No. 218: 8–32 + 15 plates. [Jap.; Eng. summ.]

Kobayashi, Y., Sudo, S. & Sugawa, T. 1958. Anatomical studies on the woods of Phdiek, Chhoeutéal and Koki from Cambodia. Bull. Govt. For. Exp. Sta., Meguro, No. 106: 217–227. [Jap.; Eng. summ.]

Kobayashi, Y. & Sugawa, T. 1959. Identification of wood of some Castanopsis species in Japan. Bull. Govt. For. Exp. Sta., Meguro, No. 118: 139–178. [Jap.; Eng. summ.]

Kobayashi, Y. & Sugawa, T. 1960; 1961; 1962; 1963; 1964; 1966a; 1972. Structure of imported woods. Bull. Govt. For. Exp. Sta., Meguro, Nos. 126: 133–138 (1960); 130: 179–192 (1961); 138: 177–186 (1962); 146: 99–118; 150: 123–142; 159: 105–134 (1963); 171: 135–154 (1964); 194: 107–126 (1966a); 243: 51–62 (1972). [Jap. only.]

Kobayashi, Y. & Sugawa, T. 1966b. Structure of meranti woods grown in Sarawak. Bull. Govt. For. Exp. Sta., Meguro, No. 190: 111–127. [Jap.; Eng. summ.]

Koek-Noorman, J. 1968. Wood-anatomical studies in the Rubiaceae of Surinam and of some other tropical South-American countries. Acta bot. neerl. 17: 226–227.

Koek-Noorman, J. 1969. A contribution to the wood anatomy of South American (chiefly Suriname) Rubiaceae. I, II. Acta bot. neerl. 18: 108–123; 377–395.

Koek-Noorman, J. 1970. A contribution to the wood anatomy of the Cinchoneae, Coptosapelteae and Naucleeae (Rubiaceae). Acta bot. neerl. 19: 154–164.

Koek-Noorman, J. 1972. The wood anatomy of Gardenieae, Ixoreae and Mussaendeae (Rubiaceae). Acta bot. neerl. 21: 301–320.

Koek-Noorman, J. 1976. Juvenile characters in the wood of certain Rubiaceae with special reference to Rubia fruticosa Ait. IAWA Bull 1976/3: 38–42.

Koek-Noorman, J. 1977. Systematische Holzanatomie einiger Rubiaceen. Ber. dt. bot. Ges. 90: 183–190.

Koek-Noorman, J. 1980. Wood anatomy and classification of Henriquezia Spruce, Platycarpum Humb. et Bonpl. and Gleasonia Standl. Acta bot. neerl. 29: 117–126.

Koek-Noorman, J. & Hogeweg, P. 1974. The wood anatomy of Vanguerieae, Cinchoneae, Condamineae, and Rondeletieae (Rubiaceae). Acta bot. neerl. 23: 627–653.

Koek-Noorman, J., Hogeweg, P., Van Maanen, W.H.M. & Welle, B.J.H. ter 1979. Wood anatomy of the Blakeeae (Melastomataceae). Acta bot. neerl. 28: 21–43.

Koek-Noorman, J. & Puff, C. 1983. The wood anatomy of Rubiaceae tribes Anthospermeae and Paederieae. Pl. Syst. Evol. 143: 17–45.

Koek-Noorman, J. & Puff, C. 1991. The wood anatomy of Paederia L. (Rubiaceae–Paederieae). In: The genus Paederia L. (Rubiaceae–Paederieae): a multidisciplinary study (ed. Puff, C.). Opera Bot. Belg. 3: 35–40.

Koek-Noorman, J. & Van Rijckevorsel, P. 1983. Wood and leaf anatomy of Opiliaceae. Willdenowia 13: 147–174.

Koek-Noorman, J., Topper, S.M.C. & Welle, B.J.H. ter 1984a, b, c. The systematic wood anatomy of the Moraceae (Urticales). I. Tribe Castilleae. IAWA Bull. n.s. 5: 138–195 (1948a). II. Tribe Dorstenieae. Ibid.: 317–329 (1948b). III. Tribe Ficeae. Ibid.: 330–334 (1948c).

Koeppen, R.C. 1963. Observations on Androcalymma (Cassieae, Caesalpiniaceae). Brittonia 15: 145–150.

Koeppen, R.C. 1967. Revision of Dicorynia (Cassieae, Caesalpiniaceae). Brittonia 19: 42–61.

Koeppen, R.C. 1980. Silica bodies in wood of arborescent Leguminosae. IAWA Bull. n.s. 1: 180–184.

Koeppen, R. & Iltis, H.H. 1962. Revision of Martiodendron (Cassieae, Caesalpiniaceae). Brittonia 14: 191–209.

Kollmann, F. 1941. Die Esche und ihr Holz. Schriftenreihe Eigenschaften und Verwertung der deutschen Nutzhölzer, No. 1: 147 pp.

Korovin, V.V. 1987. Common features in the structure of anomalous woods. Bot. Zh. SSSR 72: 472–476. [Russ. only.]

Kostermans, A.J.G.H. 1973. Cinnadenia Kosterm., genus novum Lauracearum. Adansonia, sér. 2, 13: 223–227.

Kostermans, A.J., Pinkley, H.V. & Stern, W.L. 1969. A new Amazonian arrow poison: Ocotea venenosa. Bot. Mus. Leafl., Harvard Univ. 22 (7): 241–252.

Kowal, E. & Cutler, D.F. 1975. The wood anatomy of Schouwia purpurea subsp. arabica and Fabrisinapis fruticosus (Cruciferae). Kew Bull. 30: 503–507.

Kramer, P.R. 1939. The woods of Billia, Cashalia, Henoonia, and Juliania. Trop. Woods 58: 1–5.

Krasnitskij, A.M. 1959. The microscopic structure of the wood of Fraxinus excelsior growing under various conditions. Dokl. Akad. Nauk SSSR 126: 884–885. [Russ.] Transl. in: Dokl. Akad. Nauk SSSR, bot. sci. sect. (Transl.) 126: 125–127.

Krempl, H. 1963. Das Holz der Linde. Centralbl. Ges. Forstwesen 80 (2): 123–125.

Kribs, D.A. 1927. Comparative anatomy of the woods of the Juglandaceae. Trop. Woods 12: 16–21.

Kribs, D.A. 1928a. The Persaud collection of British Guiana woods. Trop. Woods 13: 7–46.

Kribs, D.A. 1928b. The wood of Carya tonkinensis H. Lecomte. Trop. Woods 16: 50–52.

Kribs, D.A. 1930. Comparative anatomy of the woods of the Meliaceae. Amer. J. Bot. 17: 724–738.

Kribs, D.A. 1935. Salient lines of structural specialization in the wood rays of dicotyledons. Bot. Gaz. 96: 547–557.

Kribs, D.A. 1937. Salient lines of structural specialization in the wood parenchyma of dicotyledons. Bull. Torrey bot. Cl. 64: 177–186.

Kribs, D.A. 1959. Commercial foreign woods on the American market. Pennsylvania State Univ. 203 pp. [Corrected edn. 1968. Dover Publ.: New York. 241 pp.]

Krishnamurthy, K.V. & Sigamani, K. 1987. Wood anatomy of two South Indian species of Avicennia. Feddes Repert. 98: 537–542.

Kubitzki, K., Kurz, H. & Richter, H.G. 1979. Reinstatement of Clinostemon (Lauraceae). J. Arnold Arbor. 60: 515–522.

Kubitzki, K. & Richter, H.G. 1987. Williamodendron Kubitzki & Richter, a new genus of neotropical Lauraceae. Bot. Jb. 109: 49–58.

Kukachka, B.F. 1962. Wood anatomy of Petenaea cordata Lundell (Elaeocarpaceae). Wrightia 3: 36–40.

Kukachka, B.F. 1978–1982. Wood anatomy of the neotropical Sapotaceae. I. Bumelia. U.S. Dept. Agric., For. Prod. Lab., Res. Pap. FPL 325: 9 pp. II. Mastichodendron. FPL 326: 6 pp. III. Dipholis. FPL 327: 7 pp. IV. Achrouteria. FPL 328: 8 pp. V. Calocarpum. FPL 329: 5 pp. VI. Chloroluma. FPL 330: 5 pp. VII. Chrysophyllum. FPL 331: 9 pp. (1978). VIII. Diploon. FPL 349: 4 pp. IX. Pseudoxythece. FPL 350: 4 pp. X. Micropholis. FPL 351: 16 pp. XI. Prieurella. FPL 352: 8 pp. XII. Neoxythece. FPL 353: 10 pp. XIII. Podoluma. FPL 354: 4 pp. (1979). XIV. Elaeoluma. FPL 358: 6 pp. XV. Sandwithiodoxa. FPL 359: 4 pp. XVI. Paralabatia. FPL 360: 6 pp. XVII. Gambeya. FPL 361: 6 pp. XVIII. Gomphiluma. FPL 362: 3 pp. XIX. Chromolucuma. FPL 363: 4 pp. (1980). XX. Manilkara. FPL 371: 14 pp. XXI. Barylucuma. FPL 372: 4 pp. XXII. Pradosia. FPL 373: 10 pp. XXIII. Gayella. FPL 374: 4 pp. XXIV. Ecclinusa. FPL 395: 6 pp. XXV. Ragala. FPL 396: 6 pp. XXVI. Myrtiluma. FPL 397: 5 pp. XXVII. Sarcaulus. FPL 398: 5 pp. (1981). XXVIII. Labatia. FPL 416: 8 pp. XXIX. Eglerodendron. FPL 417: 4 pp. XXX. Pseudocladia. FPL 418: 4 pp. XXXI. Pouteria. FPL 419: 18 pp. XXXII. Richardella. FPL 420: 7 pp. XXXIII. Englerella. FPL 421: 6 pp. XXXIV. Franchetella–Eremoluma. FPL 422: 10 pp. XXXV. Urbanella. FPL 423: 6 pp. XXXVI. Syzygiopsis. FPL 424: 5 pp. XXXVII. Genus novo? FPL 425: 4 pp. XXXVIII. Miscellaneous. FPL 426: 8 pp. (1982).

Kukachka, F. & Rees, L.W. 1943. Systematic anatomy of the woods of the Tiliaceae. Univ. Minnesota Agric. Exp. Sta., Tech. Bull. 158: 70 pp.

Kulkarni, A.R. & Kazi, M.B. 1969–1970. On the wood anatomy of Martynia annua Glox. J. Shivaji Univ. 2–3: 77–83.

Kumazawa, M. 1935. The structure and affinities of Paeonia. Bot. Mag., Tokyo 49: 306–315. [Jap.; Eng. summ.]

Kundu, B.C. & De, A. 1968 [1969]. Taxonomic position of the genus Nyctanthes. Bull. bot. Surv. India 10: 397–408.

Kundu, B.C. & Guha, S. 1975 [1978]. Tiliacora acuminata (Lam.) Miers. Bull. bot. Surv. India 17: 147–156.

Kunz, M. 1913. Die systematische Stellung der Gattung Krameria unter besonderer Berücksichtigung der Anatomie. Beih. bot. Zbl. 30 (2): 412–427.

Kuo, J. & Pate, J.S. 1981. Intraxylary (medullary) phloem in Macrotyloma uniflorum Lam. (Fabaceae). Ann. Bot. 48: 403–406.

Kuroda, K. 1987. Hardwood identification using a microcomputer and IAWA codes. IAWA Bull. n.s. 8: 69–77.

Kusheva Nadson, L.S. 1964. Structure and physical-mechanical properties of xylem of Gymnocladus canadensis Lam. Byull. glav. Bot. Sada 56: 11–17. [Russ.]

Kutuzova, V.B. 1965. Peculiarities in stem anatomical structure of Solanaceae. Trudy prikl. Bot. Genet. Selek. 37 (2): 46–55. [Russ.; Eng. summ.]

Lacey, C.J. & Jahnke, R. 1984. The occurrence and nature of lignotubers in Notelaea longifolia and Elaeocarpus reticulatus. Aust. J. Bot. 32: 311–321.

Lal, K. & Dayal, R. 1984. Wood structure of Clematis barbellata Edgw. with particular reference to the occurrence of radial vessels and perforated ray cells. Indian For. 110: 660–661.

Lamb, A.F.A. 1968. Fast growing timber trees of the lowland tropics, No.1. Gmelina arborea. Comm. For. Inst., Oxford. 31 pp. No. 2. Cedrela odorata. Comm. For. Inst., Oxford. 46 pp.

Lamb, A.F.A. 1969. Especies maderables de crecimiento rapido en la terra baja tropical. Cedrela odorata. Inst. Forest. Latinoamer., Bol. No. 30–31: 15–59.

Lamb, A.F.A. & Ntima, O.O. 1971. Fast growing timber trees of the lowland tropics, No. 5. Terminalia ivorensis. Comm. For. Inst., Oxford. 72 pp.

Laming, P.B. 1966. The structure of Guibourtia arnoldiana J. Léonard (Mutenye). Holzforsch. Holzverwert. (1): 8 pp.

Landrum, L.R. 1981. A monograph of the genus Myrceugenia (Myrtaceae). Flora Neotropica Mon., No. 29: 1–135.

Langdon, L.D.M. 1918. The ray system of Quercus alba. Bot. Gaz. 65: 313–323.

Lanyon, J.W. 1979. The wood anatomy of three proteaceous timbers Placospermum coriaceum, Dilobeia thouarsii and Garnieria spathulaefolia. IAWA Bull. 1979/2–3: 27–33.

LaPasha, C.A. & Wheeler, E.A. 1987. A microcomputer based system for computer-aided wood identification. IAWA Bull. n.s. 8: 347–354.

La Rivière, H.C.C. 1921. L'épaississement des tiges du Vitis lanceolaria Wall. Ann. Jard. bot. Buitenzorg 31: 141–166 + plates XXV–XXVIII.

Larrieu, P. 1930. Deux Mitragyna africains, le Bahia (M. macrophylla Hiern.) et le Diou (M. africana Korth.). Etude botanique, chimique et pharmacodynamique. Thèse: Univ. Paris. 91 pp. Also in: Trav. Lab. Mat. méd., Paris 21 (1930) [1931], (4): 91 pp.

Lashevski, V. 1925 [1926]. On the liane structure in the subterraneous stem of Daphne julia K. Pol. Bull. Soc. nat. Voroneje 1: 29–36. [See Just's Jber. 1926, 2: 447.]

Latorre A., F. 1979. Estudio de la madera del Prunus capuli Cav. Ciencia y Naturaleza (Ecuador) 20: 54–62.

Latorre A., F. 1980. Juglans neotropica Diels. Toctenogal. Ciencias y Naturaleza (Ecuador) 21: 66–68 + Figs. 1–8.

Latorre A., F. 1983. Wood anatomy of eleven legumes from southeast Ecuador. Ciencia y Naturaleza (Ecuador) 24 (1): 83–92.

Latorre, F., Vivero, W. & Barrera, M.E. 1975. Leno de tres especies arboreas Ecuatorianas. Ciencia y Naturaleza (Ecuador) 16 (1): 3–12. [Eng. summ.]

Léandri, J. 1928. Le liber interne chez les Daphne. Bull. Soc. bot. Fr. 75: 497–504.

Léandri, J. 1931. Observations sur les rhizomes à structure anormale de quelques espèces africaines de Gnidia. Bull. Soc. bot. Fr. 78: 307–312.

Léandri, J. 1937. Sur l'aire et la position systématique du genre Malgache Didymeles Thouars. Annls. Sci. nat., Bot., sér. 10, 19: 309–318.

Lebacq, L. 1955; 1957; 1963. Atlas anatomique des bois du Congo belge. Vols. I–II (1955). Vols. III–IV (1957). Vol. V (1963). Publ. Inst. nat. Etude agr. Congo: Bruxelles.

Lebacq, L. & Dechamps, R. 1964. Essais d'identification anatomique des bois d'Afrique centrale. Ann. Mus. roy. Afr. Cent., Tervuren, Sér. IN-8, Sci. econ. No. 3: 101 pp.

Lebacq, L. & Dechamps, R. 1967. Contribution à un inventaire de forêts du Nord-Kasai. Ann. Mus. roy. Afr. Cent., Tervuren, Sér. IN-8, Sci. econ., No. 5: 497 pp.

Lebacq, L., Hinostroza C., D., Bravo M., M. & Ayuque A., C. 1973. Classification de bois de l'Amazonie péruvienne. (Caractères anatomiques et physiques). Documentation Economique, Mus. roy. Afr. Cent., Tervuren, No. 3: 125 pp.

Lebacq, L. & Istas, J.R. 1950. Les bois des Meliacées du Congo Belge. Ann. Mus. Congo belge, Sér. IN-8vo, Sci. hist. econ. 2: 127 pp.

Lebacq, L. & Staner, P. 1964. Anatomie comparée des bois d'Amérique latine et d'Afrique centrale. Ann. Mus. roy. Afr. Cent., Tervuren, Sér. IN-8, Sci. econ., No. 4: 162 pp.+ 18 plates.

Lebedenko, L.A. 1959. The formation of wood in roots and stems of eastern oak (Quercus macranthera F. et M.). Nauch. Dokl. Vyssh. Shkoly. Biol. Nauki (2): 126–131; Ref. Zhur., Biol. (1960) No. 38941 (transl.).

Lebendenko, L.A. 1959 [1960]. The ontogeny of the wood of the roots and stems of several representatives of Fagales. Dokl. Akad. Sci. Bot. Sci. Sect. [Transl.] 127: 193–195. [Transl. from: Dokl. Akad. Nauk SSSR 127: 213–216 (1959).]

Lebedenko, L.A. 1961. On some regularities of wood root and trunk ontogenesis in edible chestnut. Byull. mosk. Obshch. Ispyt. Prir., Otdel. Biol. 66 (4): 66–71. [Oxford Forestry Translation No. 2588.]

Lebedenko, L.A. 1962a. A brief anatomical description and the key for the identification of some most important commercial woods of Ethiopia. Bot. J. USSR 47: 79–91. [Russ.; Eng. summ. & key.]

Lebedenko, L.A. 1962b. Anatomy of Salix arctica. Trudy Inst. Lesa Akad. Nauk SSSR (Sib. Otdel.) No. 51: 135–141. [Russ.]

Lechner, S. 1914. Anatomische Untersuchungen über die Gattungen Actinidia, Saurauia, Clethra und Clematoclethra mit besonderer Berücksichtigung ihrer Stellung im System. Beih. bot. Zbl. 32(1): 431–467.

Lecomte, H. 1921. Une Juglandacée du genre Carya en Indo-Chine. Bull. Mus. natn. Hist. nat., Paris 27: 437–440.

Lecomte, H. 1922. Madagascar. Les bois de la forêt d'Analamazaotra. A.Challamel: Paris. 189 pp.

Lecomte, H. 1926a. Les bois de l'Indochine. Agence Economique de l'Indochine, Paris. Publ. No. 13: 311 pp. + Atlas of 68 Plates.

Lecomte, H. 1926b. Une Ochnacée nouvelle d'Indochine. Bull. Mus. natn. Hist. nat., Paris 32: 95–100.

Lee, C.-S. [= Li, C.-H.] 1968. Comparative wood anatomy of the Fagaceae of Taiwan. Quart. J. Chin. For., Taipei 2(1): 1–54. [Eng.]

Lee, K. 1988. Crystals and their growth in the wood of Populus maximowiczii. Res. Bull. Coll. exp. For., Hokkaido Univ. 45: 717–788. [Jap.; Eng. summ.]

Lee, P.W., Eom, Y.G. & Chung, Y.J. 1987. The distribution and shape of crystals in the xylem of Korean hardwoods. Kor. Wood Sci. Technol. 15(4): 1–11.

Lee, P.W., Kim, H.S. & Eom, Y.G. 1989. Wood anatomy of genus Carpinus grown in Korea. J. agric. Sci. Seoul natn. Univ. 14(1): 41–48. [Eng.]

Lemesle, R. 1933. De l'ancienneté des caractères anatomiques des Magnoliacées. Rev. gén. Bot. 45: 341–355.

Lemesle, R. 1936. Les vaisseaux à perforations scalariformes de l'Eupomatia et leur importance dans la phylogénie des Polycarpes. C.R. Acad. Sci., Paris 203: 1538–1540.

Lemesle, R. 1938. Contribution à l'étude du genre Eupomatia R. Br. Rev. gén. bot. 50: 693–712.

Lemesle, R. 1943. Les trachéides à ponctuations aréolées de Sargentodoxa cuneata Rehd. et Wils. et leur importance dans la phylogénie des Sargentodoxacées. Bull. Soc. bot. Fr. 90: 104–107.

Lemesle, R. 1946a. Les divers aspects de fibres à ponctuations aréolées chez les apocarpées archaique et le critérium de la trachéide du type cycadéen. C.R. Acad. Sci., Paris 222: 195–196.

Lemesle, R. 1946b. Contribution à l'étude morphologique et phylogénétique des Eupteleacées, Cercidiphyllacées, Eucommiacées (ex-Trochodendracées). Annls. Sci. nat., Bot, sér. 11, 7: 41–52.

Lemesle, R. 1947a. Fibres aréolées conductrices chez certaines Apocarpales et divers aspects des trachéides du type cycadéen chez les dicotylédones heteroxylées. C.R. Acad. Sci., Paris 225: 587–588.

Lemesle, R. 1947b. Trachéides à ponctuations aréolées à ouvertures circulaires dans le genre Calycanthus. C.R. Acad. Sci., Paris 225: 761–763.

Lemesle, R. 1947c. La constitution anatomique du bois secondaire chez les ipecacuanhas vrais. Rev. gén. Bot. 54: 138–152.

Lemesle, R. 1948a. Trachéides aréolées du type cycadéen dans le genre Paeonia; leur intérêt au point de vue systématique et phylogénétique. C.R. Acad. Sci., Paris 226: 2171–2173.

Lemesle, R. 1948b. Position phylogénétique de l'Hydrastis canadensis L. et du Crossosoma californicum Nutt., d'après les particularités histologiques du xylème. C.R. Acad. Sci., Paris 227: 221–223.

Lemesle, R. 1950a. Persistance des caractères archaiques du bois secondaire chez les Canellacées. C.R. Acad. Sci., Paris 231: 455–456.

Lemesle, R. 1950b. L'Hydrastis canadensis L. et ses principales falsifications. Rev. gén. Bot. 57: 5–22.

Lemesle, R. 1951. De l'existence de trachéides à ponctuations aréolées dans le bois de quelques Ombellifères frutescentes. C.R. Acad. Sci., Paris 233: 811–813.

Lemesle, R. 1952. Trachéides à face interne striée dans le bois de deux Ombellifères Apioidées à port arbustif. C.R. Acad. Sci., Paris 235: 896–898.

Lemesle, R. 1953. Les caractères histologiques du bois secondaire des Magnoliales. Phytomorphology 3: 430–446.

Lemesle, R. 1955a. Contribution à l'étude de quelques familles de dicotylédones considérées comme primitives. Phytomorphology 5: 11–45.

Lemesle, R. 1955b. Nature histologique des éléments du bois secondaire chez les Bruniacées; leur intérêt au point de vue phylogénétique. C.R. Acad. Sci., Paris 241: 1831–1835.

Lemesle, R. 1956a. Mise en évidence de pseudotrachéides dans le bois secondaire de quelques Bruniacées. C.R. Acad. Sci., Paris 242: 165–167.

Lemesle, R. 1956b. Revue d'histologie végétale. Les éléments du xylème dans les Angiospermes à caractères primitifs. Bull. Soc. bot. fr. 103: 629–677.

Lemesle, R. 1956c. Particularités histologiques de la tige de l'Eryngium bupleuroides Hook. Trav. Lab. bot. crypt. Inst. bot. 7 pp.

Lemesle, R. 1958a. Mise en évidence de trachéides et de pseudo-trachéides dans le cylindre ligneux de quelques Ombellifères frutescentes ou suffrutescentes. C.R. Acad. Sci., Paris 247: 1027–1029.

Lemesle, R. 1958b. Particularités histologiques du bois de quelques Peucedanum; les divers types de fibres aréolées dans le cylindre ligneux des Ombellifères. C.R. Acad. Sci., Paris 247: 1128–1129.

Lemesle, R. 1963a. Homoxylie vraie et pseudo-homoxylie. Bull. Soc. Pharm. Bordeaux 102: 305–312.

Lemesle, R. 1963b. Structure de la tige chez le genre Monimia Thou.; applications de l'histologie du xylème à la phylogénie. C.R. Acad. Sci., Paris 257: 225–228.

Lemesle, R. & Duchaigne, A. 1955. Particularités histologiques des constituants du bois chez les Dégénériacées; leur rôle dans la phylogénie de cette famille. C.R. Acad. Sci., Paris 240: 1122–1123.

Lemesle, R. & Dupuy, P. 1966. Particularités histologiques de la tige chez le Nothopanax anomalum Seem. (Araliacée); pseudo-homogénéité du bois secondaire. C.R. Acad. Sci., Paris D, 262: 88–90.

Lemesle, R. & Pichard, Y. 1954. Les caractères histologiques du bois des Monimiacées. Difficultés d'application à la phylogénie. Rev. gén. Bot. 61: 69–95.

Lemesle, R. & Rousseau, J. 1959. Structure écologique des tiges de quelques Peucedanum africains. Bull. Soc. pharm. Bordeaux 98: 86–96.

Lemke, D.E. 1987. Morphology, wood anatomy, and relationships of Neopringlea (Flacourtiaceae). Syst. Bot. 12: 609–616.

Léonard, J. 1989. Révision du genre africain Martretia Beille (Euphorbiaceae) et la nouvelle tribu des Martretieae. Bull. Jard. bot. natn. Belg. 59: 319–332.

Lepe, B.G. 1959. Estructura anatómica e histológica de un grupo de 21 especies del bosque Chiapaneco. Vol. II. Inst. Mex. Invest. Tec., México. 199 pp.

Leprince, M. 1911. Etude pharmacognosique de l'Adenium hongkell D.C. et du Xanthoxylum ochroxylum D.C. Thèse: Univ. Paris. Also in : Trav. Lab. Mat. méd., Paris 8 (1911) [1912] (1): 75 pp.

Leroy, J.F. 1946. Le genre Aphananthe (Ulmacées). Révision systématique et distribution géographique des espèces. Bull. Mus. natn. Hist. nat., Paris, sér. 2, 18: 118–123, 180–184.

Leroy, J.F. 1953. La structure du bois d'Annamocarya. Notes sur le bois des noyers et autres Juglandacées. Rev. Bot. appl. Agric. trop. 33: 216–220.

Leroy, J.F. 1960. Structure du bois et classification. Mém. Soc. bot. fr. 107: 20–29.

Leroy, J.F. 1964. Contributions à l'étude des forêts de Madagascar. VII. Recherches sur les Meliaceae: le Malleastrum (Baill.) J.F. Ler., genre nouveau endémique de la Grande Île et des Comores. J. Agric. trop. Bot. appl. 11: 127–149.

Leroy, J.F. 1973. Recherches sur la spéciation et l'endémisme dans la flore malgache III. Note sur le genre Dialyceras R. Cap. (Sphaerosépalacées). Adansonia, sér. 2, 13: 37–53.

Leroy, J.F. 1975. Taxogénétique: étude sur la sous-tribu des Mitragyninae (Rubiaceae–Naucleeae). Adansonia, sér. 2, 15: 65–88.

Letouzey, R. & Mouranche, R. 1952. Ekop du Cameroun. Publ. Centre tech. For. trop., No. 4: 81 pp.

Li, H. & Chao, C. 1954. Comparative anatomy of the woods of the Cornaceae and allies. Quart. J. Taiwan Mus. 7: 119–136.

Li, Y.-F., Wu, D.-Q., Zhou, L. & Jing, Z.-H. 1983. The wood structure, property and use of Xinjiang diversiform-leafed poplar. J. Nanjing tech. Coll. for. Prod. (4): 65–74 [Chin.; Eng. summ.] + 3 plates.

Li, Y.-L. & Zhang, X.-Y. 1990. Studies on comparative wood anatomy of 16 species of vines and trees in Celastraceae. Acta bot. sin. 32: 252–261. [Chin.; Eng. summ.] + 2 plates.

Li, Z.-L. 1993. Perforation plates of vessels in dicotyledon woods. Chin. Bull. Bot. 10, Suppl.: 18–25. [Chin.]

Liben, L. & Dechamps, R. 1966. Entandrophragma congoënse (De Wild.) A. Chev. espèce méconnue du Congo. Bull. Jard. bot. État, Bruxelles 36: 415–424.

Lidén, M. 1986. Synopsis of Fumarioideae (Papaveraceae) with a monograph of the tribe Fumarieae. Opera Bot. 88: 1–133.

Liese, J. 1924. Beiträge zur Anatomie und Physiologie des Wurzelholzes der Waldbäume. Ber. dt. bot. Ges. 42: (91)–(97).

Lim, D.O. & Soh, W.Y. 1991a. Comparative anatomy of secondary xylem in normal and dwarf individuals of some wood[y] plants. Korean J. Bot. 34 (1): 9–18. [Kor.; Eng. summ.]

Lim, D.O. & Soh, W.Y. 1991b. Comparative anatomy of the secondary xylem in the stem of Malvales plants in Korea. Korean J. Bot. 34 (1): 67–76. [Kor.]

Lim, S.C. & Lau, L.C. 1982. Further siliceous woods in Peninsular Malaysia. Malay. For. 45: 122–123.

Lima, J.T. & Marcati, C.R. 1989. Anatomia da madeira de Kielmeyera coriacea Mart. (Pausanto) – Guttiferae. Resumos XL Congr. nac. Bot., Cuiaba, Mato Grosso, Jan. 1989, 1: 301. [Abstr.]

Lin, S. 1990. Systematic wood anatomy of Lauraceae in Guangdong Province. J. South China Agric. Univ. 11(4): 79–85. [Chin.; Eng. summ.]

Lin, T.-P. & Wang, Y.-S. 1991. Paulownia taiwaniana, a hybrid between P. fortunei and P. kawakamii (Scrophulariaceae). Pl. Syst. Evol. 178: 259–269.

Lindorf, H. 1988. Contribución al establecimiento de diferencias anatómicas entre madera caulinar y radical. Bol. Soc. venez. Cienc. nat. 42 (145): 143–178.

Linnemann, G. 1953. Untersuchungen über den Markstrahlanteil am Holz der Buche. Ber. dt. bot. Ges. 66: 37–63.

Lins, A.L.F.A. 1982. Estudo anatômico do lenho do "Sarabatucu": Heteropterys orinocensis (H.B.K.) Adr. Juss. (Malpighiaceae). Resumos XXXIII Congr. nac. Bot., Soc. bot. Brasil, Maceió 1982: 55. [Abstr.]

Lisboa, P.L.B. 1982. Anatomia das madeiras de duas novas espécies de Iryanthera: Iryanthera campinae W. Rodr. e Iryanthera inpae W. Rodr. Bol. Mus. para. Emílio Goeldi (NS), Bot., No. 57: 1–8.

Lisboa, P.L.B. 1989a. Contribuição ao estudo dendrológico de Glycoxylon inophyllum (Mart. ex Miquel) Ducke (Sapotaceae). Bol. Mus. para. Emílio Goeldi, Bot. 5 (1): 57–67.

Lisboa, P.L.B. 1989b. Aspectos da anatomia sistematica do lenho de Iryanthera Warb. (Myristicaceae). Bol. Mus. para. Emílio Goeldi, ser. Bot. 5 (2): 83–134. [Eng. summ.]

Lisboa, P.L.B. 1990. Considerações sobre a anatomia da madeira e a filogenia do gênero Iryanthera (Myristicaceae). Cienc. Cult. 42: 74–75. [Eng. summ.]

Lisboa, P.L.B., Silva, J.C.A. da, Loureiro, A.A. & Dos Santos, G.M. dos A. 1987. Morphology of the vessel elements in the secondary xylem of the Myristicaceae from Brazilian Amazonia. IAWA Bull. n.s. 8: 202–212.

Liu, D.-Y., Wu, S.-M. & Li, Z.-L. 1987. Comparative anatomical studies on the vessel elements of Chinese Magnolia and Michelia. Acta bot. sin. 29: 22–28 + 1 plate. [Chin.; Eng. summ.]

Lleras, E. 1978. Trigoniaceae. Flora Neotropica Mon., No. 19: 1–73.

Lobzanidze, E.D. 1961. The cambium, and the formation of annual rings in wood. Izdat. Akad. Nauk gruz. SSR, Tbilisi. 159 pp. [Russ.]

Loesener, T. & Solereder, H. 1905. Ueber die bisher wenig bekannte südmexikanische Gattung Rigiostachys. Verh. bot. Ver. Prov. Brandenburg 47: 35–62.

Lomibao, B.A. 1973a. Wood anatomy of eight Terminalia species of the Philippine Combretaceae. Forpride Digest 2 (3/4): 22–34.

Lomibao, B.A. 1973b. Guide to the identification of the woods of Philippine Dipterocarpaceae. Forpride Digest 2 (2): 26–73.

Lomibao, B.A. 1973c. Wood anatomy of seven potentially commercial Philippine species. Philipp. Lumberman 19 (11): 22, 24–29. [Eng.]

Lomibao, B.A. 1975. Wood anatomy of 9 Rubiaceae species. II. Forpride Digest 4: 70–71.

Lomibao, B.A. 1978. Wood anatomy of Philippine mangrove species. Forpride Digest 7 (1): 23–34.

Lomibao, B.A. & Salva, R.M. 1972. Wood structure, characteristics and properties of six Vitex species of the Philippine Verbenaceae. Philipp. Lumberman 18 (3): 24–26, 28, 29.

Lopes, C.A.C., Pinto, R.G., Dourado, R.S.A., Peres, A.S.G. & Brandao, A.T. de O. 1983. Contribuição ao estudo anatômico de algumas madeiras da Amazônia. Superintêndencia do Desenvolvimento da Amazônia, Dept. Recursos nat.: Belém, Brazil. 23 pp.

López, H. & Ortega, F. 1989. Angiospermas arboreas de Mexico. 2. Anatomia de once especies. Madera u Su Uso, No. 23: 128 pp. [Eng. summ.]

López Naranjo, H. & Espinoza de Pernía, N. 1990 [1992]. Anatomía y ecología de los órganos subterráneos de Anacardium humile St. Hil. (Anacardiaceae). Revta. for. venez. 24 (34): 55–76. [Eng. summ.]

Lörcher, H. 1990. Achsenverdickung und Sprossanatomie bei Valerianaceae. Trop. subtrop. Pflwelt. 74: 1–121. [Eng. summ.]

Lörcher, H. & Weberling, F. 1982. Zur Achsenverdickung hochandiner Valerianaceen. Ber dt. bot. Ges. 95: 57–74.

Lörcher, H. & Weberling, F. 1984. Anatomie und Achsenverdickung brasilianischer Valerianaarten (Series Polystachyae). Trop. subtrop. Pflwelt 47: 1–31.

Lörcher, H. & Weberling, F. 1985. Zur Achsenanatomie hochandiner Valeriana-Arten (Valeriana micropterina Wedd., V. thalictroides Graebn.). Flora 176: 197–212. [Eng. summ.]

Lotova, L.I. 1958. Comparative anatomy investigations of woody tall and dwarf forms of Malus. Bot. J. USSR 43: 1728–1734. [Russ.]

Lotova, L.I. 1960. Some observations on the anatomical structure of the brittle woody dwarf wild apple trees. Soobshch. mosk. Otdel. Vses. bot. Obshch. Akad. Nauk SSSR (1): 125–128. [Russ. only]

Lotova, L.I. & Timonin, A.K. 1985. Character of secondary growth of axial organs in Amaranthus L. Byull. mosk. Obshch. Ispyt. Prir., Otdel. biol. 90 (4): 77–88. [Russ.; Eng. summ.]

Louis, J. & Fouarge, J. 1943; 1944; 1947; 1948. Essences forestières et bois du Congo. Publ. Inst. nat. Agron. Congo Belge, (1): 22 pp.; (3): 38 pp.; (4): 75 pp.; (5): 14 pp.

Louis, J. & Fouarge, J. 1949. Essences forestières et bois du Congo. Macrolobium dewevrei. Publ. Inst. nat. Agron. Congo Belge (6): 44 pp.

Loureiro, A.A. 1968. Contribuição ao estudo anatômico de Croton lanjouwensis (Muell. Arg.) Jablonski e Croton matourensis Aublet (Euphorbiaceae). Inst. nac. Pesq. Amazonia, Bot. Publ. No. 24: 1–16.

Loureiro, A.A. 1969; 1970. Contribuição ao estudo anatômico da madeira de Anonáceas de Amazonia. I. Unonopsis guatterioides (A. DC.) R.E. Fries, Fusaea longifolia (Aubl.) Saff., Xylopia aromatica Baill. e Rollinia insignis R.E. Fries var. pallida R.E. Fries. Inst. nac. Pesq. Amazonia, Bol. Bot. No. 30: 1–10 (1969). II. Bocageopsis multiflora (Mart.) R.E. Fries, Guatteria scytophylla Diels, Xylopia benthami R.E. Fries e Guatteria olivacea R.E. Fries. Inst. nac. Pesq. Amazonia, Bol. Pesq. florest., No. 15: 1–10 (1970).

Loureiro, A.A. 1971 [1972]. Contribuição ao estudo anatômico da madeira de Anonáceas da Amazonia. III. Annona sericea Dun., Annona paludosa Aubl. e Guatteria paranensis R.E. Fries. Acta Amazonica 1 (2): 85–90.

Loureiro, A.A. 1971 [1973]. Contribuição ao estudo anatômico da espécie Dialium guianense (Aubl.) Sandw. (Leguminosae). Acta Amazonica 1 (3): 85–87.

Loureiro, A.A. 1976. Estudo anatômico macro e microscópico de 10 espécies do gênero Aniba (Lauraceae) da Amazônia. Acta Amazonica 6 (2), Supl.: 85 pp.

Loureiro, A.A., Freitas, M.C. de & Vasconcellos, F.J. de 1989. Estudo anatômico de 24 espécies do gênero Virola (Myristicaceae) da Amazônia. Acta Amazonica 19: 415–465.

Loureiro, A.A. & Lisboa, P.L.B. 1979. Anatomia do lenho de seis espécies de Ormosia (Leguminosae) da Amazônia. Acta Amazonica 9: 731–746.

Loureiro, A.A. & Rodrigues, W.A. 1975. Estudo anatômico da madeira do gênero Swartzia (Leguminosae) da Amazônia. I. Acta Amazonica 5 (1): 79–86. [Eng. summ.]

Loureiro, A.A. & Silva, M.F. da 1972. Contribuição ao estudo dendrológico de 5 Parkias (Leguminosae) da Amazônia. Acta Amazonica 2 (2): 71–85.

Loureiro, A.A. & Silva, M.F. da 1973. Contribuição para o estudo dendrológico de cinco Leguminosas da Amazônia. Acta Amazonica 3 (2): 17–32. [Eng. summ.]

Loureiro, A.A. & Silva, M.F. da 1977. Contribuição para o estudo dendrológico e anatômico da madeira de três espécies de Qualea (Vochysiaceae) da Amazônia. Acta Amazonica 7: 407–416.

Loureiro, A.A. & Silva, M.F. da 1981. Estudo dendrológico e anatômico do lenho de 7 espécies e 3 subespécies de Dimorphandra (Leguminosae–Caesalpinioideae). Acta Amazonica 11: 561–581. [Summarized by Silva, M.F. da in: Flora Neotropica Mon., No. 44: 1–128 (1986).]

Loureiro, A.A., Silva, M.F. da & Vasconcellos, F.J. de 1984. Contribuição ao estudo anatômico do lenho de 7 espécies de Dimorphandra (Leguminosae–Caesalpinioideae). Acta Amazonica 14: 289–313.

Loureiro, A.A., Vasconcellos, F.J. de & Albuquerque, B.W.P. de 1981. Anatomia do lenho de 4 espécies de Zanthoxylum Linnaeus (Rutaceae) da Amazônia. Acta Amazonica 11: 809–820.

Loureiro, A.A., Vasconcellos, F.J. de & Freitas, J.A. de 1983. Contribuição ao estudo anatômico do lenho de 5 espécies de Sclerolobium e 5 espécies de Tachigalia (Leguminosae) da Amazônia. Acta Amazonica 13: 149–170.

Lowe, R.G. 1962. The wood parenchyma of Triplochiton scleroxylon K. Schum. Ann. Bot. 26: 599–601.

Lowell, C. & Lucansky, T.W. 1986. Vegetative anatomy and morphology of Ipomoea hederifolia (Convolvulaceae). Bull. Torrey bot. Cl. 113: 382–397.

Lowell, C. & Lucansky, T.W. 1990. Vegetative anatomy and morphology of Ipomoea quamoclit (Convolvulaceae). Bull. Torrey bot. Cl. 117: 232–246.

Luca, L. de & Edlmann Abbate, M.L. 1983. Alterazioni anatomiche riscontrate in un campione di legno cileno: Eucryphia cordifolia Cav. Rivta. Agric. subtrop. trop. 77: 381–395. [Eng. summ.]

Luo, L.C. 1989. Economic timbers in Yunnan. Yunnan People's Publ. House: Kunming. 452 pp. + 16 colour and 123 half-tone plates. [Chin. only except Latin names.]

Luteyn, J.L. 1983. Ericaceae. I. Cavendishia. Flora Neotropica Mon., No. 35: 290 pp.

Luxova, M. 1992. Structural properties of the leaf and stem of Daphne arbuscula Celak. Biologia, Bratislava 47 (1): 3–14. [Eng.]

Lyr, H. & Bergmann, J.H. 1960. Zur Frage der anatomischen Unterscheidbarkeit des Holzes einiger Salix-Arten. Ber. dt. bot. Ges. 73: 265–276.

Maas, P.J.M., Baas, P., Boeswinkel, F.D., Hiepko, P., Lobreau-Callen, D., Van den Oever, L. & Welle, B.J.H. ter 1992. The identity of "Unknown Z": Maburea Maas, a new genus of Olacaceae in Guyana. Bot. Jb. 114: 275–291.

Maas, P.J.M. & Westra, L.Y.T. 1984; 1985. Studies in Annonaceae. II. A monograph of the genus Anaxagorea A. St. Hil. Bot. Jb. 105: 73–134; 145–204.

Maas, P.J.M., Westra, L.Y.T. et al. 1992. Rollinia. Flora Neotropica Mon., No. 57: 1–189.

Maas, P.J.M. et al. 1983. Systematic studies in neotropical Gentianaceae – the Lisianthus complex. Acta bot. neerl. 32: 371–374. [Abstr.]

Mabberley, D.J. 1974a. Pachycauly, vessel-elements, islands and the evolution of arborescence in 'herbaceous' families. New Phytol. 73: 977–984.

Mabberley, D.J. 1974b. The pachycaul lobelias of Africa and St. Helena. Kew Bull. 29: 535–584.

Mabberley, D.J. 1975. The pachycaul Senecio species of St. Helena, 'Cacalia paterna' and 'Cacalia materna'. Kew Bull. 30: 413–420.

Mabberley, D.J. 1982. On Dr Carlquist's defence of paedomorphosis. New Phytol. 90: 751–755.

MacDuffie, R.C. 1921. Vessels of the gnetalean type in angiosperms. Bot. Gaz. 71: 438–445.

Machado, O. 1944. Estudos novos sobre uma planta velha o cajueiro (Anacardium occidentale L.). Rodriguésia 8: 19–48 + 20 plates.

Machado, O. 1945. Contribuição ao estudo das plantas medicinais do Brasil: Maytenus obtusifolia Mart. Rodriguésia 9 (18): 9–15 + 6 plates.

Machado, R.D., Mattos Filho, A. de & Pereira, J.M.G. 1966. Estrutura microscópica e submicroscópica da madeira de Bauhinia forficata Link. (Leg. Caes.). Rodriguésia 25: 312–334. [Eng. summ.]

Machado, R.D. & Schmid, R. 1962–1965. Estrutura das pontuações guarnecidas de Goniorrhachis marginata Taub. (Leg. Caes.). Arq. Jard. bot. Rio de Janeiro 18: 285–292. [Eng. summ.]

Mägdefrau, K. 1970. Das abnorme Dickenwachstum von Haematoxylon brasiletto Karsten. Mitt. Inst. Colombo-Aleman Invest. Cient. Punta de Betin (4): 35–44.

Mägdefrau, K. & Wutz, A. 1961. Leichthölzer und Tonnenstämme in Schwarzwassergebieten und Dornbuschwäldern des tropischen Südamerika. Forstw. Cbl. 80: 17–28.

Maguire, B. et al. 1977. Pakaraimoideae, Dipterocarpaceae of the western hemisphere. Taxon 26: 341–385.

Maguire, B. & Pires, J.M. 1978. Saccifoliaceae. In: The botany of the Guayana Highland. X, by Maguire, B. et al.: 230–245. Mem. N.Y. bot. Gard. 29.

Maguire, B. & Steyermark, J.A. 1981. Tepuianthaceae, Sapindales. In: The botany of the Guayana Highland. XI, by Maguire, B. et al.: 4–21. Mem. N.Y. bot. Gard. 32.

Maguire, B., Zeeuw, C. de, Huang, Y.-C. & Clare, C.C. 1972. Tetrameristaceae. In: The botany of the Guayana Highland. IX, by Maguire, B. et al.: 165–192. Mem. N.Y. bot. Gard. 23.

Maheshwari, P. 1930. Contributions to the morphology of Boerhaavia diffusa (II). J. Indian bot. Soc. 9: 42–61.

Mahmood, I. & Nasir, G.M. 1991. A note on anatomical, physical and mechanical properties of Conocarpus lancifolius Engler wood. Pakist. J. For. 41: 218–221.

Mainieri, C. 1958. Madeiras denominadas Caixeta. Inst. Pesq. tec. São Paulo, Publ. No. 572: 1–94.

Mainieri, C. 1960. Estudo macro e microscópico de madeiras conhecidas por Pau Brasil. Inst. Pesq. tec. São Paulo, Publ. No. 612: 62 pp.

Mainieri, C. 1962. Madeiras leves da Amazônia empregadas em caixotaria. Estudo anatômico macro e microscópico. Inst. Pesq. tec. São Paulo, Publ. No. 686: 39 pp. + 20 plates. Also in: Anu. bras. Econ. flor. 18 (18): 121–173 (1967).

Mainieri, C. 1964. Contribuição ao estudo anatômico do lenho de Parahancornia da Amazônia. An. XIV Congr. Soc. bot. Brasil, Manaus 1963: 274–283. Also in: Publ. Inst. Pesq. Amazônia, Brasil, Bot., No. 19: 6 pp.

Mainieri, C. 1967. Contribuição ao estudo anatômico da madeira de Mandigau ou Tatu (Tetrastylidium spp.) e de Acariquara (Minquartia spp.) Olacaceae. Silvicultura, São Paulo 6: 285–300. [Eng. summ.]

Mainieri, C. 1978. Fichas de características das madeiras brasileiras. Inst. Pesq. tec. São Paulo, Publ. No. 966 (120 fichas).

Mainieri, C. & Chimelo, J.P. 1989. Fichas de características das madeiras brasileiras. 2nd edn. Inst. Pesq. tec. São Paulo. 418 pp.

Mainieri, C. & Loureiro, A.A. 1964. Madeiras de Symphonia globulifera L., Platonia insignis Mart., Moronobea coccinea Aubl. e Moronobea pulchra Ducke (Guttiferae). Estudo anatômico macro e microscópico, como contribuição para a sua identificação. An. XIV Congr. Soc. bot. Brasil, Manaus 1963: 245–273. [Eng. summ.] Also in: Publ. Inst. nac. Pesq. Amazônia, Bot., No. 18: 28 pp. (1964).

Mainieri, C. & Primo, B.L. 1964; 1968. Madeiras denominadas "Angelim", estudo anatômico macro e microscópico. Anu. bras. Econ. flor. 19: 39–87 (1968). Also in: Publ. Inst. Pesq. tec. São Paulo, No. 739: 35 pp. (1964).

Mainieri, C. & Primo, B.L. 1971. Contribuição ao estudo anatômico das madeiras de faveiro (Pterodon sp.), combarú (Coumarouna alata (Vog.) Taub.) e sucupira amarela (Ferreirea spectabilis Fr. Allem.). Brasil Florestal 2 (7): 7–22.

Mainieri, C. & Steigleder, M.V. 1968. Contribuição ao estudo anatômico do lenho da Canela de Veado (Helietta cuspidata Engl.). Bol. Inst. tec. Rio Grande do Sul, Porto Alegre 4: 3 pp.

Majumdar, G.P. 1941. Anomalous structure of the stem of Nyctanthes arbortristis L. J. Indian bot. Soc. 20: 119–122.

Manchester, S.R. 1979. Triplochitioxylon (Sterculiaceae): a new genus of wood from the Eocene of Oregon and its bearing on xylem evolution in the extant genus Triplochiton. Amer. J. Bot. 66: 699–708.

Manchester, S.R. 1980. Chattawaya (Sterculiaceae): a new genus of wood from the Eocene of Oregon and its implications for xylem evolution of the extant genus Pterospermum. Amer. J. Bot. 67: 59–67.

Manchester, S.R. 1983. Fossil wood of the Engelhardieae (Juglandaceae) from the Eocene of North America: Engelhardioxylon gen. nov. Bot. Gaz. 144: 157–163.

Manchester, S.R. & Wheeler, E.A. 1993. Extinct juglandaceous wood from the Eocene of Oregon and its implications for xylem evolution in the Juglandaceae. IAWA Jl. 14: 103–111.

Marano, I. 1953. Accrescimento del legno in Phillyrea latifolia L. Nuovo G. bot. ital. 60: 197–224. [Eng. summ.]

Marcati, C.R. & Lima, J.T. 1989. Anatomia da madeira de Stryphnodendron adstringens Coville (Barbatimão) – Leguminosae Mimosoideae. Resumos XL Congr. nac. Bot., Cuiabá, Mato Grosso, Jan. 1989, 1: 255. [Abstr.]

Marchiori, J.N.C. 1986a. Anatomia descritiva da madeira de amarilho, Terminalia australis Camb. (Combretaceae). Revisto Centro Ciências Rurais 16: 329–340. [Eng. summ.]

Marchiori, J.N.C. 1986b. Estudo anatômico da madeira de mataolho, Pouteria salicifolia (Spreng.) Radlk. Revisto Centro Ciências Rurais 16: 341–352. [Eng. summ.]

Marchiori, J.N.C. 1987. Anatomia da madeira de limoeiro-do-mato, Randia armata (Sw.) DC. Revisto Centro Ciências Rurais 17: 39–48. [Eng. summ.]

Marco, H.F. 1933. The wood of Sarcosperma paniculatum. Trop. Woods 33: 1–4.

Marco, H.F. 1935. Systematic anatomy of the woods of the Rhizophoraceae. Trop. Woods 44: 1–20.

Mariani, P.C. 1968. Relazione tra livelli altitudinale e caratteristiche del legno del faggio dei Nebrodi (Sicilia). Ann. Accad. ital. Sci. forest. 17: 387–407. [Eng. summ.] Also in: Lavori Bot., Padova 32, No. 21 (1970).

Mariaux, A. 1959. Contribution à l'étude de Humbertia madagascariensis Lamk. II. Note sur le bois. J. Agric. trop. Bot. appl. 6: 616–619.

Mariaux, A. 1963. Wacapou et bois semblables. Comment les reconnaître. Bois For. Trop., No. 90: 39–49.

Mariaux, A. 1966. Croissance du kad (Acacia albida). Etude des couches d'accroissement de quelques sections d'arbres provenant de Senegal. Centre tech. For. trop.: Nogent-sur-Marne. 18 pp.

Mariaux, A. 1970. La périodicité de formation des cernes dans le bois de l'okoumé. Bois For. Trop., No. 131: 37–50.

Mariaux, A. 1971. Anatomie du bois de Crioceras dipladeniiflorus (Stapf) K. Schum. Adansonia, sér. 2, 11: 309–311.

Mariaux, A. 1974. Anatomie du bois de Leeuwenbergia africana R. Let. & N. Hallé. Adansonia, sér. 2, 14: 389–397.

Mariaux, A. 1980. Formation of silica grains in wood as a function of growth rate. IAWA Bull. n.s. 1: 140–142.

Martawijaya, A., Kartasujana, I., Kadir, K. & Prawira, S.A. 1986. Indonesian wood atlas. Vol. I. Dept. For., Agency For. Res. & Develop. & For. Prod. Res. & Develop. Centre, Bogor. 166 pp. [Eng.]

Martawijaya, A., Kartasujana, I., Mandang, Y.I., Prawira, S.A. & Kadir, K. 1989. Atlas kayu Indonesia. Jilid II. [Indonesian wood atlas. Vol. II.] Dept. For., Agency For. Res. & Develop. & For. Prod. Res. & Develop. Centre, Bogor. 167 pp. [Indonesian]

Martijena, N. 1987. Wood anatomy of Lithraea ternifolia (Gill.) Barkley & Rom. (Anacardiaceae). IAWA Bull. n.s. 8: 47–52.

Martin, B. & Cossalter, C. 1976. Les Eucalyptus des Îles de la Sonde. 7. Bois For. Trop., No. 169: 3–13.

Martin, L.G. 1953. Primera contribución al conocimiento de las maderas de la Guinea continental española. II. Inst. Estudios Africanos: Madrid. 204 pp.

Maruzzo, M.M. & America, W.M. 1981. Wood anatomy of three strains of giant ipil-ipil (Leucaena leucocephala (Lam.) De Wit.). Forpride Digest 10 (1–2): 16–27.

Matejčić, B.A. 1974. Dicorynia guianensis Amsh. A monograph. Ligna Orbis. Konink. Inst. voor de Tropen, Amsterdam. 92 pp.

Mathew, L. & Shah, G.L. 1982. Occurrence of scalariform perforation plates in some Verbenaceae. Curr. Sci. 51: 1032–1033.

Mathew, L. & Shah, G.L. 1983. Vestured pits and warts in Verbenaceae. IAWA Bull. n.s. 4: 39–40.

Mathews, M. & Rao, A.N. 1986. Development of included phloem and growth rings in Avicennia spp. J. Singapore natn. Acad. Sci. 15: 63–67.

Matović, A. 1977 [1978]. Charakteristika anatomických elementov dreva Fraxinus excelsior L. a Fraxinus angustifolia Vahl ssp. pannonica Soó et Simon. Drev. Výskum 22: 213–226. [Slovak.; Germ. & Eng. summ.]

Mattos, J.R. & Pinho, R.A. 1968. Contribuição ao estudo da "Erva doce do mato". Anais Soc. bot. brasil. XIX Congr. nac. Bot., Fortaleza 1968: 123–125.

Mattos Filho, A. de 1949. As madeiras do gênero Johannesia. Arq. Jard. bot. Rio de Janeiro 9: 209–221.

Mattos Filho, A. de 1954. Anatomia do lenho do gênero Peltogyne Vog. Arq. Serv. Florestal, Rio de Janeiro 8: 45–146.

Mattos Filho, A. de 1959. Contribuição ao estudo anatômico do lenho do gênero Plathymenia. Rodriguésia 21–22: 45–67.

Mattos Filho, A. de 1959–1961. Contribuição ao estudo anatômico de duas espécies de Capparis L. Arq. Jard. bot. Rio de Janeiro 17: 237–250.

Mattos Filho, A. de 1960. A estrutura do lenho de sassafras. Anu. bras. Econ. flor. 12: 289–296.

Mattos Filho, A. de 1960–1961. Contribuição ao estudo de Vochysia thyrsoidea Pohl (Vochysiaceae). Rodriguésia 23–24: 83–98. [Eng. summ.]

Mattos Filho, A. de 1962–1965. Contribuição ao estudo anatômico do lenho de Goniorrhachis marginata Taub. (Leg. Caes.). Arq. Jard. bot. Rio de Janeiro 18: 215–222.[Eng. summ.]

Mattos Filho, A. de 1967; 1969. Contribuição ao estudo anatômico do lenho de Dalbergia cearensis Ducke. Anu. bras. Econ. flor., Inst. nac. Pinho 18(18): 213–225 (1967). [Eng. summ.] Paper with same title in: Anais Soc. bot. brasil. 20: 5–12 (1969). [Eng. summ.]

Mattos Filho, A. de 1971. Estudo comparativo de duas espécies de Leguminosae latescentes do Cerrado e da Caatinga. Rodriguésia 26: 9–35.

Mattos Filho, A. de 1973. Anatomia do lenho de Peltogyne recifensis Ducke. Arq. Jard. bot. Rio de Janeiro 19: 125–131.

Mattos Filho, A. de 1980. Estudo anatômico do lenho de Itaobimia (Leguminosae–Lotoideae). Arq. Jard. bot. Rio de Janeiro 24: 13–18 [Eng. summ.]; 165–177 (figs.).

Mattos Filho, A. de 1989. Estudio morfológico da madeira do par de espécies vicariantes de Pithecellobium anajuliae Rizz. e Pithecellobium tortum Mart. (Leguminosae–Mimosoideae). Revta. bras. Biol. 49(1): 143–154.

Mattos Filho, A. de 1990. Taxonomia e anatomia das madeiras de Apterokarpos gardneri (Engl.) Rizz. e Loxopterygium sagotii Hook. f. (Anacardiaceae). Revta. bras. Biol. 50: 433–442. [Eng. summ.]

Mattos Filho, A. de & Coimbra Filho, A.F. 1957. Ensaios e apontamentos sobre Dalbergia nigra Fr. Allem. Arq. Serv. Florestal, Rio de Janeiro 11: 157–174.

Mattos Filho, A. de & Rizzini, C.T. 1978. Vochysia haenkeana Mart., uma Vochysiaceae completamente divergente das espécies congenéricas. Rodriguésia 30, No. 47: 33–71. [Eng. summ.]

Mauseth, J.D. 1989. Comparative structure-function studies within a strongly dimorphic plant, Melocactus intortus (Cactaceae). Bradleya 7: 1–12.

Mauseth, J.D. 1992. Comparative wood anatomy of Jasminocereus and Armatocereus in Ecuador and the Galapagos Islands. IAWA Bull. n.s. 13: 245–246. [Abstr.]

Mauseth, J.D. 1993a. Water-storing and cavitation-preventing adaptations in wood of cacti. Ann. Bot. 72: 81–89.

Mauseth, J.D. 1993b. Medullary bundles and the evolution of cacti. Amer. J. Bot. 80: 928–932.

Mauseth, J.D. & Ross, R.G. 1988. Systematic anatomy of the primitive cereoid cactus Leptocereus quadricostatus. Bradleya 6: 49–64.

McDonald, J.A. 1992. Evolutionary implications of typical and anomalous secondary growth in arborescent Ipomoea (Convolvulaceae). Bull. Torrey bot. Cl. 119: 262–267.

McLaughlin, J. 1959. The woods and flora of the Florida Keys. Wood anatomy and phylogeny of Batidaceae. Trop. Woods 110: 1–15.

McLaughlin, R.P. 1933. Systematic anatomy of the woods of the Magnoliales. Trop. Woods 34: 3–39.

McLean, J.D. & Richardson, P.E. 1973 [1974]. Vascular ray cells in woody stems. Phytomorphology 23: 59–64.

Medonça, R.C. de & Paula, J.E. de 1979. Investigações eco-morfológicas e anatômicas da Pinha-do-Brejo (Talauma ovata St. Hil.) da mata ciliar do Distrito Federal. Anais Soc. bot. brasil. 30: 37–44.

Meeuse, A.D.J. 1982. Cladistics, wood anatomy and angiosperm phylogeny – a challenge. Acta bot. neerl. 31: 345–354.

Mele, L.S. 1972. Anatomy of some high-mountain shrubs of Eastern Pamir. Izv. Akad. Nauk tadzh. SSR, Otd. biol. Nauk (2): 25–30. [Russ.]

Mello, E.C.: see Cunha Mello, E.

Mendes, M.J.B. & Paula, J.E. de 1980. Contribuição para o conhecimento do Ouratea nitida (Sw.) Engl., ocorrente no Estado de Alagoas. Brasil Florestal 10(41): 51–61.

Meniado, J.A. 1966. Wood anatomy of 'Philippine mahogany' and their identification. For. Leav. 17: 49–56.

Meniado, J.A. 1971. Wood anatomy of Philippine Dipterocarpaceae (Vatica spp.). Philipp. Lumberman 17 (1): 48, 50, 52, 54.

Meniado, J.A., America, W.M. & Valbuena, R.R. 1978. The Oleaceae family with emphasis on wood anatomy and uses of Philippine Linociera spp. Forpride Digest 7 (2/3): 23–36.

Meniado, J.A., Robillos, Y.U. & Zamuco, I.T. 1970. Crystals in some Philippine woods. Philipp. Lumberman 16 (6): 30–33, 35.

Meniado, J.A. & Valbuena, R.R. 1966. Wood anatomy of 'Manggachapui' group and their identification. Lumberman, Manila 12 (6): 32, 34, 36.

Meniado, J.A., Valbuena, R.R. & Tamolang, F.N. 1974. Timbers of the Philippines. I. For. Prod. Res. Ind. Develop. Commission. (Forpridecom): Manila, Philippines. 180 pp. [Eng.]

Mennega, A.M.W. 1966. Wood anatomy of the genus Euplassa and its relation to other Proteaceae of the Guianas and Brazil. Acta bot. neerl. 15: 177–129.

Mennega, A.M.W. 1969. The wood structure of Dicranostyles (Convolvulaceae). Acta bot. neerl. 18: 173–179.

Mennega, A.M.W. 1972a. A survey of the wood anatomy of the New World Hippocrateaceae. In: Research trends in plant anatomy (eds. Ghouse, A.K.M. & Yunus, M.): 61–72. Tata McGraw-Hill Publ. Co.: Bombay & New Delhi.

Mennega, A.M.W. 1972b. 'Soft-rot' in a wood sample of Dicranostyles: a rectification. Acta bot. neerl. 21: 343–345.

Mennega, A.M.W. 1972c. Wood structure of the genus Talisia (Sapindaceae). Acta bot. neerl. 21: 578–586.

Mennega, A.M.W. 1973. An unusual type of parenchyma strand occurring in the wood of Cedrelinga catenaeformis Ducke (Mimosaceae). IAWA Bull. 1973/1: 3–5.

Mennega, A.M.W. 1975. On unusual wood structures in Scrophulariaceae. Acta bot. neerl. 24: 359–360. [Abstr.]

Mennega, A.M.W. 1976. Changes in the identification of herbarium vouchers of wood samples of the Stahel wood collection (Suriname). IAWA Bull. 1976/1: 16.

Mennega, A.M.W. 1980a. Anatomy of the secondary xylem. In: Die natürlichen Pflanzenfamilien (eds. Engler, A. & Prantl, K.) 2nd edn. 28B1: 112–161. Angiospermae: Ordnung Gentianales. Fam. Loganiaceae. Duncker & Humblot: Berlin.

Mennega, A.M.W. 1980b. Wood structure of Trigonobalanus excelsa G. Lozano-C., HDZ-C. and Henao (Fagaceae). Caldasia 13 (61): 97–101.

Mennega, A.M.W. 1982. Stem structure of the New World Menispermaceae. J. Arnold Arbor. 63: 145–171.

Mennega, A.M.W. 1984. Wood structure of Jablonskia congesta (Euphorbiaceae). Syst. Bot. 9: 236–239.

Mennega, A.M.W. 1987. Wood anatomy of the Euphorbiaceae, in particular of the subfamily Phyllanthoideae. Bot. J. Linn. Soc. 94: 111–126.

Mennega, A.M.W. 1993. Comparative wood anatomy of Ruptiliocarpon caracolito (Lepidobotryaceae). Novon 3: 418–422.

Mennega, A.M.W. & Lanzing-Vinkenborg, M. 1977. On the wood anatomy of the tribe "Olmedieae" (Moraceae) and the position of the genus Olmedia R. & P. Acta bot. neerl. 26: 1–27.

Men'shchikova, E.A. 1964. Anomalous thickening of the stem in some species of dock (Rumex, Polygonaceae). Tr. Sverdlovskogo Sel'skokhoz. Inst. (11): 186–188. [Russ.]. From: Ref. Zhur., Biol. (1965) No. 4V122 (transl.).

Men'shchikova, E.A. 1965. Anomalies caused by thickening of the stem in various dock species. Nauch. Rab. Aspir. Sel'skokhoz. Voronezh. Sel'skokhoz. Inst. ser. Biol. Agron. (1): 8–11. [Russ.] From.: Ref. Zh. Biol. (1966) No. 11B253 (transl.).

Messeri, A. 1938. Studio anatomico-ecologico del legno secondario di alcune piante del Fezzan. Nuovo G. bot. ital. 45: 267–356.

Metcalfe, C.R. 1933. The structure and botanical identity of some scented woods from the East. Kew Bull.: 3–15.

Metcalfe, C.R. 1935. The structure of some sandalwoods and their substitutes and of some other little-known scented woods. Kew Bull.: 165–195.

Metcalfe, C.R. 1938. Anatomy of Fraxinus oxycarpa and F. Pallisae. Kew Bull.: 258–262.

Metcalfe, C.R. 1948. The elder tree (Sambucus nigra L.) as a source of pith, pegwood and charcoal, with some notes on the structure of the wood. Kew Bull.: 163–169.

Metcalfe, C.R. 1952a. Medusandra richardsiana Brenan. Anatomy of the leaf, stem and wood. Kew Bull.: 237–244.

Metcalfe, C.R. 1952b. Notes on the anatomy of the leaf and stem of Anisophyllea guianensis Sandwith. Kew Bull.: 291–293.

Metcalfe, C.R. 1956a. Scyphostegia borneensis Stapf. Anatomy of stem and leaf in relation to its taxonomic position. Reinwardtia 4: 99–104.

Metcalfe, C.R. 1956b. The taxonomic affinities of Sphenostemon in the light of the anatomy of its stem and leaf. Kew Bull.: 249–253.

Metcalfe, C.R. 1962. Notes on the systematic anatomy of Whittonia and Peridiscus. Kew Bull. 15: 472–475.

Metcalfe, C.R. 1987. Anatomy of the dicotyledons. Vol. III. Magnoliales, Illiciales, and Laurales (sensu Armen Takhtajan). 2nd edn. Clarendon Press: Oxford. 224 pp.

Metcalfe, C.R. & Chalk, L. 1950. Anatomy of the dicotyledons. 2 vols. Clarendon Press: Oxford. 1500 pp.

Metcalfe, C.R. & Chalk, L. 1983. Anatomy of the dicotyledons. Vol. II. Wood structure and conclusion of the general introduction. 2nd edn. Clarendon Press: Oxford. 297 pp.

Metcalfe, C.R., Lescot, M. & Lobreau, D. 1968. A propos de quelques caractères anatomiques et palynologiques comparés d'Allantospermum borneense Forman et d'Allantospermum multicaule (Capuron) Nooteboom. Adansonia, sér. 2, 8: 337–351.

Metcalfe, G. 1939. Observations on the anatomy of the Cricket-bat willow (Salix caerulea Sm.). New Phytol. 38: 150–158.

Meyer, R.E., Morton, H.L., Haas, R.H., Robison, E.D. & Riley, T.E. 1971. Morphology and anatomy of honey mesquite. U.S. Dept. Agric., Tech. Bull. 1423: 1–186.

Meyer-Uhlenried, K.-H. 1958a. Holzanatomische Untersuchungen an der Pappel. Holzforschung 11: 150–157.

Meyer-Uhlenried, K.-H. 1958b. Untersuchungen über die Vererbung eines anatomischen Merkmals bei Kreuzungen von Pappeln verschiedener Sektionen. Züchter 28: 209–216.

Meylan, B.A. & Butterfield, B.G. 1972. Three-dimensional structure of wood. A scanning electron microscope study. Chapman & Hall Ltd.: London. 80 pp.

Meylan, B.A. & Butterfield, B.G. 1974. Occurrence of vestured pits in the vessels and fibres of New Zealand woods. N.Z. Jl. Bot. 12: 3–18.

Meylan, B.A. & Butterfield, B.G. 1975. Occurrence of simple, multiple, and combination perforation plates in the vessels of New Zealand woods. N.Z. Jl. Bot. 13: 1–18.

Meylan, B.A. & Butterfield, B.G. 1978a. Occurrence of helical thickenings in the vessels of New Zealand woods. New Phytol. 81: 139–146.

Meylan, B.A. & Butterfield, B.G. 1978b. The structure of New Zealand woods. N.Z. Dept. Sci. Ind. Res., Bull. 222: 250 pp. Wellington, New Zealand.

Michener, D.C. 1981. Wood and leaf anatomy of Keckiella (Scrophulariaceae): ecological considerations. Aliso 10: 39–57.

Michener, D.C. 1983. Systematic and ecological wood anatomy of Californian Scrophulariaceae. I. Antirrhinum, Castilleja, Galvezia, and Mimulus sect. Diplacus. Aliso 10: 471–487.

Michener, D.C. 1986. Systematic and ecological wood anatomy of Californian Scrophulariaceae. II. Penstemon subgenus Saccanthera. Aliso 11: 365–375.

Middleton, T.M. 1987a. Aggregate rays in New Zealand Nothofagus Blume (Fagaceae) stem wood and their influence on vessel distribution. IAWA Bull. n.s. 8: 53–57.

Middleton, T.M. 1987b. Perforation plates and vessel elements of the stem sapwood in New Zealand Nothofagus Blume (Fagaceae) with particular reference to their lengths. Mauri Ora 14: 1–8.

Middleton, T.M. 1987c. Vessel distribution grouping and frequency in the stem wood of New Zealand Nothofagus (Fagaceae) taxa. Mauri Ora 14: 9–14.

Middleton, T.M. 1988. Intervessel pits in the stem wood of New Zealand Nothofagus (Fagaceae). IAWA Bull. n.s. 9: 327–331.

Mikesell, J.E. 1979. Anomalous secondary thickening in Phytolacca americana L. (Phytolaccaceae). Amer. J. Bot. 66: 997–1005.

Milanez, F.R. 1934. Estrutura do lenho do Mimusops Huberi. Arq. Inst. Biol. veg. Rio de Janeiro 1 (1): 49–62.

Milanez, F.R. 1935. Anatomia de Paradrypetes ilicifolia. Arch. Inst. Biol. veg. Rio de Janeiro 2 (1): 133–156. [Eng. summ.]

Milanez, F.R. 1936a. Anatomia do lenho do "Pau mulato". Arch. Inst. Biol. veg. Rio de Janeiro 3 (1): 111–129.

Milanez, F.R. 1936b. Estructura secundaria das raizes de Rhipsalis. Rodriguésia 5: 165–175.

Milanez, F.R. 1937. Anatomia do lenho de Ampelocera glabra Kuhlmann. Arch. Inst. Biol. veg. Rio de Janeiro 3: 211–215.

Milanez, F.R. 1938. Anatomia do lenho de Aspidosperma aquaticum Ducke. Arch. Inst. Biol. veg. Rio de Janeiro 4: 65–70 + 3 plates.

Milanez, F.R. 1939. Estudo anatômico do lenho de trinta especies do genero Aspidosperma. Physis (Rev. Soc. argent. Ci. nat.) 15: 429–490.

Milanez, F.R. 1943; 1945. Anatomia das principais madeiras brasileiras das Rutaceae. Rodriguésia 7 (16): 5–22 (1943); 9 (19): 45–47 (1945).

Milanez, F.R. 1966. Contribuição ao conhecimento anatômico de Cryptostegia grandiflora. III. Nota sôbre a estrutura secundária. Rodriguésia 25: 335–350.

Milanez, F.R. & Mattos Filho, A. de 1956. Nota sôbre a ocorrencia de silica no lenho de leguminosas. Rodriguésia 18/19: 7–26. [Eng. summ.]

Milanez, F.R. & Mattos Filho, A. de 1959. Contribuição ao estudo anatômico das madeiras do gênero Dicorynia. Rodriguésia 21/22: 25–44.

Miles, A. 1978. Photomicrographs of world woods. H.M.S.O.: London. 233 pp. [Illustrations to Brazier & Franklin 1961; indexed under Brazier & Franklin only.]

Miller, H.J. 1975. Anatomical characteristics of some woody plants of the Angmagssalik district of southeast Greenland. Medd. Grønland 198 (6): 1–30. Also in: Meded. bot. Mus. Utrecht, No. 422: 30 pp.; 1975.

Miller, R.B. 1920. The wood of Machaerium whitfordii. Bull. Torrey bot. Cl. 47: 73–79.

Miller, R.B. 1975. Systematic anatomy of the xylem and comments on the relationships of Flacourtiaceae. J. Arnold Arbor. 56: 20–102.

Miller, R.B. 1976a. Reticulate thickenings in some species of Juglans. Amer. J. Bot. 63: 898–901.

Miller, R.B. 1976b. Wood anatomy and identification of species of Juglans. Bot. Gaz. 137: 368–377.

Miller, R.B. 1977. Vestured pits in Boraginaceae. IAWA Bull. 1977/3: 43–48.

Miller, R.B. 1978. Potassium calcium sulfate crystals in the secondary xylem of Capparis. IAWA Bull. 1978/2 & 3: 50. [Abstr.]

Miller, R.B. 1980. Wood identification via computer. IAWA Bull. n.s. 1: 154–160.

Miller, R.B. 1982. Wood anatomy of Carya Nutt. and its systematic relationship within Juglandaceae. Abstr. Bot. Soc. Amer., 1982: 19 [Abstr.]

Miller, R.B. 1983. Wood anatomy of Alfaroa Standley, Oreomunnea Oerst., and Engelhardia Leschen. (Juglandaceae) and their inter- and intra-generic relationships. IAWA Bull. n.s. 4: 8–9. [Abstr.]

Miller, R.B. 1989. Wood anatomy of Obolinga (Mimosaceae). Brittonia 41: 178–182.

Miller, R.B. 1990. Comparison of the 1981 standard list and the 1989 IAWA list for hardwood identification. IAWA Bull. n.s. 11: 167–172.

Miller, R.B. 1991. Wood anatomy of Phragmotheca (Bombacaceae). Brittonia 43: 88–92.

Miller, R.B. & Cahow, E. 1989. Wood identification of commercially important North American species of birch (Betula). IAWA Bull. n.s. 10: 364–373.

Miller, R.B., Pearson, R.G. & Wheeler, E.A. 1987. Creation of a large database with IAWA Standard List characters. IAWA Bull. n.s. 8: 219–232.

Milne-Redhead, E. 1956. Montiniaceae. Tab. 3541–3544. Hooker's Icones Plantarum 36: 16 pp.

Minaki, M., Noshiro, S. & Suzuki, M. 1988. Hemiptelea mikii sp. nov. (Ulmaceae), fossil fruits and seeds from the Pleistocene of central Japan. Bot. Mag., Tokyo 101: 337–351.

Mirande, M. 1922. Sur l'origine morphologique du liber interne des Nolanacées et la position systématique de cette famille. C.R. Acad. Sci., Paris 175: 375–376.

Mogollón, A.P.: see Pérez Mogollón, A.

Moiseeva, M.N. 1940. Anatomical structure of maple stems in connection with their phylogeny. Zh. Inst. Bot. Vuan 31: 13–26 + 1 plate. [Ukrain.; Eng. summ.]

Moll, J.W. & Janssonius, H.H. 1906–1936. Mikrographie des Holzes der auf Java vorkommenden Baumarten. 6 vols. E.J. Brill: Leiden.

Molle, C.C. 1936. Anatomia de la madera de Arechavaletaia uruguayensis Spegazz. Rev. Sudamer. Bot. (Montevideo) 3: 105–109.

Molle, C.C. 1939. Estructura anatómica del leño de las Ramnáceas argentinas del género Condalia ("piquillines"). Physis 15: 409–420.

Molnar, S. 1986 [1987]. Wood structure of locust, Robinia pseudo-acacia L. Erdes. Faipari Tud. Kozl. (2): 123–132. [Hung.]

Money, L.L., Bailey, I.W. & Swamy, B.G.L. 1950. The morphology and relationships of the Monimiaceae. J. Arnold Arbor. 31: 372–404.

Monnier, L.J.M.J. 1909. Recherches sur les Ulex. Thèse: Rennes. Oberthur: Rennes. 97 pp. Also in: Trav. Lab. Mat. méd., Paris 7 (1910) [1911] (4): 97 pp.

Monteiro, R.F.R. 1967. Essências florestais de Angola. Estudo das suas madeiras. Espécies do Maiombe. Mem. Trab. Inst. Invest. Cient. Angola, Luanda, No. 4: 74 pp. [Eng. summ.]

Monteiro, R.F.R. & Frade, E.C. 1960. Essências florestais de Angola. Estudo das suas madeiras. I. Região dos Dembos. Ecologia e anatomia. Ensaios físicos. Mem. Trab. Inst. Invest. Cient. Angola, No. 1: 135 pp. [Eng. summ.]

Monteiro, R.F.R. & França, O.F.P. de 1965. Three forest species of Angola. Bol. Inst. Invest. Cient. Angola 2: 209–218. [Port.; Eng. summ.] [For. Abstr. 31 (1970) No. 1258.]

Monteiro, R.F.R. & França, O.M.V.P. de 1971. Essências florestais de Angola. Estudo das suas madeiras. II. Região dos Dembos. Anatomia, ecologia e utilização. Mem. Trab. Inst. Invest. Cient. Angola, No.1, Vol. 2: 9–118. [Eng. & French summ.]

Monteiro, R.F.R., Pinto, M.F. & França, O.P. de 1962. Carapa procera DC. Junta Invest. Ultramar: Lisbon. 12 pp.

Mork, E. 1946. Vedanatomi. Johan Grundt Tanum: Oslo. 65 pp. + 26 Plates.

Morton, C.M. 1993. Wood anatomy of a new species of Dipterocarpaceae from Amazonian Colombia. Abstr. XV intn. Bot. Congr., Yokohama: poster no. 3195. [Abstr.]

Moseley, M.F. 1948. Comparative anatomy and phylogeny of the Casuarinaceae. Bot. Gaz. 110: 231–280.

Moseley, M.F. 1956. The anatomy of the water storage organ of Ceiba parvifolia. Trop. Woods 104: 61–79.

Moseley, M.F. 1973 [1974]. Vegetative anatomy and morphology of Amentiferae. Brittonia 25: 356–370.

Moseley, M.F. & Beeks, R.M. 1955. Studies of the Garryaceae. I. The comparative morphology and phylogeny. Phytomorphology 5: 314–346.

Moss, E.H. 1936. The ecology of Epilobium angustifolium with particular reference to rings of periderm in the wood. Amer. J. Bot. 23: 114–120.

Moss, E.H. 1940. Interxylary cork in Artemisia with a reference to its taxonomic significance. Amer. J. Bot. 27: 762–768.

Mouranche, R. 1951. Note sur les bois de Fagus et de Nothofagus. Rev. Bot. appl. Agric. trop. 31: 84–90.

Mouton, J. & Jacquet, P. 1977. Contribution à l'inventaire floristique et xylologique de la Guyane française. 3. Elaeocarpaceae. C.R. 102e Congr. Soc. sav., Limoges, Sect. sci. 1977, l: 309–322.

Muhammad, A.F. 1984. Perforation plate structure in Comptonia peregrina (Myricaceae). IAWA Bull. n.s. 5: 217–223.

Muhammad, A.F. & Sattler, R. 1982. Vessel structure of Gnetum and the origin of angiosperms. Amer. J. Bot. 69: 1004–1021.

Mujica, M.B. & Cutler, D.F. 1974. Taxonomic implications of anatomical studies on the Oliniaceae. Kew Bull. 29: 93–123.

Mullenders, W. 1947. L'origine du phloème interxylémien chez Stylidium et Thunbergia. Etude anatomique. Cellule 51: 7–48.

Müller, R. 1903. Das Rhodiser-Holz. Pharm. Post (Nos. 29–40): 68 pp.

Müller-Stoll, H. 1951. Vergleichende Untersuchungen über die Abhängigkeit der Jahrringfolge von Holzart, Standort, und Klima. Bibl. Bot. 122 (30): 93 pp.

Müller-Stoll, W.R. & Mädel, E. 1962. Ein Myricaceen-Holz aus dem ungarischen Tertiär, Myricoxylon hungaricum n.g., n.sp. Senck. leth. 43: 323–333.

Müller-Stoll, W.R. & Süss, H. 1969 [1970]. Über aussergewöhnlich gestaltete vielfache Gefässdurchbrechungen bei Aeschynomene virginica (L.) B.S.P. (Papilionaceae). Ber. dt. bot. Ges. 82: 613–619.

Muñiz, G.I.B. de, Gomes, A.V. & Hofmeister, R.M. 1987. Anatomia comparada das madeiras de Jodina rhombifolia Hook. et Arn. e Castela coccinea Gris. Resumos XXXVIII Congr. nac. Bot., Univ. São Paulo 1987: 305. [Abstr.]

Murthy, G.S.R., Aleykutty, K.M., Rao, V.S. & Inamdar, J.A. 1978. Vessels of Oleaceae and Verbenaceae. Feddes Repert. 89: 359–368.

Murthy, L.S.V. 1965. Silica in Sarawak timbers. Malayan For. 28 (1): 27–45.

Mziray, W. 1992. Taxonomic studies in Toddalieae Hook.f. (Rutaceae) in Africa. Symb. bot. upsal. 30 (1): 1–95.

Nagy, F. & Veress, E. 1961. Cercetări anatomice în lemnul secundar al speciei Sorbus borbasii Jav. Studia Univ. Babes-Bolyai, Biol. 2: 89–98. [French summ.]

Nair, M.N.B. 1987. Occurrence of helical thickenings on the vessel element walls of dicotyledonous woods. Ann. Bot. 60: 23–32.

Nair, M.N.B. 1988. Wood anatomy and heartwood formation in neem (Azadirachta indica A. Juss.). Bot. J. Linn. Soc. 97: 79–90.

Nair, M.N.B. 1991 [1992]. Wood anatomy of some members of the Meliaceae. Phytomorphology 41: 63–73.

Nair, M.N.B. 1992. Vestured pits in the wood of Syzygium cumini. In: Proc. 2nd Pacific Regional Wood Anat. Conf. 1989 (eds. Rojo, J.P., Aday, J.U., Barile, E.R., Araral, R.K. & America, W.M.): 158–163. For. Prod. Dev. Inst.: College, Laguna, Philippines.

Nair, M.N.B. 1993. Structure of stem and cambial variant in Spatholobus roxburghii (Leguminosae). IAWA Jl. 14: 191–204.

Nair, M.N.B. & Ram, H.Y.M. 1989. Vestured pits and vestured vessel member walls in some Indian dicotyledonous woods. Bot. J. Linn. Soc. 100: 323–336.

Nair, M.N.B. & Ram, H.Y.M. 1990. Structure of wood and cambial variant in the stem of Dalbergia paniculata Roxb. IAWA Bull. n.s. 11: 379–391.

Nair, M.N.B. & Ram, H.Y.M. 1992. Structure of Sola wood: the traditional Indian art material. Curr. Sci. 62: 746–751.

Nájera Angulo, F. 1959. Sección de maderas. Estudio de cinco especies de la flora forestal de Canarias, notables par las características de sus maderas. An. Inst. for. Invest. exp. (Madrid) 31 (4): 55–74.

Nájera Angulo, F. & López Fraile, V. 1969. Estudio de las principales maderas comerciales de frondosas peninsulares. Inst. Forest. Invest. Exp.: Madrid. 279 pp.

Nardi Berti, R. & Edlmann Abbate, M.L. 1988; 1992. Legnami tropicali importati in Italia: anatomia e identificazione. I. Africa. Ribera Editore: Milan. 320 pp. (1988). II. America latina. CNR: Firenze. 406 pp. (1992).

Nassonov, V.A. 1934. The anatomy of the pistachio, Pistacia vera L. Trudy Prikl. Bot. Gen. Selek., ser. 3, No. 4: 113–34. [Russ.; Eng. summ.]

Nast, C.G. & Bailey, I.W. 1946. Morphology of Euptelea and comparison with Trochodendron. J. Arnold Arbor. 27: 186–192.

Nazma, Sundarsivarao, B. & Vijendrarao, R. 1981. Occurrence of perforated ray cells in the wood of Drypetes roxburghii (Wall.) Hurusawa. IAWA Bull. n.s. 2: 201–203.

Nel, E., Robbertse, J. & Grobbelaar, N. 1982. A morphological study of Dichapetalum cymosum (Hook.) Engl. 1. The underground stem and root systems. S. Afr. J. Bot. 1: 14–17.

Nicoloff, T. 1911. Contribution à l'histologie et à la physiologie des rayons médullaires chez les dicotylédones arborescentes. Rev. gén. Bot. 23: 369–403.

Nielsen, I. & Baretta-Kuipers, T. 1984. The genus Archidendron (Leguminosae–Mimosoideae). Opera Bot. 76: 1–120.

Nielsen, I., Guinet, P. & Baretta-Kuipers, T. 1983; 1984. Studies in the Malesian, Australian and Pacific Ingeae (Leguminosae–Mimosoideae): the genera Archidendropsis, Wallaceodendron, Paraserianthes, Pararchidendron and Serianthes (1). Bull. Mus. natn. Hist. nat., Paris, B, Adansonia, sér. 4, 5: 303–329 (1983); (3) sér. 4, 6: 79–111 (1984).

Niesemann, H.W. 1927. Das anomale Dickenwachstum von Mendoncia velloziana Mart. und Afromendoncia lindaviana Gilg. Diss.: Berlin. Walter de Gruyter: Berlin. 53 pp. + 37 plates.

Nikitin, A.A. 1934. Anatomy of the wood of Phellodendron amurense Rupr. Sov. Bot. (4): 136–143. [Russ. only.]

Nikitin, A.A. 1938. Comparative anatomical investigation of woody members of Rhamnaceae in the flora of the SSSR. Trudy bot. Inst. Akad. Nauk SSSR, ser. 5, Rast. sir. 1: 215–288. [Russ. only]

Nikitin, A.A. 1962. Comparative anatomical studies of certain resin-bearing Astragalus species. Trudy bot. Inst. Akad. Nauk SSSR, ser. 5, (10): 262–299. [Russ. only.]

Nikolov, S. & Bl"skova, G. 1980. Structure and properties of wood of Elaeagnus angustifolia. Nauch. Trud. Vissh. Lesotek. Inst. Sofiya 26: 35–39. [Bulg.; Germ. summ.]

Nikolov, S., Bl"skova, G., Kostov, K.D. & Arabov, A. 1984. Structure and properties of the wood of Rila oak. Gorsk. Nauka 21 (1): 63–73. [Bulg.; Eng. summ.]

Nikolov, S., Denev, D., Bl"skova, G. & Dragonzov, I. 1981. Structure and properties of the wood of some forms of the Vardim oak. Gorsk. Nauka 18 (3): 28–36. [Bulg.; Eng. summ.]

Niloofari, P. 1961. Textbook of wood technology. Vol. I. Structure, identification, defects and uses of the Iranian timbers with notes on commercial timbers of the world. Univ. Tehran Publ. No. 738.

Niloufari, P. 1977. Les tamaris de l'Iran, Turquie et Pakistan avec les remarques sur les tamaris du monde. Istanb. Univ. Orman Fak. Derg., ser. A, 27: 45–73. [French & Turkish.]

Nishida, A., Tsuchiya, K., Aida, T. & Hirai, S. 1966. On the wood of Matoa (Pometia pinnata Forster) from New Guinea. Bull. Tokyo Univ. For. 62: 197–211. [Jap.; Eng. summ.]

Nooteboom, H.P. 1985. Notes on Magnoliaceae with a revision of Pachylarnax and Elmerrillia and the Malesian species of Manglietia and Michelia. Blumea 31: 65–121.

Normand, D. 1931. Note sur Gmelina arborea Roxb., essence de repeuplement pour la forêt tropicale asiatique. Rev. Bot. appl. Agric. trop. 11: 168–174.

Normand, D. 1933a. Le bois de Guarea thompsonii, succedanée du Bossé. Rev. Bot. appl. Agric. trop. 13: 23–30.

Normand, D. 1933b. Les bois de Myristicacées du Gabon. Rev. Bot. appl. Agric. trop. 13: 471–479.

Normand, D. 1933c. Note sur les bois d'Enantia (Annonacées). Bull. Jard. bot. État Bruxelles 9: 317–322.

Normand, D. 1934. Note sur le bois de Difou. Rev. Bot. appl. Agric. trop. 14: 253–256.

Normand, D. 1935. Sur le Maesopsis de l'Ouest Africain et le bois de Nkanguele. Rev. Bot. appl. Agric. trop. 15: 252–263.

Normand, D. 1937. Le bois de Landa, Erythroxylum du Cameroun. Rev. Bot. appl. 17: 883–889.

Normand, D. 1938. Description du bois d'Ibadja walkeri A.Chev. Rev. Bot. appl. 18: 789–791.

Normand, D. 1939. Identification et emplois des bois d'Afzelia. Rev. Bot. appl. 19: 488–494.

Normand, D. 1944. Note sur l'anatomie du bois du genre nouveau Okoubaka. Bull. Soc. bot. Fr. 91: 20–25.

Normand, D. 1946. Anatomie des bois d'Endodesmia et de Lebrunia. Bull. Soc. bot. Fr. 93: 245–248.

Normand, D. 1947. Note sur les bois de Zingana et autres Césalpiniées africaines à très petites folioles. Rev. Bot. appl. 27: 139–150.

Normand, D. 1948a. Vrais et faux Tchitola du Mayumbé. Bois For. Trop., No. 6: 145–157.

Normand, D. 1948b. Note sur les bois de Dacryodes et de Santiria africains. Bois For. Trop., No. 8: 399–402.

Normand, D. 1950a. Note sur les bois de Guibourtia arnoldiana et de Copaifera religiosa du Mayumbe. Bull. Jard. bot. État Bruxelles 20: 19–30.

Normand, D. 1950b; 1955; 1960. Atlas des bois de la Côte d'Ivoire. Centre tech. For. trop.: Nogent-sur-Marne. Vol. I: 1–146 + Plates 1–56 (1950). Vol. II: 147–262 + Plates 57–112 (1955). Vol. III: 263–393 + Plates 113–168 (1960).

Normand, D. 1951. Remarques à propos de la classification du parenchyme ligneux chez les dicotylédones. IAWA Newsbull.: 12–18.

Normand, D. 1952. Ekop ou andoung. Une des essences intéressantes à retenir. Bois For. Trop., No. 26: 381–387.

Normand, D. 1958. Anatomie du bois et taxinomie II. J. Agric. trop. Bot. appl. 5: 297–303.

Normand, D. 1962. Observations xylologiques sur les espèces africaines de Dacryodes. C.R. 4e Réunion plén. Assoc. Etude tax. Fl. Afr. trop., Lisbon: 289–298.

Normand, D. 1966; 1967. Le kouali, Vochysiacées de Guyane, et leurs bois. Bois For. Trop., No. 110: 3–11 (1966). Ibid. No. 111: 5–17 (1967).

Normand, D. 1970. Les Aniègré, Sapotacées de Côte d'Ivoire et leurs bois. Bois For. Trop., No. 134: 3–13.

Normand, D. 1972. Manuel d'identification des bois commerciaux. 1. Généralités. Centre tech. For. trop., Nogent-sur-Marne. 171 pp.

Normand, D. 1977. Identification botanique du "Kouali-Neyrat" de Guyane française. Adansonia, sér. 2, 17: 11–17.

Normand, D. 1988 [1990]. A propos des bois de rose de Madagascar. Bois For. Trop., No. 217: 89–94.

Normand, D. 1993. Sur la structure anatomique du bois des espèces de Leonardoxa Aubrév. (Caesalpiniacées africaines). Bull. Jard. bot. natn. Belg. 62: 429–432.

Normand, D. & Cavaco, A. 1951. Observations taxonomiques et xylologiques sur le genre Pinacopodium Exell et Mendonça. Bull. Jard. bot. État, Bruxelles 21: 451–463.

Normand, D. & Chatelet, R. 1955. Sur le bois de quatre espèces africaines (Césalpiniacées, Ochnacée et Huacée). J. Agric. trop. Bot. appl. 2: 19–27.

Normand, D. & Détienne, P. 1992. Excoecaria parvifolia, Euphorbiaceae: une question de nomenclature. Bois For. Trop., No. 231: 52–54.

Normand, D. & Mariaux, A. 1962. Peut-on distinguer les bois d'Ozigo des Safoukala, Igaganga et autres Dacryodes? Bois For. Trop., No. 85: 33–40.

Normand, D. & Paquis, J. 1976 [1977]. Manuel d'identification des bois commerciaux. 2. Afrique guinéo-congolaise. Centre tech. For. trop.: Nogent-sur-Marne. 335 pp.

Normand, D. & Sallenave, P. 1958. Caracteristiques et propriétés des acajous (Swietenia et Khaya). Bois For. Trop., No. 59: 43–52.

Norverto, C.A. 1989. Estudio comparativo de la estructura de la madera de Lycium cestroides y L. elongatum (Solanaceae). Bol. Soc. argent. Bot. 26 (1–2): 45–52.

Norverto, C.A. 1993. Perforated ray cells and primary wall remnants in vessel element perforations of Symplocos uniflora. IAWA Jl. 14: 187–190.

Noshiro, S. & Suzuki, M. 1987. Fossil root- and stemwood of Chionanthus retusus Lindl. et Paxt. from the Late Pleistocene of Akashi, Japan. IAWA Bull. n.s. 8: 125–133.

Noskowiak, A.F. 1978. Distribution of aggregate rays in red alder. Wood & Fiber 10: 58–68.

Novruzova, Z.A. 1962a. The anatomical structure of the wood of the linden, Tilia prilipkoana Wagn. et A. Grossh. Dokl. Akad. Nauk azerb. SSR 18 (1): 71–75. [Russ.]

Novruzova, Z.A. 1962b. The effect of dry conditions on the structure of mechanical elements in the secondary xylem of some woody plants. Dokl. Akad. Nauk azerb. SSR 18 (12): 59–62. [Russ.] Referat. Zhur. Biol. (1963) No. 18V 104 (Transl.).

Novruzova, Z.A. 1962c. Anatomical structure of the wood of Ficus hyrcana. Dokl. Akad. Nauk azerb. SSR 18 (2): 69–75. [Russ.] Referat. Zhur., Biol. (1963), No. 24V 98 (Transl.).

Novruzova, Z.A. 1962d. The wood of Ulmus spp. in Azerbaijan in relation to ecology. Izv. Akad. Nauk azerb. SSR (2): 9–15. [Russ.]

Novruzova, Z.A. 1963a. Elements of the xylem in trunks of certain species of the genus Populus relative to ecology. Izv. Akad. Nauk azerb. SSR (3): 13–17. [Russ.]

Novruzova, Z.A. 1963b. The structure of xylem in some species of Astragalus as related to their ecology. Bot. J. USSR 48: 108–112. [Russ.]

Novruzova, Z.A. 1964a. Comparative anatomical study of the secondary xylem of several Crataegus species. Trudy Akad. Nauk azerb. SSR, Inst. Bot. 24: 27–35. [Russ.]

Novruzova, Z.A. 1964b. The structure of wood of the forest-forming species of oak in Azerbaijan in relation to their ecology. Bot. J. USSR 49: 1160–1167. [Russ.; Eng. summ.]

Novruzova, Z.A. 1964c. Comparative anatomical data on the woods of Cerasus species in connection with ecology. Izv. Akad. Nauk azerb. SSR, ser. biol. Nauk (4): 19–23. [Russ.]

Novruzova, Z.A. 1968. The water-conducting system of trees and shrubs in relation to ecology. Izdat. Akad. Nauk azerbaidz. SSR: Baku. 230 pp. [Russ. only.]

Novruzova, Z.A. & Gadzhieva, G.G. 1974. Comparative morphology and anatomy of roses of the Azerbaijan SSR. Izv. Akad. Nauk azerb. SSR, biol. Nauk (5–6): 9–14. [Russ.]

Novruzova, Z.A. & Shamsieva, T.A. 1964. Endomorphology of Caucasian species of the genus Berberis L. with respect to their ecology. Izv. Akad. Nauk azerb. SSR, biol. Nauk (5): 11–17. [Russ.]

Obaton, M. 1960. Les lianes ligneuses à structure anormale des forêts denses d'Afrique occidentale. Masson & Cie: Paris. 220 pp. Also in: Annls. Sci. nat., Bot., sér. 12, 1: 1–220.

Occhioni, P. 1947. Nova espécie de Canellaceae. Arq. Jard. bot. Rio de Janeiro 7: 157–163.

Occhioni, P. 1948. Contribuição ao estudo da família Canellaceae. Arq. Jard. bot. Rio de Janeiro 8: 3–165. [See pp. 72–80.]

Occhioni, P. 1949. Contribuição ao estudo anatômico de Cinnamodendron sampaioanum Occh. Arq. Jard. bot. Rio de Janeiro 9: 101–108.

Occhioni, P. 1954. Contribuição ao estudo da família Chloranthaceae com especial referência ao gênero Hedyosmum Sw. Thesis: Univ. Brasil, Rio de Janeiro. 176 pp. (publ.).

Occhioni, P. & Mattos Filho, A. 1947. Estudo anatômico do lenho secundario do Puchury-Rana. Ocotea fragrantissima Ducke. Rodriguésia 10: 1–8.

Occhioni, P. & Souza H. de 1949. "Pau rosa" brasileiro e seu oleo essencial. Lilloa 16: 213–242.

Ocloo, J.H. & Laing, E. 1991. Anatomical properties of the wood of some Celtis spp. indigenous to Ghana. Discovery Innovation 3 (2): 89–98.

Oda, K. & Nakasone, H. 1975. Crystals and crystalliferous cells in Okinawan hardwoods. Sci. Bull. Coll. Agric. Univ. Ryukyus No. 22: 713–720. [Jap.; Eng. summ.]

Oda, K. & Nakasone, H. 1976. Distribution of calcium oxalate crystals in the stem of some species grown in Okinawa. Mokuzai Gakkaishi (J. Jap. Wood Res. Soc.) 22: 703–706. [Jap.; Eng. summ.]

O'Donell, C. A. 1937. Anatomia comparada del leno de tres Simarubaceas argentinas. Lilloa 1: 263–282.

O'Donell, C. A. 1941. La posición sistemática de Diclidanthera Mart. Lilloa 6: 207–212 + 2 plates.

Ogata, K. 1967. A systematic study of the genus Acer. Bull. Tokyo Univ. For., No. 63: 89–206. [Eng.]

Ogata, K. 1975. Anatomical characters and identification of tropical woods: I. Elaeocarpus and Sloanea (Elaeocarpaceae). Bull. Govt. For. Exp. Sta., Meguro 276: 63–75 + 3 plates. [Eng.]

Ogata, K. 1975–1983; 1985. Identification of woods of South East Asia and the Pacific Region, 1–95. Wood Industr. (Jap.) 30: 171–172, 214–215, 265–266, 306–307, 357–358, 411–412, 463–464, 559–560 (1975); 31: 21–22, 66–67, 111–112, 162–163, 210–211, 248–249, 305–306, 350–351, 400–401, 444–445, 560–561 (1976); 32: 31–32, 71–72, 119–120, 163–164, 216–217, 260–261, 304–305, 353–354, 399–400, 448–449, 558–559 (1977); 33: 33–34, 74–75, 117–118, 162–163, 215–216, 251–252, 294–295, 342–343, 392–393, 438–439, 541–542 (1978); 34: 28–29, 72–73, 122–123, 160–161, 211–212, 256–257, 296–297, 353–354, 395–396, 446–447, 543–544 (1979); 35: 29–30, 80–81, 119–120, 169–170, 217–218, 265–266, 309–310, 373–374, 415–416, 469–470, 531–532 (1980); 36: 37–38, 81–82, 141–142, 181–182, 249–250, 287–288, 351–352, 395–396, 443–444, 501–502, 623–624 (1981); 37: 33–34, 99–100, 147–148, 207–208, 251–252, 303–304, 353–354, 403–404, 451–452, 505–506, 619–620 (1982); 38: 39–40, 95–96, 149–150, 207–208, 249–250, 287–288, 351–352, 385–386, 449–450, 497–502 (1983). [Jap.] Also published in book form by Wood Technological Assn. of Japan. 206 pp. (1985). [Jap.]

Ogata, K. 1988. Wood anatomy of the Caprifoliaceae of Japan. IAWA Bull. n.s. 9: 299–316.

Ogata, K. 1991. Wood anatomy of Zabelia (Caprifoliaceae): evidence for generic recognition. IAWA Bull. n.s. 12: 111–121.

Ogata, K. 1992. Some examples of contribution of wood anatomy to plant taxonomy. In: Proc. 2nd Pacific Regional Wood Anat. Conf. 1989 (eds. Rojo, J.P., Aday, J.U., Barile, E.R., Araral, R.K. & America, W.M.): 242–250. For. Prod. Dev. Inst.: College, Laguna, Philippines.

Ogata, S. 1953. Anatomical structure of eucalypt timbers. J. Jap. For. Soc. 35: 62–64. [Jap.]

Ogden, J. & West, C.J. 1981. Annual rings in Beilschmiedia tawa (Lauraceae). N.Z. Jl. Bot. 19: 397–400.

Ohtani, J. 1983. SEM investigation on the micromorphology of vessel wall sculptures. Res. Bull. Coll. Exp. For. Hokkaido Univ. 40: 323–386. [Eng.]

Ohtani, J. 1986. Vestures in axial parenchyma cells. IAWA Bull. n.s. 7: 39–45.

Ohtani, J. 1987. Vestures in septate wood fibres. IAWA Bull. n.s. 8: 59–67.

Ohtani, J. & Ishida, S. 1976. Study on the pit of wood cells using scanning electron microscopy. 5. Vestured pits in Japanese dicotyledonous woods. Res. Bull. Coll. Exp. For. Hokkaido Univ. 33: 407–435 + 11 plates. [Eng.]

Ohtani, J. & Ishida, S. 1978a. An observation on the perforation plates in Japanese dicotyledonous woods using scanning electron microscopy. Res. Bull. Coll. Exp. For. Hokkaido Univ. 35: 65–98 + 18 plates. [Eng.]

Ohtani, J. & Ishida, S. 1978b. An observation on the spiral thickenings in the vessel members in Japanese dicotyledonous woods using scanning electron microscopy. Res. Bull. Coll. Exp. For. Hokkaido Univ. 35: 433–464 + 16 plates. [Eng.]

Ohtani, J., Jing, W., Fukazawa, K. & Xian, S.Q. 1989. Multiple perforation plates in Gmelina arborea Roxb. (Verbenaceae). IAWA Bull. n.s. 10: 35–41.

Ohtani, J., Meylan, B.A. & Butterfield, B.G. 1983. Occurrence of warts in the vessel elements and fibres of New Zealand woods. N.Z. Jl. Bot. 21: 359–372.

Okeke, R.E. 1966. Comparative anatomy of three Nigerian Afzelia species. For. Prod. Res. Rep., No. F.P.R.L./9: 8 pp. Lagos.

Oliveira, J.S., Freitas, M.C.P.G. de, et al. 1970. Eucalypts of Namaacha. Revta Ciênc. agron., Lourenço Marques 3B (2): 1–230. [Port.; Eng. summ.] [For. Abstr. 32 (1971) No. 5823.]

Oprea, C. 1972 [1974]. Contributii privind structura tulpinii la citeva Pomoidee si Prunoidee cultivate si spontane. Lucr. ştiinţ. Inst. agron. Nicolae Bǎiescu, B, 15: 213–233. [Eng. summ.]

Oprea, V. & Oprea, I.V. 1986. Cercetǎri xilotomice referitoare la principalele specii de Acer L. din România şi importanţa lor aplicativǎ. Stud. cerc. Biol., ser. Biol. veg. 38: 99–105.

Orchard, A.E. 1975. Taxonomic revisions in the family Haloragaceae. I. The genera Haloragis, Haloragodendron, Glischrocaryon, Meziella and Gonocarpus. Bull. Auckland Inst. Mus. 10: 299 pp.

Ortega, F., Guerrero, L., Carmona, T. & Córdoba, C. 1988? (no date). Angiospermas arbóreas de Mexico. 1. Anatomía de la madera de veintiocho especies de Cosautlan de Carvajal, Veracruz. Madera u Su Uso, Bol. téc. No. 19: 206 pp. [Eng. summ.]

Ortega G., M. 1958. Estructura anatómica e histológica de un grupo de 28 especies del bosque Chiapaneco. Vol. I. Inst. Mex. Invest. Tec., Mexico. 241 pp.

Ortiz Cespedes, M. 1959. Etude anatomique de quelques-uns des principaux bois chiliens. Centre Tech. Bois: Paris. 25 pp.

Outer, R.W. den: see Den Outer, R.W.

Paddon, T.W. 1953. Les nouveaux hêtres du Chili. Rev. Bois (Paris) 8 (5): 9–11.

Page, V.M. 1993. Anatomical variation in the wood of Robinia pseudoacacia L. and the identity of Miocene fossil woods from southwestern United States. IAWA Jl. 14: 299–314.

Pal, S. 1981. Structure of secondary xylem in some Indian Lauraceae and its bearing on the taxonomy of the family. J. Indian bot. Soc. 60: 197–203.

Palandzhyan, V.A. 1953. Structure of the woods of the elm family in connection with their evolution and systematics. Trudy bot. Inst. Akad. Nauk arm. SSR 9: 121–178. [Russ.]

Paliwal, G.S. & Srivastava, L.M. 1969. The cambium of Alseuosmia. Phytomorphology 19: 5–8.

Pan, K.-Y., Lu, A.-M. & Wen, J. 1991. A systematic study on the genus Disanthus Maxim. (Hamamelidaceae). Cathaya 3: 1–28. [Eng.]

Panikkar, A.O.N. & Bhambie, S. 1974. Anomalous secondary growth in some vascular plants. In: Biology of the land plants (eds. Puri, V. et al.): 100–109. Sarita Prakashan, Meerut, India.

Panshin, A.J. 1932. An anatomical study of the woods of the Philippine mangrove swamps. Philipp. J. Sci. 48: 143–207.

Panshin, A.J. 1933. Comparative anatomy of the woods of the Meliaceae, subfamily Swietenioideae. Amer. J. Bot. 20: 638–668.

Panshin, A.J. 1937. Wood anatomy of certain South American rotenone-yielding plants. Amer. J. Bot. 24: 587–591.

Panshin, A.J. & Zeeuw, C. De 1970; 1980. Textbook of wood techonology. I. Structure, identification, uses, and properties of the commercial woods of the United States and Canada. McGraw-Hill: New York. 3rd edn. 705pp. (1970). 4th edn. 722 pp. (1980). [Only 4th edn. indexed.]

Panshin, A.J., Zeeuw, C. De & Brown, H.P. 1964. Textbook of wood technology. Vol. I. Structure, identification, uses, and properties of the commercial woods of the United States. McGraw-Hill Book Co. 2nd edn. 643 pp. [Panshin & Zeeuw 1980 indexed.]

Pant, D.D. & Bhatnagar, S. 1975. Morphological studies in Argyreia Lour. (Convolvulaceae). Bot. J. Linn. Soc. 70: 45–69.

Paolis, D. de 1950. Considerazioni sulla variabilita della cerchia legnosa del mandorlo. La luce e un fattore importante? Nuovo G. bot. ital. (NS) 57: 210–222.

Papaïoannou, J.C. 1948. Encore une nouvelle espèce de chêne en Grèce. Quercus euboica, spec. nov. (Forme, anatomie, répartition géographique, tempérament et exigences, importance au point de vue forestier). Anatypon 23: 336–352.

Parameswaran, N. & Conrad, H. 1982. Wood and bark anatomy of Balanites aegyptiaca in relation to ecology and taxonomy. IAWA Bull. n.s. 3: 75–88.

Parameswaran, N. & Gomes, A.V. 1981. Fine structural aspects of helical thickenings and pits in vessels of Ligustrum lucidum Ait. (Oleaceae). IAWA Bull. n.s. 2: 179–185.

Parameswaran, N. & Gottwald, H. 1979. Problematic taxa in the Dipterocarpaceae. Their anatomy and taxonomy. Mém. Mus. natn. Hist. nat., Paris, B (NS), 26: 69–75.

Parameswaran, N. & Liese, W. 1969. On the formation and fine structure of septate wood fibres of Ribes sanguineum. Wood Sci. Technol. 3: 272–286.

Parameswaran, N. & Liese, W. 1973. Scanning electron microscopy of multiperforate perforation plates. Holzforschung 27: 181–186.

Parameswaran, N. & Metcalfe, C.R. 1966. Notes on the wood structure of Panda oleosa and Galearia celebica. (Appendix II to paper by L.L. Forman). Kew Bull. 20: 319–321.

Parameswaran, N. & Richter, H.-G. 1984. The ultrastructure of crystalliferous cells in some Lecythidaceae with a discussion of their terminology. IAWA Bull. n.s. 5: 229–236.

Parente, M.Z.G. 1959–1961. Anatomia do lenho secundário de Triplaris gardneriana Wedd. Arq. Jard. bot. Rio de Janeiro 17: 251–254 + 3 plates.

Parham, B.E. 1933. New Zealand beech timbers: their structure and identification. N.Z. Jl. Sci. Technol. 14: 233–240, 372–382.

Parham, R.A. & Baird, W.M. 1974. Warts in the evolution of angiosperm wood. Wood Sci. Technol. 8: 1–10.

Parham, R.A. & Kaustinen, H. 1973. On the morphology of spiral thickenings. IAWA Bull. 1973/2: 8–17.

Park, S.J. & Soh, W.Y. 1984. Systematic studies on some Korean woody plants: Anatomy of lauraceous stem woods. Korean J. Bot. 27 (2): 81–94. [Korean; Eng. summ.]

Parsa Pajouh, D. & Schweingruber, F.H. 1985. Atlas des bois du nord de l'Iran. Institut federal de Recherches forestières: Birmensdorf, Switzerland. 144 pp.

Patel, R.N. 1965. A comparison of the anatomy of the secondary xylem in roots and stems. Holzforschung 19: 72–79.

Patel, R.N. 1973, 1974, 1975, 1978, 1986, 1987, 1988, 1989, 1990, 1991, 1992. Wood anatomy of the dicotyledons indigenous to New Zealand. 1, Cornaceae. N.Z. Jl. Bot. 11: 3–22. 2, Escalloniaceae. Ibid.: 421–434. 3, Monimiaceae and Atherospermataceae. Ibid.: 587–598 (1973). 4, Winteraceae. Ibid. 12: 19–32. 5, Verbenaceae. Ibid.: 33–44. 6, Meliaceae. Ibid.: 159–166. 7, Santalaceae. Ibid.: 431–444 (1974). 8, Corynocarpaceae. Ibid. 13: 19–29. 9, Sapindaceae. Ibid.: 131–140. 10, Chloranthaceae. Ibid.: 141–148 (1975). 11, Oleaceae. Ibid. 16: 1–6 (1978). 15, Fagaceae. Ibid. 24: 189–202 (1986). 16, Lauraceae. Ibid. 25: 477–488 (1987). 17, Tiliaceae. Ibid. 26: 337–343 (1988). 18, Elaeocarpaceae. Ibid. 27: 325–335 (1989). 19, Gesneriaceae. Ibid. 28: 85–94. 20, Cunoniaceae. Ibid.: 347–355 (1990). 21, Loranthaceae. Ibid. 29: 429–449 (1991). 22, Proteaceae. Ibid. 30: 415–428 (1992).

Patel, R.N. & Bowles, A. 1978, 1980. Wood anatomy of the dicotyledons indigenous to New Zealand. 12, Icacinaceae. N.Z. Jl. Bot. 16: 7–12. 13, Moraceae. Ibid.: 13–19 (1978). 14, Piperaceae. Ibid. 18: 507–513 (1980).

Patterson, R. & Tanowitz, B.D. 1989. Evolutionary and geographic trends in adaptive wood anatomy in Eriastrum densifolium (Polemoniaceae). Amer. J. Bot. 76: 706–713.

Paula, J.E. de 1972a. Estudos anatomico e polinologico de Antonia ovata Pohl (Loganiaceae). Acta Amazonica 2 (2): 55–70.

Paula, J.E. de 1972b. Estudos sobre Vochysiaceae: VI. Anatomia de Salvertia convallariodora St. Hil.: Analise comparativa entre especimes dos Cerrados Equatoriais do Amapa, e do Brasil Central. Acta Amazonica 2 (3): 5–23. [Eng. summ.]

Paula, J.E. de 1974. Anatomia de madeira: Guttiferae. Acta Amazonica 4 (1): 27–64. [Eng. summ.]

Paula, J.E. de 1975. Estudios sobre Bombacaceae II. Anatomia do lenho secundario de Catostemma albuquerquei. Acta Amazonica 5 (3): 297–299. [Eng. summ.]

Paula, J.E. de 1976a. Estudos sobre Bombacaceae. V. Investigações anatômicas das madeiras de Catostemma commune Sandwich, C. sclerophyllum Ducke e Scleronema micranthum (Ducke) Ducke, com vistas à polpa, papel e taxinomia. Acta Amazonica 6: 115–161. [Eng. summ.]

Paula, J.E. de 1976b. Anatomia de Lorostemon coelhoi Paula, Caraipa valioi Paula e Clusia aff. macropoda Klotzsch (Guttiferae da Amazônia). Acta Amazonica 6: 273–291. [Brief Eng. summ.]

Paula, J.E. de 1977. Estudos sobre Bombacaceae. III. Anatomia do lenho secundário de Catostemma milanezii Paula. Trab. XXVI Congr. nac. Bot., Rio de Janeiro 1975: 443–447.

Paula, J.E. de 1979. Estudo comparativo da estrutura anatômica das madeiras de setenta e duas espécies brasileiras pouco conhecidas. Brasil Florestal 9 (40): 29–63.

Paula, J.E. de 1980. Estudo anatômico das madeiras de Virola sebifera Aubl. e Pseudobombax tomentosum (Mart. et Zucc.) A. Robyns visando o seu aproveitamento tecnológico. Brasil Florestal 10 (42): 35–52. (This paper is actually on pp. 25–34 but with wrong title).

Paula, J.E. de 1981. Estudo das estruturas internas das madeiras de dezesseis espécies da flora brasileira, visando seu aproveitamento para produção de álcool, carvão, coque e papel. Brasil Florestal 11 (47): 23–50. [Eng. summ.]

Paula, J.E. de & Alves, J.L. de H. 1973. Anatomia de Anacardium spruceanum Bth. ex Engl. (Anacardiaceae de Amazônia). Acta Amazonica 3 (1): 39–52. [Eng. summ.]

Paula, J.E. de & Alves, J.L. de H. 1980. Estudo das estruturas anatômicas e de algumas propriedades físicas da madeira de 14 espécies ocorrentes em áreas de caatinga. Brasil Florestal 10 (43): 47–58. [Eng. summ.]

Paula, J.E. de & Alves, J.L. de H. 1989. Estrutura anatômica de madeiras indígenas para produção de energia e papel. Pesq. agropec. bras. 24: 1461–1471. [Eng. summ.]

Paula, J.E. de & Heringer, E.P. 1977; 1979. Anatomia comparada das espécies Annona glabra L. e A. salzmannii DC. (Annonaceae) ocorrentes no nordeste Brasileiro (Pernambuco). Trab. XXVI Congr. nac. Bot., Rio de Janeiro 1975: 465–474 (1977). Also in: Brasil Florestal 9 (38): 21–28 (1979).

Pawar, J.S. & Kulkarni, A.R. 1971. Contribution to the morphology of the Pedaliaceae: IV. Wood anatomy of Sesamum alatum Thonn. J. Shivaji Univ. 4: 117–120.

Pearson, R.G. & Wheeler, E.A. 1981. Computer identification of hardwood species. IAWA Bull. n.s. 2: 37–40.

Pearson, R.S. & Brown, H.P. 1932. Commercial timbers of India. Their distribution, supplies, anatomical structure, physical and mechanical properties and uses. Central Publ. Branch, Govt. of India, Calcutta. 2 vols. 1150 pp.

Pedro, E.R., Seabra L. de, Ferreirinha, M.P. & Sousa, A.E. de 1955. Pterocarpus angolensis DC. Garcia de Orta 3: 11–31. [Port.; Eng. summ.]

Penhallow, D.P. 1905. A systematic study of the Salicaceae. Amer. Nat. 39: 509–535, 797–838.

Pennington, T.D. 1969. Materials for a monograph of the Meliaceae. I. A revision of the genus Vavaea. Blumea 17: 351–366.

Pennington, T.D. & Styles, B.T. 1975. A generic monograph of the Meliaceae. Blumea 22: 419–540.

Peraza Oramas, C. & Lopez De Roma, A. 1967. Estudio de las principales maderas de Canarias. Inst. For. Invest. Exp., Madrid. 220 pp. [Eng. summ.]

Pereira, A.J. do R., Vasconcellos, J.M.C. de, Tavares, S. & Tavares, E.J. de S. 1970. Caracteres tecnológicos de 25 espécies de madeiras do nordeste do Brasil. Bol. Recurs. Nat., Recife 8: 5–148. [Eng. summ.]

Pereira, J. A. 1933. Contribuição para a identificação micrographica das nossas madeiras. Lab. Ensaio Mat., Esc. polytech. São Paulo, Bol. 9: 165 pp.

Perez-Jimenez, L. A. 1982. Jatropha chamelensis (Euphorbiaceae), nueva especie de la Costa de Jalisco, Mexico. Bol. Soc. bot. Mex. 42: 35–39.

Pérez Mogollón, A. 1973. Estructura anatómica de 37 maderas de la Guayana venezolana y clave para su identificación. Acta bot. venez. 8: 9–109.

Pérez Mogollón, A. 1991a. Anatomía de la madera de Sapium stylare y Tetrorchidium rubrivenium (Euphorbiaceae) del bosque La Mucuy, Estado Merida. Pittieria 19: 25–34.

Pérez Mogollón, A. 1991b. Observaciones submicroscópicas del leño de "saqui saqui", Bombacopsis quinata (Bombacaceae). Pittieria 19: 35–40.

Pérez Mogollón, A. 1993. Anatomia e identificacion de 40 maderas del bosque La Mucuy, Estado Merida, Venezuela. Pittieria 20: 5–77.

Pérez Olvera, C. de la P. 1974. Anatomia de la madera de cinco especies de encinos de Durango. Bol. téc. Inst. nac. Invest. forest., México, No. 43: 35 pp. (2nd edn. 1982.) [Eng. summ.]

Pérez Olvera, C. de la P. 1976. Características anatómicas de cinco encinos de México. Bol. téc. Inst. nac. Invest. forest., México, No. 46: 1–43. [Eng. summ.]

Pérez Olvera, C. de la P. 1982. Estructura anatómica de cinco especies del género Quercus. Bol. téc. Inst. nac. Invest. forest., México, No. 88: 62 pp.

Pérez Olvera, C. de la P. 1985. Características anatómicas de siete especies del género Quercus. Bol. téc. Inst. nac. Invest. forest., México, No. 123: 70 pp. [Eng. summ.]

Pérez Olvera, C. de la P. 1993. Anatomía de la madera de ocho especies con importancia en las artesanías del estado de Michoacán. Acta bot. México, No. 23: 103–136.

Pérez Olvera, C. de la P. & Aguilar Entíquez, M. de L. 1978. Diferencias morfológicas externas y anatómicas de la madera de los encinos blancos y rojos. Bol. téc. Inst. nac. Invest. forest., México, No. 59: 19 pp. [Eng. summ.]

Pérez Olvera, C. de la P., Carmona Valdovinos, T. F. & Rogel Gomez, M. de los A. 1980 [1981]. Estudio anatómico de la madera de 43 especies tropicales. Bol. téc. Inst. nac. Invest. forest., México, No. 63: 276 pp.

Pérez Olvera, C. de la P. & Corral Lopez, G. 1980. Estudio anatómico de la madera de once especies de angiospermas. Bol. téc. Inst. nac. Invest. forest., México, No. 64: 79 pp. [Eng. summ.]

Pérez Olvera, C. de la P., Olvera Coronel, P. & Corral Lopez, G. 1982 [1985]. Estudio anatómico de la madera de 26 especies de angiospermas de clima templado. Bol. téc. Inst. nac. Invest. forest., México, No. 91: 126 pp.

Pérez Olvera, C. de la P., Robles Gálvez, F. & Simental Serrano, A. 1979. Determinación de la características anatómicas y fisicomecánicas de la madera de 4 especies de Leguminosas. Bol. téc. Inst. nac. Invest. forest., México, No. 61: 35 pp. [Eng. summ.]

Perrot, E. 1912. Les caractères histologiques du Panda oleosa Pierre, et sa place dans la classification. Bull. Soc. bot. Fr. 59: 159–165.

Perrot, E. & Gérard, G. 1907. Recherches sur les bois de différentes espèces de Légumineuses africaines. In: Les végétaux utiles de l'Afrique tropicale française (ed. Chevalier, A.) III: 155 pp. Also in: Trav. Lab. Mat. méd., Paris 5 (1907) [1908] (3): 155 pp.

Persinos, G. J. & Quimby, M. W. 1968. Studies on Nigerian plants. V. Comparative anatomy of Lophira lanceolata and Lophira alata. Econ. Bot. 22: 206–220.

Petersen, A. E. 1953. A comparison of the secondary xylem elements of certain species of the Amentiferae and Ranales. Bull. Torrey Bot. Cl. 80: 365–384.

Petrić, B. & Šcukanec, V. 1975. Ray tissue percentages in wood of Yugoslavian hardwoods. IAWA Bull. 1975/3: 43–44.

Petriella, B. 1966. Estudio anatomico del tallo de Vernonia fulta (Compositae). Bol. Soc. argent. Bot. 11: 19–25. [Eng. summ.]

Pfeiffer, H. 1924a. Kritische Untersuchungen über die Entstehung der Zuwachsringe und der Xylemzerkluftungen bei Erycibe Roxb. Bot. Archiv 5: 171–176.

Pfeiffer, H. 1924b. Über Spaltenbildung und Vorbeigleiten der Bastkörper im unterbrochenen Holzkörper der Bignoniaceen. Ber. dt. bot. Ges. 42: 32–35.

Pfeiffer, H. 1925. Anatomische Betrachtung brasilianischer Hölzer. Beih. bot. Zbl. 41 (1): 165–178.

Pfeiffer, H. 1926. Das abnorme Dickenwachstum. [Linsbauer's Handbuch der Pflanzenanatomie Abt. 9, No. 15.] Gebrüder Borntraeger: Berlin. 273 pp.

Pfeiffer, H.H. 1951. Die Verbenaceenhölzer von Uraguay. Rev. Sudamer. Bot., Montevideo 10: 7–12.

Pfeiffer, H.H. 1953. Über Moraceenhölzer des aussertropischen Südamerica. Rev. Sudamer. Bot., Montevideo 10: 133–138.

Pfeiffer, J.P. 1926. De houtsoorten van Suriname I. Meded. konink. Ver. Kolon. Inst., Amsterdam, No. 22: 505 pp. + Atlas of 24 plates.

Philipson, W.R. 1967. Griselinia Forst. fil. - anomaly or link. N.Z. Jl. Bot. 5: 134–165.

Philipson, W.R. 1975. Evolutionary lines within the dicotyledons. N.Z. Jl. Bot. 13: 73–91.

Philipson, W.R. 1990. Anomalous cambia. In: The vascular cambium (ed. Iqbal, M.): 201–212. Research Studies Press, Taunton.

Philipson, W.R., Stone, B.C. et al. 1980. The systematic position of Aralidium Miq. – a multidisciplinary study. Taxon 29: 391–416.

Philipson, W.R., Ward, J.M. & Butterfield, B.G. 1971. The vascular cambium. Its development and activity. Chapman & Hall: London. 182 pp.

Pickel, D.B.J., Mainieri, C., Guimarães, O.P. & Lima, A.O. 1961. A Caviúna Vermelha e suas propriedades. Anu. bras. Econ. flor. No. 13: 238–245.

Pinho, R.A. de 1984. Estudo anatômico do lenho das Araliáceas arbóreas nativas no Parque Estadual das Fontes do Ipiranga (São Paulo, Brasil). Hoehnea 11: 39–45.

Pinho, R.A. de, Bassetto, E. & Sajo, M. das G. 1986a. Estudo anatômico do lenho de Solanáceas arbóreas nativas no Parque Estadual das Fontes do Ipiranga (São Paulo, Brasil): I. Hoehnea 13: 43–49.

Pinho, R.A. de, Gorgatti, L. & Sajo, M. das G. 1986b. Estudo anatômico do lenho das Anonáceas arbóreas nativas no Parque Estadual das Fontes do Ipiranga (São Paulo, Brasil). Hoehnea 13: 35–42.

Pinker, K. & Linskens, H.F. 1958. Vergleichende Untersuchungen der anatomischen und physikalischen Eigenschaften des Holzes von Populus simonii und Populus robusta. Holz Roh- u. Werkst. 16: 325–327.

Pinto M., L.A. 1978. Descripción anatómica del leño de Uladendron codesurii Marcano-Berti (Malvaceae). Pittieria 7: 31–34.

Pipoly, J.J. 1983. Contributions toward a monograph of Cybianthus (Myrsinaceae): III. A revision of subgenus Laxiflorus. Brittonia 35: 61–80.

Pipoly, J.J. 1987. A systematic revision of the genus Cybianthus subgenus Grammadenia (Myrsinaceae). Mem. N.Y. bot. Gard. 43: 1–76.

Plank, S. 1976. Histologie und Verkernung des Holzes von Sambucus nigra und Sambucus racemosa. I. Histologie und jahreszeitliche cytologische Veränderungen. Phyton (Austria) 17: 195–212.

Plank, S. & Wolkinger, F. 1976. Holz von Vitis vinifera im Raster-Elektronenmikroskop. Vitis 15: 153–159.

Poller, S. 1967. Beitrag zur Kenntnis wenig bekannter vietnamesischer Hölzer. Arch. Forstw. 16: 1321–1336. [Eng. summ.]

Pompert, M.G. de 1989. Estudio morfo-anatomico de dos especies de Sapium (Euphorbiaceae). Bonplandia 6(3): 197–210.

Pozhidaeva, L.F. 1970. The anatomical structure of hornbeam wood. Khim. Drev., No. 5: 3–9. [Russ.]

Prabhakar, M. & Ramayya, N. 1979. Anatomical studies in the Indian Portulacaceae: I. Stem wood. Indian J. Bot. 2: 96–106.

Prakash, N. 1972. Root-wood anatomy of some tropical economic plants. Notes Jodrell Lab. VII: 1–19.

Prakash, N. & Lau, Y.Y. 1976. Morphology of Ploiarium alternifolium and the taxonomic position of Ploiarium. Bot. Notiser 129: 279–285.

Prakash, U. 1961. Fibers in the secondary xylem of Aeschynomene. J. Arnold Arbor. 42: 442–446.

Prance, G.T. 1965. The systematic position of Stylobasium Desf. Bull. Jard. bot. État, Bruxelles 35: 435–448.

Prance, G.T. 1968. The systematic position of Rhabdodendron Gilg & Pilg. Bull. Jard. bot. natn. Belg. 38: 127–146.

Prance, G.T. 1972a. Dichapetalaceae. Flora Neotropica Mon., No. 10: 1–84.

Prance, G.T. 1972b. Rhabdodendraceae. Flora Neotropica Mon., No. 11: 1–22.

Prance, G.T. & Freitas da Silva, M. 1973. A monograph of Caryocaraceae. Flora Neotropica Mon., No. 12: 1–75.

Prance, G.T. & White, F. 1988. The genera of Chrysobalanaceae: a study in practical and theoretical taxonomy and its relevance to evolutionary biology. Phil. Trans. roy. Soc. Lond., B, 320: 1–184.

Primo, B.L. 1971. Contribuição ao estudo anatômico da madeira de matamatá, de jarana e de ihaiba. Brasil Florestal 2 (6): 24–32.

Psaras, G.K. & Hatzopoulou-Belba, C.C. 1984. Tracheary element morphology of some sclerophyllous plants common in Mediterranean formations in Greece. Flora 175: 319–328.

Puglia, M. de la Paz & Norverto, C.A. 1990. Estructura y ontogenia del leño anómalo de Pisonia zevallo. Parodiana 6 (2): 227–239.

Puławska, Z. 1973. The parenchymo-vascular cambium and its derivative tissues in stems and roots of Bougainvillea glabra Choisy (Nyctaginaceae). Acta Soc. bot. pol. 42: 41–61.

Puławska, Z. 1982. Tissues development in stems of Aristolochia clematitis L. in the point of view of multicellular complexes formation. Acta Soc. bot. pol. 51: 107–125.

Purkayastha, S.K. 1958. Growth and development of septate and crystalliferous fibres in some Indian trees. Proc. Nat. Inst. Sci. India 24 B: 239–244.

Purkayastha, S.K. 1980. Wood anatomy in relation to taxonomy. In: Glimpses in plant research. V. Modern trends in plant taxonomy (ed. Nair, P.K.K.): 192–198. Vikas: India.

Purkayastha, S.K. & Bahadur, K.N. 1977. A note on the taxonomy and wood anatomy of the Indian Cornaceae with special reference to the genus Cornus. Indian Forester 103: 240–250.

Purkayastha, S.K., Juneja, K.B.S. & Kazmi, S.M.H. 1976. Anatomy of more important Andaman commercial timbers (with notes on their supply, properties and uses). Indian For. Rec. (NS) Wood anatomy 2 (1): 1–48.

Qian, H. 1988. A study on the genus Berchemiella Nakai (Rhamnaceae) endemic to eastern Asia. Bull. bot. Res. N.E. for. Univ. (China) 8 (4): 119–128. [Chin.; Eng. summ.]

Qian, L., Zhou, W., Jin, Y. & Tao, Y. 1989. Wood anatomy of Magnolia amoena Cheng. J. Zhejiang For. Sci. Tech. 9 (1): 26–29. [Chin.; Eng. summ.]

Queiroz, P.F. & Van der Burgh, J. 1988–1989 [1989]. Wood anatomy of Iberian Ericales. Rev. biol., Lisboa 14: 95–134.

Quirk, J.T. 1980. Wood anatomy of the Vochysiaceae. IAWA Bull. n.s. 1: 172–179.

Quirk, J.T. 1983. Data for a computer-assisted wood identification system. I. Commercial legumes of tropical Asia and Australia. IAWA Bull. n.s. 4: 118–130.

Quirk, J.T. & Miller, R.B. 1983. Nonvestured pits in Koompassia Maingay (Leguminosae). IAWA Bull. n.s. 4: 191–195.

Quirk, J.T. & Miller, R.B. 1985. Vestured pits in the tribe Cassieae Bronn. (Leguminosae). IAWA Bull. n.s. 6: 200–212.

Rabechault, H. 1955. Sur l'anatomie du giroflier, Syzygium aromaticum (L.) Merrill et Perry. Agron. trop. 10: 449–484.

Ragonese, A.M. 1961. Estructura del xilema secundario de las Araliaceae argentinas. Revta Invest. agric. 15: 361–391 + 6 plates.

Ragonese, A.M. 1976. Consideraciones sobre el problema de la clasificación de los elementos traqueales no perforados de las dicotiledóneas y en especial de algunas Mirtáceas. Darwiniana 20: 476–490. [Eng. summ.]

Ragonese, A.M. 1977 [1978]. Caracteres anatómicos del parénquima radial y axial en el leño de los Mirtáceas. Darwiniana 21: 27–41.

Ragonese, A.M. 1980. Las placas de perforacion en los vasos de Pterocaulon (Compositae). Bol. Soc. argent. Bot. 19: 139–147.

Rakouth, B.R. 1989. Wood anatomy of Malagasy and African Montiniaceae. IAWA Bull. n.s. 10: 345. [Abstr.]

Ramalho, R.S., Lelles, J.G. de & Burger, L.M. 1981. Estudo tecnológico da "quaresminha" (Miconia candolleana Trian.) I. Características dendrológicas e anatômicas da madeira. Revta. Arvore 5 (1): 104–114. [Eng. summ.]

Rancusi, H.-M., Nishida, M. & Nishida, H. 1987. Xylotomy of important Chilean woods. In: Contributions to the botany in the Andes II (ed. Nishida, M.): 68–158 + plates 8–66. Academia Scientific Book Inc.: Tokyo.

Ranjani, K. & Krishnamurthy, K.V. 1987. A comparative study of root and stem woods of some members of the Mimosoideae (Leguminosae). J. Arnold Arbor. 68: 349–355.

Ranjani, K. & Krishnamurthy, K.V. 1988. Tyloses of the root wood of Cassia fistula L. Feddes Repert. 99: 147–149 + Plate XIII.

Ranjani, K. & Krishnamurthy, K.V. 1991. Chambered crystal strands in the wood of Caesalpiniaceae. Feddes Repert. 102: 57–62 + 1 plate.

Rao, A.N. 1979. Vessel elements in Vaccinium buxifolium Hook. J. Indian bot. Soc. 58: 21–25.

Rao, B.H., Surya Kamala, S.V.R. & Kumar, K.V.R. 1989. Anatomical studies of some boraginaceous woods. J. Swamy bot. Cl. 6: 39–44.

Rao, B.S. 1962. Variation in the structure of wood in some dicotyledonous trees. Proc. Summer School Bot., 1960, Darjeeling (ed. Maheshwari, P., Johri, B.M. & Vasil, I.K.): 469–476. Min. Sci. Res. & Cult. Aff., New Delhi.

Rao, B.S. & Rao, P.S.P. 1972. Variability in the secondary xylem of Terminalia tomentosa. J. Indian bot. Soc. 51: 113–117.

Rao, B.S.S. & Rao, R.V. 1979. Wood anatomy of Gouania lupuloides (L.) Urban. Curr. Sci. 48: 269–270.

Rao, K.K. & Ramayya, N. 1984. Structure and distribution of calcium oxalate crystals in the stem wood of Ficus L., in relation to taxonomy. Indian J. For. 7: 25–30.

Rao, K.R. 1966 [1970]. Intercellular canals in the secondary xylem and their importance in the classification and identification of Indian woods. Proc. Autumn School Botany, Mahabaleshwar 1966 (ed. Mahabalé, T.S.): 279–294.

Rao, K.R. & Dayal, R. 1992. The secondary xylem of Aquilaria agallocha (Thymelaeaceae) and the formation of 'Agar'. IAWA Bull. n.s. 13: 163–172.

Rao, P.S.P. 1972. Wood anatomy of some Combretaceae. J. Jap. Bot. 47: 358–377. [Eng.]

Rao, R.V., Bisen, S.S., Sharma, B. & Dayal, R. 1987a. SEM observations of perforation plates in Sonneratia Linn. (Sonneratiaceae). IAWA Bull. n.s. 8: 331–336.

Rao, R.V., Dayal, R. & Raturi, R.D. 1992a. Wood anatomy of Indian Myristicaceae with critical remarks on some foreign genera. Indian For. 118: 125–141.

Rao, R.V., Dayal, R., Sharma, B.L. & Chauhan, L. 1992b. Reinvestigation of the wood structure of Thottea siliquosa (Aristolochiaceae). IAWA Bull. n.s. 13: 17–20.

Rao, R.V., Sharma, B., Chauhan, L. & Dayal, R. 1987b. Reinvestigations of the wood anatomy of Duabanga and Sonneratia with particular reference to their systematic position. IAWA Bull. n.s. 8: 337–345.

Rao, R.V., Sharma, B. & Dayal, R. 1984. Occurrence of perforated ray cells in Santalaceae. IAWA Bull. n.s. 5: 313–315.

Rao, R. V., Sharma, B. & Dayal, R. 1989. Anatomy of aerial rootwood of Sonneratia caseolaris (L.) Engler (Sonneratioideae). IAWA Bull. n. s. 10: 374–378.

Rao, R. V., Sharma, B., Dayal, R. & Raturi, R. D. 1991. Occurrence of broad rays in Indian Castanopsis (D.Don) Spach; Lithocarpus Blume and Quercus semiserrata Roxb. (Fagaceae). J. Indian Acad. Wood Sci. 22 (2): 25–40.

Rasa, E. A. 1981. Anatomy proves taxonomy. A comparative anatomical study of ten leguminous trees. Nat. Res. Counc. Philipp., Res. Bull. 36 (1): 150–161. Also in: Philipp. J. Sci. 109: 23–32 (1980).

Raturi, R. D. & Dayal, R. 1988. Wood structure of Clethra monostachya Rehder and Wilson. Indian For. 114: 865–867.

Rauh, W. & Dittmar, K. 1970. Weitere Untersuchungen an Didiereaceen. III. Vergleichend-anatomische Untersuchungen an den Sprossachsen und den Dornen der Didiereaceen. S.B. Heidelberg. Akad. Wiss., math. naturwiss. Kl., No. 4: 88 pp.

Ravololomaniraka, D. & Koechlin, J. 1970. Sur la structure anatomique de quelques lianes ligneuses de Madagascar. Ann. Univ. Madagascar, Sci. nat. math. (7): 215–230.

Rebollar Domínguez, S. 1977. La madera de Alnus firmifolia y sus usos. Ciencia forestal 2 (8): 51–63.

Rebollar Domínguez, S., Perez Olvera, C. de la P. & Quintanar Isaías, P. A. 1987. Maderas de la península de Yucatán, México. I. Estudio anatómico de la madera de tres especies del estado de Yucatán. Biotica, Méx. 12: 159–179.

Record, S. J. 1918; 1921. Intercellular canals in dicotyledonous woods. J. Forestry 16: 428–441 (1918). Further notes on intercellular canals in dicotyledonous wood. Ibid. 19: 255–266 (1921).

Record, S. J. 1919. Storied or tier-like structure of certain dicotyledonous woods. Bull. Torrey bot. Cl. 46: 253–273.

Record, S. J. 1921a. The wood of the Venezuelan Mahogany (Swietenia candollei Pittier). Bol. Com. Indust., Caracas, No. 18: 577–581.

Record, S. J. 1921b. Lignum-vitae: a study of the woods of the Zygophyllaceae with reference to the true Lignum-vitae of commerce – its sources, properties, uses, and substitutes. Bull. Yale Sch. For., No. 6: 48 pp.

Record, S. J. 1925a. Secretory cells in dicotyledonous woods. Trop. Woods 1: 9–12.

Record, S. J. 1925b. Occurrence of intercellular canals in dicotyledonous woods. Trop. Woods 4: 17–20.

Record, S. J. 1926a. The wood of Saurauia villosa DeCandolle. Trop. Woods 8: 11–13.

Record, S. J. 1926b. The wood of Krugiodendron ferreum (Vahl) Urban. Trop. Woods 8: 13–15.

Record, S. J. 1926c. The wood of Koeberlinia spinosa Zuccarini. Trop. Woods 8: 15–17.

Record, S. J. 1927a. A new species of Mollia of British Guiana. Trop. Woods 9: 8–10.

Record, S. J. 1927b. The wood of Tapura cubensis (Poepp. & Endl.) Grisebach. Trop. Woods 9: 18–19.

[Record, S. J.] 1927c. The Butterfly Tree of British Honduras. Trop. Woods 11: 4.

Record, S. J. 1927d. The wood of Tetrapodenia glandifera Gleason. Trop. Woods 11: 22–24.

[Record, S. J.] 1928a. "Pink ivory" wood. Trop. Woods 13: 4–5.

Record, S. J. 1928b. The "Palo Prieto" of West Central Mexico. Trop. Woods 14: 8–12.

Record, S. J. 1929a. The West African Abachi, Ayous, or Samba (Triplochiton scleroxylon). Trop. Woods 18: 43–54. Fresh wood of Triplochiton is malodorous - a correction. Trop. Woods 20: 19.

Record, S. J. 1929b. No oil cells in wood of Physocalymma. Trop. Woods 20: 23.

Record, S. J. 1931a. West African Avodiré (Turraeanthus africana). Trop. Woods 26: 1–9.

Record, S. J. 1931b. The wood of Escallonia tortuosa. Trop. Woods 26: 12–13.

Record, S. J. 1932a. Notes on new species of Brazilian woods. Trop. Woods 31: 22–29.

Record, S. J. 1932b. Woods of the Ericales, with particular reference to Schizocardia. Trop. Woods 32: 11–14.

Record, S.J. 1932c. The wood of Gleasonia duidana. Trop. Woods 32: 18–20.

Record, S.J. 1933. The woods of Rhabdodendron and Duckeodendron. Trop. Woods 33: 6–10.

Record, S.J. 1934. Identification of the timbers of temperate North America. John Wiley & Sons: New York. 196 pp. [Keys; not indexed under families.]

Record, S.J. 1935. Note on the wood of Cephalohibiscus. Trop. Woods 44: 21.

Record, S.J. 1936. Classifications of various anatomical features of dicotyledonous woods. Trop. Woods 47: 12–27.

Record, S.J. 1938a. The American woods of the Orders Celastrales, Olacales, and Santalales. Trop. Woods 53: 11–38.

Record, S.J. 1938b. The American woods of the family Euphorbiaceae. Trop. Woods 54: 7–40.

Record, S.J. 1938c. American woods of the family Loganiaceae. Trop. Woods 56: 9–13.

Record, S.J. 1939a. American woods of the family Rhamnaceae. Trop. Woods, 58: 6–24.

Record, S.J. 1939b. American woods of the family Bombacaceae. Trop. Woods 59: 1–20.

Record, S.J. 1939c. American woods of the family Sapotaceae. Trop. Woods 59: 21–51.

Record, S.J. 1939d. American woods of the family Anacardiaceae. Trop. Woods 60: 11–45.

Record, S.J. 1941a. American timbers of the mahogany family. Trop. Woods 66: 7–33.

Record, S.J. 1941b. American woods of the family Flacourtiaceae. Trop. Woods 68: 40–57.

Record, S.J. 1942a. American woods of the family Theaceae. Trop. Woods 70: 23–33.

[Record, S.J.] 1942b. Review of: A new genus of Rubiaceae from Mexico. By M. Martinez. Bull. Torrey bot. Cl. 69: 438–441 (1942). Trop. Woods 71: 36–37.

Record, S.J. 1942c; 1943; 1944a. Keys to American woods. I. Ring-porous woods. II. Woods with pores in ulmiform or wavy tangential arrangement. III. Woods with pores in flame-like or dendritic arrangement. Trop. Woods 72: 19–35 (1942). IV. Vessels virtually all solitary. V. Vessels with spiral thickenings. 73: 23–42. VI. Vessels with scalariform perforation plates. VII. Vessels with very fine pitting. 74: 17–43. VIII. Vessels with opposite or scalariform pitting. IX. Woods with conspicuous rays. 75: 8–26 (1943). X. Woods with storied structure. 76: 32–47. XI. Woods with resin or gum ducts. XII. Parenchyma reticulate. 77: 18–38. XIII. Woods with septate fibers. 78: 35–45. XIV. Dicotyledonous woods with xylem rays virtually all uniseriate. 79: 25–34. XV. Fibers with conspicuous bordered pits. XVI. Woods with oil (or similar) cells. 80: 10–15 (1944). [For XVII–XXI see Hess, R.W.]

Record, S.J. 1944b. Random observations on tropical American timbers. Trop Woods 77: 1–10.

Record, S.J. 1945. Notes on tropical timbers. Trop. Woods 81: 2–5.

Record, S.J. & Chattaway, M.M. 1939. List of anatomical features used in classifying dicotyledonous woods. Trop. Woods 57: 11–16.

Record, S.J. & Garratt, G.A. 1923. Cocobolo. Bull. Yale Sch. For., No. 8: 42 pp.

Record, S.J. & Garratt, G.A. 1925. Boxwoods. Bull. Yale Sch. For., No. 14: 81 pp.

Record, S.J. & Hess, R.W. 1940a. American woods of the family Moraceae. Trop. Woods 61: 11–54.

Record, S.J. & Hess, R.W. 1940b. American timbers of the family Bignoniaceae. Trop. Woods 63: 9–38.

Record, S.J. & Hess, R.W. 1940c. American woods of the family Rutaceae. Trop. Woods 64: 1–28.

Record, S.J. & Hess, R.W. 1941a. American woods of the family Verbenaceae. Trop. Woods 65: 4–21.

Record, S.J. & Hess, R.W. 1941b. American woods of the family Boraginaceae. Trop. Woods 67: 19–33.

Record, S.J. & Hess, R.W. 1942. American timbers of the family Lauraceae. Trop. Woods 69: 7–33.

Record, S.J. & Hess, R.W. 1943. Timbers of the New World. Yale School of Forestry: New Haven. 640 pp.

Record, S.J. & Mell, C.D. 1924. Timbers of tropical America. Yale Univ. Press: New Haven. 610 pp.

Reed, C.F. 1955. The comparative morphology of the Olacaceae, Opiliaceae and Octoknemaceae. Mem. Soc. Brot. 10: 29–79.

Reid, J.S. 1947. Silica in beech timbers. N.Z. Jl. For. 5: 330–331.

Reinders, E. 1935. Fiber-tracheids, libriform wood fibers, and systematics in wood anatomy. Trop. Woods 44: 30–36.

Reinders-Gouwentak, C.A. 1948. Key to lauraceous woods from Java. Meded. Landbouwhogesch. Wageningen 49 (1): 3–12.

Reinders-Gouwentak, C.A. 1949. Homogeneous and heterogeneous rays, their characteristics and a key for their identification. Meded. Landbouwhogesch. Wageningen 49 (6): 216–236.

Reinders-Gouwentak, C.A. 1950. Ray terminology in wood anatomy. Proc. konink. Ned. Akad. Wetensch. 53 (8): 1265–1275.

Reinders-Gouwentak, C.A. 1955. The storied-structure-features and the taxonomic rank of the leguminous taxa. Acta bot. neerl. 4: 460–470.

Reinders-Gouwentak, C.A. & Rijsdijk, J.F. 1955. Wood anatomical characterization of the leguminous taxa. Proc. konink. Ned. Akad. Wetensch., C, 58: 41–50.

Reinders-Gouwentak, C.A. & Rijsdijk, J.F. 1968. Hout van Leguminosae uit Suriname. H. Veenman & Zonen N.V.: Wageningen. 152 pp.

Reinders-Gouwentak, C.A. & Stahel, G. 1948. Wood anatomy and systematic position of Ropourea guianensis Aubl. Meded. Landbouwhogesch. Wageningen 49 (3): 19–24.

Rendle, B.J. & Clarke, S.H. 1934. The diagnostic value of measurements in wood anatomy. Trop. Woods 40: 27–37.

Renner, S.S. 1989. Systematic studies in the Melastomataceae: Bellucia, Loreya, and Macairea. Mem. N.Y. bot. Gard. 50: 1–112.

Reyes, L.J. 1923. Woods of the Philippine dipterocarps. Philipp. J. Sci. 22: 291–344.

Richter, H.G. 1979; 1980. On the occurrence, morphology and taxonomic implications of crystalline and siliceous inclusions in the secondary xylem of Lauraceae and related families. In: Wood quality and utilization of tropical species (ed. Tamolang, F.N.): 65–73. Proc. IUFRO Conf., Forpridecom, Philippines, 1978. Paper with similar title in: Wood Sci. Technol. 14: 35–44 (1980).

Richter, H.G. 1981a. Wood and bark anatomy of Lauraceae. I. Aniba Aublet. IAWA Bull. n.s. 2: 79–87.

Richter, H.G. 1981b. Anatomie des sekundären Xylems und der Rinde der Lauraceae. Sonderbände des Naturwiss. Vereins Hamburg 5. Verlag Paul Parey: Hamburg & Berlin. 148 pp.

Richter, H.G. 1982. The wood structure of Couratari Aubl. and Couroupita Aubl. (Lecythidaceae). IAWA Bull. n.s. 3: 45–55.

Richter, H.G. 1985; 1990. Wood and bark anatomy of Lauraceae. II. Licaria Aublet. IAWA Bull. n.s. 6: 187–199 (1985). III. Aspidostemon Rohwer & Richter. Ibid. 11: 47–56 (1990).

Richter, H.G. & Charvet, L.M. 1973. Estudo e pesquisa sobre Mimosa scabrella. Floresta 4 (2): 68–71.

Richter, H.G., Nock, H.P. & Reichmann Neto, F. 1975. Bicuiba (Virola oleifera). I. Aspectos dendrológicos da espécie e descrição macro e microscópica da madeira. Floresta 6 (1): 36–42. [Eng. summ.]

Richter, H.G. & Roth, E. 1985. Inorganic inclusions as an important aid in differentiating the West African commercial timbers 'aningré' and 'longhi'. Proc. Symp. For. Prod. Res. Intn. Achievements and the Future, April 1985, Pretoria, vol. 1, Paper 16–8: 10 pp. CSIRO: S. Africa.

Richter, H.G. & Schmitt, U. 1987. Unusual crystal formations in the secondary xylem of Cosmocalyx spectabilis Standl. (Rubiaceae). IAWA Bull. n.s. 8: 323–329.

Richter, H.G. & Trockenbrodt, M. 1993. IAWA list of microscopic features for hardwood identification adapted to the DELTA system. Federal Research Centre for Forestry and Forest Products, Hamburg. 44 pp. [Available from the authors on request.]

Richter, H.G. & Van Wyk, A.E. 1990. Wood and bark anatomy of Lauraceae IV. Dahlgrenodendron J.J.M. van der Merwe & Van Wyk. IAWA Bull. n.s. 11: 173–182.

Ridsdale, C.E., Bakhuizen van den Brink, R.C. & Koek-Noorman, J. 1972. Notes on New Guinea Rubiaceae. Versteegia and Maschalodesme. Blumea 20: 339–348.

Riedl, H. 1937. Bau und Leistungen des Wurzelholzes. Jb. wiss. Bot. 85: 1–75.

Riera, P.F. 1947. Primera contribución al conocimiento de las maderas de la Guinea continental española. Edic. Inst. Estudios Afr. Madrid. 250 pp.

Riggins, R. & Farris, J.S. 1983. Cladistics and the roots of angiosperms. Syst. Bot. 8: 96–100.

Rivera, S.M. 1988 [1989]. Revisión xilologica del género Nothofagus Bl. para la Argentina. In: Simposio sobre Nothofagus, Neuquén, Argentina, Mar. 1987 (ed. Gamundi, I.J.): 73–81. Monografías Acad. nac. Cien. Exact. Fis. Nat., Buenos Aires, No. 4.

Rizzini, C.T. & Mattos Filho, A. de 1960–1961. Contribuição ao estudo da Cabiúna do cerrado. Rodriguésia 23/24: 213–228. [Eng. summ.]

Rizzini, C.T. & Mattos Filho, A. de 1962–1965. Mimosa laticifera n.sp., leguminosa latescente do Cerradão. Arq. Jard. bot. Rio de Janeiro 18: 73–85. [Eng. summ.]

Rizzini, C.T. & Mattos Filho, A. de 1967. Sôbre cinco importantes madeiras da Bahia ainda não classificadas. Anu. bras. Econ. flor., Inst. Nac. Pinho 18(18): 175–204.

Rizzini, C.T. & Mattos Filho, A. de 1972. Sobre Arapatiella trepocarpa n.g. + sp. (Leguminosae, Caesalpinioideae). Revta. bras. Biol. 32: 323–333.

Rizzini, C.T. & Mattos Filho, A. de 1977. Sobre Luetzelburgia Harms (Leguminosae). Rodriguésia 29(42): 7–31.

Robbertse, P.J. & Teichman, I. von 1979. The morphology of Acacia redacta J.H. Ross. Jl. S. Afr. Bot. 45: 11–23.

Robbertse, P.J., Venter, G. & Van Rensburg, H.J. 1980. The wood anatomy of the South African Acacias. IAWA Bull. n.s. 1: 93–103.

Robyns, A., Nilsson, S. & Dechamps, R. 1977. Sur la position systématique du genre Maxwellia Baillon. Bull. Jard. bot. natn. Belg. 47: 145–153.

Rock, B.N. 1972. The woods and flora of the Florida Keys: "Pinnatae". Smithsonian Contrib. Bot., No. 5: 1–35.

Rodrigues, W.A. 1972. A ucuuba de várzea e suas aplicações. Acta Amazonica 2(2): 29–47.

Rodriguez, E.M. 1958. El leño de las Sapindáceas arbóreas argentinas. Estructura, características y aplicaciones. Rev. Fac. Agron. Buenos Aires 14: 271–305.

Rodríguez, R.L. 1957a. Systematic anatomical studies on Myrrhidendron and other woody Umbellales. Univ. Calif. Publ. Bot. 29: 145–318.

Rodríguez, R.L. 1957b. Anotaciones a la anatomía comparada de las Umbelíferas. Rev. Biol. Trop. 5: 157–171. [Eng. summ.]

Rodríguez, R.L. 1971. The relationships of the Umbellales. In: The biology and chemistry of the Umbelliferae (ed. Heywood, V.H.): 63–91. Bot. J. Linn. Soc. 64, Suppl. 1: 438 pp.

Rogel Gomez, M. de los A. 1982. Caracteristicas anatomicas de la madera de siete especies tropicales. Bol. téc. Inst. nac. Invest. for., México, No. 86: 55 pp.

Rogel Gomez, M. de los A. 1982 [1985]. Estudio anatomico de la madera de seis especies tropicales. Bol. téc. Inst. nac. Invest. for., México, No. 89: 70 pp.

Rogers, G.K. 1981. The wood of Gleasonia, Henriquezia, and Platycarpum (Rubiaceae) and its bearing on their classification: some new considerations. Brittonia 33: 461–465.

Rogers, G.K. 1984. Gleasonia, Henriquezia, and Platycarpum (Rubiaceae). Flora Neotropica Mon., No. 39: 135 pp.

Rohweder, O & Urmi-Konig, K. 1975. Centrospermen-Studien. 8. Beiträge zur Morphologie, Anatomie und systematischen Stellung von Gymnocarpos Forsk. und Paronychia argentea Lam. (Caryophyllaceae). Bot. Jb. 96: 375–409.

Rohwer, J.G. & Richter, H.G. 1987. Aspidostemon, a new lauraceous genus from Madagascar. Bot. Jb. 109: 71–79.

Rohwer, J.G., Richter, H.G. & Van der Werff, H. 1991. Two new genera of neotropical Lauraceae and critical remarks on the generic delimitation. Ann. Missouri bot. Gard. 78: 388–400.

Roig J., F.A. 1986. The wood of Adesmia horrida and its modifications by climatic conditions. IAWA Bull. n.s. 7: 129–135.

Roig J., F.A. 1986 [1987]. Un inusual tipo de placa de perforacion en Discaria Hook. (Rhamnaceae). Parodiana 4: 205–211. [Eng. summ.]

Rojo, J.P. 1968. The wood anatomy of Allantospermum borneense Forman and Allantospermum multicaule (Capuron) Nooteboom. Adansonia 8: 73–83.

Rojo, J.P. 1992. Xylem anatomy of the world's Dialium (Cassieae–Caesalpinioideae). In: Proc. 2nd Pacific Regional Wood Anat. Conf. 1989 (eds. Rojo, J.P., Aday, J.U., Barile, E.R., Araral, R.K. & America, W.M.): 179–190. For. Prod. Dev. Inst.: College, Laguna, Philippines.

Roth, I. & Ascensio, J. 1977. Crecimiento anomalo del eje de varias especies de Bauhinia y su relacion con la filotaxis. Acta bot. venez. 12: 12–77. [Eng. summ.]

Rozens, A. 1978. Apses (Populus tremula L.) stumbra un zaru koksnes anatomiska uzbuve. [Anatomic structure of the wood of Populus tremula trunk and branches.] Tr. Latv. Lauksaimn. Akad., No. 163: 45–49. [Latvian]

Rozmarin, G., Toma, C., Koumou, A., Aly, H.I.M., Bordy, J.E.E. & Tudor-Bălan, M. 1983. Cîteva consideratii privind lemnul tropical din R.P. Congo. 1. Aspecte de structură anatomomorfologică. Celuloza Hirtie 32 (2): 56–69. [Eng. summ.]

Rudall, P. 1981. Wood anatomy in the Hyptidinae (Labiatae). Kew Bull. 35: 735–741.

Rudall, P.J. 1982. An unusual type of perforation plate in Canthium barbatum Seem. (Rubiaceae). IAWA Bull. n.s. 3: 127–129.

Rudall, P.J. 1985. Perforated ray cells in Hyptis hagei – a new record for Labiatae. IAWA Bull. n.s. 6: 161–162.

Rudall, P.J. 1987. Laticifers in Euphorbiaceae – a conspectus. Bot. J. Linn. Soc. 94: 143–163.

Rudall, P. 1989. Laticifers in vascular cambium and wood of Croton spp. (Euphorbiaceae). IAWA Bull. n.s. 10: 379–383.

Ruffin, J. 1974 [1975]. Wood anatomy of Amphiachyris, Amphipappus, Thurovia, Gymnosperma and the Xanthocephalum complex. Sida 5: 341–352.

Rury, P.M. 1981. Systematic anatomy of Erythroxylum P. Browne: practical and evolutionary implications for the cultivated cocas. J. Ethnopharm. 3: 229–263.

Rury, P.M. 1985. Systematic and ecological wood anatomy of the Erythroxylaceae. IAWA Bull. n.s. 6: 365–397.

Rury, P.M. & Dickison, W.C. 1984. Structural correlations among wood, leaves and plant habit. In: Contemporary problems in plant anatomy (eds. White, R.A. & Dickison, W.C.): 495–540. Academic Press: Orlando, etc.

Ryu, H.Y. & Soh, W.Y. 1988. Anatomical comparison of the secondary xylem in the branch, stem and root of Salix glandulosa and Quercus variabilis. J. Korean for. Soc. 77: 283–293. [Kor.; Eng. summ.]

Saccardy, L. & Muzard, J.R. 1938. Notes sur la bruyère arborescente et l'exploitation de la souche de bruyère en Algéria. Bull. Sta. Rech. forest. N. Afr. 2: 461–489.

Sachsse, H. 1980. Das Holz der chilenischen Nothofagus procera Oerst. aus einem westdeutschen Versuchsanbau. Forstarchiv 51: 149–153 [Eng. summ.].

Sacchse, H. & Schulte, A. 1991. Holzeigenschaften der Anden-Erle (Alnus acuminata O. Ktze.). Forstarchiv 62 (5): 196–199. [Eng. summ.]

Sahri, M.H., Ibrahim, F.H. & Shukor, N.A.A. 1993. Anatomy of Acacia mangium grown in Malaysia. IAWA Jl. 14: 245–251.

Saiki, H. 1982. The structure of domestic and imported woods in Japan. An atlas of scanning electron micrographs. Japan Forest Technical Assn.: Rokubancho, Tokyo, Japan. 218 pp. [Jap.; Eng. intro. & captions.]

Saiki, H. & Ohnishi, K. 1976. Radial strands of the included phloem in jongkong wood (Dactylocladus stenostachys Oliv.). Bull. Kyoto Univ. For. 48: 160–166. [Jap.; Eng. summ.]

Saint-Laurent, J. de 1926; 1928. Etudes sur les caractères anatomiques des bois d'Algérie. Bull. Sta. Rech. forest. N. Afr. 1 (7): 241–255 (1926); 1 (9): 351–417 (1928).

Saint-Laurent, J. de 1932a. Etudes sur les caractères anatomiques du bois et du liber secondaire dans les essences du Sahara et particulièrement du Hoggar. Bull. Sta. Rech. forest. N. Afr. 2: 1–48.

Saint-Laurent, J. de 1932b. Etudes sur les caractères anatomiques du bois et du liber secondaire dans quelques essences forestières du Maroc dernièrement recoltées par M. le Dr. R. Maire. Bull. Sta. Rech. forest. N. Afr. 2: 49–60.

Saint-Laurent, J. de 1934. Etude anatomique des rameaux chez les essences forestières d'Algérie avec quelques observations sur les modifications amenées par l'âge. Bull. Sta. Rech. forest. N. Afr. 2: 61–201.

Saitoh, T., Ohtani, J. & Fukazawa, K. 1993. The occurrence and morphology of tyloses and gums in the vessels of Japanese hardwoods. IAWA Jl. 14: 359–371.

Sajo, M. das G. & Menezes, N.L. de 1986. Anatomia do rizóforo de espécies de Vernonia Screb. (Compositae) da Serra do Cipó, MG. Revta. bras. Biol. 46: 189–196.

Samant, D.D. & Shete, R.H. 1989 [1990]a. Wood anatomy of Cassia glauca Lamk. Indian Reporter 8: 131–133.

Samant, D.D. & Shete, R.H. 1989 [1990]b. Wood anatomy of Cassia kolabensis. Indian Reporter 8: 147–148.

Şanli, I. 1977. Doğu Kayini (Fagus orientalis Lipsky.) 'nin Türkiyé de çeşitli yörelerde oluşan odunlari üzerine anatomik araştirmalar. [Recherches anatomiques sur les bois du hêtre (Fagus orientalis Lipsky.) des differentes regions de Turquie.] Istanb. Univ. Orman Fak. Derg. ser. A, 27: 207–282. [French summ. 250–5].

Şanli, I. 1981. Certaines caracteristiques d'Ulmus leavis Pall. en Thrace. Instanb. Univ. Orman Fak. Derg., ser.A, 31: 192–202. [In French.]

Şanli, I. 1985 [1986]. Trakya'nin iki akmese türünün bazi iç morfolojik özellikleri. [Certaines caracteristiques morphologiques internes de deux espèces de chêne de la Thrace.] Istanb. Univ. Orman Fak. Derg., ser. A, 35 (2): 55–71. [French summ.]

Şanli, I. 1988 [1989]. Ostrya carpinifolia Scop. (Kayacik) odununun iç morfolojisi üzerinde bazi incelemeler. [Recherches xylologiques chez le charme-houblon (Ostrya carpinifolia Scop.).] Istanb. Univ. Orman Fak. Derg., ser. A, 38 (1): 91–104. [French summ.]

Santos, J.K. 1931. Anomalous stem structure in Archangelisia flava and Anamirta cocculus from the Philippines. Philipp. J. Sci. 44: 385–407.

Sarayar, C.G. 1976. Struktur anatomi kaya meranti Indonesia. [Anatomical structure of Indonesian meranti.] Lembaga Penelitian Hasil Hutan, Bogor, Indonesia, Laporan (Report) No. 71: 34 pp. + appendices. [Eng. summ. & captions.]

Sárkány, S. & Stieber, J. 1959. Untersuchungen über die quantitativ-ökologische Xylotomie von Fagus silvatica. Ann. Univ. Sci. Budapest. (Biol.) 2: 239–257. [Eng. summ.]

Sárkány, S., Stieber, J. & Fillo, Z. 1957. Investigations on the wood of Hungarian Populus species by means of quantitative xylotomy. Ann. Univ. Sci. Budapest. (Biol.) 1: 219–229. [Eng.]

Sastrapradja, D.S. & Lamoureux, C. 1969. Variations in wood anatomy of Hawaiian Metrosideros (Myrtaceae). Ann. bogor. 5: 1–83.

Sastre, C. 1975a. L'importance des caractères anatomiques dans la systématique des Ochnacées. C.R. 100e Congr. natn. Soc. sav., Paris 1975, II: 185–196.

Sastre, C. 1975b. Etude du genre Cespedesia Goudot (Ochnacées). Cespedesia 4: 191–214. [Span. transl. on pp. 215–225.]

Satabié, B. 1991. Compte-rendu de l'étude de quelques éléments de la biosystématique à l'interprétation de la vicariance des deux espèces de Lophira (Ochnacées) au Cameroun. Candollea 46: 85–94.

Sax, K. & Abbe, E.C. 1932. Chromosome numbers and the anatomy of secondary xylem in the Oleaceae. J. Arnold Arbor. 13: 37–48.

Saya, I. 1957. Contributo alla conoscenza del legno dei principali arbusti mediterranei. Ann. Accad. ital. Sci. for. 6: 299–312.

Saya, I. 1959. Secondo contributo alla conoscenza del legno dei principali arbusti mediterranei. Ann. Accad. ital. Sci. for. 8: 309–326 + 3 plates.

Saya, I. 1961. Caratteri anatomici del legno di esemplare adulto e di polloni di Ailanthus glandulosa Desf. Ann. Accad. ital. Sci. for. 10: 163–172.

Scala, A.C. 1924. Contribución al estudio histológico de la flore chileana. VI. Lomatia obliqua. Rev. chil. Hist. nat. 28: 19–25.

Scala, A.C. 1929. Contribución al estudio histológico de las maderas chilenas. Rev. chil. Hist. nat. 33: 257–268.

Scala, A.C. 1934. La estructura histologica del leño de "Guayaibi" Patagonula americana L. (Borraginaceae). Rev. Sudamer. Bot. 1 (1): 1–7.

Scaramuzzi, F. 1960. Evoluzione della cerchia legnosa in Quercus aegilops L. a Tricase. Nuovo G. bot. ital. (NS) 67: 525–545.

Scharai-Rad, M. & Kambey, E. 1989. The wood of Acacia mangium Willd., its properties and possible uses. German Forestry Group Rep. No. 14: 1–12.

Scharai-Rad, M. & Sulistyobudi, A. 1985. Anatomical, physical, and mechanical characteristics of ulin (Eusideroxylon zwageri). Forestry & Forest Products. German Forestry Group Rep. No. 3: 5–13.

Schenck, H. 1893. Beiträge zur Anatomie der Lianen. (Schimpers bot. Mitth. aus den Tropen, Heft 5.) Jena. 291 pp.

Schirarend, C. 1987. Zur Holz- und Blattanatomie der neotropischen Gattung Krugiodendron Urban (Rhamnaceae). Feddes Repert. 98: 515–519.

Schirarend, C. 1991. The systematic wood anatomy of the Rhamnaceae Juss. (Rhamnales). I. Tribe Zizipheae. IAWA Bull. n.s. 12: 359–388.

Schirarend, C. & Süss, H. 1985. Zur Holzanatomie und systematischen Stellung der Gattung Maesopsis Engler (Rhamnaceae). Gleditschia 13: 41–45 + plate I.

Schmid, A. 1915. Beiträge zur Kenntnis bolivianischer Nutzhölzer. Promotionsarbeit: Zürich. Winterthur. 176 pp.

Schmid, R. 1980. Comparative anatomy and morphology of Psiloxylon and Heteropyxis, and the subfamilial and tribal classification of Myrtaceae. Taxon 29: 559–595.

Schmid, R. & Baas, P. 1984. The occurrence of scalariform perforation plates and helical vessel wall thickenings in wood of Myrtaceae. IAWA Bull. n.s. 5: 197–215.

Schmid, R., Carlquist, S., Hufford, L.D. & Webster, G.L. 1984. Systematic anatomy of Oceanopapaver, a monotypic genus of the Capparaceae from New Caledonia. Bot. J. Linn. Soc. 89: 119–152.

Schmid, R. & Machado, R.D. 1963. Über den Feinbau der 'verzierten' Tüpfel bei der Gattung Plathymenia. Holz Roh- u. Werkst. 21: 41–47.

Schmid, R. & Machado, R.D. 1964. Zur Entstehung und Feinstruktur skulpturierter Hoftüpfel bei Leguminosen. Planta 60: 612–626. [Eng. summ.]

Schmid, W. 1928. Das anomale sekundäre Dickenwachstum der Amarantaceae. Vierteljahrsschr. naturf. Ges. Zurich 73, Beiblatt No.15: 542–553. [Festschrift Hans Schinz.]

Schmidt, E. 1951–1952. Überseehölzer. 30 Holzartenbeschreibungen wichtiger Handelshölzer Holzeigenschaften. Fritz Haller: Berlin-Grunewald (1951). Beilage der Z. Weltforstwirtsch. 15 (2) (3) (4) (5) (1952).

Schmidt, E. 1964. Helical structures in the ray cell-walls of Fagus sylvatica. Holz Roh- u. Werkst. 22 (12): 453–455.

Schmidt, W.G. de 1922. Studies on the distribution and volume of wood rays in slippery elm (Ulmus fulva). J. For. 20: 353–362.

Schultz, A.R., Almeida, O.M. de & Steigleder, M. de V. 1964. Dendrologia do Rio Grande do
    Sul. III. Magnoliaceae, Winteraceae. IV. Casuarinaceae, Fagaceae, Guttiferae. Inst. tec. Rio
    Grande do Sul, Bol. No. 36: 1–52.
Schultz, A.R. & Wollheim, O.M. 1962. Dendrologia do Rio Grande do Sul II. Malvales. Inst.
    tec. Rio Grande do Sul, Bol. No. 35: 51 pp.
Schweingruber, F.H. 1974. Holzanatomische Differenzierung der mitteleuropäischen Pomo-
    ideen (Rosaceae). Mitt. dt. dendrol. Ges., Nr. 67: 62–72.
Schweingruber, F.H. 1978. Mikroskopische Holzanatomie. Anatomie microscopique du bois.
    Microscopic wood anatomy. Structural variability of stems and twigs in recent and subfossil
    woods from Central Europe. Swiss Fed. Inst. For. Res., Birmensdorf. Edition Zürcher:
    Zug, Switzerland. 226 pp. [Germ., French, Eng.]
Schweingruber, F.H. 1990. Anatomie europäischer Hölzer. Anatomy of European woods. Ver-
    lag Paul Haupt: Bern & Stuttgart. 800 pp. [Germ. & Eng.]
Scott, M.H. 1927. Notes on the characteristics and minute structure of thirty woods indigenous
    to South Africa. S. Afr. J. Sci. 24: 298–317.
Scurfield, G., Anderson, C.A. & Segnit, E.R. 1974. Silica in woody stems. Aust. J. Bot. 22:
    211–229.
Scurfield, G., Michell, A.J. & Silva, S.R. 1973. Crystals in woody stems. Bot. J. Linn. Soc.
    66: 277–289.
Seabra, L. de & Ferreirinha, M.P. 1959. Terminalia superba Engl. & Diels (Limba). Ficha tec-
    nológica e florestal. Garcia de Orta 7: 509–531.
Seabra, L. de & Ferreirinha, M.P. 1960. Gossweilerodendron balsamiferum Harms (Tola bran-
    ca). Ficha tecnológica e florestal. Garcia de Orta 8: 279–293. [Eng. summ].
Seabra, L. de, Ferreirinha, M.P. & Freitas, M.C.P.G. de 1957; 1959. Contribuições para o
    conhecimento tecnológico da flora do ultramar. Garcia de Orta 5: 711–726 (1957). Ibid. 7:
    77–88 (1959).
Sebastine, K.M. 1955. Studies on the variations on the structure and size of rays in the sec-
    ondary wood. J. Indian bot. Soc. 34: 299–306.
Senkevich, N.G. 1977. Age features of the anatomical structure of wood of Ulmus pumila in
    the Trans-Baikal region. Lesovedenie (2): 59–65. [Russ.; Eng. summ.]
Senni, L. 1905. Contributo alla conoscenza di alcuni legnami della Colonia Eritrea. Boll. Orto
    bot. Palermo 4: 89–98.
Serizawa, T. 1985. Wood anatomy and identification of family Anacardiaceae in Sabah. Forest
    Res. Centre, Sabah, FRC Publ. No. 24: 194 pp. [For. Abstr. 52 (1991) No. 8931.]
Shafranova, L.M. 1968. The anatomical structure of shoots in Potentilla fruticosa L., P. parvi-
    folia Fisch. and P. bifurca L., associated with the transformation of shrubs into herbs in
    Potentilla L. (s.l.). Byull. mosk. Obshch. Ispyt. Prir., Otdel. Biol. 73 (1): 140–154. [Russ.;
    Eng. summ.]
Shah, A.M. & Kachroo, P. 1979. The structure of wood in some species of Morus and Ficus.
    In: Recent Research in Plant Science (ed. Bir, S.S.): 174–186.
Sharma, B.L., Rao, R.V., Bisen, S.S. & Dayal, R. 1985. Modified scalariform and reticulate
    perforation plates in species of Euodia (Rutaceae). IAWA Bull. n.s. 6: 39–41.
Sharma, M. 1971. A note on silica content in teak. J. Indian Acad. Wood Sci. 2 (1): 25–26.
Sharma, M. & Rao, K.R. 1970. Investigations on the occurrence of silica in Indian timbers.
    Indian For. 96: 740–754.
Sharma, M.R. 1962. Morphological and anatomical investigations on Artocarpus Forst. I.
    Vegetative organs. Proc. Indian Acad. Sci., B, 56: 243–258.
Shaw, H.K.A., Cutler, D.F. & Nilsson, S. 1973. Pottingeria, its taxonomic position, anat-
    omy and palynology. Kew Bull. 28: 97–104.
Sheahan, M.C. & Cutler, D.F. 1993. Contribution of vegetative anatomy to the systematics of
    the Zygophyllaceae R.Br. Bot. J. Linn. Soc. 113: 227–262.
Shen, Y.-F. 1954. Phylogeny and wood anatomy of Nandina. Taiwania 5: 85–92.

Shilkina, I.A. 1973. On the xylem anatomy of the genus Punica L. Bot. Zh. SSSR 58: 1628–1630. [Russ. only.]

Shilkina, I.A. 1977. The comparative anatomy of the wood of the genus Oncotheca (Order Theales). Bot. Zh. SSSR 62: 1273–1275. [Russ.; brief Eng. summ.]

Shilova, N.V. 1965. Wood- and leaf-structure in Piptanthus D. Don and Ammopiptanthus Cheng f. Bot. J. USSR 50: 396–403. [Russ. only.]

Shimaji, K. 1952. Anatomical studies on the wood of some Fagus species. Bull. Tokyo Univ. Forests, No. 42: 181–195. [Eng.]

Shimaji, K. 1954. Anatomical studies on the wood of Japanese Quercus. I. On subgenus Lepidobalanus (Nara group). Bull. Tokyo Univ. Forests, No. 46: 193–210. II. On subgenus Cyclobalanopsis (Kashi group). Ibid., No. 47: 125–148. [Eng.]

Shimaji, K. 1959. Anatomical studies on the wood of Japanese Pasania, Castanea and Castanopsis. (With a key to the 22 Japanese representative species of the Fagaceae.) Bull. Tokyo Univ. Forests, No. 55: 81–99. [Eng.]

Shimaji, K. 1962. Anatomical studies on the phylogenetic interrelationship of the genera in the Fagaceae. Bull. Tokyo Univ. Forests, No. 57: 1–64. [Eng.]

Shimaji, K. 1964. Illustrated wood anatomy. Chikyushuppan Press, Tokyo. 113 pp. [Jap. only. Shimaji & Itoh 1982 indexed.]

Shimaji, K. & Itoh, T. 1982. Illustrated wood anatomy. Revised edn. Chikyushuppan Press: Tokyo. 176 pp. [Title and text in Jap. only.]

Shimaji, K. & Itoh, T. 1988. Comparative survey of wooden articles excavated from relics in Japan. Yuhzankaku Press, Tokyo. 296 pp. [Jap. only.]

Shipchanov, I. 1973. Study on the anatomical structure of wood of some forms of Quercus rubra. Gorsk. Nauka 10(6): 3–9. [Bulg.; Germ. summ.]

Shulkina, T.V. & Zikov, S.E. 1980. The anatomical structure of the stem in the family Campanulaceae s.str. in relation to the evolution of life forms. Bot. Zh. SSSR 65: 627–639. [Russ.; Eng. summ.]

Shutts, C.F. 1960. Wood anatomy of Hernandiaceae and Gyrocarpaceae. Trop. Woods 113: 85–123.

Siddiqi, M.R. & Wilson, T.K. 1974. Wood anatomy of the genus Knema (Myristicaceae). Bull. Torrey bot. Cl. 101: 354–362.

Sieber, M. 1985. Anatomical structure of roots of two species of Khaya in Ghana. In: Xylorama (ed. Kučera, L.J.): 176–183. Birkhäuser Verlag: Basel, etc.

Sieber, M. & Kučera, L.J. 1980. On the stem anatomy of Clematis vitalba L. IAWA Bull. n.s. 1: 49–54.

Sillans, R. & Normand, R.D. 1953. Sur le fruit et la structure du bois de Neochevalierodendron stephanii. Rev. int. Bot. appl. Agr. trop. 33: 565–570.

Silva, A. 1991. Anatomía de la madera de ocho especies propias del Bosque de Galeria (vertiente sur) del Parque Nacional "El Avila". Bol. Soc. venez. Ci. nat. 44: 85–136.

Silva, A., Blanco, C. & Lindorf, H. 1989. Anatomía de la madera de nueve Leguminosas de Venezuela. Acta bot. bras. 2(1) Supl.: 115–133.

Silva, M.R.M. da 1971. Espécies lenhosas da floresta alberta de Angola. Publ. Inst. Invest. agron. Angola, sér. Cien., No. 18: 15 pp.

Šimić, P. 1956–1957. Prilog poznavanju anatomske građe bukovog drveta vrste Fagus moesiaca iz Karaormana. [The anatomical structure of Fagus moesiaca from Karaorman.] God. Zborn. zemjod.-shumar. Fak. Univ. Skopje, Shumar., No. 10: 217–252.

Šimić, P. 1964. Anatomical structure of the wood of indigenous pyramidal poplars (Populus nigra var. italica and P. thevestina) from Jugoslavian Macedonia. God. Zborn. zemjod.-shumar. Fak. Univ. Skopje, Shumar., No. 17: 183–233. [Serbo-Croat; Germ. summ.]

Šimić, P. 1964–1965. Anatomical structure of the wood of Populus nigra cv. italica Moench, P. pannonica Kit syn. P. thevestina Dode from Macedonia. God. Zborn. zemjod.-shumar. Fak. Univ. Skopjc, Shumar., No. 18: 99–154. [Serbo-Croat; Germ. summ.]

Šimić, P. 1965. Untersuchungen über den anatomischen Aufbau des Holzes in Pyramidenpappeln (Populus nigra cv. italica Moensch und P. thevestina Dode) aus Sr. Mazedonien. Arch. Forstwes. 14: 1271–1284.

Singh, B. 1943. The origin and distribution of inter- and intraxylary phloem in Leptadenia. Proc. Indian Acad. Sci. 18 B: 14–19.

Singh, B. 1944. A contribution to the anatomy of Salvadora persica L. with special reference to the origin of the included phloem. J. Indian bot. Soc. 23: 71–78.

Singh, B. 1945. An anatomical study of Tiliacora acuminata Miers. J. Indian bot. Soc. 24: 135–146.

Skvortzova, N.T. 1965. A contribution to the morphology of the genus Hamamelis. Bot. J. USSR 50: 1143–1148. [Russ. only.]

Skvortsova, N.T. 1975. Comparative morphological study of representatives of the family Hamamelidaceae R. Br. and their phylogenetic relations. In: Voprosy sravnitel'noi morfologii semennykh rastenii (ed. Budantsev, L. Yu.): 7–24 + 11 plates at end of volume. [Russ.]

Slatter, E.M. 1948. The wood structure of Senecio meruensis Cotton and Blakelock. Kew Bull.: 51–53.

Sleumer, H. 1937. Peekeliodendron, eine neue Icacinaceen-Gattung mit Schwimmfrüchten. Notizbl. Bot. Gart. Mus. Berlin-Dahlem 13: 509–512.

Sleumer, H. 1971. Lophopyxidaceae. In: Flora Malesiana, ser. I, 7 (1): 89–91.

Small, J. 1914. The botanical source of Lignum nephriticum. Pharm. J., ser. 4, 38: 4–6.

Smilga, Ya.-Ya. 1967. Anatomical structure of aspen wood, growing in the Latvian SSR. Lesovedenie, SSSR (4): 71–76. [Russ.]

Smith, A.C. & Ayensu, E.S. 1964. The identity of the genus Calyptosepalum S. Moore. Brittonia 16: 220–227.

Smith, A.C. & Bailey, I.W. 1941. Brassiantha, a new genus of Hippocrateaceae from New Guinea. J. Arnold Arbor. 22: 389–394.

Snezhkova, S.A. 1974. Anatomical characteristics of the wood of some maples in the Maritime Province. Izv. vyssh. ucheb. Zaved., lesn. Zh. 17 (3): 23–27. [Russ.]

Snezhkova, S.A. 1977. Anatomical characteristics of the wood of Sorbus species in the Maritime Territory of the USSR. Izv. vyssh. ucheb. Zaved., lesn. Zh. 20 (3): 164–165. [Russ.]

Snezhkova, S.A. 1979. On anatomical characteristics of hawthorn woods of Primorie. Byull. glav. bot. Sada 113: 79–81. [Russ. only.]

Snezhkova, S.A. 1986. Wood structure in some lianes of the Far East. Bot. Zh. SSSR 71: 768–773. [Russ. only.]

Snezhkova, S.A. 1990. Structure of woods of some representatives of Hydrangeaceae and Grossulariaceae. Byull. glav. bot. Sada 158: 78–80. [Russ. only.]

Soerianegara, I. & Lemmens, R.H.M.J. (eds.) 1993. Plant resources of South-east Asia. No. 5 (1). Timber trees: major commercial timbers. Pudoc Scientific Publishers, Wageningen. 610 pp.

Soh, W.Y. & Han, K.S. 1985. Comparative anatomy of the secondary xylem in the root and stem of some Korean Betulaceae. Korean J. Bot. 28 (2): 127–140. [Korean; Eng. summ.]

Soh, W.Y. & Lim, D.O. 1987. Comparative anatomy of the secondary xylem in the root and stem of some Korean Lauraceae. J. Korean for. Soc. 76: 317–329. [Korean; Eng. summ.]

Soh, W.Y. & Park, S.J. 1984. Systematic studies on some Korean woody plants. Anatomy of lauraceous root wood. Korean J. Bot. 27 (3): 149–162. [Korean; Eng. summ.]

Soh, W.Y. & Park, S.J. 1985. Systematic studies on some Korean woody plants: comparative wood anatomy of Magnoliaceae, Winteraceae and Schisandraceae. Korean J. Bot. 28 (4): 271–284. [Korean; Eng. summ.]

Soh, W.Y. & Sun, B.Y. 1986. Systematic studies on some Korean woody plants – a comparative wood anatomy of Theaceae. Korean J. Bot. 29: 317–327. [Korean; Eng. summ.]

Solereder, H. 1908. Systematic anatomy of the dicotyledons. 2 Vols. Clarendon Press: Oxford. 1183 pp. [Eng. transl. of Systematische Anatomie der Dicotyledonen. F. Enke: Stuttgart (1899).]

Solereder, H. 1915. Über die Versetzung der Gattung Heteranthia von den Scrophulariaceen zu den Solanaceen. Beih. bot. Zbl. 33 (2): 113–117.

Solheim, S.L. 1987. Reevesia (Sterculiaceae, Helictereae): systematics and biogeography of an Asian-eastern American disjunction. Amer. J. Bot. 74: 754. [Abstr.]

Soper, K. 1956–1957. Comparative morphology of the New Zealand species of Pseudopanax and Nothopanax. Trans. roy. Soc. N. Zealand 84: 749–755.

Sosnowsky, D. 1933. Die relikten Birken des Kaukasus. Tr. Tifl. bot. Inst. 1: 31–48. [Russ.; Germ. summ.]

Souza, J.P. de & Gusmão, E.F. de 1984. Contribuição ao conhecimento do lenho de Bursera leptophloeos (Martius) Engler ou imburna de cambão. An. XXXIV Congr. nac. Bot., Soc. Bot. Brasil, Porto Alegre 1983, 2: 557–564.

Souza, J.P. de, Oliveira, A.L.P.C. de & Souza, M.M. de 1982. Contribuição ao conhecimento do lenho de Laguncularia racemosa (L.) Gaertn. Silvicultura, São Paulo 16A: 280–292. [Eng. summ.]

Souza, J.P. de, Pereira, S.A. & Lemos, M.B.N. 1982. Contribuição ao conhecimento da madeira de Rhizophora mangle Linnaeus. Silvicultura, São Paulo 16A: 269–279. [Eng. summ.]

Špoljarić, Z. 1953. Anatomska grada drva tilovine. [Wood structure of Petteria ramentacea (Sieber) Presl.] Ann. exp. Forest. 2: 311–320. [Eng. summ.]

Sporne, K.R. 1980. A re-investigation of character correlations among dicotyledons. New Phytol. 85: 419–449.

Sprague, T.A. & Boodle, L.A. 1914. West Indian Boxwood (Casearia praecox Griseb.). Kew Bull. 214–219.

Stahel, J. 1971. Anatomische Untersuchungen an Brettwurzeln von Khaya ivorensis A.Chev. und Piptadeniastrum africanum (Hook.f.) Brenan. Holz Roh- u. Werkst. 29: 314–318.

Stark, E.W. 1953a. Wood anatomy of the Betulaceae indigenous to the United States. Sta. Bull. Indiana Agric. Exp. Sta. No. 602: 31 pp. Purdue Univ.

Stark, E.W. 1953b. Wood anatomy of the Juglandaceae indigenous to the United States. Sta. Bull. Indiana Agric. Exp. Sta. No. 595: 42 pp. Purdue Univ.

Stark, E.W. 1954a. Wood anatomy of the Aceraceae indigenous to the United States. Sta. Bull. Indiana Agric. Exp. Sta. No. 606: 26 pp. Purdue Univ.

Stark, E.W. 1954b. Wood anatomy of the Magnoliaceae indigenous to the United States. Sta. Bull. Indiana Agric. Exp. Sta. No. 607: 20 pp. Purdue Univ.

Steigleder, M. de V. 1970. Dendrologia do Rio Grande do Sul. V. Moraceae. Bol. Inst. tec. Rio Grande Sul, No. 51: 37 pp.

Stemmermann, L. 1980 [1981]. Vegetative anatomy of the Hawaiian species of Santalum (Santalaceae). Pacific Sci. 34: 55–75.

Stern, W.L. 1952. The comparative anatomy of the xylem and the phylogeny of the Julianiaceae. Amer. J. Bot. 39: 220–229.

Stern, W.L. 1954. Comparative anatomy of xylem and phylogeny of Lauraceae. Trop. Woods 100: 1–73.

Stern, W.L. 1955. Xylem anatomy and relationships of Gomortegaceae. Amer. J. Bot. 42: 874–885.

Stern, W.L. 1957. Guide to institutional wood collections. Trop. Woods 106: 1–29.

Stern, W.L. 1967. Kleinodendron and xylem anatomy of Cluytieae (Euphorbiaceae). Amer. J. Bot. 54: 663–676.

Stern, W.L. 1974; 1978. Comparative anatomy and systematics of woody Saxifragaceae. Escallonia. Bot. J. Linn. Soc. 68: 1–20 (1974). Hydrangea. Ibid. 76: 83–113 (1978).

Stern, W.L. 1988. Index xylariorum. Institutional wood collections of the world. 3. IAWA Bull. n.s. 9: 203–252.

Stern, W.L. & Brizicky, G.K. 1957. The woods and flora of the Florida Keys. Introduction. Trop. Woods 107: 36–65.

Stern, W.L. & Brizicky, G.K. 1958a. The comparative anatomy and taxonomy of Heteropyxis. Bull. Torrey bot. Cl. 85: 111–123.

Stern, W.L. & Brizicky, G.K. 1958b, c. The woods and flora of the Florida Keys. Goodeniaceae. Trop. Woods 109: 38–44 (1958b). Passifloraceae. Ibid.: 45–53 (1958c).

Stern, W.L. & Brizicky, G.K. 1960. The morphology and relationships of Diomma, gen. inc. sed. Mem. N.Y. Bot. Gard. 10(2): 38–64.

Stern, W.L., Brizicky, G.K. & Eyde, R.H. 1969. Comparative anatomy and relationships of Columelliaceae. J. Arnold Arbor. 50: 36–75.

Stern, W.L., Brizicky, G.K. & Tamolang, F.N. 1963. The woods and flora of the Florida Keys: Capparaceae. Contrib. U.S. Nat. Herb. 34(2): 25–43.

Stern, W.L. & Chambers, K.L. 1960. The citation of wood specimens and herbarium vouchers in anatomical research. Taxon 9(1): 7–13.

Stern, W.L. & Greene, S. 1958. Some aspects of variation in wood. Trop. Woods 108: 65–71.

Stern, W.L. & Sweitzer, E.M. 1972. The woods and flora of the Florida Keys. Ulmaceae. In: Research trends in plant anatomy (eds. Ghouse, A.K.M. & Yunus, M.): 53–59. Tata McGraw-Hill Publ. Co.: Bombay & New Delhi.

Stern, W.L., Sweitzer, E.M. & Phipps, R.E. 1970. Comparative anatomy and systematics of woody Saxifragaceae. Ribes. In: New research in plant anatomy (eds. Robson, N.K.B, Cutler, D.F. & Gregory, M.): 215–237. Bot. J. Linn. Soc. 63, Suppl. 1.

Stern, W.L. & Zamuco, I.T. 1964. Identity of 'Tiaong' (Dipterocarpaceae). Brittonia 17: 35–46.

Stieber, J. 1965. Variations in some properties of the wood in Turkey Oak (Quercus cerris). Studies in quantitative xylotomy. Drev. Výskum (1): 11–26. [Eng.]

Studholme, W.P. & Philipson, W.R. 1966. A comparison of the cambium in two woods with included phloem: Heimerliodendron brunonianum and Avicennia resinifera. N.Z. Jl. Bot. 4: 355–365.

Styer, C.H. 1977. Comparative anatomy and systematics of Moutabeae (Polygalaceae). J. Arnold Arbor. 58: 109–145.

Styer, C.H. & Stern, W.L. 1979a, b. Comparative anatomy and systematics of woody Saxifragaceae. Philadelphus. Bot. J. Linn. Soc. 79: 267–289 (1979a). Deutzia. Ibid.: 291–319 (1979b).

Suciu, P.N. 1960. Lemnul de ulm. [Elm wood.] Industr. Lemn. (9): 353–355. [Ruman.; Eng. summ.]

Sudo, S. 1959. Identification of Japanese hardwoods. Bull. Govt. For. Exp. Sta., Meguro, No. 118: 1–138 + 36 plates. [Jap.; Eng. summ.]

Sudo, S. 1963. Identification of tropical woods. Bull. Govt. For. Exp. Sta., Meguro, No. 157: 1–262. [Jap.; Eng. summ.]

Sudo, S. 1988. Anatomical characters and identification of Papua New Guinea timber species. Bull. Forestry Forest Products Research Institute, Tsukuba, Ibaraki, Japan, No. 350: 199 pp. + 131 plates. [Jap.; Eng. captions and tables.]

Sudo, S. & Fujii, T. 1987. Latex tubes in the rays of Pimelodendron amboinicum Hassk. (Euphorbiaceae). IAWA Bull. n.s. 8: 109–112.

Sudo, S., Iidaka, K., Yamane, M. & Iwami, M. 1967. Silica inclusions in timbers from tropical Asia. Bull. Govt. For. Exp. Sta., Meguro, No. 200: 43–55. [Jap.; Eng. table & summ.]

Sudworth, G.B. & Mell, C.D. 1911a. The identification of important North American oak woods, based on a study of the anatomy of the secondary wood. U.S. Dept. Agric., For. Serv., Bull. No. 102: 46 pp.

Sudworth, G.B. & Mell, C.D. 1911b. Distinguishing characteristics of North American gum woods. U.S. Dept. Agric., For. Serv., Bull. No. 103: 20 pp.

Sudworth, G.B. & Mell, C.D. 1911c. Fustic wood: its substitutes and adulterants. Circ. U.S. For. Serv., No. 184: 14 pp.

Sugawa, T. 1967a. Contributions to the knowledge on the wood anatomy of Dipterocarpaceae. Occurrence of horizontal intercellular canals in rays of the secondary xylem of Shorea kalunti Merr. J. Jap. Wood Res. Soc. 13: 71–74. [Jap.; Eng. summ.]

Sugawa, T. 1967b. Anatomical characters of keruing woods grown in Kalimantan. Bull. Govt. For. Exp. Sta., Meguro, No. 206: 1–16 + 4 plates. [Jap.; Eng. summ.]

Sugawa, T. 1968a. The wood anatomy of para rubber timber (Hevea brasiliensis). Wood Industr., Tokyo 23 (9): 23–24. [Jap.]

Sugawa, T. 1968b. Identification and anatomical characters of Apitong woods grown in the Philippines. Bull. Govt. For. Exp. Sta., Meguro, No. 208: 94–105. [Jap.; Eng. summ.]

Sugawa, T. 1968c. Identification and anatomical characters of thirteen species of Kalimantan woods. Bull. Govt. For. Exp. Sta., Meguro, No. 218: 109–128, 14 plates. [Jap.; Eng. summ.]

Sugawa, T. 1969. Identification and anatomical characters of Keruing woods grown in Malaya. Bull. Govt. For. Exp. Sta., Meguro, No. 221: 60–72 + 5 plates. [Jap.; Eng. summ.]

Sugawa, T. 1971a. Variation in density and anatomical features in stems of red lauan. Wood Industr. 26 (3): 19–22. [Jap.]

Sugawa, T. 1971b. The anatomical characters of Red Lauan wood from the Philippines. Bull. Govt. For. Exp. Sta., Meguro, No. 234: 9–19 + 2 plates. [Jap.; Eng. summ.]

Sugawa, T., Fujii, T., Noshiro, S. & Ogata, K. 1993. Silica grains in the wood of Heritiera s.l. (Sterculiaceae). Abstr. XV intn. Bot. Congr., Yokohama: poster no. 3161. [Abstr.]

Sulochana, C.B. 1959. Indian species of Rauvolfia. J. Indian bot. Soc. 38: 575–594.

Surya Kamala, S.V.R., Rao, B.H. & Kumar, K.V.R. 1988. Xylotomy of Echium fastuosum Aig. J. Swamy bot. Cl. 5: 133–136.

Surya Kamala, S.V.R., Rao, B.H. & Kumar, K.V.R. 1989. Xylotomical studies of some Boraginaceae. Proc. Indian Acad. Sci., Pl. Sci. 99: 417–422.

Süss, H. 1969. Über reniforme Gefässdurchbrechungen im Holz einiger Kakteen. Ber. dt. bot. Ges. 82: 183–189.

Süss, H. 1973. Zur Evolution des Holzstammes der Laubhölzer unter besonderer Berücksichtigung seiner Festigkeit. Feddes Repert. 84: 517–531.

Süss, H. 1974. Die Anatomie des Holzes von Dendrocereus nudiflorus (Engelm.) Britt. et Rose (Cactaceae). Feddes Repert. 85: 759–765.

Süss, H. & Müller-Stoll, W.R. 1973. Zur Anatomie des Ast-, Stamm- und Wurzelholzes von Platanus × accrifolia (Ait.) Willd. Öst. bot. Z. 121: 227–249.

Süss, H. & Müller-Stoll, W.R. 1975. Zur Frage der Unterscheidung von Platanus-Arten nach dem Bau des Holzes. Feddes Repert. 86: 57–70.

Suzuki, M., Joshi, L., Fujii, T. & Noshiro, S. 1991. The anatomy of unusual tracheids in Tetracentron wood. IAWA Bull. n.s. 12: 23–33.

Suzuki, M. & Nishida, M. 1974. Chionanthus mesozoica sp. nov., a dicotyledonous wood from the Lower Cretaceous of Choshi, Chiba Prefecture, with references to comparison with recent Chionanthus. J. Jap. Bot. 49: 47–53. [Eng.]

Suzuki, M. & Noshiro, S. 1988. Wood structure of Himalayan plants. In: The Himalayan plants. Vol. 1 (eds. Ohba, H. & Malla, S.B.): 341–379 + Plates 52–96. Univ. Museum, Univ. Tokyo, Bull. No. 31.

Suzuki, M., Noshiro, S., Takahashi, A., Yoda, K. & Joshi, L. 1991. Wood structure of Himalayan plants. II. In: The Himalayan plants. Vol. II (eds. Ohba, H. & Malla, S.B.): 17–65 + plates 5–62. Univ. Tokyo Press.

Suzuki, M. & Ohba, H. 1988. Wood structural diversity among Himalayan Rhododendron. IAWA Bull. n.s. 9: 317–326.

Suzuki, M. & Yoda, K. 1986. Comparative wood anatomy of Coriaria of east Asia (1), (2). J. Jap. Bot. 61: 289–296; 333–341 + plates IV–VII. [Eng.]

Suzuki, M. & Yoda, K. 1992. Comparative wood anatomy of Coriaria. In: Proc. 2nd Pacific Regional Wood Anat. Conf. 1989 (eds. Rojo, J.P., Aday, J.U., Barile, E.R., Araral, R.K. & America, W.M.): 164–172. For. Prod. Dev. Inst.: College, Laguna, Philippines.

Swamy, B.G.L. 1949. The comparative morphology of the Santalaceae: node, secondary xylem, and pollen. Amer. J. Bot. 36: 661–673.

Swamy, B.G.L. 1953a. The morphology and relationships of the Chloranthaceae. J. Arnold Arbor. 34: 375–408.

Swamy, B.G.L. 1953b. Comments on Ascarina alticola Schlechter. Proc. Nat. Inst. Sci. India 19: 143–147.

Swamy, B.G.L. 1953c. Sarcandra irvingbaileyi, a new species of vesselless dicotyledon from South India. Proc. Nat. Inst. Sci. India 19: 301–306.

Swamy, B.G.L. 1975. A new type of anomalous secondary thickening of plant axis in Adenia palmata. Phytomorphology 25: 271–279.

Swamy, B.G.L. & Bailey, I.W. 1949. The morphology and relationships of Cercidiphyllum. J. Arnold Arbor. 30: 187–210.

Swamy, B.G.L. & Bailey, I.W. 1950. Sarcandra, a vesselless genus of the Chloranthaceae. J. Arnold Arbor. 31: 117–129.

Swart, J.P.J. & Van der Walt, J.J.A. 1985. Systematic wood anatomy of the southern African Lauraceae. Proc. Symp. For. Prod. Res. Intn. Achievements and the Future, April 1985, Pretoria, vol. 1, Paper 16-9: 13 pp. CSIRO: S. Africa.

Swart, J.P.J. & Vos, J. 1985. Systematic wood anatomy: a computer-based research system. S. Afr. for. J. (132): 50–53.

Sweitzer, E.M. 1971. Comparative anatomy of Ulmaceae. J. Arnold Arbor. 52: 523–585.

Szalai, I. & Varga, M.B. 1955. Über den Einfluss des Lebensalters und der Lebensbedingungen auf den Markstrahlenanteil im Holzkörper der Esche. (Studien über Fraxinus excelsior L.I.). Acta biol. szeged. (NS) 1: 71–94.

Tabata, H. 1964. Vessel elements of Japanese birches as viewed from ecology and evolution. Physiol. Ecol. (Kyoto) 12 (1-2): 7–16. [Eng.]

Tabatabai, M. 1962. A study on the Iranian timber species. Bull. For. Wood Technol. Lab. Univ. Teheran, Nos. 32, 34–40. [Nos. 37–40 by Tabatabai, M. & Jowlani, B.] [Each part with 4–6 pp.]

Tabatabai, M., Jowlani, B. & Soleymani, P. 1963. A study on the Iranian wood species. Bull. For. Wood Technol. Lab. Univ. Teheran, Nos. 41–50. [Eng.]

Tabatabai, M. & Soleymani, P. 1964. A study on the Iranian wood species. 19. Estabrag (Calotropis procera Willd.). Asclepiadaceae. Bull. For. Wood Technol. Lab. Univ. Teheran, No. 57: 12 pp. [Persian.] 20. Daar-doost (Hedera helix L.). Araliaceae. Ibid., No. 58: 10 pp. [Persian.]

Tabatabai, M., Soleymani, P. & Nagdi, F. 1964. A study on the Iranian wood species. 21. Garre-baadaam (Periploca sp.?). Asclepiadaceae. Bull. For. Wood Technol. Lab. Univ. Teheran, No. 59: 14 pp.

Tabatabai, M., Terver, P. & Boullanger, M. 1967. Quercus castaneifolia C.A.M. (Boland-Mazou) of the forests of N.E. Iran. Bull. Fac. For., Univ. Teheran, No. 7: 16 pp. [Persian & French.]

Tabatabai, M. et al. 1969. Bois de l'Iran Betulaceae et Corylaceae. Centre français de documentation technique de Teheran. 19 + 16 pp.

Tabirih, P.K. & Seehann, G. 1981. On biological characteristics of Abachi wood (Triplochiton scleroxylon K. Schum.). Holzforschung 35: 207–212.

Tainter, F.H. 1968. Microscopic identification of commercial Chilean woods. Special Publ., Montana Forest & Conservation Exp. Sta., Missoula, No. 3: 27 pp. [Eng. & Span.]

Takahashi, A. 1984. Comparative wood anatomy of Chloranthaceae. Proc. Pacific Regional Wood Anatomy Conf., Tsukuba, Japan, 1984: 150–152.

Takahashi, A. 1985. Wood anatomical studies of Polycarpicae. I. Magnoliales. Sci. Rep. Osaka Univ. 34: 29–83. II. Ranunculales. Ibid.: 121–144.

Takahashi, A. 1988. Wood anatomy of Hedyosmum orientale Merr. et Chun (Chloranthaceae). J. Phytogeog. Taxon. 36: 51–53. [Eng.]

Takahashi, A. 1989. Wood anatomical report of some Magnoliaceae from Borneo. J. Phytogeog. Taxon. 37: 93–100. [Eng.]

Takahashi, A. & Tamura, M. 1990a. An evolutionary trend in dimension of the tracheary elements of the woody Polycarpicae. J. Jap. Bot. 65: 45–57. [Eng.]

Takahashi, A. & Tamura, M. 1990b. Occurrence of vessel elements in the stem of Sarcandra glabra. J. Jap. Bot. 65: 81–85. [Eng.]

Takaki, T. 1963. Studies of tropical woods. 1. Studies on the anatomical characters of some species of Dipterocarpaceae in Sarawak. J. Agr. Sci., Setagaya 9: 104–116. [Jap.; Eng. summ.]

Takhtajan, A.L., Shilkina, I.A. & Yatsenko-Khmelevsky, A.A. 1986. Wood anatomy of Didymeles madagascariensis in the connection with the systematic status of the family Didymelaceae. Bot. Zh. SSSR 71: 1203–1206. [Russ. only.] + 2 plates.

Takizawa, T., Takahashi, M., Kawaguchi, N. & Yamamoto, H. 1980. Anatomical properties of species of poplars. J. Hokkaido for. prod. Res. Inst., No. 338: 6–9. [Jap.; Eng. summ.]

Tang, Y. 1932; 1935. Timber studies of Chinese trees. I. Timber anatomy of Rhoipteleaceae. Bull. Fan Mem. Inst. Biol. Peking 3(10): 127–131 (1932). 7. Notes on the systematic position of Bretschneideraceae as shown by its timber anatomy. Ibid. 6(3): 153–157 (1935). [Eng.]

Tang, Y. 1943. Systematic anatomy of the woods of the Hamamelidaceae. Bull. Fan Mem. Inst. Biol. Peking (NS) 1: 8–62. [Eng.]

Tang, Y. 1973. The tropical and subtropical woods of Yunnan Province. Science Press: Peking. 274 pp. + 79 plates. [Chin.]

Tang, Y. 1992a. A study on Melhania hamiltoniana in relation to the systematic position of the genus. Acta bot. yunnan. 14(1): 13–20. [Chin.; Eng. summ.] + 1 plate.

Tang, Y. 1992b. The systematic position of Corchoropsis Sieb. & Zucc. Cathaya 4: 131–150. [Eng.]

Tang, Y. 1993. On the systematic position of Paradombeya Stapf. Acta phytotax. sin. 31: 297–308 + 3 plates. [Eng.]

Taniguchi, T., Harada, H. & Nakato, K. 1982. Mineral deposits in some tropical woody plants. Ann. Bot. 50: 559–562.

Taranenko, P.Kh. 1972. Anatomical characteristic of the Quercus borealis Michx. xylem. Ukrain. bot. Zh. 29: 446–451. [Ukrain.; brief Eng. summ.]

Taras, M.A. & Kukachka, B.F. 1970. Separating Pecan and Hickory lumber. For. Prod. J. 20(4): 58–59.

Tavares, E.J. de S. 1968. Anatomia do lenho de "cabata-de-leite" Thyrosodium schomburgkianum Benth. Bol. tec. secret. viac. obras. Publ. (90): 13–16.

Tavares, E.J. de S. 1970. Anatomia do lenho de Schinus terebinthifolius Raddi. Bol. Recurs. Nat., Recife 8: 195–201. [Eng. summ.]

Tavares, S. 1957. Contribuição para o estudo botânico do "guajeru" (Chrysobalanus icaco L.). Publ. Inst. Pesq. Agron. Pernambuco 1: 1–12.

Tavares, S. 1959. Estudo sôbre a anatomia do lenho do "Visgueiro", Parkia pendula Benth. Inst. Pesq. Agron. Pernambuco, Publ. No. 8: 19 pp.

Tavares, S. & Tavares, E.J.S. 1967. Anatomia do lenho de Virola gardneri (D.C.) Warb. Publ. Inst. tec. Estado Pernambuco, Recife, 9. Also in: Revista Clube Engenharia Pernambuco 27: 17–22 (1967).

Taylor, F.H. 1972. The secondary xylem of the Violaceae: a comparative study. Bot. Gaz. 133: 230–242.

Taylor, F. 1973. Anatomical wood properties of South African grown Eucalyptus grandis. S. Afr. for. J. 84: 20–24.

Teixeira, L.L. 1983. Some unusual features in the wood of Sloanea lasiocoma K. Schum. (Elaeocarpaceae) and Casearia obliqua Spreng. (Flacourtiaceae). IAWA Bull. n.s. 4: 213–217.

Teixeira, L.L., Burger, L.M. & Karstedt, P. 1978. Estudos microscópicos do xilema e da casca do gênero Dalbergia baseados em quatro espécies do sul do Brasil. Arq. Jard. bot. Rio de Janeiro 22: 115–133.

Teles, A.A. & Paula, J.E. de 1980. Estudo de madeiras da Amazônia visando o seu aproveitamento para polpa e papel. Brasil Florestal 10 (42): 25–34.

Tellini, G. 1939 [1940]. Ricerche anatomiche su Dianthus arboreus L. verus (= D. aciphyllus
Sieb.). Nuovo G. bot. ital. 46: 615–642.

Temu, R.P.C. 1990a. Seedling morphology, wood anatomy and notes on the distribution of
Scorodophloeus fischeri (Taub.) J. Léonard (African Leguminosae–Caesalpinioideae).
Bull. Jard. bot. natn. Belg. 60: 213–221.

Temu, R.P.C. 1990b. Taxonomy and biogeography of woody plants in the eastern Arc Mts,
Tanzania: case studies in Zenkerella, Scorodophloeus and Peddiea. Acta Univ. upsal. 286:
68 pp. + 4 reprinted papers.

Ter-Abraamyan, B. 1951. Structure of wood of species of the genus Carpinus L. Izv. Akad.
Nauk arm. SSR 4 (4): 327–335. [Russ.]

Terrazas, T. 1988. Sintesis historica de los estudios de la anatomia de la madera en Mexico.
Agrociencia (Mex.), No. 71: 43–58. [Eng. summ.]

Terrazas, T. 1993. Wood anatomy of the Anacardiaceae – ecological and phylogenetic inter-
pretation. Abstr. XV intn. Bot. Congr., Yokohama: 3.5.4-2. [Abstr.]

Tewari, D.N. 1992. Monograph on neem (Azadirachta indica A. Juss.). International Book
Distributors: Dehra Dun. 279 pp.

Tewfik, S.A. & Al-Dawoody, D.M. 1982. Anatomical features of some Iraq Quercus and
Populus woods. Ain. Shams Univ. Fac. Agric. Res. Bull., No. 1804: 1–9. [Eng.]

Theron, G.K., Schweickerdt, H.G. & Van der Schijff, H.P. 1968. 'N anatomiese studie van
Plinthus karooicus Verdoorn. T. Nat.-Wetensk., Suid-Afr. 8 (2): 69–104. [Eng. summ.]

Thieme, H.W. 1929. Das Bongosiholz und seine Abstammung. Bot. Archiv 26: 164–223.

Thomas, J.L. 1960. A monographic study of the Cyrillaceae. Contrib. Gray Herb. Harvard
Univ. No. 186: 1–114.

Thompson, W.P. 1911. On the origin of the multiseriate ray of the dicotyledons. Ann. Bot. 25:
1005–1014.

Thompson, W.P. 1918. Independent evolution of vessels in Gnetales and angiosperms. Bot.
Gaz. 65: 83–90.

Thompson, W.P. 1923. The relationships of the different types of angiospermic vessels. Ann.
Bot. 37: 183–192.

Thompson, W.P. & Bailey, I.W. 1916. Are Tetracentron, Trochodendron and Drimys special-
ized or primitive types? Mem. N.Y. bot. Gard. 6: 27–32.

Thunell, B. & Perem, E. 1947. Identifiering av träslag. Medd. Svenska Träforskningsinst. Trät.
Avdel. 12: 12 pp.

Tiêp, N.V. 1980. Beiträge zur Sippenstruktur der Gattung Manglietia Bl. (Magnoliaceae).
Feddes Repert. 91: 497–576.

Tillson, A.H. & Muller, C.H. 1942. Anatomical and taxonomic approaches to subgeneric seg-
regation in American Quercus. Amer. J. Bot. 29: 523–529.

Timmermans, A.S. 1931. Beiträge zur Kenntnis der Anatomie und des anormalen Dicken-
wachstums von Phytocrene macrophylla Bl. Ann. Jard. bot. Buitenzorg 41: 65–104.

Timonin, A.K. 1987. Anomalous secondary thickening of the axial organs of the centrosperms
(on the example of the Amaranthaceae Juss.). 1. The concepts of thickening, thickening
patterns in some species. Byull. mosk. Obshch. Ispyt. Prir., Otdel. biol. 92 (4): 63–81.
2. Evolutionary aspects. Ibid. (6): 92–103. [Russ.; Eng. summ.]

Timonin, A.K. 1988a. On some interpretations of the anomalous thickening patterns in Centrosperms. Nauch. Dokl. vyssh. Shk., biol. Nauki (1): 67–71. [Russ.]

Timonin, A.K. 1988b. On the evolution of anomalous secondary thickening in centrosperms.
Zh. Obshch. Biol. 42: 185–201. [Russ.]

Tineo, B., Rodríguez, P. & Castillo, A. 1992 [1993]. Morfoanatomia de organos vegetativos de
Machaerium robiniaefolium (DC) Vog. (Leguminosae: Papilionoideae, Dalbergieae). Mem.
Soc. Cienc. nat. La Salle 52 (137): 37–51.

Tippo, O. 1938. Comparative anatomy of the Moraceae and their presumed allies. Bot. Gaz. 100: 1–99.

Tippo, O. 1940. The comparative anatomy of the secondary xylem and the phylogeny of the Eucommiaceae. Amer. J. Bot. 27: 832–838.

Tippo, O. 1946. The role of wood anatomy in phylogeny. Amer. Midl. Nat. 36: 362–372.

Titman, P.W. 1949. Studies in the woody anatomy of the family Nyssaceae. J. Elisha Mitchell Sci. Soc. 65: 245–261.

Tochigi, T., Shiokura, T., Lantican, C.B., Salud, C.C. & Madamba, C.B. 1984. Computer assisted tropical wood identification (CATWI). Proc. Pacific Regional Wood anatomy Conf., Tsukuba, Japan, 1984: 174–176.

Toker, R. 1963. The wood properties of Fagus orientalis in Turkey. Holz-Zbl. 89: 1516–1517. [Germ.]

Toledo Rizzini, C. & Occhioni, P. 1949. Dialypetalanthaceae. Lilloa 17: 243–248 [Eng. summ.]

Tomazello Filho, M. 1985. Estrutura anatômica da madeira de oito espécies de eucalipto cultivadas no Brasil. Inst. Pesq. Estud. Florest., No. 29: 25–36. [Eng. summ.]

Tomazello Filho, M., Chimelo, J.P. & Garcia, P.V. 1983. Madeiras de especies florestais do estado do Maranhão: II. Caracterização anatômica. Inst. Pesq. Estud. Florest. (IPEF) No. 23: 29–35. [Eng. summ.] [For. Prod. Abstr. 12 (1989) No. 1369.]

Tomlinson, P.B. & Craighead, F.C. 1972. Growth-ring studies on the native trees of subtropical Florida. In: Research trends in plant anatomy (eds. Ghouse, A.K.M. & Yunus, M.): 39–51. Tata McGraw-Hill Publ. Co.: Bombay & New Delhi.

Tondeur, G. 1939. Monographie forestière du Chlorophora excelsa Benth. et Hook. Bull. agric. Congo Belge, Brussels 30: 163–198.

Topper, S.M.C. & Koek-Noorman, J. 1980. The occurrence of axial latex tubes in the secondary xylem of some species of Artocarpus J.R. & G. Forster (Moraceae). IAWA Bull. n.s. 1: 113–119.

Tôrres, J.P. de 1941. Estudos do lenho de algumas espécies florestais de Timor. Rev. agron. Lisboa 29: 56–86.

Tortorelli, L.A. 1937 [1938]. Estructura anatomica del leño de la tiaca (Caldcluvia paniculata). Revta chil. Hist. nat. 41: 187–191.

Tortorelli, L.A. 1941. Tratamiento florestal y caracteres xilológicos del maitén (Maytenus boaria) arbol forrajero de la Patagonia. Univ. Buenos Aires, Fac. Agron. Vet., Inst. Frutivit. Silv. 1 (2): 32 pp.

Tortorelli, L.A. 1944 [1945]. Estudio xilológico del Drimys winteri. Rev. Fac. Agron. Vet. Univ. Buenos Aires 11 (1): 5–11.

Tortorelli, L.A. 1945. La disposición estratificada de los elementos leñosos en el 'ibira-ita' (Muellera glaziovii). Pub. tec. No. 5, Rev. Inst. Bot. Darwinion 7: 58–61.

Tortorelli, L.A. 1948a. Estudio dendrológico de las especies de Piptadenia de la flora argentina. Revta argent. Agron. 15: 90–112.

Tortorelli, L.A. 1948b. The Argentine Piptadenia timbers. Trop. Woods 94: 1–27.

Tortorelli, L.A. 1956. Maderas y bosques argentinos. Editorial Acme, S.A.C.I., Buenos Aires. 910 pp.

Tortorelli, L. & Castiglioni, J.A. 1949. Estudio dendrológico de las Estiracáceas argentinas. Lilloa 16: 125–139.

Trabut, L. 1926. Le tlaia; Tamarix articulata Vahl. Bull. Sta. Rech. forest. Alger. 1: 336–349.

Trautner-Jäger, E. 1962. La formación de zonas generatrices en plantas leñosas del limite selvático Andino. Acta. cient. venez. 13: 126–131.

Troll, W. 1933. Botanische Mitteilungen aus den Tropen. XII. Camptostemon schultzii Mast. und Camptostemon philippinensis (Vid.) Becc. als neue Vertreter der austral-asiatischen Mangrovevegetation. Flora 128: 348–360.

Tschchubianischvili, I.I. 1933. Beiträge zur Anatomie von Corylus colchica Alb. Tr. Tifl. bot. Inst. 1: 285–290. [Russ.; Germ. summ.]

Tschinkel, H.M. 1966. Annual growth rings in Cordia alliodora. Turrialba 16: 73–80.

Tumanyan, S. 1947. On the anatomical characterization of the Armenian species of Pyrus and Malus. Dokl. Akad. Nauk arm. SSR 6 (1): 9–16. [Russ.; Eng. summ.]

Tumanyan, S.A. 1949. Anatomical characters of the genus Sorbus. Trudy Inst. Lesa, Mosk. 85–90. [Russ.]

Tumanyan, S. [Tumanjan, S.] 1950. Anatomical structure of the woods of the Caucasian representatives of the sub-family Pomoideae, family Rosaceae. Trud. bot. Inst. Akad. Nauk arm. SSR 7: 69–103. [Russ. only.]

Tumanyan, S.A. 1953. Comparative anatomical investigation on the wood of representatives of the genus Quercus. Trudy Inst. Lesa, Mosk. 9: 39–69. [Russ.]

Tumanyan, S.A. 1954. The wood structure of Pyrus rossica A. Dan. Izv. Akad. Nauk arm. SSR, biol. Nauki 7 (3): 99–102. [Russ.]

Tumanyan, S.A. 1969. Parenchyma in the wood of broad-leaved trees. Biol. Zh. arm. 22 (6): 54–63. [Russ.]

Tumanyan, S.A. 1975. Comparative anatomical study of the timber of two Caucasian birches, Betula megrelica Sosn., Betula raddeana Trautv. Biol. Zh. arm. SSSR 28 (10): 60–70. [Russ.]

Tunman, O. 1908. Zur Anatomie des Holzes und der Wurzel von Morinda citrifolia L. mit besonderer Berücksichtigung der mikrochemischen Verhältnisse. Pharmac.-zentralhalle 1013–1017. [See Just's Jber. 1908, 1: 488.]

Tupper, W.W. 1931. An unusual seasonal growth ring in Eucalyptus. Pap. Mich. Acad. Sci. Arts Lett. 13: 217–219.

Tupper, W.W. 1934. Preliminary report on the wood structure of the Flacourtiaceae. Trop. Woods 38: 11–14.

Tyshkevich, G.L. 1976. Anatomical structure of beech wood in relation to growth conditions. Lesovedenie (1): 59–64. [Russ.]

Uhlarz, H. & Kunschert, A. 1975 [1976]. Das Holz von Euphorbia grandicornis Goeb. Beitr. Biol. Pfl. 51: 391–406.

Umarov, M.U. & Chavchavadze, E.S. 1990. Structural changes of wood in Periploca graeca (Asclepiadaceae) in connection with environmental conditions. Bot. Zh. SSSR 75: 675–682. [Russ. only] + 2 plates.

Urling, G.P. & Smith, R.B. 1953. An anatomical study of twenty lesser known woods of Florida. Quart. J. Fla. Acad. Sci. 16: 163–180.

Ursem, B.W.N.J. & Welle, B.J.H. ter 1992. Anomalous growth patterns in South American lianas, with special reference to their ontogeny. In: Proc. 2nd Pacific Regional Wood Anat. Conf. 1989 (eds. Rojo, J.P., Aday, J.U., Barile, E.R., Araral, R.K. & America, W.M.): 399–408. For. Prod. Dev. Inst.: College, Laguna, Philippines.

Valente, M. da C. 1974. Observações sobre a anatomia de Ecclinusa balata Ducke. Rodriguésia 27, No. 39: 7–24. [Eng. summ.]

Vales, M.A. 1983a. Verzierte einfache Gefässdurchbrechungen im Holz einiger endemischer Rubiaceen-Arten aus Kuba. Feddes Repert. 94: 493–495.

Vales, M.A. 1983b. Verzierte Gefäss- und Holzfaser-Hoftüpfel im Holz einiger endemischer Rubiaceen-Arten aus Kuba. Feddes Repert. 94: 497–500.

Vales, M.A. 1984. Anatomía de la madera de Brunellia comocladifolia H. & B. (Brunelliaceae). Revta Jard. bot. nac. Univ. La Habana 5 (1): 157–168. [Eng. summ.]

Vales, M.A. & Babos, K. 1977. Wood anatomy of Ceratopyxis Hooker f. ex Hooker (Rubiaceae) a monotypic endemic genus of West Cuba. Acta. bot. hung. 23 (1/2): 275–283.

Vales, M.A., Babos, K. & Borhidi, A. 1977. On the wood anatomy of Bombacopsis cubensis A. Robyns (Bombacaceae) and Magnolia cubensis Urb. ssp. cubensis (Magnoliaceae). Acta bot. hung. 23: 427–437.

Vales, M.A., Borhidi, A. & Del-Risco, E. 1982. Anatomía de la madera de Myricaceae en Cuba: consideraciones ecologicas. Acta bot. Acad. sci. hung. 28 (1/2): 241–253.

Vales, M.A. & Carreras, R. 1986; 1987. Anatomía de maderas de Cuba, I. Acta bot. hung. 32: 231–245 (1986). III. Ibid. 33: 333–351 (1987).

Vales, M.A. & Martinez, C. 1983. Contribución al estudio anatómico del xilema de la familia Simarubaceae en Cuba, I. Alvaradoa Liebm. y Simaruba Aubl. Acta bot. hung. 29: 231–240.

Vales, M.A., Moncada, M. & Machado, S. 1988. Anatomía comparada de Clethraceae en Cuba. Revta. Jard. bot. nac. Univ. La Habana 9 (3): 69–73.

Vales, M.A. & Süss, H. 1985a. Die Holzanatomie der in Kuba endemischen Rubiaceae Acunaeanthus tinifolius (Griseb.) Borhidi, Ariadne shaferi (Standl.) Urb. und Neomazaea phiallanthoides (Griseb.) Krug et Urb. Feddes Repert. 96: 215–225 + plates 9–11.

Vales, M.A. & Süss, H. 1985b. Die Holzanatomie der in Kuba endemischen Rubiaceae Phyllomelia coronata Griseb. und Ceratopyxis verbenacea (Griseb.) Hook.f. ex Hook. Feddes Repert. 96 : 227–233 + plates 12, 13.

Vales, M.A., Vilamajó, D. & Martínez, C. 1983. Caracterización ecoanatómica del xilema de especies lignificadas de las estaciones de Sierra del Rosario y Yaguaramas, Cuba. Cienc. biol., Cuba 9: 47–54. [Brief Eng. summ.]

Van den Oever, L. 1984. Comparative wood anatomy of the Olacaceae. Proc. Pacific Regional Wood Anatomy Conf., Tsukuba, Japan, 1984: 177–178.

Van den Oever, L., Baas, P. & Zandee, M. 1981. Comparative wood anatomy of Symplocos and latitude and altitude of provenance. IAWA Bull. n.s. 2: 3–24.

Van den Oever, L., Welle, B.J.H. ter & Koek-Noorman, J. 1993. Wood and timber. In: Flora of the Guianas (ed. Görts-van Rijn, A.R.A.). 102. Olacaceae: 44–64. Koeltz: Koenigstein.

Van der Graaff, N.A. & Baas, P. 1974. Wood anatomical variation in relation to latitude and altitude. Blumea 22: 101–121.

Van der Slooten, H.J. 1968. Informe sobre un programa de ensayo de maderas realizado para el proyecto UNDP 192, investigacion y desarrollo de zonas forestales selectas de C.R. por el Laboratorio de Technologia de la Madera del Inst. Inter-americano de Ciencias agricolas (IICA), Turrialba, Costa Rica. FAO, 131 pp.

Van der Slooten, H.J. 1969. Maderas latinoamericanas. I. Objetivos y especificaciones generales de los estudios. Turrialba 19: 409–411.

Van der Slooten, H.J., Acosta-Contreras, I. & Aas, P.S. 1969; 1970. Maderas latinoamericanas. II. Quercus aáata, Q. costaricensis y Q. eugeniaefolia. Turrialba 19: 412–418 (1969). III. Podocarpus standleyi, Podocarpus oleifolius, Drimys granadensis, Magnolia poasana y Didymopanax pittieri. Ibid. 20: 105–115. IV. Nectandra sp., Ocotea austinii, Persea sp. aff. vesticula, Persea schiedeana. Ibid.: 223–232 (1970).

Van der Slooten, H.J., Corothie, H. & Perez, J.A. 1962. Caracteristicas anatómicas y propiedades físico-mecánicas de algunas especies maderables del Brasil. Bol. Inst. Forest. Latinoamer. Invest. Capac. 10: 39–93. [Eng. summ.]

Van der Slooten, H.J. & Gonzalez, M.E. 1970 [1971]; 1971. Maderas latinoamericanas. V. Carapa sp., Virola koschnyi, Terminalia lucida y Brosimum costaricanum. Turrialba 20: 503–510 (1970). VI. Bursera simaruba, Poulsenia armata, Pterocarpus officinalis y Ficus werckleana. Ibid. 21: 69–76 (1971).

Van der Veken, P. 1960. Blighiopsis genre nouveau de Sapindacées du Congo. Bull. Jard. Bot. État, Bruxelles 30: 413–419.

Van der Walt, J.J.A., Schweickerdt, H.G. & Van der Schijff, H.P. 1969. Afwykende sekondêre diktegroei in die stingels van die liane Cyphostemma anatomicum (C.A. Sm.) Wild & Drummond (Vitaceae) en Adenia gummifera (Harv.) Harms (Passifloraceae). Tydskr. Nat.-Wetensk., Suid-Afr. 9: 89–123. [Eng. summ.]

Van der Walt, J.J.A., Schweickerdt, H.G. & Van der Schijff, H.P. 1970. Afwykende sekondêre diktegroei in die stingels van die liane Cocculus hirsutus (L.) Diels (Menispermaceae) en Pyrenacantha grandiflora Baill. (Icacinaceae). Tydskr. Nat.-Wetensk., Suid-Afr. 10: 173–199. [Eng. summ.]

Van der Walt, J.J.A., Van der Schijff, H.P. & Schweickerdt, H.G. 1973. Anomalous secondary growth in the stems of the lianes Mikania cordata (Burm. f.) Robins. (Compositae) and Paullinia pinnata Linn. (Sapindaceae). Kirkia 9: 109–138.

Van der Walt, J.J.A., Werker, E. & Fahn, A. 1987. Wood anatomy of Pelargonium (Geraniaceae). IAWA Bull. n.s. 8: 95–108.

Van der Werff, H. & Richter, H.G. 1985. Caryodaphnopsis Airy Shaw (Lauraceae), a genus new to the neotropics. Syst. Bot. 10: 166–173.

Vander Wyk, R.W. & Canright, J.E. 1956. The anatomy and relationships of the Annonaceae. Trop. Woods 104: 1–24.

Van Donselaar, J. 1972. Aspidosperma helstonei (Apocynaceae), a new species from Surinam. Acta bot. neerl. 21: 253–256.

Van Iterson, G. 1934. The significance of the anatomy of wood for the preservation of marine structures against the shipworm (teredo). Proc. 5th Pacific Sci. Congr., Canada: 3907–3911.

Van Steenis, C.G.G.J. 1973. Woodiness in island floras. Taiwania 18: 45–48.

Van Veenendaal, W.L.H. & Den Outer, R.W. 1978. A provisional determination key to 54 continental African Dichapetalum species, based on anatomical characters of the secondary xylem. Meded. Landbouwhogesch. Wageningen 78 (18): 1–23.

Van Veenendaal, W.L.H. & Den Outer, R.W. 1993. Development of included phloem and organisation of the phloem network in the stem of Strychnos millepunctata (Loganiaceae). IAWA Jl. 14: 253–265.

Van Vliet, G.J.C.M. 1975. Wood anatomy of Crypteroniaceae sensu lato. J. Microsc. 104: 65–82.

Van Vliet, G.J.C.M. 1976a. Wood anatomy of the Rhizophoraceae. In: Wood structure in biological and technological research (eds. Baas, P., Bolton, A.J. & Catling, D.M.): 20–75. Leiden Botanical Series No. 3. Leiden Univ. Press.

Van Vliet, G.J.C.M. 1976b. Radial vessels in rays. IAWA Bull. 1976/3: 35–37.

Van Vliet, G.J.C.M. 1978. Vestured pits of Combretaceae and allied families. Acta bot. neerl. 27: 273–285.

Van Vliet, G.J.C.M. 1979. Wood anatomy of the Combretaceae. Blumea 25: 141–223.

Van Vliet, G.J.C.M. 1981. Wood anatomy of the palaeotropical Melastomataceae. Blumea 27: 395–462.

Van Vliet, G.J.C.M. & Baas, P. 1982. Wood anatomy and classification of the Myrtales. Ann. Missouri bot. Gard. 69: 1–22. [1984 paper indexed.]

Van Vliet, G.J.C.M. & Baas, 1984. Wood anatomy and classification of the Myrtales. Ann. Missouri bot. Gard. 71: 783–800.

Van Vliet, G.J.C.M., Koek-Noorman, J. & Welle, B.J.H. ter 1981. Wood anatomy, classification and phylogeny of the Melastomataceae. Blumea 27: 463–473.

Van Vuuren, D.R.J. 1973. Afwykende sekondêre diktegroei by die stingels van die houtagtige verteenwoordigers van die genus Adenia Forsk. in Suid-Afrika: I. Afwykende diktegroei by die stingel van Adenia spinosa Burtt Davy. Tydskr. Nat.-Wetensk., Suid-Afr. 13: 27–51. [Eng. summ.]

Van Wyk, A.E., Robbertse, P.J. & Kok, P.D.F. 1983. The genus Eugenia (Myrtaceae) in southern Africa: structure and taxonomic value of wood. S. Afr. J. Bot. 2: 135–151.

Vasilevskaya, V.K. 1933. The development of the wood in the trees and shrubs of the sand desert Kara-Kum. Bull. appl. Bot., Genet., Plant Breed. Leningrad, ser. 1, No. 1: 231–260. [Russ.; Eng. summ.]

Vasilevskaya, V.K. 1972. Special type of anatomical structure in the family Chenopodiaceae. Bot. Zh. SSSR 57: 103–108 [Russ. only.]

Vasilevskaya, V.K. & Borisovskaya, G.M. 1981. Life forms and their evolutional transformations in the Buxaceae Dum. Trudy mosk. Obshch. Ispyt. Prir. 56: 90–104. [Russ.; Eng. summ.]

Vasilevskaya, V.K. & Petrov, M.P. 1964. Central Asian endemic Tetraena mongolica Maxim. Bot. J. USSR 49: 1506–1513. [Russ.]

Vasilevskaya, V.K. & Shulkina, T.V. 1976. The morphological and anatomical structure of the arborescent plant Azorina vidalii Feer. (Campanula vidalii Wats.). Trudy mosk. Obshch. Ispyt. Prir. 42: 131–140. [Russ.; Eng. summ.]

Vasilevskaya, V.K. & Trubochkina, S.I. 1963. Anatomical structure of the wood of Tetraena Maxim, Zygophyllum L. and Nitraria L. In: Opyt raboty Repetekskoi peschanopustynoi statsii. Akad. Nauk Turkmensk. SSR, Ashkhabad: 88–106 (1963) [Russ.]; Referat. Zhur., Biol. (1964) No. 2V79 [Transl.]

Vasiljević, S. 1950. O širini traka lignuma nekih vrsta roda Acer. [The width of the xylem rays in some species of Acer.] Glasn. šum. Fak., Beograd, No. 1: 116–151. [Serb.; Eng. summ.]

Vasiljević, S. 1954. O nekim razlikama u mikroskopskoj gradi lignuma medu domaćim vrstama roda Acer. [Some differences in microscopic wood structure between Acer species in Jugoslavia.] Glasn. šum. Fak., Beograd, No. 8: 65–132. [Eng. summ.]

Veldkamp, J.F. 1988. Notes on Pteleocarpa, incertae sedis. Flora Males. Bull. 10: 47–50.

Venkateswarlu, J. & Rao, P.S.P. 1964. The wood anatomy and the taxonomic position of Sonneratiaceae. Curr. Sci. 33: 6–9.

Venkateswarlu, J. & Rao, P.S.P. 1971. Wood anatomy and systematic position of Strephonema. New Phytol. 70: 767–771.

Vent, W., Meinhardt, U. & Vobach, V. 1973. Beiträge zur Kenntnis der infraspezifischen Struktur von Frangula alnus Mill. (Rhamnaceae). Gleditschia 1: 17–31.

Verhoeven, R.L. & Van der Schijff, H.P. 1974 [1975]. Anatomical aspects of Combretaceae in South Africa. Phytomorphology 24: 158–164.

Verna, M.M. 1979. El leno secundario de las Meliaceas argentinas. Folleto Tecnico Forestal, Instituto Forestal Nacional, No. 53: 29 pp.

Versteegh, C. 1968. An anatomical study of some woody plants of the mountain flora in the tropics (Indonesia). Acta bot. neerl. 17: 151–159.

Vestal, P.A. 1937. The significance of comparative anatomy in establishing the relationship of the Hypericaceae to the Guttiferae and their allies. Philipp. J. Sci. 64: 199–256.

Vestal, P.A. & Vestal, M.R. 1940. The formation of septa in the fiber-tracheids of Hypericum androsaemum L. Bot. Mus. Leafl. Harvard Univ. 8: 169–188.

Viana, V.R.C. 1992. Contribuição ao estudo anatômico de eixo vegetativo de Amaranthus viridis L. (Amaranthaceae). Arq. Jard. bot. Rio de Janeiro 31: 15–70.

Vigne, C. & Record, S.J. 1929. Panda oleosa Pierre. Trop. Woods 20: 14–17.

Vigodsky-De Philippis, A. 1938 [1939]. Solenostemma argel (Delile, 1802) Hayne (Solenostemma oleifolium (Nect.) Bull. et Bruce) morfologia ed anatomia. Nuovo G. bot. ital. 45: 572–585.

Vijendra Rao, R.: see Rao, R.V.

Vikhrov, V.E. 1954. The structure and physico-mechanical properties of oak wood. Inst. Lesa, Akad. Nauk SSSR, Moscow. 264 pp. [Russ.]

Villalba, R. 1985. Xylem structure and cambial activity in Prosopis flexuosa DC. IAWA Bull. n.s. 6: 119–130.

Vintoniv, I.S. 1976. Features of the wood structure of sycamore growing in the Ukrainian Carpathians. Izv. vyssh. ucheb. Zaved., lesn. Zh. (4): 80–84. [Russ.]

Visser, C. 1966. Anatomie van die stingels van Protea repens (L.) L. en Leucadendron abscendens R. Br. II. Anatomie van die stingels. Jl. S. Afr. Bot. 32: 347–377. [Eng. summ.]

Vitalis-Brun, A. & Mariaux, A. 1982. Séparation anatomique de bois de Sapotacées par des méthodes d'analyse multidimensionnelle. Bois For. Trop., No. 196: 59–71.

Vonk, G.J.A. & Leeuwenberg, A.J.M. 1989. A taxonomic revision of the genus Tabernanthe and a study of wood anatomy of T. iboga. Wageningen Agric. Univ. Pap. 89 (4): 1–18. [Also in: Belmontia (NS) 23, No. 144; 1991.]

Wagemann Wiedenbrug, G. 1949. Maderas chilenas. Contribucion a su anatomia e identificacion. Lilloa 16: 263–375 + 29 plates.

Wagenführ, R. 1961. Die Klassifizierung des Holz-Parenchyms – ein Beitrag zur Bestimmung der Holzarten. I. & II. Holztechnologie, Dresden 2: 110–118; 207–211.

Wagenführ, R. 1989. Anatomie des Holzes unter besonderer Berücksichtigung der Holztechnik. VEB Fachbuchverlag: Leipzig. 4th edn. 334 pp.

Wagenführ, R. 1990. Vergleichende holzanatomische Betrachtungen einiger Nutzhölzer Kambodschas. Wiss. Z. tech. Univ. Dresden 39: 163–166.

Wagenführ, R., Röber, B. & Weiss, B. 1988. Rechnergestützte Holzarteninformation und -identifizierung. Holztechnologie, Dresden 29 (1): 33–34.

Wagenführ, R. & Scheiber, C. 1974; 1985. Holzatlas. VEB Fachbuchverlag, Leipzig. 690 pp. (1974). 2nd edn. 720 pp. (1985).

Wagenführ, R. & Steiger, A. 1963. Mahagoni und mahagoniähnliche Hölzer – Probleme ihrer Identifizierung. Holztechnologie, Dresden 4: 137–146.

Wagenführ, R. & Steiger, A. 1986. Vergleichende holzanatomische Untersuchungen an der Holzart Sapelli aus unterschiedlichen Provenienzen. Holztechnologie, Dresden 27: 258–259.

Wagenführ, R. & Weiss, B. 1990. Erkennung, Eigenschaften und Verwendung von Meranti-Hölzern aus Südostasien. Holztechnologie, Dresden 31: 321–323.

Wagner, K. A. 1946. Notes on the anomalous stem structure of a species of Bauhinia. Amer. Midl. Nat. 36: 251–256.

Waisel, Y. & Fahn, A. 1965. The effects of environment on wood formation and cambial activity in Robinia pseudacacia L. New Phytol. 64: 436–442.

Wałek-Czernecka, A. 1952. Anatomia porownawcza drewna Populus alba L., Populus tremula L., Populus canescens Sm. Roczn. dendrol. polsk. Tow. bot. 8: 1–31. [Polish; French summ.]

Wałek-Czernecka, A. & Smoliński, M. 1956. Anatomia drewna bukowego normalnego i ciągliwego. Roczn. dendrol. polsk. Tow. bot. 11: 21–69. [Polish; French summ.]

Walker, F. S. 1978. Pedunculate and sessile oaks: species determination from differences between their wood. In: Dendrochronology in Europe; principles, interpretations and applications to archaeology and history (ed. Fletcher, J.): 329–338. Res. Lab. Archaeol. Hist. Art, Oxford.

Wallace, G. D. 1986. Wood anatomy of Cassiope (Ericaceae). Aliso 11: 393–415.

Walsh, M. A. 1975. Xylem anatomy of Hibiscus (Malvaceae) in relation to habit. Bot. Gaz. 136: 30–40.

Wang, D. & Gao, S. 1991. Study on the relationships of Cercidiphyllaceae. II. Anatomy and morphology study on secondary xylem. Acta bot. bor.-occ. sin. 11: 287–291. [Chin.; Eng. summ.] + 2 plates.

Wang, H. 1965; 1966. Anatomical studies on the commercial timbers of Taiwan (I). Tech. Bull. Exp. For. Taiwan Univ., No. 41: 19 pp. (1965). (II). Ibid., No. 45: 20 pp. (1966). [Chin. & Eng.]

Wang, L.-J., Zhang, Y.-M., Zhong, Y. & Gu, A.-G. 1991. Studies on the secondary vascular tissue in the stem of Actinidia arguta (Sieb. et Zucc.) Planch. ex Miquel. Bull. bot. Res. N.E. For. Univ. (China) 11 (1): 79–83. [Chin.; Eng. summ.]

Wang, M., Gu, A.-G. & Wang, L.-J. 1990. Advanced studies on Metalonicera. Bull. bot. Res. N.E. For. Univ. (China) 10 (1): 105–109. [Chin.; Eng. summ.]

Wang, S.-Y. 1984. The characteristics of tree and wood of Dipterocarpaceae. For. Prod. Indust. 3 (1): 99–107. [Chin. only.]

Wang, S.-Y. 1984–1988. Wood identification and property of southeast Asian woods (I–X). For. Prod. Indust. 3 (4): 129–134 (1984); 4 (1): 111–118; (2): 124–132; (3): 125–134; (4): 101–112 (1985); 5 (1): 92–100; (2): 114–123 (1986); 6 (4): 50–61 (1987); 7 (1): 135–147; (2): 79–90 (1988). [Chin. only.]

Wang, W.-Y. 1982. Comparative anatomy of nine species of the genus Rhododendron from Qinghai Plateau and their systematic position. Acta phytotax. sin. 20: 49–58. [Chin.; Eng. summ.] + 2 plates.

Wang, Y.-F. & Li, Z.-L. 1989. Comparative studies on woods of three species of normal and dwarf trees. Acta bot. sin. 31: 12–18. [Chin.; Eng. summ.] + 1 plate.

Watari, S. 1950. Studies in the wood anatomy of several species of Meliosma. Misc. Rep. Res. Inst. nat. Resources, Nos. 17-18: 25–32. [Jap.]

Watari, S. 1951. Studies on the fossil woods from the Tertiary of Japan. VII. Leea (Vitaceae) from the Miocene of Simane. Bot. Mag., Tokyo 64: 1–7. [Eng.]

Webber, I.E. 1934a. The wood of Hibiscus tiliaceus L. Trop. Woods 37: 14–18.

Webber, I.E. 1934b. Systematic anatomy of the woods of the Malvaceae. Trop. Woods 38: 15–36.

Webber, I.E. 1936a. The woods of sclerophyllous and desert shrubs of California. Amer. J. Bot. 23: 181–188.

Webber, I.E. 1936b. Systematic anatomy of the woods of the Simarubaceae. Amer. J. Bot. 23: 577–587.

Webber, I.E. 1938. Intercellular cavities in the rays of dicotyledonous woods. Lilloa 2: 465–469.

Webber, I.E. 1941. Systematic anatomy of the woods of the Burseraceae. Lilloa 6: 441–465.

Webber, I. 1945. The wood of Ambelania laxa Muell. Arg. Lilloa 11: 49–54.

Weberling, F., Lörcher, H. & Bohnke, F. 1980. Die Stipeln der Irvingioideae und Recchioideae und ihre systematische Wertung nebst Bemerkungen zur Holzanatomie und Palynologie. Pl. Syst. Evol. 133: 261–283.

Webster, G.L. 1982. Systematic status of the genus Kleinodendron (Euphorbiaceae). Taxon 31: 535–539.

Wei, N. 1991. A comparative anatomy on the vegetative organs of Tetraena mongolica Maxim and Zygophyllum xanthoxylum (Bunge) Maxim. Acta Scient. nat. Univ. Intramongolicae 22: 528–533. [Chin.; Eng. summ.] + 2 plates.

Wei, Z. 1984. Studies on the genus Acmena. Acta bot. yunnan. 6: 195–204. [Chin.; Eng. summ.] + 2 plates.

Welch, M.B. 1924 [1925]a. Note on the structure of some Eucalyptus woods. J. Proc. roy. Soc. N.S. Wales 58: 169–176.

Welch, M.B. 1924 [1925]b. A further contribution to the knowledge of the silky oaks. J. Proc. roy. Soc. N.S. Wales 58: 255–267.

Welch, M.B. 1925 [1926]. The identification of the principal ironbarks and allied woods. J. Proc. roy. Soc. N.S.Wales 59: 329–345.

Welch, M.B. 1926. Notes on the principal indigenous timbers of the natural order Saxifrageae. J. Proc. roy. Soc. N.S. Wales 59: 276–292.

Welch, M.B. 1926 [1927]. The wood structure of certain eucalypts belonging chiefly to the "ash" group. J. Proc. roy. Soc. N.S.Wales 60: 147–166.

Welch, M.B. 1929a. Walnut Bean (Endiandra palmerstoni). Trop. Woods 20: 4–9.

Welch, M.B. 1929b. Notes on some Australian timbers of the Monimiaceae. J. Proc. roy. Soc. N.S.Wales 62: 350–365.

Welch, M.B. 1929 [1930]. Some properties of Red Satinay, Syncarpia hillii. J. Proc. roy. Soc. N.S.Wales 63: 122–130.

Welch, M.B. 1931a. Queensland "maple" (Flindersia spp.). Trop. Woods 25: 18–23.

Welch, M.B. 1931b. The occurrence of intercellular canals in the wood of some species of Flindersia. J. Proc. roy. Soc. N.S.Wales 64: 352–362.

Welle, B.J.H. ter 1975. Spiral thickenings in the axial parenchyma of Chrysobalanaceae. Acta bot. neerl. 24: 397–405.

Welle, B.J.H. ter 1976a. On the occurrence of silica grains in the secondary xylem of the Chrysobalanaceae. IAWA Bull. 1976/2: 19–29.

Welle, B.J.H. ter 1976b. Silica grains in woody plants of the Neotropics, especially Surinam. In: Wood structure in biological and technological research (eds. Baas, P., Bolton, A.J. & Catling, D.M.): 107–142. Leiden Botanical Series No. 3. Leiden Univ. Press.

Welle, B.J.H. ter 1980. Cystoliths in the secondary xylem of Sparattanthelium (Hernandiaceae). IAWA Bull. n.s. 1: 43–48.

Welle, B.J.H. ter 1984. Variation and diversity in the Annonaceae. Proc. Pacific Regional Wood Anatomy Conf., Tsukuba, Japan, 1984: 144–146.

Welle, B.J.H. ter 1985. Wood anatomy of Streblus s.l. (Moraceae). Proc. Symp. For. Prod. Res. Intn. Achievements and the Future, April 1985, Pretoria, vol. 1, Paper 16-6: 7 pp. CSIRO: S. Africa.

Welle, B.J.H. ter & Détienne, P. 1986. Wood and timber. In: Flora of the Guianas (ed. Görts-van Rijn, A.R.A.). 85. Chrysobalanaceae (by Prance, G.T.): 109–140. Koeltz: Koenigstein.

Welle, B.J.H. ter & Détienne, P. 1988. Wood and timber. In: Flora of the Guianas (ed. Görts-van Rijn, A.R.A.). 148. Verbenaceae (by Jansen-Jacobs, M.J.): 87–99. Koeltz: Koenigstein.

Welle, B.J.H. ter & Détienne, P. 1993. Wood and timber. In: Flora of the Guianas (ed. Görts-van Rijn, A.R.A.). 99. Melastomataceae: 337–363. Koeltz: Koenigstein.

Welle, B.J.H. ter & Koek-Noorman, J. 1978. On fibres, parenchyma and intermediate forms in the genus Miconia (Melastomataceae). Acta bot. neerl. 27: 1–9.

Welle, B.J.H. ter & Koek-Noorman, J. 1981. Wood anatomy of the neotropical Melastomataceae. Blumea 27: 335–394.

Welle, B.J.H. ter, Koek-Noorman, J. & Topper, S.M.C. 1986. The systematic wood anatomy of the Moraceae (Urticales). IV. Genera of the tribe Moreae with urticaceous stamens. IAWA Bull. n.s. 7: 91–128. V. Genera of the tribe Moreae without urticaceous stamens. Ibid.: 175–193.

Welle, B.J.H. ter, Loureiro, A.A., Lisboa, P.L.B. & Koek-Noorman, J. 1983. Systematic wood anatomy of the tribe Guettardeae (Rubiaceae). Bot. J. Linn. Soc. 87: 13–28.

Welle, B.J.H. ter & Mennega, A.M.W. 1977. On the presence of large styloids in the secondary xylem of the genus Henriettea (Melastomataceae). IAWA Bull. 1977/2: 31–35.

Welle, B.J.H. ter & Van Rooden, J. 1982. Systematic wood anatomy of Desmopsis, Sapranthus and Stenanona (Annonaceae). IAWA Bull. n.s. 3: 15–23.

Wellendorf, M. 1966. Millettia laurentii. Micrography of the wood. Bot. Tidsskr. 62: 223–230.

Westra, L.Y.T. 1985. Studies in Annonaceae. IV. A taxonomic revision of Tetrameranthus R.E. Fries. Proc. konink. Ned. Akad. Wetensch., C, 88: 449–482.

Whalen, M.A. 1987. Wood anatomy of the American Frankenias (Frankeniaceae): systematic and evolutionary implications. Amer. J. Bot. 74: 1211–1223.

Wheat, D. 1977. Successive cambia in the stem of Phytolacca dioica. Amer. J. Bot. 64: 1209–1217.

Wheeler, E.A. 1981. Intervascular pitting in Fraxinus americana L. IAWA Bull. n.s. 2: 169–174.

Wheeler, E.A. & Baas, P. 1991. A survey of the fossil record for dicotyledonous wood and its significance for evolutionary and ecological wood anatomy. IAWA Bull. n.s. 12: 275–332.

Wheeler, E.A., Baas, P. & Gasson, P.E. (eds.) 1989. IAWA list of microscopic features for hardwood identification. IAWA Bull. n.s. 10: 219–332.

Wheeler, E.A., LaPasha, C.A. & Miller, R.B. 1989. Wood anatomy of elm (Ulmus) and hackberry (Celtis) species native to the United States. IAWA Bull. n.s. 10: 5–26.

Wheeler, E.A., Pearson, R.G. & LaPasha, C.A. 1987. Objectives of computerised databases for wood. IAWA Bull. n.s. 8: 355–362.

Wheeler, E.A., Pearson, R.G., LaPasha, C.A., Zack, T. & Hatley, W. 1986. Computer-aided wood identification. Reference manual. Bull. N. Carolina Agric. Res. Serv., No. 474: 160 pp.

Wilkes, J. 1988. Variations in wood anatomy within species of Eucalyptus. IAWA Bull. n.s. 9: 13–23.

Wilkins, A.P. & Papassotiriou, S. 1989. Wood anatomical variation of Acacia melanoxylon in relation to latitude. IAWA Bull. n.s. 10: 201–207.

Willeitner, H., Richter, H.G. & Brandt, K. 1982. Farbreagenz zur Unterscheidung von Weisseichen- und Roteichenholz. Holz Roh- u. Werkst. 40: 327–332.

Williams, L. 1928. Studies of some tropical American woods. Trop. Woods 15: 14–24.

Williams, L. 1929. The wood of Caryodendron angustifolium Standley. Trop. Woods 20: 26–27.

Williams, L. 1935. A study of the Caryocaraceae. Trop Woods 42: 1–18.

Williams, L. 1936. Woods of northeastern Peru. Field Mus. nat. Hist., Bot. ser. 15: 1–587. Chicago.

Williams, L. 1938. Note on Calatola venezuelana Pittier. Trop. Woods 56: 6–9.

Williams, S. 1939–1942. Secondary vascular tissues of the oaks indigenous to the United States. I. The importance of secondary xylem in delimiting Erythrobalanus and Leucobalanus. Bull. Torrey bot. Cl. 66: 353–365 (1939). II. Types of tyloses and their distribution in Erythrobalanus and Leucobalanus. Ibid.: 69: 1–10. III. A comparative and anatomical study of the wood of Leucobalanus and Erythrobalanus. Ibid.: 115–129 (1942).

Wilson, C.L. 1979. Idiospermum australiense (Idiospermaceae) – aspects of vegetative anatomy. Amer. J. Bot. 66: 280–289.

Wilson, K. & White, D.J.B. 1986. Anatomy of wood: its diversity and variability. Stobart, London. 309 pp.

Wilson, T.K. 1960. The comparative morphology of the Canellaceae I. Synopsis of genera and wood anatomy. Trop. Woods 112: 1–27.

Wiraj Chunwarin & Damrong Sri-Aran 1973. Macroscopic and microscopic structure of commercial woods in series Thalamiflorae and Disciflorae of Thailand. For. Res. Bull. Kasetsart Univ., Thailand, No. 25: 245 pp. [Thai; Eng. summ.]

Wiraj Chunwarin & Damrong Sri-Aran 1974. Macroscopic and microscopic structure of important woods in series Calyciflorae, Inferae, Heteromerae, Bicarpellatae, Micembryae, Daphnales, and Unisexuales. For. Res. Bull. Kasetsart Univ., Thailand, No. 29: 174 pp. [Thai; Eng. summ.]

Withner, C.L. 1941. Stem anatomy and phylogeny of the Rhoipteleaceae. Amer. J. Bot. 28: 872–878.

Włoch, W. & Szendera, W. 1989. The storeyed and non-storeyed arrangement of rays in the storeyed cambium of Tilia cordata Mill. Acta Soc. bot. pol. 58: 211–228.

Wolkinger, F. 1969–1971. Morphologie und systematische Verbreitung der lebenden Holzfasern bei Sträuchern und Bäumen. I. Zur Morphologie und Zytologie. Holzforschung 23: 135–144 (1969). II. Histologie. Ibid., 24: 141–147 (1970). III. Systematische Verbreitung. Ibid., 25: 29–30 (1971). [Eng. summ.]

Wolkinger, F. 1970. Das Vorkommen lebender Holzfasern in Sträuchern und Bäumen. Phyton (Austria) 14: 55–67.

Wong, T.M. & Lim, S.C. 1983. Interxylary phloem in Cynometra (Kekatong). Malay. Forester 46: 93–97.

Woodworth, R.H. 1935. Fibriform vessel members in the Passifloraceae. Trop. Woods 41: 8–16.

Worbes, M. 1984. Periodische Zuwachszonen an Bäumen zentralamazonischer Überschwemmungswälder. Naturwissenschaften 71: 157–158.

Worbes, M. 1986. Lebensbedingungen und Holzwachstum in zentralamazonischen Überschwemmungswäldern. Scripta Geobotanica XVII. Erich Goltze: Göttingen. 112 pp. [Eng. summ., p. 75.]

Worbes, M. 1988. Variety in structure of annual growth zones in Tabebuia barbata (E.Mey.) Sandw., Bignoniaceae, a tropical tree species from Central Amazonian inundation forests. Dendrochronologia, No. 6: 71–89.

Worsdell, W.C. 1915; 1919. The origin and meaning of medullary (intraxylary) phloem in the stems of dicotyledons. I. Cucurbitaceae. Ann. Bot. 29: 567–590 (1915). II. Compositae. Ibid. 33: 421–458 (1919).

Wu, S.C., Hsieh, R.S. & Wang, Y.J. 1988. Studies on the anatomical structure of Acacia mangium. Q. Jl. exp. For. natn. Taiwan Univ. 2(2): 27–43. [Chin.]

Wu, S.C. & Tsai, C.S. 1973. Studies on the wood structure of order Laurales grown in Taiwan (1, 2). Q. Jl. chin. For. 6(2): 35–79; (3): 45–77. [Chin.; Eng. summ.]

Wu, S.C. & Tsai, C.S. 1975. Studies on the structure and identification of wood in South-Eastern Asia. 1. The minute structural features. Q. Jl. chin. For. 8(1): 3–17. – 2. Wood of genus Shorea. Ibid.: 19–55. [Chin.; Eng. summ.]

Wu, S.C. & Wang, S.H. 1976. The wood structure and fiber morphology of the commercial hardwoods grown in Taiwan. 1. The wood structure. Bull. Exp. For. natn. Taiwan Univ., No. 117: 43–98. [Chin.; Eng. summ.]

Wu, S.-M. & Li, Z.-L. 1988. Comparative anatomical studies on the vessel elements of eight genera in Magnoliaceae. Acta bot. sin. 30: 33–39. [Chin.; Eng. summ.] + 2 plates.

Wu, S.-M. & Li, Z.-L. 1989. Spiral thickenings of vessel elements in Magnoliaceae in China. Acta bot. sin. 31: 280–284. [Chin.; Eng. summ.] + 1 plate.

Wu, S.-M., Lin, J.-X. & Li, Z.-L. 1993. Comparative anatomical studies on the wood rays of sixty-six species in nine genera of Magnoliaceae in China. Acta bot. sin. 35: 268–279 + 2 plates. [Chin.; Eng. summ.]

Wu, S.-M. & Xiao, S.Q. 1989. Comparative anatomical studies on the woods of Castanea Mill. and Trigonobalanus Forman in China. Guihaia 9: 341–346. [Chin.; Eng. summ.] + 3 plates.

Wuang, B.C. 1979. Shensi timbers. Their identification, properties and uses. People's Publishing House of Shensi: Sian, China. 244 pp. [Chin.]

Xie, F.-H. & Mo, S.-L. 1987. Studies on the wood structure of Apterosperma Chang. Guihaia 7: 107–109. [Chin.; Eng. summ.]

Xie, F.H., Zu, F. & Liang, S.-Y. 1987. On the wood structure of Camellia terminalis. Guihaia 7: 319–323. [Chin.; Eng. summ.] + 1 plate.

Xu, F., Mou, J.-P. & Liang, S.-Y. 1990. Wood anatomy of the Bhesa – new recorded genus of Chinese Celastraceae. Chin. Bull. Bot. 7(3): 52–53. [Chin. only.]

Xu, F., Xie, F.H. & Liang, S.Y. 1989. Studies on wood anatomy of Camellia Section Chrysantha from China. Guihaia 9: 249–254. [Chin.; Eng. summ.] + 1 plate.

Yadav, R.R. & Bhattacharyya, A. 1989 [1990]. Occurrence of unusual perforations in Michelia champaca L. Phytomorphology 39: 331–333.

Yaghmaie, M. & Catling, D. 1984. The occurrence of vascular tracheids in Betula and some other Betulaceae genera. Pl. Syst. Evol. 147: 125–131.

Yakovlev, G.P., Yatsenko-Khmelevsky, A.A. & Zoubkova, I.G. 1968. Taxinomie et phylogénie du genre Angylocalyx et de la tribu des Angylocalyceae. Adansonia, sér. 2, 8: 317–335.

Yaltirik, F. 1968. Memleketimizin doğal akçaağaç (Acer L.) türlerinin odunlarinin anatomik özellikleri ile yetişme yeri arasindaki münasebet. [Comparison of anatomical characteristics of woods in Turkish maples with the relation of the humidity of the sites.] Istanb. Univ. Orman Fak. Derg. A, 18(2): 77–89. [Eng. summ.]

Yaltirik, F. 1970. Comparison of anatomical characteristics of wood in Turkish maples with relation to the humidity of the sites. J. Inst. Wood Sci. 5(1), No. 25: 43–48.

Yaltirik, F. 1971. Yerli akçaağaç (Acer L.) türleri üzerinde morfologik ve anatomik araştirmalar. [The taxonomical study on the macro- and micro-morphological characteristics of indigenous maples (Acer L.) in Turkey.] Istanb. Univ. Orman Fak. Yayinlari No. 179: 232 pp. [Eng. summ. 219–225.]

Yamabayashi, N. 1933. Identification of Corean woods (Fagaceae). For. Exp. Sta., Govt. Chosen, Japan. 82 pp. [Jap.; Eng. keys & tables.]

Yamabayashi, N. 1938. Identification of Corean woods. For. Exp. Sta., Chosen, Keijo, Japan, Bull. 27: 484 pp. [Jap.; Eng. summ.]

Yamauchi, F. 1962. Anatomical identification of the woods in Japanese Acer. Misc. Rep. Res. Inst. nat. Resources, Tokyo 58-59: 3–11 + 10 plates. [Jap.; Eng. summ.]

Yamauchi, F. 1967. The crystalliferous parenchyma in Japanese woods. Misc. Rep. Res. Inst. nat. Resources, Tokyo 69: 115–122. [Jap.; Eng. summ.]

Yamauchi, F. 1971. Observation of the perforation plates of vessels in the wood of Japanese Lauraceae. Misc. Rep. Res. Inst. nat. Resources, Tokyo 75: 25–30. [Jap.; Eng. summ.]

Yamauchi, F. 1972. Wood structure of Acer mono Maxim. var. glabrum (Lev. et Vnt.) Hara. Mem. natn. Sci. Mus., Tokyo, No. 5: 179–181. [Jap.; Eng. summ.]

Yamauchi, F. 1976. Anatomical studies of woods in Japanese Elaeagnus. Bull. natn. Sci. Mus., Tokyo, B, 2: 107–118. [Jap.; Eng. summ. & captions.]

Yamauchi, F. 1979. Anatomical studies of woods in Japanese species of Palura and Dicalyx (Symplocaceae). Bull. natn. Sci. Mus., Tokyo, B, 5: 61–66. [Jap.; Eng. summ.]

Yamauchi, F. 1980. Wood structure of Japanese species of Stewartia (Theaceae). Bull. natn. Sci. Mus., Tokyo, B, 6: 61–64. [Jap.; Eng. summ.]

Yang. J. & Cheng, F. 1990. Microcomputer-assisted wood identification system WIP-89. J. Beijing For. Univ. 12 (4): 88–94. [Chin.; Eng. summ.]

Yang, K.-C. 1981. Trochodendron – a hardwood without vessel. Q. Jl. chin. For. 14 (2): 11–19. [Eng.]

Yang, K.-C. & Huang-Yang, Y.-S. 1987. Minute structure of Taiwanese woods – a guide to their identification with micrographs. Hua Shiang Yuan Publ. Co.: Taipei, Taiwan. 172 pp. [Not seen.]

Yao, X. 1988. Scanning electron microscope structure of main Chinese woods. China Forestry Publ.: Beijing, China. 262 pp. [Chin.]

Yaskevich, R.T. 1956. Observations on the anatomical structure of the wood of species of almond. Bot. J. USSR 41: 1172–1177. [Russ. only.]

Yatsenko-Khmelevsky, A.A. 1933. The crystalliferous parenchyma in the wood of certain Caucasian Rosaceae. Tr. Tifl. bot. Inst. 1: 291–301. [Russ.; Eng. summ.]

Yatsenko-Khmelevsky, A.A. 1939. On the determination of the Caucasian representatives of the genus Acer by the structure of their woods. Zamet. Sist. Geog. Rast. Tbilisi Bot. Inst. (7): 23–36. [Russ. only]

Yatsenko-Khmelevsky, A. 1945. The wood structure of some species of the genus Nothofagus Bl. in connection with its systematic position. Dokl. Akad. Nauk arm. SSR 2: 109–113. [Russ.; brief Eng. summ.]

Yatsenko-Khmelevsky, A. 1946a. Variations in structure of wood of oriental beech (Fagus orientalis Lipsky), as influenced by age, level and the environment. Bull. Acad. Sci. arm. SSR, No. 5. [Russ.]

Yatsenko-Khmelevsky, A.A. 1946b. The wood structure of the Caucasian Ericaceae and its systematical and phylogenetical value. Izv. Akad. Nauk arm. SSR, Estest. Nauki 6, No. 9: 33–58. [Russ.; brief Eng. summ.]

Yatsenko-Khmelevsky, A.A. 1946c. Some peculiarities of the wood of Hippophae rhamnoides. Dokl. Akad. Nauk arm. SSR 4 (4): 109–114. [Russ.]

Yatsenko-Khmelevsky, A.A. 1954a. Drevesiny Kavkaza. [Caucasian woods.] Vol. I. Akad. Nauk Armyanskoi SSR: Erevan. 674 pp. [Russ.]

Yatsenko-Khmelevsky, A.A. 1954b. Foundation and methods of the anatomical investigation of wood. Akad. Nauk. SSSR, Moscow. 337 pp. [Russ.]

Yoda, K. & Suzuki, M. 1992. Comparative wood anatomy of Coriaria. Bot. Mag., Tokyo 105: 235–245.

Young, D.A. 1974. Comparative wood anatomy of Malosma and related genera (Anacardiaceae). Aliso 8: 133–146.

Young, D.A. 1981. Are the angiosperms primitively vesselless? Syst. Bot. 6: 313–330.

Young, D.A. 1982. Wood anatomy of Actinocheita (Anacardiaceae). Madroño 29: 61–62.

Young, D.A. & Richardson, P.M. 1982. A phylogenetic analysis of extant seed plants: the need to utilize homologous characters. Taxon 31: 250–254.

Youngs, R.L. 1955. The xylem anatomy of Orthopterygium (Julianiaceae). Trop. Woods 101: 29–43.

Yu, C.H. 1948. Anatomy of the commercial timbers of Kansu. Bot. Bull. Acad. sin. 2: 127–131. [Eng.]

Yu, C.H. & Li, Y. 1954. The wood structure of Annamocarya sinensis (Dode) Leroy with reference to its phylogeny. Acta bot. sin. 3: 330–332. [Eng.]

Zamora, V.-N., Poveda, A.-L.J. & Canessa, A.-E. 1988. Una nueva especie de Caryodaphnopsis Airy Shaw (Lauraceae) para la region neotropical. Ann. Missouri bot. Gard. 75: 1160–1166.

Zamski, E. 1979. The mode of secondary growth and the three-dimensional structure of the phloem in Avicennia. Bot. Gaz. 140: 67–76.

Zamuco, I.T. 1967. Bark and wood anatomy of four important Philippine bast-fibre producing trees. Philipp. Lumberman 13(12): 10–20. Also in: Philipp. J. For. 21: 127–146 (1965) [1970].

Zamuco, I.T., Vela, B.C. de, Robillos, Y.U. & Meniado, J.A. 1964. Wood anatomy of Philippine red mahogany and Shorea teysmanniana. Lumberman, Manila 10(5): 10, 12, 14, 16. Also in: Forestry Leaves 15(3): 75–82 (1964). Same paper in: Philipp. J. For. 20: 55–65 (1964) [1968].

Zarucchi, J.L. 1987. A revision of the tribe Ambelanieae (Apocynaceae-Plumerioideae). Series of revisions of Apocynaceae. XXIV. Agric. Univ. Wageningen Pap. 87(1): 1–106. [Also in: Belmontia (NS) 23, No. 142; 1991.]

Zeeuw, C.H. de 1990. Secondary xylem of neotropical Lecythidaceae. In: Lecythidaceae–II. The zygomorphic-flowered New World genera (Couroupita, Corythophora, Bertholletia, Couratari, Eschweilera, & Lecythis) (by Mori, S.A. & Prance, G.T.): 4–59. Flora Neotropica Mon. 21(II): 1–375.

Zeeuw, C.H. de 1992 [1993]. Wood and timber. In: Flora of the Guianas (ed. Görts-van Rijn, A.R.A.). 53. Lecythidaceae (by Mori, S.A. & Prance, G.T.): 89–113. Koeltz: Champaign/ Königstein.

Zeeuw, C. de & Mori, S.A. 1987. Wood anatomy. In: The Lecythidacae of a lowland neotropical forest: La Fumée mountain, French Guiana (by Mori, S.A. et al.): 100–112. Mem. N.Y. bot. Gard. 44.

Zgurovskaya, L.N. 1958. Investigations on the anatomy and physiology of absorbing, extension and conducting roots of woody species. Trud. Inst. Lesa, Mosk. 41: 5–32. [Russ.]

Zhang, Q.C., Cheng, F. & Lian, Y.H. 1986. Microcomputer identification of hardwood species. Scientia Silvae sin. 22(2): 213–217. [Chin.; Eng. summ.]

Zhang, S.-S., Lei, L.-G., Liu, H.-Q. & Su, Q.-Y. 1990. A preliminary study on tracheary elements in the endemic species Sarcandra hainanensis from China – evidence for the occurrence of vessels in Sarcandra. Acta bot. bor.-occ. sin. 10(2): 95–98. [Chin.; Eng. summ.] + 1 plate.

Zhang, S.-Y. 1992. Systematic wood anatomy of the Rosaceae. Blumea 37: 81–158.

Zhang, S.-Y. & Baas, P. 1992. Wood anatomy of trees and shrubs from China. III. Rosaceae. IAWA Bull. n.s. 13: 21–91.

Zhang, S.-Y., Baas, P. & Zandee, M. 1992. Wood structure of the Rosaceae in relation to ecology, habit and phenology. IAWA Bull. n.s. 13: 307–349.

Zhang, X., Baas, P. & Mennega, A.M.W. 1990. Wood anatomy of Bhesa sinica (Celastraceae). IAWA Bull. n.s. 11: 57–60.

Zhang, X., Deng, L. & Baas, P. 1988. The ecological wood anatomy of the lilacs (Syringa oblata var. giraldii) on Mount Taibei in northwestern China. IAWA Bull. n.s. 9: 24–30.

Zhang, X.-Y. & Cao, W.-H. 1990. Studies on the secondary xylem anatomy of Hippophae rhamnoides under different habitats. Acta bot. sin. 32: 909–915. [Chin.; Eng. summ.] + 2 plates.

Zhang, Z.-S. 1984. A preliminary study on the wood anatomy of Manglietia aromatica Dandy (Paramanglietia aromatica (Dandy) Hu and Cheng) and Paramichelia baillonii (Pierre) Hu of Magnoliaceae from China. Acta bot. sin. 26: 479–483. [Chin.; Eng. summ.] + 1 plate.

Zhang, Z.-Y., Lu, A.-M., Pan, K.-Y. & Wen, J. 1990. The anatomy, embryology and systematic relationships of Eucommiaceae. Acta phytotax. sin. 28: 430–441. [Chin.; Eng. summ.] + 6 plates.

Zheng, P. & Gao, S.-Z. 1990. Wood anatomy of Tetracentraceae. Acta bot. bor.-occ. sin. 10 (3): 185–189. [Chin.; Eng. summ.] + 1 plate.

Zhong, Y., Baas, P. & Wheeler, E.A. 1992. Wood anatomy of trees and shrubs from China. IV. Ulmaceae. IAWA Bull. n.s. 13: 419–453.

Zhu, J., Zhang, H., Ma, D. & Tao, W. 1992. Anomalous secondary structure and growth in the stem of Ceratoides latens. Acta bot. bor.-occ. sin. 12: 135–141. [Chin.; Eng. summ.] + 2 plates.

Ziliani, G. 1987. Presencia de silice en maderas de especies arbóreas del Uruguay. Bol. Invest., Fac. Agron., Univ. Repub. (Uruguay) No. 6: 1–10. [Eng. summ.]

Ziliani, G. 1989. Anatomia de maderas del Uruguay. III. Sapotaceae. Resumos XL Congr. nac. Bot., Cuiabá, Mato Grosso, Jan. 1989, 1: 263. [Abstr.]

Zimmermann, A. 1922. Die Cucurbitaceen. Beiträge zur Anatomie, Physiologie, Morphologie, Biologie, Pathologie und Systematik. G. Fischer: Jena. 391 pp.

Zobel, B.J. & Van Buijtenen, J.P. 1989. Wood variation – its causes and control. Springer Verlag: Berlin, etc. 363 pp.

Zou, S., Wu, Y. & Wang, H. 1989. A study on the tropical fast-growing and drought resistant tree species – Anogeissus acuminata var. lanceolata. Acta bot. yunnan. 11: 81–90. [Chin.; Eng. summ.]

Zürcher, E., Kučera, L. & Bosshard, H.H. 1985. Bildung und Morphologie der Thyllen: eine Literaturübersicht. Vierteljahrsschr. naturf. Ges. Zürich 130: 311–333.